FEATURES AND BENEFITS
Core-Plus Mathematics, Course 1 TEACHER'S GUIDE PART A ©2008

Content and Organization

	See page(s):
• Alignment to the NCTM Grades 9–12 Content Standards.	x
• Introduction and Organization of Course 1.	xi–xvii
• Access, Equity, and Differentiation.	xvi–xvii
• Implementing the Curriculum.	xvii–xxviii

Student and Teacher Friendly

• Engaging student-centered applications invite students to read and do more mathematics on their own. Read *Cause and Effect* and *Trying to Get Rich Quick*.	2, 11
• Lesson development organizes problems for students into easy-to-understand instructions. See *Translating Words into Symbols* problems 1 to 4.	49
• Full-color Student Edition page alongside Teacher's Guide page for easy reference.	89–T89
• Effective *Teacher's Guide* design provides point-of-use support to make it easier for you to focus on managing students' progress in completing investigations.	75–T75B

Extensive and Varied Practice

• **Applications** help students use and apply ideas from each lesson.	90–93
• **Connections** connect each lesson's topics with other mathematics students know.	255–257
• **Reflections** help students avoid developing misconceptions and help them rethink key ideas that were developed in the lesson.	95–97
• **Extensions** provide opportunities to explore further or more deeply important ideas developed in the lesson.	97–101
• **Review** tasks help students maintain important skills.	284–285

Test Preparation and Assessment

• **Think About This Situation** assesses students' prior knowledge before the start of the lesson.	323
• **Summarizing the Mathematics** assesses students' ability to correctly articulate the mathematics developed after each investigation in the lesson.	122
• **Check Your Understanding** assesses students' ability to solve problems based upon the mathematics developed in each investigation in the lesson.	270
• **Looking Back** lessons help students review and practice key ideas that were developed in the unit.	232

Technology

• *CPMP-Tools*™ expands student use of technology by including software tools for algebra, geometry, statistics, and discrete mathematics and time-saving access to selected lesson data sets.	xi

- *StudentWorks*™ **CD-ROM** includes the Student Edition, Student Study Guide, and more on one convenient CD.
- *ExamView*® *Pro Assessment Suite* **CD-ROM** is a powerful state-of-the art test generator that combines ease of use with enormous flexibility in creating customized assessments.
- *TeacherWorks*™ *Plus* **CD-ROM** is the latest in all-in-one planne[r] resource center including the ability to edit many of your print re[sources]
- *Core-Plus Mathematics* Web site resources at **www.cpmp.gle**[n]

Teacher's Guide Part A

Course **1** Core-Plus Mathematics

Contemporary Mathematics in Context

2nd Edition

Christian R. Hirsch • James T. Fey • Eric W. Hart
Harold L. Schoen • Ann E. Watkins
with
Beth E. Ritsema • Rebecca K. Walker • Sabrina Keller
Robin Marcus • Arthur F. Coxford • Gail Burrill

New York, New York   Columbus, Ohio   Chicago, Illinois   Peoria, Illinois   Woodland Hills, California

 **Glencoe**

The *McGraw·Hill* Companies

 This material is based upon work supported, in part, by the National Science Foundation under grant no. ESI 0137718. Opinions expressed are those of the authors and not necessarily those of the Foundation.

Send all inquiries to:
Glencoe/McGraw-Hill
8787 Orion Place
Columbus, OH 43240-4027

ISBN: 978-0-07-877247-4   **Core-Plus Mathematics**
MHID: 0-07-877247-8   *Contemporary Mathematics in Context*
                              Course 1 Teacher Edition, Part A

ISBN: 978-0-07-877248-1   **Core-Plus Mathematics**
MHID: 0-07-877248-6   *Contemporary Mathematics in Context*
                              Course 1 Teacher Edition, Part B

Printed in the United States of America.

3 4 5 6 7 8 9 10 079/043 15 14 13 12 11 10 09

Core-Plus Mathematics 2 Development Team

Senior Curriculum Developers

Christian R. Hirsch (Director)
Western Michigan University

James T. Fey
University of Maryland

Eric W. Hart
Maharishi University of Management

Harold L. Schoen
University of Iowa

Ann E. Watkins
California State University, Northridge

Contributing Curriculum Developers

Beth E. Ritsema
Western Michigan University

Rebecca K. Walker
Grand Valley State University

Sabrina Keller
Michigan State University

Robin Marcus
University of Maryland

Arthur F. Coxford (deceased)
University of Michigan

Gail Burrill
Michigan State University
(First edition only)

Principal Evaluator

Steven W. Ziebarth
Western Michigan University

Advisory Board

Diane Briars
Pittsburgh Public Schools

Jeremy Kilpatrick
University of Georgia

Robert E. Megginson
University of Michigan

Kenneth Ruthven
University of Cambridge

David A. Smith
Duke University

Mathematical Consultants

Deborah Hughes-Hallett
University of Arizona / Harvard University

Stephen B. Maurer
Swarthmore College

William McCallum
University of Arizona

Doris Schattschneider
Moravian College

Richard Scheaffer
University of Florida

Evaluation Consultant

Norman L. Webb
University of Wisconsin-Madison

Collaborating Teachers

Mary Jo Messenger
Howard County Public Schools, Maryland

Jacqueline Stewart
Okemos, Michigan

Technical Coordinator

James Laser
Western Michigan University

Production and Support Staff

Angie Reiter
Teri Ziebarth
Western Michigan University

Graduate Assistants

Allison BrckaLorenz
Christopher Hlas
University of Iowa

Michael Conklin
University of Maryland

Jodi Edington
Karen Fonkert
Dana Grosser
Anna Kruizenga
Diane Moore
Western Michigan University

Undergraduate Assistants

Cassie Durgin
University of Maryland

Rachael Kaluzny
Jessica Tucker
Ashley Wiersma
Western Michigan University

Core-Plus Mathematics 2 Field-Test Sites

Core-Plus Mathematics 2 builds on the strengths of the 1st edition which was shaped by multi-year field tests in 36 high schools in Alaska, California, Colorado, Georgia, Idaho, Iowa, Kentucky, Michigan, Ohio, South Carolina, and Texas. Each revised text is the product of a three-year cycle of research and development, pilot testing and refinement, and field testing and further refinement. Special thanks are extended to the following teachers and their students who participated in the testing and evaluation of 2nd Edition Course 1.

Hickman High School
Columbia, Missouri
  Peter Doll

Holland Christian High School
Holland, Michigan
  Jeff Goorhouse
  Tim Laverell
  Brian Lemmen
  Mike Verkaik

Jefferson Junior High School
Columbia, Missouri
  Marla Clowe
  Lori Kilfoil
  Martha McCabe
  Paul Rahmoeller
  Evan Schilling

Malcolm Price Lab School
Cedar Falls, Iowa
  James Maltas
  Josh Wilkinson

North Shore Middle School
Holland, Michigan
  Sheila Schippers
  Brenda Katerberg

Oakland Junior High School
Columbia, Missouri
  Teresa Barry
  Erin Little
  Christine Sedgwick
  Dana Sleeth

Riverside University High School
Milwaukee, Wisconsin
  Cheryl Brenner
  Alice Lanphier
  Ela Kiblawi

Rock Bridge High School
Columbia, Missouri
  Nancy Hanson

Sauk Prairie High School
Prairie du Sac, Wisconsin
  Joel Amidon
  Shane Been
  Kent Jensen
  Scott Schutt
  Dan Tess
  Mary Walz

Sauk Prairie Middle School
Sauk City, Wisconsin
  Julie Dahlman
  Janine Jorgensen

South Shore Middle School
Holland, Michigan
  Lynn Schipper

Washington High School
Milwaukee, Wisconsin
  Anthony Amoroso
  Debbie French

West Junior High School
Columbia, Missouri
  Josephus Johnson
  Rachel Lowery
  Mike Rowson
  Amanda Schoenfeld
  Patrick Troup

UNIT 1 PATTERNS OF CHANGE

Patterns of Change develops student ability to recognize and describe important patterns that relate quantitative variables, to use data tables, graphs, words, and symbols to represent the relationships, and to use reasoning and calculating tools to answer questions and solve problems.

Topics include variables and functions, algebraic expressions and recurrence relations, coordinate graphs, data tables and spreadsheets, and equations and inequalities.

UNIT 2 PATTERNS IN DATA

Patterns in Data develops student ability to make sense of real-world data through use of graphical displays, measures of center, and measures of variability.

Topics include distributions of data and their shapes, as displayed in dot plots, histograms, and box plots; measures of center including mean and median, and their properties; measures of variability including interquartile range and standard deviation, and their properties; and percentiles and outliers.

UNIT 3 LINEAR FUNCTIONS

Linear Functions develops student ability to recognize and represent linear relationships between variables and to use tables, graphs, and algebraic expressions for linear functions to solve problems in situations that involve constant rate of change or slope.

Topics include linear functions, slope of a line, rate of change, modeling linear data patterns, solving linear equations and inequalities, equivalent linear expressions.

Overview

UNIT 4   VERTEX-EDGE GRAPHS

Vertex-Edge Graphs develops student understanding of vertex-edge graphs and ability to use these graphs to represent and solve problems involving paths, networks, and relationships among a finite number of elements, including finding efficient routes and avoiding conflicts.

Topics include vertex-edge graphs, mathematical modeling, optimization, algorithmic problem solving, Euler circuits and paths, matrix representation of graphs, vertex coloring and chromatic number.

Lesson 1   Euler Circuits: Finding the Best Path

Lesson 2   Vertex Coloring: Avoiding Conflict

Lesson 3   Looking Back

UNIT 5   EXPONENTIAL FUNCTIONS

Exponential Functions develops student ability to recognize and represent exponential growth and decay patterns, to express those patterns in symbolic forms, to solve problems that involve exponential change, and to use properties of exponents to write expressions in equivalent forms.

Topics include exponential growth and decay functions, data modeling, growth and decay rates, half-life and doubling time, compound interest, and properties of exponents.

Lesson 1   Exponential Growth

Lesson 2   Exponential Decay

Lesson 3   Looking Back

UNIT 6   PATTERNS IN SHAPE

Patterns in Shape develops student ability to visualize and describe two- and three-dimensional shapes, to represent them with drawings, to examine shape properties through both experimentation and careful reasoning, and to use those properties to solve problems.

Topics include Triangle Inequality, congruence conditions for triangles, special quadrilaterals and quadrilateral linkages, Pythagorean Theorem, properties of polygons, tilings of the plane, properties of polyhedra, and the Platonic solids.

Lesson 1   Two-Dimensional Shapes

Lesson 2   Polygons and Their Properties

Lesson 3   Three-Dimensional Shapes

Lesson 4   Looking Back

Overview

UNIT 7 QUADRATIC FUNCTIONS

Quadratic Functions develops student ability to recognize and represent quadratic relations between variables using data tables, graphs, and symbolic formulas, to solve problems involving quadratic functions, and to express quadratic polynomials in equivalent factored and expanded forms.

Topics include quadratic functions and their graphs, applications to projectile motion and economic problems, expanding and factoring quadratic expressions, and solving quadratic equations by the quadratic formula and calculator approximation.

UNIT 8 PATTERNS IN CHANCE

Patterns in Chance develops student ability to solve probability problems by constructing sample spaces of equally-likely outcomes and to approximate solutions for more complex problems by using simulation.

Topics include sample spaces, equally-likely outcomes, probability distributions, mutually exclusive events, Addition Rule, simulation, Law of Large Numbers, and geometric probability.

Contents

Contents

NCTM Standards

Core-Plus Mathematics and the instructional and assessment practices it promotes address the focal points of the National Council of Teachers of Mathematics' (NCTM) Principles and Standards for School Mathematics. By design, the process standards on Problem Solving, Reasoning and Proof, Communication, Connections, and Representation are an integral part of each lesson of every unit in the curriculum. The chart below correlates Course 1 units with the content standards for grades 9–12 in terms of focus (Ⓕ) and connections (Ⓒ).

Correlation of Course 1 to NCTM Standards

NCTM Grades 9–12 Content Standards	Unit 1 Patterns of Change	Unit 2 Patterns in Data	Unit 3 Linear Functions	Unit 4 Vertex-Edge Graphs	Unit 5 Exponential Functions	Unit 6 Patterns in Shape	Unit 7 Quadratic Functions	Unit 8 Patterns in Chance
Number and Operations								
Understand numbers, ways of representing numbers, relationships among numbers, and number systems	Ⓒ	Ⓒ	Ⓒ	Ⓒ	Ⓒ	Ⓒ	Ⓒ	Ⓒ
Understand meanings of operations and how they relate to one another	Ⓒ	Ⓒ	Ⓒ			Ⓒ	Ⓒ	Ⓒ
Compute fluently and make reasonable estimates	Ⓒ	Ⓒ	Ⓒ			Ⓒ	Ⓒ	Ⓒ
Algebra								
Understand patterns, relations, and functions	Ⓕ	Ⓒ	Ⓕ		Ⓕ	Ⓒ	Ⓕ	Ⓒ
Represent and analyze mathematical situations and structures using algebraic symbols	Ⓕ	Ⓒ	Ⓕ		Ⓕ	Ⓒ	Ⓕ	Ⓒ
Use mathematical models to represent and understand quantitative relationships	Ⓕ	Ⓒ	Ⓕ	Ⓒ	Ⓕ	Ⓒ	Ⓕ	Ⓒ
Analyze change in various contexts	Ⓕ	Ⓒ	Ⓕ		Ⓕ	Ⓒ	Ⓕ	Ⓒ
Geometry								
Analyze characteristics and properties of two- and three-dimensional geometric shapes and develop mathematical arguments about geometric relationships				Ⓒ		Ⓕ		
Specify locations and describe spatial relationships using coordinate geometry and other representational systems				Ⓒ		Ⓒ		Ⓒ
Apply transformations and use symmetry to analyze mathematical situations		Ⓒ				Ⓕ	Ⓒ	
Use visualization, spatial reasoning, and geometric modeling to solve problems		Ⓒ			Ⓕ	Ⓕ	Ⓒ	Ⓒ
Measurement								
Understand measurable attributes of objects and the units, systems, and processes of measurement	Ⓕ	Ⓒ	Ⓒ			Ⓕ		
Apply appropriate techniques, tools, and formulas to determine measurements	Ⓕ	Ⓒ	Ⓒ			Ⓕ		
Data Analysis and Probability								
Formulate questions that can be addressed with data and collect, organize, and display relevant data to answer them	Ⓒ	Ⓒ	Ⓒ		Ⓒ	Ⓒ		Ⓕ
Select and use appropriate statistical methods to analyze data	Ⓒ	Ⓕ	Ⓕ		Ⓒ			Ⓕ
Develop and evaluate inferences and predictions that are based on data	Ⓒ	Ⓕ	Ⓕ		Ⓕ	Ⓒ		Ⓕ
Understand and apply basic concepts of probability								Ⓕ

Overview

Introduction

The first three courses in *Core-Plus Mathematics* provide a significant common core of broadly useful mathematics for all students. They were developed to prepare students for success in college, in careers, and in daily life in contemporary society. Course 4 continues the preparation of students for success in college mathematics and statistics courses. The program builds upon the theme of mathematics as sense-making. Through investigations of real-life contexts, students develop a rich understanding of important mathematics that makes sense to them and which, in turn, enables them to make sense out of new situations and problems.

Each course in *Core-Plus Mathematics* shares the following mathematical and instructional features.

• Integrated Content

Each year the curriculum advances students' understanding of mathematics along interwoven strands of algebra and functions, statistics and probability, geometry and trigonometry, and discrete mathematics. These strands are unified by fundamental themes, by common topics, and by mathematical habits of mind or ways of thinking. Developing mathematics each year along multiple strands helps students develop diverse mathematical insights and nurtures their differing strengths and talents.

• Mathematical Modeling

The curriculum emphasizes mathematical modeling including the processes of data collection, representation, interpretation, prediction, and simulation. The modeling perspective permits students to experience mathematics as a means of making sense of data and problems that arise in diverse contexts within and across cultures.

• Access and Challenge

The curriculum is designed to make mathematics accessible to more students, while at the same time challenging the most able students. Differences in students' performance and interest can be accommodated by the depth and level of abstraction to which core mathematics topics are pursued, by the nature and degree of difficulty of applications, and by providing opportunities for student choice of homework tasks and projects.

• Technology

Numeric, graphic, and programming capabilities such as those found on many graphing calculators are assumed and appropriately used throughout the curriculum. The curriculum materials also include a suite of computer software called *CPMP-Tools* that provide powerful aids to learning mathematics and solving mathematical problems. (See pages xvii–xviii for further details.) This use of technology permits the curriculum and instruction to emphasize multiple representations (verbal, numerical, graphical, and symbolic) and to focus on goals in which mathematical thinking and problem solving are central.

- ### Active Learning

  Instructional materials promote active learning and teaching centered around collaborative investigations of problem situations followed by teacher-led whole-class summarizing activities that lead to analysis, abstraction, and further application of underlying mathematical ideas and principles. Students are actively engaged in exploring, conjecturing, verifying, generalizing, applying, proving, evaluating, and communicating mathematical ideas.

- ### Multi-dimensional Assessment

  Comprehensive assessment of student understanding and progress through both curriculum-embedded assessment opportunities and supplementary assessment tasks supports instruction and enables monitoring and evaluation of each student's performance in terms of mathematical processes, content, and dispositions.

Core-Plus Mathematics is designed to make mathematics accessible and more meaningful to more students. Developing mathematics along multiple strands nurtures the differing strengths and talents of students and simultaneously helps them to develop diverse mathematical insights. Developing mathematics from a modeling perspective permits students to experience mathematics as a means of making sense of data and problems that arise in diverse contexts within and across cultures. Engaging students in collaborating on tasks in small groups develops their ability to both deal with, and find commonality in, diversity of ideas. Using technology as a means for learning and doing mathematics enables students to develop versatile ways of dealing with realistic situations and reduces the manipulative skill filter which has prevented large numbers of students from continuing their study of significant mathematics. In addition, technology-produced graphics offer powerful new ways of visualizing mathematics across each of the strands.

Integrated Mathematics

Core-Plus Mathematics replaces the traditional Algebra-Geometry-Advanced Algebra/Trigonometry-Precalculus sequence of high school mathematics courses with a sequence of courses that features concurrent and connected development of important mathematics drawn from four strands.

Algebra and Functions

The Algebra and Functions strand develops student ability to recognize, represent, and solve problems involving relations among quantitative variables. Central to the development is the use of functions as mathematical models. The key algebraic models in the curriculum are linear, exponential, power, polynomial, logarithmic, rational, and trigonometric functions. Modeling with systems of equations, both linear and nonlinear, is developed. Attention is also given to symbolic reasoning and manipulation.

Geometry and Trigonometry

The primary goal of the Geometry and Trigonometry strand is to develop visual thinking and ability to construct, reason with, interpret, and apply mathematical models of patterns in visual and physical contexts. The focus is on describing patterns in shape, size, and location; representing patterns with drawings, coordinates, or vectors; predicting changes and invariants in shapes under transformations; and organizing geometric facts and relationships through deductive reasoning.

Statistics and Probability

The primary goal of the Statistics and Probability strand is to develop student ability to analyze data intelligently, to recognize and measure variation, and to understand the patterns that underlie probabilistic situations. The ultimate goal is for students to understand how inferences can be made about a population by looking at a sample from that population. Graphical methods of data analysis, simulations, sampling, and experience with the collection and interpretation of real data are featured.

Discrete Mathematics

The Discrete Mathematics strand develops student ability to solve problems using vertex-edge graphs, recursion, matrices, systematic counting methods (combinatorics), and voting methods. Key themes are discrete mathematical modeling, optimization, and algorithmic problem-solving.

Connected Strands

Each of these four strands of mathematics is developed within focused units connected by fundamental ideas such as symmetry, matrices, functions, data analysis, and curve-fitting. The strands also are connected across units by mathematical habits of mind such as visual thinking, recursive thinking, searching for and explaining patterns, making and checking conjectures, reasoning with multiple representations, inventing mathematics, and providing convincing arguments and proofs.

   The strands are unified further by the fundamental themes of data, representation, shape, and change. Important mathematical ideas are frequently revisited through this attention to connections within and across strands, enabling students to develop a robust and connected understanding of mathematics.

Organization of Course 1

Course 1 consists of eight units. Each of the units is comprised of two to five multi-day lessons in which major ideas are developed through investigation of rich applied problems. Units vary in length from approximately two to six weeks.

Unit 1 *Patterns of Change*	**Unit 5** *Exponential Functions*
Unit 2 *Patterns in Data*	**Unit 6** *Patterns in Shape*
Unit 3 *Linear Functions*	**Unit 7** *Quadratic Functions*
Unit 4 *Vertex Edge Graphs*	**Unit 8** *Patterns in Chance*

   The 2nd Edition of Course 1 builds on the strengths of the 1st Edition. It includes mathematical content which the developers believed was the most important mathematics all ninth-grade students should have the opportunity to learn. In particular, the content of the last units in the text are not viewed as optional as is often the case with traditional textbooks. Depending on the mathematics standards and content expectations for your state, you may wish to have students complete all Course 1 units before they embark on Course 2 of the *Core-Plus Mathematics* series.

Instructional Model

The manner in which students encounter mathematical ideas can contribute significantly to the quality of their learning and the depth of their understanding. *Core-Plus Mathematics* units are designed around multi-day lessons centered on big ideas. Each lesson includes 2–5 focused mathematical investigations that engage students in a four-phase cycle of classroom activities, described in the following paragraph—*Launch, Explore, Share and Summarize,* and *Apply*. This cycle is designed to engage students in investigating and making sense of problem situations, in constructing important mathematical concepts and methods, in generalizing and proving mathematical relationships, and in communicating, both orally and in writing, their thinking and the results of their efforts. Most classroom activities are designed to be completed by students working collaboratively in groups of two to four students.

LAUNCH class discussion

Think About This Situation

The lesson launch promotes a teacher-led discussion of a problem situation and of related questions to think about. This discussion sets the context for the student work to follow and helps to generate student interest. It also provides an opportunity for the teacher to assess student knowledge and to clarify directions for the investigation to follow.

EXPLORE group investigation

Investigation

Classroom activity then shifts to investigating focused problems and questions related to the launching situation by gathering data, looking for and explaining patterns, constructing models and meanings, and making and verifying conjectures. As students collaborate in pairs or small groups, the teacher circulates among students providing guidance and support, clarifying or asking questions, giving hints, providing encouragement, and drawing group members into the discussion to help groups collaborate more effectively. The investigations and related questions posed by students and teachers drive the learning.

SHARE AND SUMMARIZE class discussion

Summarize the Mathematics

This investigative work is followed by a teacher-led class discussion (referred to as Summarize the Mathematics) in which students summarize mathematical ideas developed in their groups, providing an opportunity to construct a shared understanding of important concepts, methods, and approaches. This discussion leads to a class summary of important ideas or to further exploration of a topic if competing perspectives remain. Varying points of view and differing conclusions that can be justified should be encouraged.

APPLY individual tasks

Check Your Understanding

Students are given a task to complete on their own to check and reinforce their initial understanding of concepts and methods.

Overview

Homework

In addition to the classroom investigations, *Core-Plus Mathematics* provides sets of On Your Own tasks, which are designed to engage students in applying, connecting, reflecting on, extending, and reviewing their evolving mathematical knowledge. On Your Own tasks are provided for each lesson in the materials and are central to the learning goals of each lesson. These tasks are intended primarily for individual work outside of class. Selection of homework tasks should be based on student performance and the availability of time and technology. Also, students should exercise some choice of tasks to pursue, and, at times should be given the opportunity to pose their own problems and questions to investigate. The chart below describes the types of tasks in a typical On Your Own set.

On Your Own: Homework Tasks	
Applications	These tasks provide opportunities for students to use and strengthen their understanding of the ideas they have learned in the lesson.
Connections	These tasks help students to build links between mathematical topics they have studied in the lesson and to connect those topics with other mathematics that they know.
Reflections	These tasks provide opportunities for students to re-examine their thinking about ideas in the lesson.
Extensions	These tasks provide opportunities for students to explore further or more deeply the mathematics they are learning.
Review	These tasks provide opportunities for just-in-time review and distributed practice of mathematical skills to maintain procedural fluency.

Additional Summarizing Activities

In *Core-Plus Mathematics*, students learn mathematics by doing mathematics. However, it is important that students prepare and maintain summaries of important concepts and methods that are developed. Students should create a Math Toolkit that organizes important class-generated ideas and selected Summarize the Mathematics responses as they complete investigations. Math Toolkit Prompts are provided in this *Teacher's Guide* to assist in identifying and summarizing key concepts and methods as they are developed by students.

In addition, the final lesson in each unit is a Looking Back lesson that helps students review and synthesize the key mathematical concepts and techniques presented in the unit. The Summarize the Mathematics questions in this lesson are focused on key ideas of the unit. The Check Your Understanding asks students to prepare a summary of the important concepts and skills developed in the unit. Templates to guide preparation of these unit summaries can be found in the *Unit Resource Masters*. Completed Unit Summaries should become part of students' Math Toolkits.

Students should retain their Math Toolkits as they continue on to Courses 2–4. In some districts, teachers collect these resources at the end of the school year and return them to students in the fall.

Multiple Approaches to Assessment

Assessing what students know and are able to do is an integral part of *Core-Plus Mathematics*. There are opportunities for assessment in each phase of the instructional cycle. Initially, as students pursue the investigations that comprise the curriculum, the teacher is able to informally assess student understanding of mathematical processes and content and their disposition toward mathematics. At the end of each investigation, a class discussion to Summarize the Mathematics provides an opportunity for the teacher to assess levels of understanding that various groups of students have reached as they share and explain their findings. Finally, the Check Your Understanding tasks and the tasks in the On Your Own sets provide further opportunities to assess the level of understanding of each individual student. Quizzes, in-class tests, take-home assessment tasks, and extended projects are included in the teacher resource materials.

A more detailed description of the complete assessment program is given on pages xxi–xxv of this text and in *Implementing Core-Plus Mathematics*.

Practicing for Standardized Tests

Opportunities for additional review and practice are provided in eight Preparing for Standardized Tests practice sets. Each Practicing for Standardized Tests master presents 10 questions and a test-taking tip. The questions are presented in the form of test items similar to how they often appear in standardized tests such as state assessments tests, the Preliminary Scholastic Aptitude Test (PSAT), or the ACT PLAN. By using these practice sets, students can become familiar with the formats of standardized tests and develop effective test-taking strategies for performing well on such tests.

Access, Equity, and Differentiation

Several research studies have provided evidence that introducing activities through class discussion, teaching students to explain and justify, and making real-world contexts accessible to students promote greater access and equity in mathematics classrooms. (Boaler, J. "Learning from Teaching: Exploring the Relationship Between Reform Curriculum and Equity," *Journal for Research in Mathematics Education*, 2002, Vol. 33, No. 4, 239-258, and Brown, C.A., Stein, M.K., and Forman, E. A. "Assisting teachers and students to reform their mathematics classroom," *Education Studies in Mathematics*, 1996, 31–93). These practices that help promote equity are briefly discussed below.

Introducing Investigations Through Class Discussions Group and class discussions of the aim of investigations, the meaning of contexts, the challenging points within problems, and possible problem access points to which students might turn make tasks more evenly accessible to all students.

Teaching Students to Explain and Justify their Thinking Giving explicit attention to explaining thinking and evaluating what makes a good piece of work helps students improve their work.

Making Real-world Contexts Accessible Considering the constraints that real situations involve and connecting these situations with issues and topics in their own lives helps students view mathematics as something that will help them interpret their world.

Other Practices that Promote Equity Mixed-ability classes, a focus on problems solving, high expectations for all students, attention to a broad array of mathematical topics, and allowing students to restate problems in their own words also appear to help students from different racial, ethnic, and linguistic groups be more successful in mathematics.

Overview

Core-Plus Mathematics offers many opportunities for teachers to incorporate these practices into daily routines. One such built-in opportunity is the Think About This Situations (TATS) used to introduce lessons through discussions. Although no TATS questions are in the student text for individual investigations there are often suggestions in the *Teacher's Guide* for class launches of investigations. Since much of the mathematical content is based on real contexts, it is important that all students understand the contexts and draw on their own or a classmates background knowledge. Opportunities for students to explain and justify their thinking are built into all curriculum features. Look for opportunities to encourage the habit of mind of justifying their thinking, individually and in small group or class discussions.

In addition, in the *Teacher's Guide* periodically, notes provide specific ideas for differentiation at point of use. Look for the margin notes.

Implementing the Curriculum

Considering mathematics topics and knowledge presented at each grade level and how that knowledge is built upon in succeeding grades is key to improving student learning. To support building the teacher expertise to effectively implement *Core-Plus Mathematics* the developers recommend that districts begin adoption with Course 1 and add a course level each year. Encourage teachers to progress from Course 1 to Course 4 in stages, so they can develop an understanding of the growth of mathematical ideas in the curriculum. Realize that teachers will need time and support to improve instruction for their students.

Additional advice related to successful implementation is on the Core-Plus Mathematics Projects web site at www.wmich.edu/cpmp under Implementation.

Planning for Instruction

The *Core-Plus Mathematics* curriculum is not only changing what mathematics all students have the opportunity to learn, but also changing how that learning occurs and is assessed. Active learning is most effective when accompanied with active teaching. Just as the student text is designed to actively engage students in doing mathematics, the teacher's resource materials are designed to support teachers in planning for instruction; in observing, listening, questioning, and facilitating student work, and orchestrating classroom discussion; and in managing the classroom.

The *Teacher's Guide* provides suggestions, based on the experiences of field-test teachers, for implementing this exciting new curriculum in your classroom. You probably will find new ideas that can at first be overwhelming. The developers highly recommend that teachers who are teaching *Core-Plus Mathematics* for the first time do so at least in pairs who share a common planning period.

Each of the items listed below is included in the *Teacher's Guide* for each unit.
- Unit Overview
- Objectives, suggested timeline, and materials needed
- Instructional notes and suggestions
- Suggested assignments for each homework set
- Solutions for Investigations and homework tasks

Each *Unit Resource Masters* book includes teaching, student activity, technology tip, unit summary, and practicing for standardized test masters. Also included in each *Unit Resource Masters* book is the assessment package for the unit as outlined on pages xxi–xxv.

A first step toward planning the teaching of a unit is to review the scope and sequence of the unit. This review provides an overall feel for the goals of the unit and how it holds together. The *Scope and Sequence* guide shows where specific mathematical topics fit in the complete four-year curriculum. Working through the student investigations, if possible with a colleague, provides help in thinking about and understanding mathematical ideas that may be unfamiliar.

In the *Teacher's Guide*, at the beginning of each unit, you will find a Planning Guide to assist in overall planning. This resource gives a quick overview of lessons, suggested assignments, materials needed, and pacing suggestions.

You will also find teaching notes for each lesson, including instructional suggestions and sample student responses to investigations and homework sets. Thinking about the range of possible responses and solutions to problems proves to be very helpful in facilitating student work.

Some teachers choose to post the homework assignment at the beginning of a lesson along with the due date—usually a day or two following planned completion of the lesson. Other teachers prefer to assign particular tasks at appropriate points during the course of the multiday investigation, and then assign the remaining tasks toward the end of the lesson. Review tasks can be assigned before the completion of the investigation. Note that all recommended assignments include provision for student choice of some tasks. This is but one of many ways in which this curriculum is designed to accommodate and support differences in students' interests and performance levels.

It is strongly recommended that student solutions to Connections tasks be discussed in class. These tasks help students organize and formalize the mathematics developed in context and connect it to other mathematics they have studied. Structuring the underlying mathematics and building connections are best accomplished by comparing and discussing student work and synthesizing key ideas within the classroom.

Technology in Course 1

In the 21st century, anyone who faces the challenge of learning mathematics or using mathematics to solve problems can draw on the resources of powerful information technology tools. Calculators and computers can help with calculations, drawing, and data analysis in mathematical explorations and solving mathematical problems.

Graphing Calculators: Graphing calculators with iteration capabilities are assumed for class work and homework.

Computers: Periodically, it would be valuable to have one classroom computer for whole class discussions, 4–6 classroom computers for groups to use as stations during investigations, portable classroom sets of computers, or computer lab access. For some homework tasks, school or home computer availability is also desirable.

Overview

Computer software: The use of spreadsheet, interactive geometry, data analysis, and vertex-edge graph software, and computer algebra systems (CAS) is incorporated into Course 1 units. The curriculum materials include computer software called *CPMP-Tools* specifically designed to support student learning and problem solving.

The suite of Java-based mathematical software, includes four families of programs:

Algebra The software for work on algebra problems include an electronic spreadsheet and a computer algebra system (CAS) that produces tables and graphs of functions, manipulates algebraic expressions, and solves equations and inequalities.

Geometry The software for work on geometry problems include an interactive drawing program for constructing, measuring, and manipulating geometric figures and a set of custom tools for studying geometric models of physical mechanisms, tessellations, and special shapes.

Statistics The software for work on data analysis and probability problems provide tools for graphic display and analysis of data, simulation of probability experiments, and mathematical modeling of quantitative relationships.

Discrete Mathematics The software for work on graph theory problems provide software for constructing, manipulating, and analyzing vertex-edge graphs.

In addition to the general purpose tools provided for work on tasks in each strand of *Core-Plus Mathematics*, *CPMP-Tools* includes files that provide electronic copies of most data sets essential for work on problems in each *Core-Plus Mathematics* course. When students see an opportunity to use computer tools for work on a particular investigation, they can select the *CPMP-Tools* menu corresponding to the content involved in the problem. Then they can select the sub-menu items corresponding to the required mathematical operations and data sets. Each unit overview in the Teacher's Guide provides general information related to *CPMP-Tools* use in the unit. Technology notes at point of use alert teachers to applicable software and specific data sets included in the software.

Overview

Materials Needed for Course 1

The following is a complete list of items used in the eight units of Course 1. Each unit Planning Guide indicates the items used in that unit.

Necessary

Rubber bands and weights

Meter sticks

Compasses

Protractors

Transparent rulers in metric and English scales

Dice

Watch with second hand or stopwatch

Red and black checkers

Various balls that bounce

Coins and unpopped corn or beans

12-foot loop of rope with knots at 6-inch intervals

Spaghetti

Linkage strips

Mirror tiles (or plastic sheets) to make two- and three-mirror kaleidoscopes

Acrylic plastic mirrors

Set of tetrahedral, octagonal, decahedral, and icosahedral dice

One penny per student

Optional:

Identical weights such as small cubes or plastic interlocking blocks

Backgammon set

Colored pencils

Electronic Resources

The *Core-Plus Mathematics* student text, *Teacher's Guide,* and *Unit Resource Masters* are included for viewing and printing form the Core-Plus Mathematics TeacherWorks Plus CD-ROM. Custom tailoring of assessment items can be accomplished by using the ExamView Assessment Suites. *CPMP-Tools* is available on both the StudentWorks and TeacherWorks Plus CD-ROMs.

Orchestrating Lessons

Core-Plus Mathematics is designed to engage students in a four-phase cycle of classroom activities. The activities often require both students and teachers to assume roles quite different than those in more traditional mathematics classrooms. Becoming accustomed to these new roles usually takes time, perhaps a semester or more, but field-test teachers report that the time and effort required are well worth it in terms of student learning and professional fulfillment. Although realistic problem solving and investigative work by students are the heart of the curriculum, how teachers orchestrate the launching of an investigation and the sharing and summarizing of results is critical to successful implementation.

Students enter the classroom with differing backgrounds, experience, and knowledge. These differences can be viewed as assets. Engaging the class in a free-flowing give-and-take discussion of how students think about the launch situations serves to connect lessons with the informal understandings of data, shape, change, and chance that students bring to the classroom. Try to maximize the participation of students in these discussions by emphasizing that their ideas and possible approaches are valued and important and that definitive answers are not necessarily expected at this time.

Overview

Once launched, an investigation may involve students working together collaboratively in small groups for a period of days punctuated occasionally by brief class discussion of questions students have raised. In this setting, the investigation becomes driven primarily by the instructional materials themselves. Rather than orchestrating class discussion, the teacher shifts to circulating among the groups and observing, listening, and interacting with students by asking guiding or probing questions. These small-group investigations lead to (re)invention of important mathematics that makes sense to students. Sharing, and agreeing as a class, on the mathematical ideas that groups are developing is the purpose of the Summarizing the Mathematics (STM) in the instructional materials.

Class discussions at STMs are orchestrated somewhat differently than during the launch of a lesson. At this stage, mathematical ideas and methods still may be under development and may vary for individual groups. So class discussion should involve groups comparing their methods and results, analyzing their work, and arriving at conclusions agreed upon by the class.

The investigations deepen students' understanding of mathematical ideas and extend their mathematical language. Technical terminology and symbolism are introduced as needed. This sometimes occurs in student materials immediately following an STM and before the corresponding Check Your Understanding task. The technical terminology and symbolism should be introduced by the teacher as a natural way of closing the class discussion summarizing investigation content.

Periodically, you will find sample class discussions for Think About This Situations and Summarize the mathematics curriculum features at point of use. These sample discussions, called Promoting Mathematical Discourse, may provide some ideas for your class discussions. The following icon denotes the existence of a sample discussion.

PROMOTING MATHEMATICAL DISCOURSE

Assessment

Throughout the *Core-Plus Mathematics* curriculum, the term "assessment" is meant to include all instances of gathering information about students' levels of understanding and their disposition toward mathematics for purposes of making decisions about instruction. You may want to consult the extended section on assessment in *Implementing Core-Plus Mathematics*.

The dimensions of student performance that are assessed in this curriculum (see chart below) are consistent with the assessment recommendations of the National Council of Teachers of Mathematics in the *Assessment Standards for School Mathematics* (NCTM, 1995). They are more comprehensive than those of a typical testing program.

Assessment Dimensions		
Process	**Content**	**Disposition**
Problem Solving	Concepts	Beliefs
Reasoning	Applications	Perseverance
Communication	Representational Strategies	Confidence
Connections	Procedures	Enthusiasm

Overview

Sources of Assessment Information

Several kinds of assessment are available to teachers using *Core-Plus Mathematics*. Some of these sources reside within the curriculum itself, some of them are student-generated, and some are supplementary materials designed specifically for assessment. Understanding the nature of these sources is a prerequisite for selecting assessment tools, establishing guidelines on how to score assessments, making judgments about what students know and are able to do, and assigning grades.

Curriculum Sources

Two features of the curriculum, questioning and observation by the teacher, provide fundamental and particularly useful ways of gathering formative assessment information. The student text uses questions to facilitate student understanding of new concepts, of how these concepts fit with earlier ideas and with one another, and of how they can be applied in problem situations. Whether students are working individually or in groups, the teacher is given a window to watch how the students think about and apply mathematics as they attempt to answer the questions posed by the curriculum materials. In fact, by observing how students respond to the curriculum-embedded questions, the teacher can assess student performance across all process, content, and attitude dimensions described in the chart on the previous page.

Specific features in the student material that focus on different ways students respond to questions are the Summarize the Mathematics, Check Your Understanding, and the On Your Own homework sets. Summarize the Mathematics features are intended to bring students together, usually after they have been working in small groups, so they may share and discuss the progress each group has made during a sequence of related activities. The questions in the Summarize the Mathematics are focused on the mathematical concepts and procedures developed in the investigation. They should help the teacher and the students identify and formalize the key ideas of the investigation. Each Summarize the Mathematics is intended to be a whole-class discussion, so it should provide an opportunity for teachers to assess, informally, the levels of understanding that the various groups of students have reached.

Following each Summarize the Mathematics, the Check Your Understanding tasks are meant to be completed by students working individually. Student responses to these tasks provide an opportunity for teachers to assess the level of understanding of each student.

The tasks in the On Your Own homework sets serve many purposes, including post-investigation assessment. Each type of task in the On Your Own homework sets has a different instructional purpose. Applications tasks provide opportunities for students to demonstrate how well they understand and can use the ideas they learned in the investigations of the lesson. Work on Connections tasks demonstrates how well the students understand links between mathematical topics they studied in the lesson and their ability to connect those topics with other mathematics that they know. Reflections tasks provide insight into student's beliefs, attitudes, and judgments about their mathematical thinking and analysis. Extensions tasks show how well students are able to extend the present content beyond the level addressed in the investigations. The review tasks allow for pre-assessment of students' understanding of ideas or procedures needed in the upcoming lessons and also provide information on how well students are retaining previously learned mathematics. The performance of students or groups of students in each of these types of tasks provides the teacher with further information to help assess each student's evolving ability to use, connect, and extend the mathematics of the lesson.

Finally, an opportunity for group self-assessment is provided in the last element of each unit, the Looking Back lesson. These tasks help students pull together and demonstrate what they have learned in the unit and at the same time provide helpful review and confidence-building for students.

Student-Generated Sources

Mathematics Toolkits Students should create a Math Toolkit that organizes important class-generated ideas and selected Summarize the Mathematics responses as they complete investigations. Constructing a Math Toolkit prompts are provided in the *Teacher's Guide* to assist in identifying key concepts and methods as they are developed by students.

Unit Summaries A summary template intended to help students organize and record the main ideas learned in the unit is provided in each *Unit Resource Masters* book. The synthesis of ideas that occurs during completion of the "Looking Back" lesson and the final unit Summarize the Mathematics discussion should provide the background for student completion of the unit summary.

Assessment Resources

Each *Unit Resource Masters* book includes lesson quizzes and unit assessments in the form of tests, take-home tasks, and projects. There are also banks of questions and projects from which you can form end of semester exams following the Unit 4 and Unit 8 assessment masters. Calculators are assumed in most cases and are intended to be available to students. Teacher discretion should be used regarding student access to their textbook and Math Toolkit for assessments. In general, if the goals to be assessed are problem solving and reasoning, while memory of facts and procedural skill are of less interest, resources may be allowed. However, if automaticity of procedures or unaided recall are being assessed, it is appropriate to prohibit resource materials.

The ExamView Assessment Suite software can be used to modify the problems curriculum provided assessment items or to create formal assessments using a combination of curriculum supplied items and ones by the teacher.

Lesson Quizzes Two forms of a quiz covering the main ideas of each lesson are provided. These quizzes are comprised of problems meant to determine if students have developed understanding of the important concepts and procedures of each lesson. The two forms of each quiz are not necessarily equivalent, although they assess essentially the same mathematical ideas. Since many rich opportunities for assessing students are embedded in the curriculum itself, you may choose not to use a quiz at the end of every lesson.

Overview

Unit Tests Two forms of tests are provided for each unit and are intended to be completed in a 50-minute class period. The two forms of each tests are not necessarily equivalent, although they assess essentially the same mathematical ideas. Teachers should preview the two versions carefully to be sure that the unit assessment aligns with the learning goals emphasized.

Take-Home Assessments Take-home assessment tasks are included for each unit. The students or the teacher should choose one or, at most, two of these tasks. These assessments, some of which are best done by students working in pairs or small groups, provide students with the opportunity to organize the information from the completed unit, to work with another student or group of students, to engage in in-depth problem solving, to grapple with new and more complex situations related to the mathematics of the unit, and to avoid the time pressure often generated by in-class exams. These problems may also require more extensive use of technology than is often available in the regular classroom during testing situations. You may wish to use these more in-depth problems as a replacement for a portion of an in-class end-of-unit exam.

Projects Assessment traditionally has been based on evaluating work that students have completed in a very short time period and under restricted conditions. Some assessment, however, should involve work done over a longer time period and with the aid of resources. Thus, assessment projects are included in unit assessments. These projects, which are intended to be completed by small groups of students, provide an opportunity for students to conduct an investigation that extends and applies the main ideas from the unit and to write a summary of their findings. Many of these might also allow for students to present their work in a variety of ways. You may have students who would rather prepare and present their work orally or visually using computers and/or video equipment. In this way, the projects can provide an opportunity for students to use their creativity while demonstrating their understanding of mathematics.

Midterm and Final Assessments A bank of assessment tasks, from which to construct midterm and final exams that fit your particular class needs and emphases, are provided in the Unit Resource Masters following the Unit 4 and Unit 8 assessments. In addition to problems similar in form to those on the quizzes and tests, these assessment banks include several multiple-choice problems for each unit.

   Extended assessment projects are also included with the end-of-year assessments. These projects are investigations that make use of many of the main ideas encountered in the curriculum. They require use of material from more than one unit. The projects are intended to be completed by small groups of students working over a period of time. You may wish to have different groups work on different projects and then give presentations or create posters of their work.

Portfolios The *Core-Plus Mathematics* assessment program provides many items that can be placed in students' portfolios, including reports of individual and group projects, Math Toolkits, teacher-completed observation checklists, unit assessments (especially the take-home tasks), and projects. See *Implementing Core-Plus Mathematics* for additional portfolio information.

Overview

Scoring Assessments

High expectations of the quality of students' written work will encourage students to reach their potential. Assigning scores to open-ended assessments and to observations of students' performance requires more subjective judgment by the teacher than does grading short-answer or multiple-choice tests. It is therefore not possible to provide a complete set of explicit guidelines for scoring open-ended assessment items and written or oral reports. However, some general guidelines may be helpful. When scoring student work on open-ended assessment tasks, the goal is to reward, in a fair and consistent way, the kinds of thinking and understanding that the task is meant to measure. To score open-ended assessment tasks, teachers should have a general rubric, or scoring scheme, with several response levels in mind; a specific rubric and anchor items. (See *Implementing Core-Plus Mathematics* for more details.) The general rubric is the foundation for scoring across a wide range of types of open-ended tasks. The following general rubric can be used for most assessment tasks provided with *Core-Plus Mathematics*.

General Scoring Rubric	
4 points	Contains complete response with clear, coherent, and unambiguous explanation; includes clear and simple diagram, if appropriate; communicates effectively to identified audience; shows understanding of question's mathematical ideas and processes; identifies all important elements of question; includes examples and counterexamples; gives strong supporting arguments
3 points	Contains good solid response with some, but not all, of the characteristics above; explains less completely; may include minor error of execution but not of understanding
2 points	Contains complete response, but explanation is muddled; presents incomplete arguments; includes diagrams that are inappropriate or unclear, or fails to provide a diagram when it would be appropriate; indicates some understanding of mathematical ideas, but in an unclear way; shows clear evidence of understanding some important ideas while also making one or more fundamental, specific errors
1 point	Omits parts of question and response; has major errors; uses inappropriate strategies
0 points	No response; frivolous or irrelevant response

Assigning Grades

Since the *Core-Plus Mathematics* approach and materials provide a wide variety of assessment information, the teacher will be in a good position to assign appropriate grades. With such a wide choice for assessment, a word of caution is appropriate. It is easy to overassess students. The developers believe it is best to vary assessment methods from lesson to lesson, and from unit to unit. If information on what students understand and are able to do is available from their homework and in-class work, it may not be necessary to take the time for a formal quiz after each lesson. Similarly, information from take-home assessments or project work may replace all or portions of an in-class test.

Deciding exactly how to weigh the various kinds of assessment information is a decision that the teacher will need to make and communicate clearly to students.

Managing Classroom Activities

Active Learning and Collaborative Work

The *Core-Plus Mathematics* curriculum materials are designed to promote active, collaborative learning and group work for two important reasons. First, a collaborative environment fosters students' ability to make sense of mathematics and develop deep mathematical understandings. Collaborative learning is an effective method for engaging all the students in the learning process, particularly students who have been under represented in mathematics classes. Second, practice in collaborative learning in the classroom is practice for real life: students develop and exercise the same skills in the classroom that they need in their lives at home, in the community, and in the workplace.

Value of Individuals

Perhaps the most fundamental belief underlying the use of collaborative learning is that every student is viewed as a valuable resource and contributor. In other words, every student participates in group work and is given the opportunity and time to voice ideas and opinions. Implementing this concept is not easy nor does it happen automatically. In order to set a tone that will promote respect for individuals and their contributions, classroom norms should be established. Teachers should initiate a discussion and together write all the student formulated classrooms rules for both individual and group behavior. The positively states rules of behavior should be posted in the classroom and every member of the learning community should be held responsible for adhering to them.

Importance of Social Connections

Even in classrooms in which the rules for showing respect have been clearly established, experience has shown that students still cannot talk with one another about mathematics (or social studies, or literature, or any other subject) if they do not first have positive social connections.

One way to develop this kind of common base is through team-building activities. These short activities may be used at the beginning of the year to help students get acquainted with the whole class, and may be used during the year whenever new groups are formed to help groupmates know one another better. Team-building activities help students learn new and positive things about classmates with whom they may have attended classes for years, but have not known in depth. The time taken for these quick team builders pays off later in helping students feel comfortable enough to work with the members of their group.

Need for Teaching Social Skills

Experience also has shown that social skills are critical to the successful functioning of any small group. Because there is no guarantee that students of any particular age will have the social skills necessary for effective group work, it often is necessary to teach these skills to build a collaborative learning environment.

These social skills are specific skills, not general goals. Examples of specific social skills that the teacher can teach in the classroom include responding to ideas respectfully, keeping track of time, disagreeing in an agreeable way,

Overview

involving everyone, and following directions. Though goals such as cooperating and listening are important, they are too general to teach.

One of the premises of collaborative learning is that by developing the appropriate skills through practice, anyone in the class can learn to work in a group with anyone else. Learning to work in groups is a continuous process, however, and the process can be helped by decisions that the teacher makes.

One method of teaching social skills is to begin by selecting a specific skill and then having the class brainstorm to develop a script for practicing that skill. Next, the students practice that skill during their group work. Finally, in what is called the processing, the students discuss within their groups how well they performed the assigned social skill. Effective teaching of social skills requires practicing and processing; merely describing a specific social skill is not enough. The *Teacher's Guide* includes specific collaborative skills to practice and processing prompts for student self-assessment.

The culture created within the classroom is crucial to the success of this curriculum. It is important to inculcate in students a sense of inquiry and responsibility for their own learning. Without this commitment, active, collaborative learning by students cannot be effective. Some students seem satisfied with the rationale that collaboration is important in workplace. Others may need to understand that the struggle of verbalizing their thinking, listening to others' thinking, questioning themselves and other group members, and coming to an agreement increases their understanding and retention of the mathematics while contributing to the formation of important thinking skills or habits of mind.

Issues of helping students to work collaboratively will become less pressing as both you and your students experience this type of learning. *Implementing Core-Plus Mathematics* provides additional information related to the challenge of facilitating collaborative work including support to help teachers make decisions about group size, composition, method of selection, the duration of groups and dealing with student absences. This resource also offers a number of practical suggestions from *Core-Plus Mathematics* teachers on effectively pacing instruction in a student-centered classroom.

Additional Resources

Implementing Core-Plus Mathematics contains expanded information on:
- the scope and sequence of Courses 1–4,
- managing classroom activities,
- differentiation built into the program,
- the assessment program,
- communication with parents, and
- mathematics program evaluation.

You will find it useful to have the implementation guide available for reference throughout the school year.

Math Link articles that are related to *Core-Plus Mathematics* written by developers and teachers are available on the Core-Plus Mathematics Project Web Site at www.wmich.edu/cpmp under "Publications". These articles were written based on first edition experiences, but in many cases are still applicable to the second edition materials.

Topics include:

- selecting and implementing *Core-Plus Mathematics*,
- effectively using collaborative groups,
- the four-year mathematics program,
- options for acceleration paths to AP Calculus or AP Statistics
- meeting the needs of ELL and LEP students,
- college placement
- the International Baccalaureate Program, and
- achievement in Science.

Annotated Bibliography Available on the CPMP Web site under "Publications" are references to articles, book chapters, dissertations, papers presented at conferences, and field-test reports based on the program. Some of these resources can be downloaded.

Professional Development Opportunities A variety of professional development opportunities are provided by Glencoe and the Core-Plus Mathematics Project. Workshops are listed on the CPMP Web site www.wmich.edu/cpmp under "Teacher Support." Experienced *Core-Plus Mathematics* teacher-consultants can be contracted to provide onsite inservice. Contact your Glencoe sales representative or the CPMP office (cpmp@wmich.edu) for provider names.

Parent Support Information and resources for parents including helping with homework, research supporting *Core-Plus Mathematics*, evidence of success, and frequently asked questions is available at www.wmich.edu/cpmp/parentresource/index.html.

UNIT 1

PATTERNS OF CHANGE

Change is an important and often predictable aspect of the world in which we live. For example, in the thrill sport of bungee jumping, the stretch of the bungee cord is related to the weight of the jumper. A change in *jumper weight* causes change in *stretch of the cord*. Because bungee jumpers come in all sizes, it is important for jump operators to understand the connection between the key variables.

In this first unit of *Core-Plus Mathematics*, you will study ideas and reasoning methods of algebra that can be used to describe and predict patterns of change in quantitative variables. You will develop understanding and skill in use of algebra through work on problems in three lessons.

Lessons

1 Cause and Effect

Use tables, graphs, and algebraic rules to represent relationships between independent and dependent variables. Describe and predict the patterns of change in those cause-and-effect relationships.

2 Change Over Time

Use tables, graphs, and algebraic rules to describe, represent, and analyze patterns in variables that change with the passage of time. Use calculators and computer spreadsheets to study growth of populations and investments.

3 Tools for Studying Patterns of Change

Use calculator and computer tools to study relationships between variables that can be represented by algebraic rules. Explore connections between function rules and patterns of change in tables and graphs.

PATTERNS OF CHANGE

Unit Overview

The intent of this unit, which begins Core-*Plus Mathematics Course 1*, is to focus student attention on the variety of types of change inherent in problem situations. This unit will provide students with a broad picture of patterns of change. Students will explore linear, quadratic, inverse variation, and exponential patterns of change throughout the unit. Within this unit there is an effort to make a distinction between cause-and-effect change relationships and change-over-time relationships. In the third unit of this course, linear functions will be analyzed as a class of functions with a specific pattern of change.

Spreadsheets and computer algebra system symbol manipulation are introduced in Lessons 2 and 3. This content can be omitted without jeopardizing future work. Since this unit is an overview of patterns of change, *mastery is not expected at this stage*. The unit should be completed in under 4 weeks of classes that meet approximately 50 minutes each day.

Lesson 1 Lesson 1 begins with a bungee jump experiment in which students review the use of tables and graphs for representing relations between variables. In Investigation 2, relationships with random variation are explored. This foreshadows that aspect of Course 1 and gives an example in which the value of y is not precisely predictable from the value of x by an algebraic rule. Investigation 3 is designed to get a variety of functions on the table early. In general, it is not expected that students will be proficient at translating word problems into algebraic rules, but they might be able to use a given rule.

Lesson 2 The second lesson develops students' understanding and skill in analyzing situations that change over time. In particular, the iterative perspective in which one compares the value of a variable at one point in time to the value of the variable at successive, equally-spaced intervals is introduced.

Lesson 3 The main goals of Lesson 3 are to develop each student's ability to express problem conditions symbolically and to use symbolic representations with appropriate technology to answer questions about situations modeled by several basic patterns of change. In particular, students will learn to produce tables and graphs for functions in order to solve equations in one variable.

Lesson 4 Lesson 4, the Looking Back lesson, is intended to give students an opportunity to synthesize and pull together the main mathematical ideas of the unit. The concept of "function" is informally defined in this lesson.

Unit Objectives

- Begin developing students' sensitivity to the rich variety of situations in which quantities vary in relation to each other
- Develop students' ability to represent relations among variables in several ways—using tables of numerical data, coordinate graphs, symbolic rules, and verbal descriptions—and to interpret data presented in any one of those forms
- Develop students' ability to recognize important patterns of change in single variables and related variables

Access and Equity Matters

Research by Boaler (1998; 2000; 2002) and by the Quasar Project (Brown, Stein, & Favar, 1996) has identified particular teaching practices with curricula such as *Core-Plus Mathematics* that promote greater access and equity in mathematics classrooms. These practices include:

- introducing activities through class discussion,
- teaching students to explain and justify, and
- making real-world contexts accessible by discussing the contexts.

Core-Plus Mathematics offers many opportunities for teachers to incorporate these practices into daily routines. One such built-in opportunity is the Think About This Situation used to introduce lessons through discussion. You may wish to begin investigations in a similar way. Since much of the mathematical content is based in real-world contexts, it is important that all students understand the contexts and draw on their own or a classmate's background knowledge. Opportunities for students to explain and justify their thinking are built into all curriculum features. Encourage the habit of mind of justifying claims.

Technology Tools

This unit provides multiple opportunities for students to explore the use of spreadsheets and Computer Algebra Systems (CAS) in solving problems. These tools are available for a variety of platforms—calculator tools, computers, and handheld PDAs. *Core-Plus Mathematics* includes Java-based software called *CPMP-Tools*, specifically designed to be used with the curriculum.

CPMP-Tools is a suite of Java-based mathematical software, specifically designed to support student learning and problem solving in each strand of *Core-Plus Mathematics*. The software includes four families of programs: *Algebra* (spreadsheet and CAS), *Geometry* (coordinate and synthetic), *Statistics*, and *Discrete Math*. Each content-area tool includes specific custom tools and electronic copies of many data sets used in investigations and homework. Additional information about the course-specific software for Course 1 is included in the front matter of this *Course 1 Teacher's Guide* on page xix.

In this unit, Investigation 2 of Lesson 2 offers students an opportunity to track recursive change using spreadsheets. In Investigation 2 of Lesson 3, students are introduced to CAS technology. Three data sets are included under Statistics, Data Analysis, Unit 1 for student use.

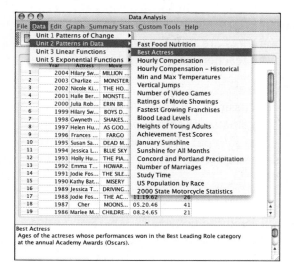
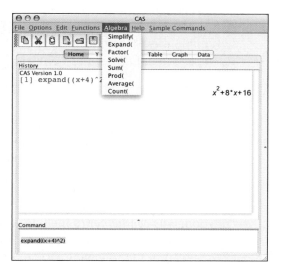

Developing a Collaborative Classroom

The CPMP curriculum materials have been designed to support learning through interactive problem-based investigations. In the first investigation, the modeling bungee jumping exploration lends itself to helping your students get to know each other in the first days of the school year and to developing collaborative group behavior guidelines like those below.

- Each member contributes to the group's work.
- Each member of the group is responsible for listening carefully when another group member is talking.
- Each member of the group has the responsibility and the right to ask questions.
- Each group member should help others in the group when asked.
- Each member of the group should be considerate and encouraging.
- Work together until everyone in the group understands and can explain the group's results.

Blackline masters to assist in developing effective collaborative groups are the first masters in the *Teaching Resources*. In addition, Collaboration Skill development suggestions occur at the beginning of selected investigations. Processing prompts for these skills occur at the Summarize the Mathematics. Holding students accountable to established group norms and giving them positive feedback regarding their group's interaction is particularly important at the early stages of developing effective working groups.

One way to help students work together effectively is to choose a collaborative skill on which to focus for a particular investigation. Introduce the skill to the class by discussing what that skill might look and sound like. Once students have worked in their groups for a class period, provide a collaborative-processing prompt that leads to a full class discussion of the particular skill. Collaboration processing prompts are often provided for your use in the *Teacher's Guide* following the Summarize the Mathematics sections. Additional resources and guidelines related to inquiry-based classrooms are in the *Implementing Core-Plus Mathematics* booklet and on the teacher planning CD.

Promoting Mathematical Discourse

Periodically, you will find sample class discussions for Think About This Situations (TATS) and Summarize the Mathematics (STM) at point of use. These sample discussions may provide some ideas for your class discussions. In this unit, Promoting Mathematical Discourse scenarios are written for the TATS on page 3 and the STMs on pages 7 and 30.

Review and Practice

Core-Plus Mathematics includes review tasks in the homework sets. The purpose of the review tasks is two-fold. Some tasks are **just-in-time review** of skills needed in the following lesson. These tasks will be designated by a clock icon in the margin of the *Teacher's Guide*. Some tasks provide **distributed practice** of mathematical skills to maintain procedural fluency. These tasks should be completed outside of class by students. If a few students are identified as needing additional assistance with specific skills, they should be given additional assistance outside of class.

Practicing for Standardized Tests

Opportunities for additional review and practice are provided in 8 Practicing for Standardized Tests practice sets. Each Practicing for Standardized Tests master presents 10 questions that draw on all content strands. The questions are presented in the form of test items similar to how they often appear in standardized tests such as state assessment tests, the Preliminary Scholastic Aptitude Test (PSAT), or the ACT PLAN. We suggest using these practice sets following the unit assessment so students can become familiar with the formats of standardized tests and develop effective test-taking strategies for performing well on such tests.

Middle School Background

If your students have experienced a functions approach to algebra in middle school, you may find that this unit is best treated as a quick review. Assigning some of the Connections and Reflections Tasks should help students deepen their understanding of the content in this unit. As indicated on page T1, mastery is not expected at this stage. Linear, exponential, and quadratic functions are developed thoroughly in Units 3, 5, and 7 of this course.

Lesson Objectives	On Your Own Assignments*	Suggested Pacing	Materials
Lesson 1 *Cause and Effect* • Develop disposition to look for cause-and-effect relationships between variables • Review and develop skills in organizing data in tables and graphs and using words to describe patterns of change shown in those representations • Review or begin to develop knowledge about common patterns of change (linear, inverse, exponential, quadratic) and ability to use symbolic rules to represent and reason about those patterns • Use tables, graphs, and rules to solve problems of cause-and-effect change	**After Investigation 1:** A1–A3, C9, R14, R15, Rv21, Rv22 **After Investigation 2:** A4, A5, C10, Rv23–Rv26 **After Investigation 3:** A6 or A7, C11–C13, R15, R16 or R17, choose one of E18–E20, Rv27, Rv28	7 days	For each group of students: • Rubber bands and fishing weights, bags of nuts and bolts, or other weights • Meter sticks • Dice • Three different coins • Unit 1 Resource Masters
Lesson 2 *Change Over Time* • Develop ability to recognize recursive patterns of change • Develop ability to use calculators to iterate stages in a recursive pattern • Develop ability to write *NOW-NEXT* rules to represent recursive patterns • Develop ability to write and use spreadsheet formulas to explore recursive patterns of change (optional investigation) • Use iteration to solve problems about population and money change over time	**After Investigation 1:** See Assignment Note below. Choose one of A1–A4, A5 or A6, C10, C11, C14, C15, R19, E22 or E23, Rv26–Rv29 **After Investigation 2:** A7, A8 or A9, C12 or C13, R20 or R21, E24 or E25, Rv30, Rv31	6 days	• Access to computers with spreadsheet software, *CPMP-Tools*, or calculators with spreadsheet capabilities • *Optional: CPMP-Tools* data analysis software for C10–12, and E23 • Unit 1 Resource Masters
Lesson 3 *Tools for Studying Patterns of Change* • Develop skill in writing rules that express problem conditions • Review perimeter and area formulas for triangles, parallelograms, and circles, and the Pythagorean Theorem • Develop skill in producing tables and graphs for functions • Develop skill in using function tables, graphs, and computer algebra manipulations to solve problems that involve functional relationships, especially solving equations in one variable • Develop informal knowledge about connections among function rules, tables, and graphs for linear, inverse, exponential, and quadratic relations	**After Investigation 1:** Choose three of A1–A5, C13, choose two of C14–C18, E25, Rv31 **After Investigation 2:** A6 or A7, A8, A9, C19, C20, R21–R23, choose one of E26–E29, Rv32 **After Investigation 3:** A10–A12, R24, E30, Rv33–Rv36	5 days	• Access to a Computer Algebra System such as in *CPMP-Tools* • Unit 1 Resource Masters
Lesson 4 *Looking Back* • Review and synthesize the major objectives of the unit		2 days (including testing)	• Unit 1 Resource Masters

* *When choice is indicated, it is important to leave the choice to the student.*

Note: *It is best if Connections tasks are discussed as a whole class after they have been assigned as homework.*

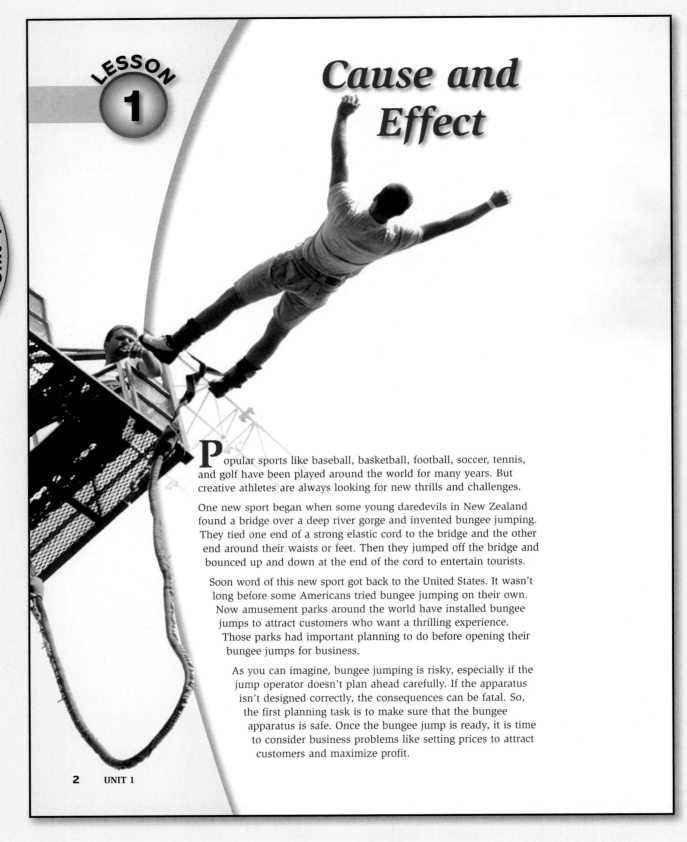

Cause and Effect

Popular sports like baseball, basketball, football, soccer, tennis, and golf have been played around the world for many years. But creative athletes are always looking for new thrills and challenges.

One new sport began when some young daredevils in New Zealand found a bridge over a deep river gorge and invented bungee jumping. They tied one end of a strong elastic cord to the bridge and the other end around their waists or feet. Then they jumped off the bridge and bounced up and down at the end of the cord to entertain tourists.

Soon word of this new sport got back to the United States. It wasn't long before some Americans tried bungee jumping on their own. Now amusement parks around the world have installed bungee jumps to attract customers who want a thrilling experience. Those parks had important planning to do before opening their bungee jumps for business.

As you can imagine, bungee jumping is risky, especially if the jump operator doesn't plan ahead carefully. If the apparatus isn't designed correctly, the consequences can be fatal. So, the first planning task is to make sure that the bungee apparatus is safe. Once the bungee jump is ready, it is time to consider business problems like setting prices to attract customers and maximize profit.

2   UNIT 1

Cause and Effect

In many practical situations, variables of interest are related so that manipulating one of the variables leads in predictable ways to changes in the second variable. Change in the *independent variable* causes change in the *dependent variable*. In this first lesson of *Core-Plus Mathematics Course 1*, we engage students in experiments and problem-solving tasks that involve a wide variety of such cause-and-effect changes. Students should develop their abilities to use tables, graphs, and (to a limited extent) equations to express relationships between independent and dependent variables and to describe the cause-and-effect patterns of those relationships.

The problems of investigations in this first lesson of the *Patterns of Change* unit are structured to help students advance development of the kind of collaborative classroom discourse community that will lead to maximum learning by all. In this lesson, there are some suggestions for skills to focus on and processing prompts to assist with discussions. Look for suggested skills at the beginning of investigations and prompts following the Summarize the Mathematics section.

Additional ideas on developing effective groups are available in an additional resource, *Implementing the Core-Plus Mathematics Curriculum,* available in print and on the Teacher Works CD.

Lesson Objectives

- Develop disposition to look for cause-and-effect relationships between variables
- Review and develop skills in organizing data in tables and graphs and using words to describe patterns of change shown in those representations
- Review or begin to develop knowledge about common patterns of change (linear, inverse, exponential, quadratic) and ability to use symbolic rules to represent and reason about those patterns
- Use tables, graphs, and rules to solve problems of cause-and-effect change

Lesson Launch

Like all Think About This Situations (TATS) in *Core-Plus Mathematics*, this opening prompt for student thinking and class discussion is designed to pique students' interest in a situation that leads to important mathematical ideas. Frequently there are no "right answers" at this point in the investigation. However, even at this introductory stage of the investigation, students should be encouraged to think through their ideas and explain the thinking that leads them to conjectures. The TATS will also allow you an opportunity to assess students' prior knowledge of the context or mathematics at hand.

PROMOTING MATHEMATICAL DISCOURSE Periodically when this icon appears you will find a sample discussion offering possible teacher-student discourse around Think About This Situation and Summarize the Mathematics questions at point of use.

Think About This Situation

Suppose that operators of Five Star Amusement Park are considering installation of a bungee jump.

a How could they design and operate the bungee jump attraction so that people of different weights could have safe but exciting jumps?

b Suppose one test with a 50-pound jumper stretched a 60-foot bungee cord to a length of 70 feet. What patterns would you expect in a table or graph showing the stretched length of the 60-foot bungee cord for jumpers of different weights?

Jumper Weight (in pounds)	50	100	150	200	250	300
Stretched Cord Length (in feet)	70	?	?	?	?	?

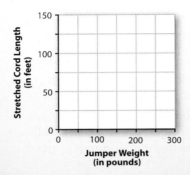

c How could the Five Star Amusement Park find the price to charge each customer so that daily income from the bungee jump attraction is maximized?

d What other safety and business problems would Five Star Amusement Park have to consider in order to set up and operate the bungee attraction safely and profitably?

As you complete the investigations in this lesson, you will learn how data tables, graphs, and algebraic rules express relations among variables. You will also learn how they can help in solving problems and making decisions like those involved in design and operation of the Five Star bungee jump.

Think About This Situation

Teaching Resources

INSTRUCTIONAL NOTE This master can be reproduced as a transparency.

Student Master 4.

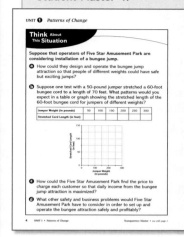

a Students' ideas about how to design a safe but exciting bungee jump will certainly vary. Possible ideas include testing the bungee cord for maximum weight or using different cords (of different elasticity) for people of different weights. They should recognize that the key relationship is between jumper weight and stretch of the bungee cord.

b Students should expect stretched length of the cord to increase as jumper weight increases. If students say they have no ideas or experience on which to base their specific numerical conjectures, ask them to use their instinct. Then be sure that as different groups or individuals report their ideas, they make an effort to explain why they completed the table in the pattern they chose. For example, a student who increases stretched cord length in constant increments should be able to say something about how he or she believes that each addition of weight has the same effect on cord length. If students complete the table in some other pattern, they should be able to give some, however conjectural, explanation of why they used the pattern they chose. (See the sample discussion in the *Teaching Resources* for this lesson.)

c Students might suggest finding out the price charged for bungee jumping at other amusement parks, taking a survey of park visitors on a given day, or lowering the price if no one signs up and raising the price if many people are interested. The goal here is to help students think about how change in one variable has an effect on the value of another variable.

d Considerations might include a concern for customers with health problems, the quality of the structure, insurance, posting a set of rules, and also an appropriate location (e.g., Is there a competitor nearby?).

Promoting Mathematical Discourse

Think About This Situation, *page 3*

Teacher: Let's think about what is involved in designing and operating a bungee jump at an amusement park. How could they design and operate the bungee jump attraction so that people of different weights could have safe but exciting jumps?

Carey: It needs to be designed so it won't break.

Sam: Yeah, and maybe there should be a safety net or a big air mattress on the ground just in case it does break.

Michael: Also, you would want to be sure the cord is strong enough to hold the weight of the person and not break and elastic enough to stretch. If the cord is too stiff, there would be no bouncing and that wouldn't be much fun.

Regina: But it can't be too stretchy or else someone might hit the ground.

Teacher: Have any of you attempted a bungee jump?

Carlotta: My older sister did. She said it was really scary but fun. The one she went on had a seat for people to sit in to prevent them from hurting their backs during the jump.

Juan: I haven't ever jumped, but if I did I would want to make sure that the straps and buckles like those in the picture on the cover page were very strong and secure. I wouldn't want the straps so tight that they choke me, though.

Teacher: Any other ideas on the design or operation of the bungee jump to make it safe but exciting?

Tessa: Maybe they could have a variety of designs for different weights. Or even offer different heights for beginners who might be afraid of the jump. Or maybe people could pick how bouncy a ride they want.

Maria: I would want to see a video first. You know, like a safety video so I would know what to expect. Otherwise, if people didn't know what to expect they might freak out and more people could be hurt.

Teacher: Interesting ideas—anything else?

Aaron: It would be more fun if the jump looked realistic. Like you are really jumping off a bridge into a gorge like the pictures in our book. Sometimes, you just jump off of a mobile bungee tower. I think more people would choose to jump if it were realistic.

Teacher: So having people want to experience the jump is important?

Aaron: Sure, otherwise the amusement park won't make any money on the ride.

Teacher: We'll think more about the money-making aspects in a few minutes. Take a look up front at the overhead screen. The Think About This Situation asks us to consider what patterns we might expect in a table or graph. We see a table of values showing the length of a 60-foot bungee cord for different weights of jumpers. *(The teacher points to the table on the overhead copy of the TATS.)* What do we know about this situation from the table?

Caroline: We know that a 50-pound jumper stretched the cord to a length of 70 feet.

Teacher: And how do we know that, Caroline?

Caroline: Because the table shows the jumper weight and the length of the stretched out cord. It says that some person weighed 50 pounds and the cord stretched to 70 feet.

Teacher: All right. Do we know anything else? *(The teacher pauses; nothing else is offered by students.)* . . . Okay. I want you to think about something for a minute and then pair up with a neighbor to discuss your thoughts. *(The teacher explicitly chooses the think-pair-share strategy so all students have time to consider possible mathematical patterns.)* This is what I want you to think about, ready? *(The teacher glances around the room to make sure she has the attention of each student.)* I want you to think about how the length of the stretched cord would change as the weight of a jumper increases. Think for a minute alone. Then share your thinking with the person next to you.

Teacher: *(The teacher allows time for students to think and discuss.)* Okay, what do you think?

Alicia: Well, we were saying that the cord would stretch more if there was more weight on it.

John: We agreed. At first we said that the cord would probably stretch 140 feet for a 100-pound person and 210 feet for a 150-pound person. But then we realized that for a 300-pound person the cord would be way too long. So, we decided that the table might go up by tens.

Teacher: That is interesting. Did you notice that John's group adjusted their thinking based on the reality of the situation? When we model situations with mathematics, we often need to consider the context along with the math we are using. Would someone from your group come up here and sketch a graph on this transparency showing your thinking?

(Tamie comes up and draws a line connecting (50, 70), (100, 80), and (110, 90)) on the overhead transparency.)

Teacher: How would you describe this pattern in mathematical language?

(Many students respond together that the pattern is linear. They know this from their work in middle school.)

Teacher: Let's see by a show of hands, how many groups thought the pattern was linear. Looks like some of you had different types of patterns. Cam, what did your group decide?

Cam: We decided that the pattern would increase but not as fast. In fact, we thought it would slow down.

Teacher: Cam, please sketch your pattern on this same grid and explain why you thought it would slow down.

Cam: *(Sketches a curve from (50, 70).)* We decided it would slow down because the cord might be reaching its limit of stretching.

Teacher: What do the rest of you think? Any other ideas about the pattern of stretched cord? *(Pause)* No, okay, we have two different ideas on the table. *(The teacher purposely does not press students to think about the y-intercept. Students did not introduce the idea themselves and it will be considered during the investigation.)*

Teacher: In a couple of minutes, we will be doing an experiment to simulate a bungee jump. We will collect some data and investigate the relationship between weight and stretch. Next, let's think about the business aspects of running a bungee jump. How could the Five Star Amusement Park figure out what price to charge each customer so that they could maximize the daily income from the attraction? *(Part c)*

Kat: They might find out how much is charged at other amusement parks.

Sandy: They could ask people who come to the park while they are building the bungee jump how much they would pay to take a ride—or whether they would do it at all. I wouldn't.

James: I think they should just charge a lot since the ride will be new. Once the newness wears off, they could charge less for the jump.

Teacher: How do these suggestions relate to the question of maximum income?

Dawson: Well, the more you charge the more you make.

Kat: That might not be true; if you charge too much, no one will do the jump. So, you have to keep the price set where people can afford to pay.

Jenni: I agree. There is probably a maximum price that people will pay, or at least that *most* people will pay. The operators would have to figure out the best price.

Chris: If they make the ride free, then lots of people would jump but they wouldn't make any profit. But, if they make it too expensive, like Kat and Jenni were saying, then only a few people would jump.

Teacher: So, it sounds like each of you is saying that the price for a jump will have some effect on the profit made by Five Star. Do the rest of you agree? *(Students agree.)* So, if you know that the jump costs $5, how much income will be generated?

Jason: Well, you still have to know how many people jump to find the income. Your income depends on two things: the price and the number of people.

Teacher: *(Seeing some blank stares.)* Does anyone want to ask Jason a question?

Tameka: I don't know what you mean, Jason … .

Jason: Well think about it this way … . If you charge $5 and two people jump, you make $10. If 100 people jump you make $500. So, you need to know both the price and the number of people jumping to find out the income.

Teacher: So, do you agree with Jason that there are two factors needed to find the income? *(Students agree.)*

Teacher: Okay, any other safety or business problems Five Star Amusement Park has to consider? *(Part d)*

A variety of students suggest things like the quality of the structure, the strength of the cord, insurance, ride restrictions (age, height, and health).

 **Physics and Business at Five Star Amusement Park**

The distance that a bungee jumper falls before bouncing back upward *depends on* the jumper's weight. In designing the bungee apparatus, it is essential to know how far the elastic cord will stretch for jumpers of different weights.

The number of customers attracted to an amusement park bungee jump depends on the price charged per jump. Market research by the park staff can help in setting a price that will lead to maximum income from the attraction.

As you work on the problems of this investigation, look for answers to these questions:

> *How is the stretch of a bungee cord related*
> *to the weight of the bungee jumper?*

> *How are number of customers and income for a*
> *bungee jump related to price charged for a jump?*

> *How can data tables, graphs, and rules relating variables be used to*
> *answer questions about such relationships between variables?*

Bungee Physics In design of any amusement park attraction like a bungee jump, it makes sense to do some testing before opening to the public. You can get an idea about what real testing will show by experimenting with a model bungee apparatus made from rubber bands and small weights. The pattern relating jumper weight and cord stretch will be similar to that in a real jump.

When scientists or engineers tackle problems like design of a safe but exciting bungee jump, they often work in research teams. Different team members take responsibility for parts of the design-and-test process. That kind of team problem solving is also effective in work on classroom mathematical investigations.

As you collect and analyze data from a bungee simulation, you may find it helpful to work in groups of about four, with members taking specific roles like these:

Experimenters	Perform the actual experiment and make measurements.
Recorders	Record measurements taken and prepare reports.
Quality Controllers	Observe the experiment and measurement techniques and recommend retests when there are doubts about accuracy of work.

Different mathematical or experimental tasks require different role assignments. But, whatever the task, it is important to have confidence in your partners, to share ideas, and to help others.

Physics and Business at Five Star Amusement Park

In this investigation, students are asked to perform an experiment that simulates bungee jumping. While the exact physical analysis of forces involved in a real bungee jump involves piecewise and nonlinear factors, students doing the simulation are highly likely to get data that suggest an approximately linear relationship with positive slope and y-intercept. It is not at all important that students use any of that language to describe their results, but it provides teachers with an opportunity to learn what students already know about linearity.

The introduction to this bungee simulation experiment includes some guidelines about organizing for work in teams. We have suggested to students that this is a good thing to do because it is the way people work on such tasks in business and industry—not just because it is an effective way to learn mathematics.

Students should record the stretched length of the bungee cord with various weights attached, not simply the amount of stretch. With this focus, they should get an approximately linear pattern in which the y-intercept represents the cord length with no weight attached and the slope represents the amount of stretch per unit of weight. Fishing weights, bags of nuts and bolts, or other weights can be used for this experiment. You may wish to have groups use different types of weights.

To allow for class discussion about the need for establishing well-defined experimental procedures, the directions for the bungee simulation experiment are intentionally far short of what is needed. Before setting the groups off on their team work, facilitate a discussion about establishing experiment design and execution procedures that will support the collection of good data to be used for understanding the overall question. Issues like how to measure stretch accurately (since the "jumper" will rebound quickly from its maximum stretch point) are sure to come up. It is important for students to realize that a careful experiment will allow variation only in the independent variable of interest, not in other experimental conditions.

It is likely that some groups will connect the data points in their plots. After students report their bungee experiment results you may wish to discuss options of connecting dots or drawing a line or curve through the data to help visualize the pattern. For some contexts, the graph points between the real data points have no meaning. As students progress in this unit, you may wish to periodically draw their attention to cases where connecting dots, drawing curves, or curve fitting is a visual aid or allows prediction but should not imply that all independent variable values have meaning for the context. (This unit also allows the opportunity to discuss restricted domains.)

In the second part of Investigation 1, students analyze data illustrating the classic relationship between price and demand for a product or service—in this case the relationship between price for trying a bungee jump at Five Star Amusement Park and the number of daily customers who can be expected to pay for that experience. Again, the underlying idea being explored is the way that changes in an independent variable cause or effect change in another dependent variable.

> **COLLABORATION SKILL**
> Encourage contributions by all members. (Encourage students to focus on specific skills during collaborative work.) A prompt to reflect on this is provided following the Summarize the Mathematics on page T7A.

1 Make a model bungee jump by attaching a weight to an elastic cord or to a chain of rubber bands.

a. Use your model to collect test data about bungee cord stretch for at least five weights. Record the data in a table and display it as a *scatterplot* on a graph.

Weight Attached (in grams)					
Length of Stretched Cord (in cm)					

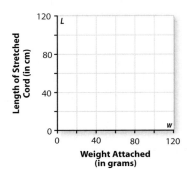

b. Use the pattern in your experimental data to predict length of the stretched bungee cord for weights different from those already tested. Then test the accuracy of your predictions.

c. Compare your results to those of others doing the same experiment. What might explain any differences in results?

2 When a group of students in Iowa did the bungee jump experiment, they proposed an algebraic rule relating the length of the stretched bungee cord L (in centimeters) to the attached weight w (in grams). They said that the rule $L = 30 + 0.5w$ could be used to predict the stretched cord length for any reasonable weight.

a. Use the Iowa students' rule to make a table and a graph of sample (w, L) values for $w = 0$ to 120 in steps of 20 grams.

b. How, if at all, do the numbers 30 and 0.5 in the Iowa students' rule relate to the pattern of (w, L) values shown in the table and graph? What do they tell about the way the length of the cord changes as the attached weight changes?

c. Is the pattern of change in the rule-based (w, L) values in Part a different from the pattern of change in your experimental data? If so, what differences in experimental conditions might have caused the differences in results?

a. In the students' recorded data, stretched cord length should increase steadily as weight attached increases steadily. The plot of the data should lie roughly in a linear pattern, though the linearity might fail at the extremes of the experimental weights.

b. Students might suggest linear interpolation (not in those words) or the mid-value of stretched cord length between two nearby data points. They might also suggest drawing a line to match the pattern and then reading intermediate point coordinates. This strategy will be developed more thoroughly in the Unit 3 *Linear Functions.*

c. Students should discuss reasons for different numbers. Some rubberbands are stronger than others, and some students may have made mistakes such as starting measurement of the length of the bungee cord at the wrong point. Some students may have performed the tests slightly differently than others giving data differences due to experimental error. The important point is to get students thinking about how variables in the experiment affect results.

2 **INSTRUCTIONAL NOTE** The goal of this problem is to see how comfortable students are in use of symbolic rules, including use of standard order of operations. At this point, do not expect students to be proficient in finding equations that match linear data patterns.

a.

w (in gm)	0	20	40	60	80	100	120
L (in cm)	30	40	50	60	70	80	90

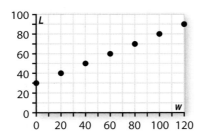

b. The number 30 represents the value of L when $w = 0$ (the original length of the cord). Thus, 30 is the L value associated with a w value of 0 in the table and with the location where the graph crosses the y-axis.

　The value 0.5 represents the change in L compared to the change in w. For each increase of 1 gram in w, the value of L increases by 0.5 centimeters. (Of course, in practice, the pattern of change in stretched cord length as attached weight increases will only approximate the pattern predicted by the formula.)

　Another way to explain the 0.5 is to say that L only changes 0.5 of what w changes. (This is a more subtle interpretation problem that will be dealt with carefully in Unit 3 on *Linear Functions,* so if students don't get it here, there is no need to belabor the point.)

c. Possible differences might include: different rate of change in length as weight is added (though students might not use the "rate" language to talk about it) or different values of L when $w = 0$.

Reasons for differences might include:

Different starting lengths of cords, different size increments of added weights, different elasticity of bungee cords, experimental errors, different experimental procedures, or different weight and length units used.

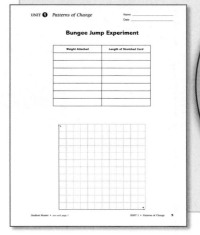

Bungee Business Designing the bungee jump apparatus is only part of the task in adding the attraction to Five Star Amusement Park. It is also important to set a *price per jump* that will make the operation profitable. When businesses face decisions like these, they get helpful information from market research. They ask people how much they would be willing to pay for a new product or service.

3 The Five Star marketing staff did a survey of park visitors to find out the *number of customers* that could be expected each day for the bungee jump at various possible *price per jump* values. Their survey produced data that they rounded off and presented in this table.

Market Survey Data

Price per Jump (in dollars)	0	5	10	15	20	25	30
Likely Number of Customers	50	45	40	35	30	25	20

   a. Plot the (*price per jump, number of customers*) data on a coordinate graph. Then describe how the predicted *number of customers* changes as *price per jump* increases from $0 to $30.

   b. The Five Star data processing department proposed the rule $N = 50 - p$ for the relationship between *number of customers N* and *price per jump p*. Does this rule represent the pattern in the market research data? Explain your reasoning.

4 The Five Star staff also wanted to know about *daily income* earned from the bungee jump attraction.

   a. If the price per jump is set at $5, the park can expect 45 bungee jump customers per day. In this case, what is the daily income?

   b. Use the market survey data from Problem 3 to estimate the *daily income* earned by the bungee jump for prices from $0 to $30 in steps of $5. Display the (*price per jump, daily income*) data in a table and in a graph. Then describe the pattern relating those variables.

   c. What do the results of the Five Star market research survey and the income estimates suggest as the best price to charge for the bungee jump attraction? How is your answer supported by data in the table and the graph of (*price per jump, daily income*) values?

5 In situations where values of one variable depend on values of another, it is common to label one variable the **independent variable** and the other the **dependent variable.** Values of the dependent variable are a function of, or depend on, values of the independent variable. What choices of independent and dependent variables make sense in:

   a. studying design of a bungee jump apparatus?

   b. searching for the price per jump that will lead to maximum income?

INSTRUCTIONAL NOTE The next three problems explore the *price* and *demand* relationship—in general, higher prices mean lower demand. Students can encounter this pattern with a linear relationship in which the *y*-intercept represents demand if the product or service is free, and the negative slope represents the rate at which demand declines as price increases. (We do not expect students to use this language.) Ask students to think about why the data pattern reflects a reasonable cause and effect relationship and how the graph illustrates the relationship.

Discussing factors other than price that will affect the number of customers on any particular day would be a good way to engage the class in the problem and to develop students' critical thinking skills. However, point out that the (*price, customers*) relationship is useful in business analysis, even if it oversimplifies the situation. This kind of simplification is the essence of mathematical modeling, as real-life situations are seldom as consistent as mathematical functions.

ASSIGNMENT OPTION
Following Problem 3, you may wish to discuss Part a of the Check Your Understanding on page 8.

③ **a.** All students should note that as the price per jump goes up, the number of customers goes down. Some students may have deeper understanding at this point and note that the drop in demand is 5 customers for every $5 increase in price or that there is a steady decline in customers as price increases.

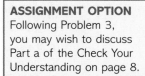

b. The proposed rule does produce pairs of (*price per jump, number of customers*) values identical to those in the table. Students should substitute values of *p* from the table into the rule $N = 50 - p$ to see that the rule accurately describes the data pattern.

④ **INSTRUCTIONAL NOTE** This problem explores the relationship between *daily income* and *price per jump*. The fact that income equals price times quantity will probably be a new idea for students. Ask students to explain that calculation as part of the launch into this segment of the problem.

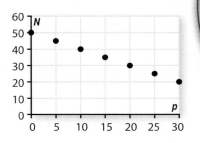

a. *Income* = 5 × 45 so the income is $225 when the price per jump is $5.

b.

Price per Jump *p* (in $)	0	5	10	15	20	25	30
Daily Income *I* (in $)	0	225	400	525	600	625	600

The pattern relating *price* and *income* shows an increase, then a decrease in *income* while *price* increases. Equal changes in price do not produce equal changes in income.

c. The best price is $25. This price yields the highest income, as evident in the correspondence of $p = 25$ with $I = 625$ in the table and by the peak in the graph at $p = 25$.

⑤ **INSTRUCTIONAL NOTE** From a technical standpoint, choice of independent and dependent variables is arbitrary. In practice, it makes sense to choose, as the independent variable, the quantity whose value can be in an experimental situation. The dependent variable changes in response to free or planned changes in the independent variable. For this reason statisticians tend to prefer the terms *explanatory* and *responding* instead of independent and dependent.

NOTE If a student suggests that there might be an intermediate price that will yield a higher income, the student can use the rule, $N = 50 - p$ to find the income for prices near $25.

a. Independent Variable: *weight of jumper*
Dependent Variable: *stretched length of bungee cord*

b. Independent Variable: *price per jump*
Dependent Variable: *daily income*

Summarize the Mathematics

To describe relationships among variables, it is often helpful to explain how one variable *is a function of* the other or how the value of one variable *depends on* the value of the other.

a How would you describe the way that:

    i. the stretch of a bungee cord depends on the weight of the jumper?

    ii. the number of customers for a bungee jump attraction depends on the price per customer?

    iii. income from the jump depends on price per customer?

b What similarities and what differences do you see in the relationships of variables in the physics and business questions about bungee jumping at Five Star Amusement Park?

c In a problem situation involving two related variables, how do you decide which should be considered the independent variable? The dependent variable?

d What are the advantages and disadvantages of using tables, graphs, algebraic rules, or descriptions in words to express the way variables are related?

e In this investigation, you were asked to use patterns in data plots and algebraic rules to make predictions of bungee jump stretch, numbers of customers, and income. How much confidence or concern would you have about the accuracy of those predictions?

Be prepared to share your thinking with the whole class.

✓ Check Your Understanding

The design staff at Five Star Amusement Park had another idea—selling raffle tickets for chances to win prizes. The prize-winning tickets would be drawn at random each day.

a. Suppose that a market research study produced the following estimates of raffle ticket sales at various prices.

Price per Ticket (in dollars)	1	2	3	4	5	10	15
Number of Tickets Sold	900	850	800	750	700	450	200

    i. Plot the (*price per ticket, number of tickets sold*) estimates on a graph. Because *price per ticket* is the independent variable in this situation, its values are used as *x*-coordinates of the graph. Because *number of tickets sold* is the dependent variable, its values are used as the *y*-coordinates of the graph.

It is important to be sure that students are articulating the mathematics correctly and also to be sure to not push the conversations into content that students will subsequently investigate.

Summarize the Mathematics

PROMOTING MATHEMATICAL DISCOURSE

Teaching Resources

Transparency Master 6.

Unit 1

a   **i.** If the weight attached to a bungee cord increases, the stretched length of the cord will increase in a fairly steady linear pattern.

ii. If the price is set too high, no customers will come. If the price is lowered, this will cause more people to become jump customers.

iii. It appears that, up to a certain point, increasing price leads to increasing income, despite a decrease in number of customers. Beyond that "certain point," the increase in price seems unable to compensate for the decrease in number of customers, so income decreases.

b   In each of the three relationships studied in this investigation, there was a relationship between variables in which changes in one variable led to changes in another variable. In two cases, the changes occurred in a steady pattern, represented in the data plots as linear patterns.

The two linear patterns were different in that one was an increasing pattern (stretched cord length), while the other was a decreasing pattern (number of customers). The third pattern was different from the first two because it did not show a steady and consistent increase or decrease of income values as price increased. Instead, it showed an increase at first (rather rapid), then a slowing rate of increase, a maximum value (and graph point), and then a decrease at an increasing rate.

c   The natural choice for independent variable is that whose values can be directly manipulated in a situation, causing or leading to changes in one or more other dependent variables. The dependent variable is the one that is a function of, depends on, or is a result of a change in the independent variable.

d   Tables show actual values, graphs help to see patterns, rules help to generate new data, and words communicate ideas about the situation. Since students might have different ideas or different preferences themselves, some discussion of the pros and cons would be helpful in getting students to reflect on their own and others' preferred information styles.

MATH TOOLKIT Explain what is meant by the dependent and independent variable. What are the ways that can be used to express how variables are related? Give an advantage for each type of variable. (Additional information on Math Toolkits is in the *Implementing the Core-Plus Mathematics Curriculum* booklet and on the TeacherWorks CD.)

(e) One of the unavoidable facts of life in using mathematical concepts and techniques to reason about real-life problem situations is that the exactness of mathematical calculations only approximate the behavior of situations being modeled. Mathematical models are idealizations or averages of messier real data patterns. The degree of confidence that one has in predictions from a mathematical model is usually based on the regularity of the data pattern used to generate the model.

When (as in the bungee jump experiment) there is an underlying physical law governing behavior of the phenomenon being studied, predictions from models tend to be more accurate than in situations (like the prediction of bungee jump demand from price information) where less deterministic variables are involved. We just want students to begin developing sensitivity to this fundamental fact of applied mathematics, which will come up again in subsequent investigations and units. At this point, student responses to the question about confidence or concerns about predictions from patterns will probably be fairly unsophisticated, but it is important to ask students "Why?" they do or do not believe that interpolation or extrapolation (not using those words) from a data pattern will yield reliable predictions.

PROCESSING PROMPT Things we said to encourage one another to contribute ideas:

1. _____   2. _____   3. _____

Promoting Mathematical Discourse

Summarize the Mathematics, *page 7*

For this first Summarize the Mathematics (STM) discussion, it would be helpful to explicitly address both the importance and structure of this feature of the curriculum with students. Collectively developing norms of behavior for the STM discussions, such as the expectation that students will respond to or add to others comments, is modeled in this scenario. Allowing groups to talk about how they would answer each question posed in the STM before moving to a class discussion should give students more confidence to respond during the discussion.

Teacher: I would like each group to take a few minutes to talk about how you would answer the Summarize the Mathematics questions. Don't write out your responses yet. Just make some notes about your thinking to keep track of it. You will be asked to share your ideas as an entire class in about 5 minutes. *(Students discuss the questions. The teacher listens purposefully to the ideas surfacing from small group discourse to be prepared to push students' thinking during the whole class discussion or to call on specific groups for their ideas.)*

Teacher: It is time to share your thinking with the entire class. Meredith, would you please read aloud the introductory sentence and the first question of Part a? And then someone else from your group can tell us what your group was thinking.

Meredith: To describe relationships among variables, it is often helpful to explain how one variable is a function of the other or how the value of one variable depends on the value of the other. How would you describe the way that the stretch of a bungee cord depends on the weight of the jumper?

Josh: We said that the cord got longer when the jumper weighed more.

Teacher: *(Pause to see if students initiate more discussion.)* Remember the expectations we set for this discussion. Others should add their thoughts to this discussion without prompting from me.

Latisha: Okay, we said the weight of the jumper caused the cord to get longer.

Angela: We said that the more the jumper weighed, the longer the cord got.

Teacher: Let's analyze the difference between these last two descriptions. *(Teacher writes Latisha's and Angela's words on the board.)* Let's consider the mathematics described in these. If someone had not done the experiment you did or did not have any idea of how the weight of a jumper might affect the cord length, which of these two descriptions would be the better one to help them understand how the cord length depends on the weight of the jumper? And why do you think that?

Carl: Everyone knows that more weight makes the cord longer, but if someone really had no idea of this, the one that says, "the more the jumper weighed" would be better; 'cause they might think that less weight makes the cord longer.

Teacher: Do others agree with Carl's choice? *(Students indicate agreement.)* Good. Notice how we are being careful about the language we use to describe relationships mathematically. We need to be very clear on whether the variables are increasing or decreasing in the relationship. Using similar mathematical language, describe the way that the number of customers for a bungee jump attraction depends on the price of the jump.

Daniel: The number of customers was high when the price was low and it went down as the price went up.

Teacher: Are there ways to make this response more mathematical or will we accept it as is?

Gian: Well, it was a pretty straight down pattern. So, maybe we could say, "As the price went up the number of customers dropped in a linear pattern."

Teacher: Are there ways to make this response more mathematical or will we accept it as is? *(Pause—students indicate they will accept this description.)* Notice how Daniel was willing to offer up a response and Gian worked at refining it to be more mathematical. This is an example of how we will work together in this class to understand and express mathematical ideas, not only in class discussions, but in your group discussions. When we reflect on the discussions in our groups during the next investigation, let's look for times when we help each other refine or improve our ideas.

Teacher: Now let's use similar language to describe the relationship between the income and price per customer.

Kyra: As the price per customer went up, the income went up too. But then the income came back down when the price got too high.

Teacher: Thanks for offering up a response, Kyra. Are there ways to make this response more mathematical or will we accept it as is? *(Students indicate they will accept this response.)*

Teacher: Good descriptions. Let's turn to Part b. What similarities and differences do you see in the relationships of variables in the physics and business questions about bungee jumping at Five Star Amusement Park? *(Silence)*

Sam: What does that mean? What physics did we do?

Teacher: Can anyone interpret this question for us?

Sara: I think we are supposed to just compare the three things we talked about in Part a.

Teacher: Well, how do we compare these three relationships? *(Writes on board: (weight/cord length), (price per customer, number of customers), and (price per customer, income).)*

Sam: Oh, that's all? Well, the first two you have up there were both pretty linear.

Jewel: I can try to make this one more mathematical. The weight/length one increased and the price/number of customers one decreased in linear patterns.

Teacher: What about the price per jump/daily income relationship?

Henri: That relationship was different from the others since the income went back down when the price got too high.

Teacher: Okay, now let's think more generally to answer Part c. In a problem situation involving two related variables, how do you decide which is the independent variable? The dependent variable? Think about how you made your decisions in Problem 5.

✔Check Your Understanding

a. The relationship between *price per ticket* and *number of tickets* sold:

i.

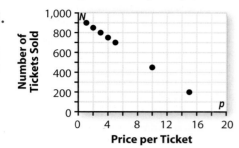

INSTRUCTIONAL NOTE
Remind students to label axes clearly and indicate the scales.

Unit 1

ii. Describe the pattern relating values of those variables and the way that the relationship is shown in the table and the graph.

iii. Does the rule $N = 950 - 50p$ produce the same pairs of (*price per ticket p, number of tickets sold N*) values as the market research study?

b. Use the data in Part a relating *price per ticket* to *number of tickets sold* to estimate the *income* from raffle ticket sales at each of the proposed ticket prices.

    i. Record those *income* estimates in a table and plot the (*price per ticket, income*) estimates on a graph.

    ii. Describe the relationship between raffle ticket price and income from ticket sales. Explain how the relationship is shown in the table and the graph of (*price per ticket, income*) estimates.

    iii. What do your results in parts i and ii suggest about the ticket price that will lead to maximum income from raffle ticket sales? How is your answer shown in the table and graph of part i?

Investigation 2 · Taking Chances

Students at Banneker High School hold an annual *Take a Chance* carnival to raise funds for special class projects. The planning committee is often puzzled about ways to predict profit from games of chance.

In one popular game, a fair die is rolled to find out whether you win a prize. Rules of the game are:

- You win a $4 prize if the top face of the die is a 4.
- You donate $1 to the school special project fund if the top face of the die is 1, 2, 3, 5, or 6.

As you work on the problems of this investigation, look for answers to these questions:

> *What is the pattern of change relating profit to number of players in the die-tossing game?*
>
> *How is that pattern of change illustrated in tables and graphs of data from plays of the game?*
>
> *How is the pattern of change in profit similar to and different from the patterns of change in bungee jump cord length and number of bungee jump customers?*

1 Use a fair die to play the die-tossing game at least 20 times. Record your results in a table like this:

Play Number	1	2	3	4	5	6	7	...
Outcome ($ won or lost for school)								...
Cumulative Profit ($ won or lost by school)								...

ii. The trend is steadily decreasing sales as price increases. In fact, it looks like a loss of 50 customers for every increase of $1 in ticket price.

iii. The rule $N = 950 - 50p$ produces the number pairs in the table.

b. **i.**

Price (in $)	1	2	3	4	5	10	15
Income (in $)	900	1,700	2,400	3,000	3,500	4,500	3,000

ii. As ticket price increases from $1 to $10, income appears to increase from $900 to $4,500. As price increases from $10 to $15, income decreases from $4,500 to $3,000. The plotted points go up from $p = 1$ to $p = 10$, and down from $p = 10$ to $p = 15$ and increase up to $p = 10$. Table values decrease after $p = 10$. There are no data points between 5 and 10 or between 10 and 15, so the trends are not certain.

iii. Ticket price that will lead to maximum income looks to be about $10. In the table, that price is paired with the highest income. In the graph, the peak shows the maximum income, and corresponding price on the horizontal axis.

Investigation 2 — Taking Chances

This investigation engages students in a hands-on experiment that leads to a random walk pattern, foreshadowing probability ideas like the Law of Large Numbers and expected value. It also provides a meaningful example of a situation in which change in one dependent variable is not deterministically predictable from change in the related independent variable (number of trials). The payoff in such an experience should be a more flexible and open student understanding of patterns of change and functions (though a formal function must have well-defined connections between input and output values). Do not expect students to have much of a feel for the concepts of probability at this time. The key point is that the pattern is not predictable but could be summarized by a linear model.

COLLABORATION SKILL Respond to ideas respectfully.

1 The long-term trend should produce an average increase in fund-raiser profit of about 17¢ per trial. Students will have different (*trial number, cumulative profit*) data. The expected value from the fund-raiser's perspective is $-4\left(\frac{1}{6}\right) + 1\left(\frac{5}{6}\right) = \frac{1}{6}$. Students should not be expected to think this way.

2 Plot the data from your test of the game on a graph that shows how *cumulative profit* for the school changes as the *number of plays* increases. Since the school can lose money on this game, you will probably need a graph (like the one below) showing points below the horizontal axis. Connecting the plotted points will probably make patterns of change in fund-raiser profit clearer. Use the graph to answer the questions that follow.

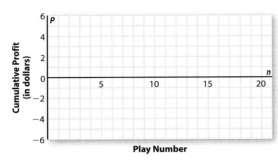

a. Describe the pattern of change in profit or loss for the school as clearly and precisely as you can. Explain how the pattern is shown in the table and the graph.

b. See if you can express the pattern as a rule relating *cumulative profit P* to *number of plays n*.

3 Combine your results from the die-tossing experiment with those of other students to produce a table showing results of many more plays. If each student or group contributes cumulative results for 20 plays, you could build a table like this:

Number of Plays	20	40	60	80	100	120	140	160
Cumulative Profit (in $)								

Plot the resulting (*number of plays, cumulative profit*) data.

a. How is the pattern in this experiment with many plays similar to or different from the patterns of your experiment with fewer plays?

b. See if you can express the pattern as a rule relating *cumulative profit P* to *number of plays n*.

4 Suppose that the game operators change the prize payoff from $4 to $6.

a. What similarities and differences would you expect in the way *cumulative profit* for the school changes as the *number of plays* increases in the new game compared to the original game? How will those patterns appear in a data table and a graph of results?

2 **a–b.** Graphs of student data will not follow any familiar or simple pattern, but as the number of plays increases, there should be a general upward drift in the *cumulative profit* points. (Students are unlikely to have ideas about how to express the random patterns with a symbolic formula—that's part of the point of this problem.)

3 **a.** As plays continue, there will be a general trend for fund-raiser profit to accumulate at a rate of about $3.33 for every 20 plays of the game. However, this is only an overall trend, and the actual plot might vary from that linear trend pattern. Overall these line graphs will be less "jagged" than from the 20-play experiments of each group.

b. Students may be able to express class plot patterns by a linear rule with slope of about 0.167 (per one trial).

4 **a.** When the prize payoff changes from $4 to $6, the odds are then with the player, and not the fund-raiser. The graph points will still oscillate, but the cumulative earnings will tend to decrease. The expected return per play will be $-6\left(\frac{1}{6}\right) + 1\left(\frac{5}{6}\right) = -\frac{1}{6}$. The table of *cumulative fund-raiser profit* will show a trend toward negative values, averaging a loss of about 17¢ per play.

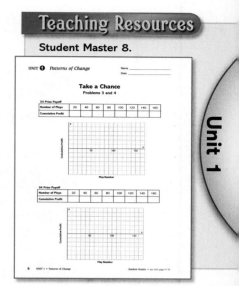

b. Repeat the die-tossing experiment to test profit prospects for the fund-raiser with the new payoff scheme. Try to explain differences between what you predicted would happen in Part a and what actually did happen.

5 What payoff amounts (for winning and losing) might make this a fair game—that is, a game in which profit for the school is expected to be zero?

Summarize
the Mathematics

In this investigation, you explored patterns of change for a variable with outcomes subject to the laws of probability. You probably discovered in the die-tossing game that *cumulative profit* is related somewhat predictably to the *number of plays* of the game.

a After many plays of the two games with payoffs of $4 or $6, who seemed to come out ahead in the long run—the players or the school fund-raiser? Why do you think those results occurred?

b How is the pattern of change in *cumulative profit* for the school fund-raiser similar to, or different from, patterns you discovered in the investigation of bungee physics and business?

Be prepared to share your ideas and reasoning with the class.

✔Check Your Understanding

Suppose that another game at the *Take a Chance* carnival has these rules:

  Three coins—a nickel, a dime, and a quarter—are flipped.

If all three turn up heads or all three turn up tails, the player wins a $5 prize.

  For any other result, the player has to contribute $2 to the school fund.

The school fund-raiser is most likely to win $2 on any individual play of the game, but there is also a risk of losing $5 to some players. The challenge is to predict change in fund-raiser profit as more and more customers play this game.

a. If you keep a tally of your *cumulative profit* (or loss) for many plays of this game:

  i. What pattern would you expect to find in your cumulative profit as the number of plays increases?

  ii. How would the pattern you described in part i appear in a graph of the recorded (*play number, cumulative profit*) data?

b. Actual data will generally not match the trend until many plays have been accumulated.

5 If the penalty for losing is kept at $1, then a payoff to winners of $5 will make this a fair game. (Students will likely select $5 based on their results from Problems 3 and 4.)

Summarize
the Mathematics

a In the original game, the operators will tend to come out ahead over the long run. However, when the payoff is increased to $6, the advantage switches to the players. At this point, we don't expect most students to be able to provide a rational explanation of why this happens. However, it seems reasonable to expect that they will have some rough ideas about the trade-offs between prize for the rare win and penalty for the more common loss by individual players.

b This pattern will not be very much like the other patterns encountered in Investigation 1, since it is unpredictable and it is neither consistent nor steady in its pattern of change. This irregularity shows up in the table data and in the graph that seems to jump up and down.

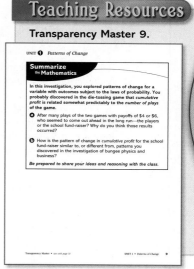
PROCESSING PROMPT
We responded to ideas
respectfully by ... .

✓ Check Your Understanding

a. **i.** Cumulative profit would tend to grow in the long run. In the long run, cumulative profit would increase by $2 three-quarters of the time and decrease by $5 one-quarter of the time.

ii. In a graph, points representing cumulative profit for the school fund-raiser will oscillate up and down, roughly around a line with a slope of about 0.25.

b. Use three coins to play the game at least 20 times. In a table, record the results of each play and the cumulative profit (or loss) after each play. Make a plot of your (*play number, cumulative profit*) data and describe the pattern shown by that graph.

c. How are the results of your actual plays similar to what you predicted in Part a? If there are differences, how can they be explained?

Investigation 3   Trying to Get Rich Quick

Relationships between independent and dependent variables occur in a wide variety of problem situations. Tables, graphs, and algebraic rules are informative ways to express those relationships. The problems of this investigation illustrate two other common patterns of change. As you work on the next problems—about NASCAR racing and pay-for-work schemes—look for answers to these questions:

> *Why are the relationships involved in these problems*
> *called nonlinear patterns of change?*
>
> *How do the dependent variables change as*
> *the independent variables increase?*

NASCAR Racing Automobile racing is one of the most popular spectator sports in the United States. One of the most important races is the NASCAR Daytona 500, a 500-mile race for cars similar to those driven every day on American streets and highways. The prize for the winner is over $1 million. Winners also get lots of advertising endorsement income.

1 The average speed and time of the Daytona 500 winner varies from year to year.

    a. In 1960, Junior Johnson won with an average speed of 125 miles per hour. The next year Marvin Panch won with an average speed of 150 miles per hour. What was the difference in race time between 1960 and 1961 (in hours)?

    b. In 1997, Jeff Gordon won with an average speed of 148 miles per hour. The next year the winner was Dale Earnhardt with an average speed of 173 miles per hour. What was the difference in race time between 1997 and 1998 (in hours)? (Source: www.nascar.com/races/)

2 Complete a table like that shown here to display sample pairs of (*average speed, race time*) values for completion of a 500-mile race.

Average Speed (in mph)	50	75	100	125	150	175	200
Race Time (in hours)							

b. If students make a table of their number of plays, individual outcomes, and the cumulative outcome, the individual outcomes will be a random sequence of +2 and −5 entries, with many more +2 entries (about $\frac{3}{4}$ of the entries). The graph will have some sequences of steady 2-unit rises and a few drops of 5 in y value.

c. The conflict or agreement between predictions and actual results will depend on what the predictions are. However, even if the prediction is theoretically correct, there is a good chance in as few as 20 plays that cumulative profit for the operator will oscillate in ways that take it away from the line with a slope of 0.25. The random nature of this game accounts for the differences.

Investigation 3 — Trying to Get Rich Quick

The goal of this investigation is to expose students to two more important nonlinear patterns of change—inverse variation ($y = \frac{k}{x}$ or $xy = k$) and exponential growth. Students who have had prior exposure to these two types of variation might recognize the symbolic forms and their relationship to the table and graph patterns of the data and the general problem conditions. For other students, this will serve primarily as a hint of things that will be studied more carefully in future units.

There is no intention that teachers should take extensive time to explain inverse variation or exponential growth, especially the corresponding symbolic formulas, to students who do not recognize those underlying patterns as familiar. Instead, we aim only for student recognition that variables can be related in cause-and-effect relations of many different types and that inspecting tables and graphs of those relationships can be informative about how the variables depend on each other.

COLLABORATION SKILL Check for agreement.

1 **a.** $\frac{2}{3}$ hours
$$\frac{500}{125} - \frac{500}{150} = \frac{2}{3}$$
b. 0.488 hours
$$\frac{500}{148} - \frac{500}{173} \approx 0.488$$

2

Average Speed (in mph)	50	75	100	125	150	175	200
Race Time (in hours)	10	6.66	5	4	3.33	2.86	2.5

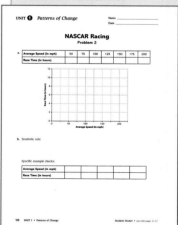

a. Plot the sample (*average speed, race time*) data on a graph. Describe the relationship between those two variables.

b. Write a symbolic rule that shows how to calculate *race time t* as a function of *average speed s* in the Daytona 500 race. Show with specific examples that your rule produces correct race time for given average speed.

(3) In the 1960–61 and 1997–98 comparisons of winning speed and time for the Daytona 500 race, the differences in average speed are both 25 miles per hour. The time differences are not the same. At first, this might seem like a surprising result.

How is the fact that equal changes in average speed don't imply equal changes in race time illustrated in the shape of the graph of sample (*average speed, race time*) data?

(4) How are the table, graph, and algebraic rule relating *average speed* and *race time* similar to or different from those you have seen in work on earlier problems?

Part-Time Work … Big-Time Dollars When Devon and Kevin went looking for part-time work to earn spending money, their first stop was at the Fresh Fare Market. They asked the manager if they could work helping customers carry groceries to their cars. When the manager asked how much they wanted to earn, Devon and Kevin proposed $2 per hour plus tips from customers.

The Fresh Fare Market manager proposed a different deal, to encourage Devon and Kevin to work more than a few hours each week. The manager's weekly plan would pay each of them $0.10 for the first hour of work, $0.20 for the second hour, $0.40 for the third hour, $0.80 for the fourth hour, and so on.

(5) Which pay plan do you think would be best for Devon and Kevin to choose? To provide evidence supporting your ideas, complete a table showing the earnings (without tips) for each student from each plan for work hours from 1 to 10. Plot graphs showing the patterns of growth in earnings for the two plans.

Hours Worked in a Week	1	2	3	4	5	6	7	8	9	10
Earnings in $ Plan 1	2	4	…							
Earnings in $ Plan 2	0.10	0.30	…							

Based on the pattern of earnings, which of the two pay plans would you recommend to Devon and Kevin?

a.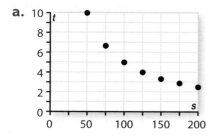

As speed increases, race time decreases. However, the race time does not decrease at a constant rate. Equal changes in speed do not produce equal changes in race time. The greatest change in race time is for speed increases from relatively low starting points.

b. $t = \frac{500}{s}$; Students should check their rule using at least two (*average speed, race time*) pairs from their table.

3 The graph relating race time to average speed drops rapidly at first (for low speeds) and then more slowly (for higher speeds). So, changes of 25 mph along the horizontal axis do not have the same vertical decrease.

4 Similarities: They all involve a cause-and-effect relationship between one independent variable and one dependent variable. In this case, as *x* increases, *y* decreases, somewhat like the relationship between price and demand for bungee jump tries.

Differences: Race time does not change at a constant rate (as bungee cord stretch and demand for the bungee jump did), this data plot shows a curved pattern (not a straight line like stretch and number of customers in the bungee jump), and the rule relating race time to average speed has a variable in the denominator.

5 The table below displays the correct values for the different plans. Recall that these values represent the cumulative earnings for Devon and Kevin. Students should suggest that if Devon and Kevin would like to work 7 hours or less per week, then Plan 1 would be the wiser choice. Beyond 7 hours, Plan 2 becomes the best choice.

INSTRUCTIONAL NOTE
You might ask, "What would you expect the graph to look like if equal changes in average speed meant equal time differences?"

ASSIGNMENT NOTE
Part a of Check Your Understanding can be completed by students following Problem 4.

Hours Worked in a Week	1	2	3	4	5	6	7	8	9	10
Earnings in $ for Plan 1	2	4	6	8	10	12	14	16	18	20
Earnings in $ for Plan 2	0.10	0.30	0.70	1.50	3.10	6.30	12.70	25.50	51.10	102.30

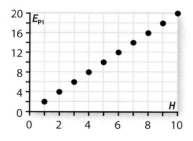

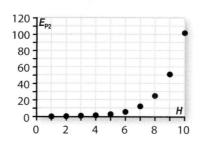

Teaching Resources

Student Master 11.

6. Would you change your choice of pay plan if the manager's offer was:

   a. Plan 3: Only $0.05 for the first hour of work, $0.10 for the second hour, $0.20 for the third hour, $0.40 for the fourth hour, and so on? Why or why not?

   b. Plan 4: Only $0.01 for the first hour of work, but $0.03 for the second hour, $0.09 for the third, $0.27 for the fourth, and so on? Why or why not?

Summarize the Mathematics

The patterns relating *race time* to *average speed* for the Daytona 500 and *earnings* to *hours worked* in Plan 2 at Fresh Fare Market are examples of nonlinear relationships.

   a What is it about those relationships that makes the term "nonlinear" appropriate?

   b You found patterns showing how to calculate *race time* from *average speed* and *total pay* from *hours worked*. How would your confidence about the accuracy of those calculations compare to that for calculations in the bungee jump and fair game problems?

Be prepared to share your ideas and reasoning with the class.

✔ Check Your Understanding

Use these problems to test your skill in analyzing nonlinear relationships like those in the NASCAR and Fresh Fare Market problems.

   a. The Iditarod Trail Sled Dog Race goes 1,100 miles from Anchorage to Nome, Alaska, in March of each year. The winner usually takes about 10 days to complete the race.

   i. What is a typical average speed (in miles per day) for Iditarod winners?

   ii. Make a table and sketch a graph showing how *average speed* for the Iditarod race depends on *race time*. Use times ranging from 2 (not really possible for this race) to 20 days in steps of 2 days.

   iii. What rule shows how to calculate *average speed s* for any Iditarod *race time t*?

   iv. Compare the table, graph, and rule showing Iditarod *average speed* as a function of *race time* to that showing Daytona 500 *race time* as a function of *average speed* in Problem 2 of this investigation. Explain how relationships in the two situations are similar and how they are different.

   b. Ethan and Anna tried to get a monthly allowance of spending money from their parents. They said, "You only have to pay us 1 penny for the first day of the month, 2 pennies for the second day of the month, 4 pennies for the third day, and so on." According to Ethan and Anna's idea, how much would the parents have to pay on days 10, 20, and 30 of each month?

6 a. Plan 3: Again, the number of hours to be worked should be critical in plan selection. In the new plan, one would have to work for 9 hours to make it more profitable than Plan 1. But the new plan also becomes more profitable beyond the 9-hour workload (though only half as profitable as Plan 2).

b. Plan 4: Despite its modest beginnings, this plan would overtake Plan 1 (and both of the other options) after 8 hours of work. In fact, after 10 hours of work it would beat the original plan by $275.24.

Summarize
the Mathematics

a The most obvious reason for calling these two relationships nonlinear is the fact that, in contrast to several earlier examples, the graphs of (x, y) value pairs do not produce linear patterns.

b In the problems of this investigation, all calculations gave exact values of the dependent variable corresponding to given values of the independent variable. There is neither experimental error nor random variation to consider when applying results to thinking about questions in the problem situations. Therefore, we can be more confident about the accuracy of the calculations in these problems than for those in the bungee jump and fair game problems.

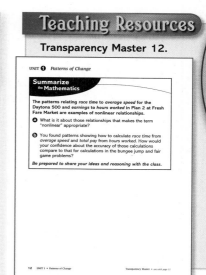

PROCESSING PROMPT We checked that we all agreed on a solution by ... and by ... .

MATH TOOLKIT Describe the patterns in tables, graphs, and symbolic expressions of the linear and nonlinear relationships you studied in this lesson.

✓ Check Your Understanding

a. i. 110 miles per day

ii.

Race Time (in days)	2	4	6	8	10	12	14	16	18	20
Average Speed (in miles per day)	550	275	183	138	110	92	79	69	61	55

Students should sketch a graph of this situation.

iii. $s = \dfrac{1{,}100}{t}$ miles per day

iv. The shapes of the graphs are similar, despite the different choice of variables for dependent and independent variables on the axes. The tables both indicate similar decreasing patterns for the dependent variable. In the symbolic rules, the two variables are switched, but the forms of the rules are the same.

b. The parents would have to pay $5.12 in pennies on day 10, $5,242.88 on day 20, and $5,368,709.12 on day 30.

On Your Own

Applications

These tasks provide opportunities for you to use and strengthen your understanding of the ideas you have learned in the lesson.

1. The table below gives data from tests of a full-size bungee jump.

Jumper Weight (in pounds)	100	125	150	175	200
Stretched Cord Length (in feet)	50	55	60	65	70

a. Which variable does it make sense to consider independent and which dependent?

b. Plot the given data on a coordinate graph.

c. Use the pattern in the table or the graph to estimate the stretched cord length for jumpers who weigh:

   i. 85 pounds   ii. 135 pounds   iii. 225 pounds

d. Would it make sense to connect the points on your data plot? Explain your reasoning.

e. Describe the overall pattern relating *stretched cord length L* to *jumper weight w*.

f. The technician who did the tests suggested that the pattern could be summarized with a symbolic rule $L = 30 + 0.2w$. Does that rule give estimates of stretched cord length that match the experimental data? Explain.

2. To help in estimating the number of customers for an amusement park bungee jump, the operators hired a market research group to visit several similar parks that had bungee jumps. They recorded the number of customers on a weekend day. Since the parks charged different prices for their jumps, the collected data looked like this:

Price per Jump (in dollars)	15	20	25	28	30
Number of Customers	25	22	18	15	14

a. In this situation, which variable makes sense as the independent variable and which as the dependent variable?

b. Plot these data on a coordinate graph.

Applications

1 **a.** *Jumper weight* is the most plausible independent variable and *stretched cord length* the dependent variable because it changes as an effect of changed *jumper weight*.

b.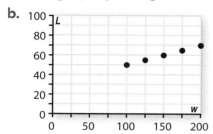

c. Reasonable estimates are:

   i. 47 feet   **ii.** 57 feet   **iii.** 75 feet

d. In this situation, it probably does make sense to connect the dots to indicate stretched cord length for weight values between the given data points because there is a clear trend and no reason to think the relationship would be any different for weight values between those in the table. Also, values between those in the table make sense (i.e., jumper weight is a continuous variable).

e. Stretched cord length increases steadily as jumper weight increases. For every 25-pound increase in jumper weight, there is a 5-foot increase in stretched cord length or about 0.2 feet per pound of weight.

f. The given rule does produce the (*jumper weight, stretched cord length*) values in the data table. For example, when $w = 100$, the rule says $L = 50$, and when $w = 200$, the rule says $L = 70$.

2 **a.** In this case, *price per jump* is the natural independent variable and *number of customers* is the natural dependent variable because it is affected by the price charged.

b.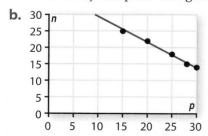

c. Does it make sense to connect the points on your data plot? Explain your reasoning.

d. Use the pattern in the table or the graph to estimate the *number of customers* if the *price per jump* is:

   i. $18   **ii.** $23   **iii.** $35

e. Describe the overall pattern of change relating *price per jump* to *number of customers.*

f. The market research staff suggested that the pattern could be summarized with a rule $n = 35 - 0.7p$. Does that rule produce estimates of number of customers n at various prices p like those in the survey data?

3 Use the data in Applications Task 2 to study the relationship between price per bungee jump and income from one day's operation at the five parks that were visited.

a. Complete a table showing sample (*price per jump, daily income*) values.

Price per Jump (in dollars)	15	20	25	28	30
Daily Income (in dollars)					

b. In this situation, what choice of independent and dependent variables makes most sense?

c. Plot the data relating *price per jump* and *daily income* on a coordinate graph.

d. Would it make sense to connect the points on the graph? Explain your reasoning.

e. Describe the overall pattern in the relationship between *price per jump* and *daily income.*

f. Use the data table and graph pattern to estimate the *price per jump* that seems likely to yield maximum *daily income.*

4 Suppose that you go to a school carnival night and play a game in which two fair coins are tossed to find out whether you win a prize. The game has these rules:

- Two heads or two tails showing—you win $1.
- One head and one tail showing—you lose $1.

a. If you keep score for yourself in 20 plays of this game:

   i. What pattern would you expect in your cumulative score as the plays occur?

   ii. How would the pattern you described in part i appear in a graph of (*play number, cumulative score*) data?

b. Use two coins to play the game 20 times. Record the results of each play and the cumulative score after each play in a table. Make a scatterplot of your (*play number, cumulative score*) data and describe the pattern shown by that graph.

c. How are the results of your actual plays similar to what you predicted in Part a? How are they different?

c. In this situation, connecting the dots is a reasonable way to visualize the pattern and to make estimates of numbers of customers for prices between those for which the given data provide direct evidence. However, since the pattern does seem linear, it may be more reasonable to draw a single line that matches the pattern well.

d. Interpolating and extrapolating in a roughly linear pattern from the given data points, expected number of customers at the suggested prices would be about:

i. 23　　　　　**ii.** 19　　　　　**iii.** 10

e. The overall pattern of change is one in which *number of customers* declines as *price per jump* increases. The pattern is roughly linear, with on average a drop of about 3–4 customers for every $5 increase in price.

f. The values produced by the rule are quite close to the actual data.

Price per Jump (in dollars)	15	20	25	28	30
Number of Customers	24.5	21	17.5	15.4	14

INSTRUCTIONAL NOTE
Problem 2 provides an opportunity to discuss the issue of rounding to whole numbers of customers.

③　a.

Price per Jump (in dollars)	15	20	25	28	30
Daily Income (in dollars)	375	440	450	420	420

b. In this case, the natural independent variable is *price per jump* while the natural dependent variable is *daily income* because the income is based on the price charged for jumps.

c. A plot of the (*price per jump, daily income*) data will look like the graph to the right:

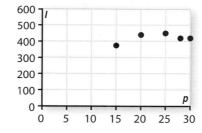

d. It would make some sense to connect the points since prices between those for which there are income estimates do make sense, and it is reasonable to believe that the incomes associated with those prices would be in the same pattern as that of the data points already known. However, since the pattern does not seem linear, it may be more reasonable to draw a smooth curve through the points.

e. The overall pattern appears to suggest an increase in income as prices approach the $20–$25 range, and then a decline as the price rises higher.

f. A jump price somewhere around $24 or $25 seems to yield the maximum daily income.

④　a.　i. Since the probability of two heads or two tails is the same as the probability of one head and one tail (each are $\frac{1}{2}$), the long-run cumulative winnings or losses from this game should be about 0.

　　ii. The graph would be points oscillating slightly above and slightly below the *x*-axis.

b. Answers will vary, but should be roughly in the pattern described in Part a.

c. Explanations will depend on the match between predicted and actual results.

5 The postage cost for U.S. first-class mail is related to the weight of the letter or package being shipped. The following table gives the regulations in 2006 for relatively small letters or packages.

Weight (in ounces)	up to 1	up to 2	up to 3	up to 4	up to 5
Postage Cost (in dollars)	0.39	0.63	0.87	1.11	1.35

a. Make a coordinate graph showing (*weight, postage cost*) values for letters or packages weighing 1, 2, 3, 4, and 5 ounces.

b. What postage costs would you expect for letters or small packages sent by first-class mail, if those items weighed:

   i. 1.5 ounces   ii. 4.25 ounces   iii. 7 ounces

c. Add the (*weight, postage cost*) values from Part b to your graph. How should the points on your graph be connected (if at all)?

6 The Olympic record for the men's 400-meter hurdle race is 46.78 seconds. It was set by Kevin Young in 1992. His average running speed was $400 \div 46.78 \approx 8.55$ meters per second.

a. Make a table and a graph showing how 400-meter *race time* changes as *average speed* increases from 2 meters per second to 10 meters per second in steps of 1 meter per second.

b. Describe the pattern of change shown in your table and graph.

c. Write a rule showing how to calculate *race time t* for any *average speed s*.

d. Which change in *average speed* will reduce the *race time* most: an increase from 2 to 4 meters per second or an increase from 8 to 10 meters per second? Explain how your answer is illustrated in the shape of your graph.

7 The Olympic record in the women's 100-meter freestyle swim race is 53.52 seconds. It was set by Australian Jodie Henry in 2004. She swam at an average speed of $100 \div 53.52 \approx 1.87$ meters per second.

a. Make a table and a graph showing the way *average speed* for the 100-meter race changes as *time* increases from 40 seconds to 120 seconds (2 minutes) in steps of 10 seconds.

5 **a.**

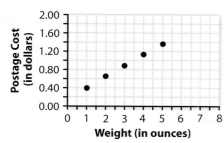

b. **i.** 1.5 ounces would cost $0.63.

ii. 4.25 ounces would cost $1.35.

iii. 7 ounces cost $1.83, assuming the pattern of increasing the cost by 24¢ for each ounce continues.

c. One possible suggestion would be as a *step function* as seen in the graph below.

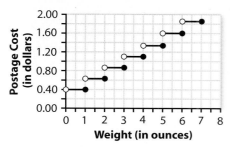

6 **a.**

Average Speed (in m/sec)	2	3	4	5	6	7	8	9	10
Race Time (in sec)	200	133	100	80	67	57	50	44	40

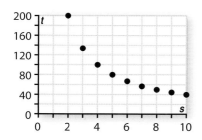

b. Race time decreases rapidly as speed increases from 2 meters per second, but for higher speeds a comparable increase in speed does not produce as significant a reduction in time.

c. $t = \dfrac{400}{s}$

d. The change from 2 m/sec to 4 m/sec produces the greater reduction in race time. That is shown by the fact that the graph drops more rapidly for increases in speed at lower speeds.

7 **a.**

Race Time (in sec)	40	50	60	70	80	90	100	110	120
Average Speed (in m/sec)	2.5	2.0	1.7	1.4	1.3	1.1	1.0	0.9	0.8

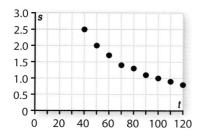

b. Describe the pattern of change shown in your table and graph.

c. Write a rule showing how to calculate *average speed s* for any *race time t*.

d. Which change in *race time* will cause the greatest change in *average speed*: an increase from 50 to 60 seconds or an increase from 110 to 120 seconds? Explain how your answer is illustrated in the shape of your graph.

8 The Water World Amusement Park has a huge swimming pool with a wave machine that makes you feel like you are swimming in an ocean. Unfortunately, the pool is uncovered and unheated, so the temperature forecast for a day affects the number of people who come to Water World.

On a summer day when the forecast called for a high temperature of 90°F, about 3,000 people visited the park. On another day, when the forecast called for a high temperature of 70°F, only 250 people came for the ocean-wave swimming.

a. Complete this table of (*temperature forecast, number of swimmers*) data in a way that you think shows the likely pattern relating *temperature forecast* to *number of swimmers*.

Temperature Forecast (in °F)	70	75	80	85	90	95
Number of Swimmers	250				3,000	

b. Graph the data in Part a. Then draw a line or curve that seems to match the pattern in your data points and could be used to predict *number of swimmers* at other temperatures.

c. Describe the pattern of change in *number of swimmers* as *temperature forecast* increases and explain how much confidence you would have in using that pattern to predict *number of swimmers* on any particular day.

d. Use your table and/or graph to estimate the number of swimmers for temperatures of:

i. 77°F   **ii.** 83°F   **iii.** 98°F

e. Suppose that Water World charges $15 for admission. Use this information and your estimates for number of swimmers at various forecast temperatures to make a table and graph showing the relationship between *forecast high temperature* and *park income*.

f. Use the information from Part e to estimate the park income when the high temperature is forecast to be:

i. 87°F   **ii.** 92°F

g. Why would you have limited confidence in using the data patterns of Parts a and e to predict park income when the forecast high temperature is 40°F or 110°F?

b. Race speed decreases rapidly as time increases from 40 seconds, but for higher times the increase in time does not produce as significant a reduction in speed.

c. $s = \frac{100}{t}$

d. The change from 50 seconds to 60 seconds produces the greater reduction in race speed. That is shown by the fact that the graph drops more rapidly for increases in time at lower times.

⑧ **a–e.** Answers to each part of this task will vary, but there ought to be a general trend for increase in temperature to cause increase in number of customers (except perhaps when it begins to get too hot).

f. The projected income should be obtained by multiplying the number of customers by $15 in each case.

g. With very low or very high temperatures, the patterns set at more reasonable swimming temperatures might have little relevance, since almost no one would go swimming in 40°F weather or even in 110°F weather.

Connections

These tasks will help you to build links between mathematical topics you have studied in the lesson and to connect those topics with other mathematics that you know.

9 The table below shows latitude of some major northern hemisphere cities and the average high temperatures in those cities in mid-summer and in mid-winter. Use that data and the scatterplots on page 19 to answer Parts a–c about the relationship between latitude and typical temperatures.

a. Does the pattern of points relating *mid-summer average high temperature* to *geographic latitude* suggest a close relationship between those variables? Explain your reasons for saying yes or no.

b. Does the pattern of points relating *mid-winter average high temperature* to *geographic latitude* suggest a close relationship between those variables? Explain your reasons for saying yes or no.

c. What factors other than latitude might influence summer and winter temperatures?

City	Latitude Degrees N	Mid-Summer Temperature °F	Mid-Winter Temperature °F
Athens, Greece	40	89	56
Bangkok, Thailand	14	90	90
Barrow, Alaska	72	45	−7
Berlin, Germany	53	74	35
Bombay, India	19	86	85
Cairo, Egypt	30	94	66
Chicago, Illinois	42	84	29
Jerusalem, Israel	32	84	53
Lagos, Nigeria	7	83	90
London, England	51	71	44
Los Angeles, California	34	84	68
Mexico City, Mexico	19	74	70
Miami, Florida	26	89	75
Manila, Philippines	14	89	86
New York City, New York	41	84	37
Reykjavik, Iceland	64	56	35
Seattle, Washington	48	75	45
Tokyo, Japan	36	84	49

Connections

  a. The scatterplot shows some trend for higher latitude cities to have lower temperatures. However, there is little midsummer variation due to latitude among cities in the lower latitudes.

b. The scatterplot shows a fairly consistent trend for higher latitude cities to have lower midwinter temperatures.

c. Among the factors students may include are those that deal with geographic differences such as distance above sea level and location near or far from large bodies of water like oceans.

Why Assign Connections and Reflections Tasks?

To help students focus on making sense, understand the overall picture, make connections, and reflect on their own thinking and to assist in retention of the concepts and skills learned in investigations, Connections and Reflections tasks have been developed for each homework set.

Connections tasks offer opportunities for students to consolidate the formal mathematics developed in the lesson and to make connections with mathematics in the current strand and other strands. Identifying and using connections among concepts and skills helps students to be more flexible in the use of their mathematical knowledge. Assigning the Connections tasks and then discussing them as a class can help develop mathematical expertise by encouraging students to see the overall picture of the mathematics they are learning.

Reflection tasks are designed to provide opportunities for students to process their learning and think about their thinking. These tasks ask students to reflect on their thinking and promote self-monitoring and self-assessment.

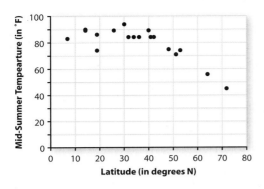

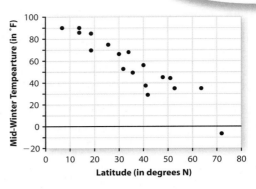

10. Random events such as the outcomes of flipping a fair coin often have predictable patterns.

   a. What is the probability of flipping a coin once and getting a head?

   b. What is the probability of flipping a coin two times and getting two heads?

   c. What is the probability of flipping a coin three times and getting three heads?

   d. What is the probability of flipping a coin four times and getting four heads?

   e. How would you describe the pattern in the probabilities of getting all heads as the number of coin tosses increases?

11. Jamal's average on history quizzes changed throughout the first quarter.

   a. After the first two quizzes, his average was 7, but he earned a 9 on the third quiz. What was his average for the first three quizzes?

   b. After the first eight quizzes, his average had slipped again to 7, but he earned 9 on the ninth quiz. What was his average for all nine quizzes of the quarter?

   c. Why did Jamal's 9 on the third quiz improve his overall average more than his 9 on the ninth quiz?

12. When the value of a quantity changes, there are several standard ways to describe *how much* it has changed. For example, if a boy who is 60 inches tall at the start of grade 8 grows to 66 inches twelve months later, we could say his height has increased:

   • by 6 inches (the *difference* between original and new height)

   • by 10% (the *relative* or *percent change* in his height)

   • by 0.5 inches per month (an *average rate of change*)

   Express each of the following quantitative changes in three ways similar to those above:

   a. The enrollment of Wayzata High School increased from 1,000 to 1,250 in the five-year period from 1998 to 2003.

   b. The balance in a student's bank savings account increased from $150 to $225 while she worked during the three-month summer break from school.

a. There are two possible equally likely outcomes, "heads" or "tails," so the probability is $\frac{1}{2}$.

b. There are four possible equally likely outcomes: HH, HT, TH, or TT. So the probability of getting two heads is $\frac{1}{4}$.

c. A tree diagram will show 8 possibilities, one of which is three heads. Thus, the probability of getting three heads is $\frac{1}{8}$.

d. A tree diagram will show 16 possibilities, one of which is four heads. Thus, the probability of getting four heads is $\frac{1}{16}$.

e. As the number of coins increases by one, the probability of getting all heads decreases by a factor of 0.5. (The rule $p = \frac{1}{2^n}$, where p is the probability of getting all heads and n is the number of coin flips, could also be used to describe the situation.)

 a. $\dfrac{7 + 7 + 9}{3} \approx 7.67$

b. $\dfrac{8 \cdot 7 + 9}{9} \approx 7.22$

c. With only three scores, the 9 score has more of an "influence" on the average. In other words, in Part a, the 9 is a higher percentage of the total points earned (23) than in Part b (65). (One way to illustrate this idea is to picture 1,000 quizzes with one 9 and 999 7s. This 9 has even less influence than the one in Part b, and the average score continues to get closer to 7.)

 a. (1) Enrollment increased by 250 students.

(2) by 25%

(3) by an average of 50 students per year

b. (1) The balance increased by $75.

(2) by 50%

(3) by an average of $25 per month

Unit 1

c. The supply of soft drinks in a school vending machine decreased from 200 to 140 during the 8 hours of one school day.

d. From the start of practice in March until the end of the track season in June, Mike's time in the 800-meter race decreased from 2 minutes 30 seconds to 2 minutes.

13 The related variables you studied in Investigations 1–3 and in Applications Tasks 1–8 are only a few of the many situations in which it helps to understand the pattern relating two or more variables.

a. Write a sentence in the form "_____ depends on _____" or "_____ is a function of _____" that describes a situation with which you are familiar.

b. For the situation you described in Part a:

 i. Explain how change in one variable relates to or causes change in the other.

 ii. Make a table showing at least 5 sample pairs of values that you would expect for the related variables.

 iii. Plot a graph of the sample data in part ii and connect the points in a way that makes sense (if at all).

Reflections

These tasks provide opportunities for you to re-examine your thinking about ideas in the lesson.

14 Experimentation with one bungee cord suggested that the rule $L = 30 + 0.2w$ would be a good predictor of the stretched cord length as a function of jumper weight. The operators of the bungee jump decided to adjust the jump-off point for each jumper to the height L calculated from the rule. What reasons can you think of to question that plan?

15 The student government at Banneker High School decided to set up a Velcro® jump (pictured at the left) as a fund-raiser for a school trip. They did a survey to see how many students would try the Velcro jump at various prices.

The data were as follows:

Price per Jump (in dollars)	0.50	1.00	2.00	3.00	5.00
Expected Number of Jumps	95	80	65	45	15

When several groups of Banneker mathematics students were asked to study the survey data about profit prospects of the rented Velcro jump, they produced different kinds of reports.

How would you rate each of the following reports, on a scale of 5 (excellent) to 0 (poor)? Explain why you gave each report the rating you did.

c. (1) The number of drinks decreased by 60.

(2) by 30%

(3) by an average of 7.5 drinks per hour

d. (1) Mike's time decreased by 30 seconds.

(2) by 20%

(3) by an average of 7.5 seconds per month

13 Answers will vary, depending on examples of situations that students choose to describe.

Reflections

14 There should be some margin of error, especially on the safe side.

Report a: *Making Money for Banneker*

The survey shows that a price of $0.50 will lead to the most customers, so that will bring in the biggest profit.

Report b: *Sticking it to the Velcro Customers*

The survey shows that the more you charge, the fewer customers you will have. If you multiply each price by the expected number of customers, you get a prediction of the income from the Velcro jump.

When we did that, we found that a price of $3.00 leads to the greatest income, so that is what should be charged. If you want to let the most kids have fun, you should charge only $0.50. If the operators don't want to work very hard, they should charge $10, because then no one will want to pay to jump.

Report c: *Velcro Profit Prospects*

Data from our market survey suggest a pattern in which the number of customers will decrease as the price increases. Each increase of $1 in the price will lead to a decrease of 15–20 customers. This pattern is shown in a plot of the survey data.

The trend in the data is matched well by the line drawn on the graph that follows. That line also helps in predicting the number of customers for prices not included in the survey.

Velcro Customer Prospects

To see how the amount of money earned by the Velcro game would be related to the price per jump, we added another row to the table, showing income. For example, 95 customers at $0.50 per jump will bring income of $47.50.

Price per Jump (in dollars)	0.50	1.00	2.00	3.00	5.00
Expected Number of Jumps	95	80	65	45	15
Expected Income (in dollars)	47.50	80.00	130.00	135.00	75.00

15 The purpose of this task is to stimulate student discussion of what constitutes good work in reporting results of a mathematical investigation. Student responses to the specific samples will vary, so the value of the item will come from full-class discussion. Obviously, we have in mind that Report c is most attractive because it is complete, illustrated by graphs and accurate in its conclusions.

Some suggestions follow.

Report a is not only incomplete but it is incorrect. It should receive a rating of 0.

Report b might receive a rating of a 3. This report reaches a reasonable conclusion from the table but does not consider the expected incomes for ticket prices other than those in the table. Since the table values jump from $2 to $3 to $5, one should consider ticket prices between those values also. Good reports would provide more detail including graphs for the reader. The last two sentences deviate from the issue of obtaining the most income.

Report c should receive the highest rating, likely a 5. This report outlines the full analysis needed to reach the conclusion and provides graphs. This report explains to the reader the thinking behind the conclusions in a way that is easily understood by the reader. The mathematics is accurate, leading to a correct conclusion.

ELL TIPS To aid English Language Learners in your classroom allow them to use their native language when answering questions whether you speak the language or not. This can enable them to build a foundation of math concepts.

Unit 1

A graph of the *price per jump* and *income* data is shown at the right. It suggests that a price between $2 and $3 per jump will lead to the greatest income. Since the rental charge is a fixed dollar amount, greatest income means greatest profit.

Velcro Profit Prospects

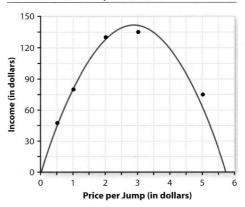

16 If you were asked to look for a pattern relating the values of two variables in a problem, would you prefer to have:

- a table of (x, y) data,
- a plot of points with coordinates (x, y), or
- a symbolic rule showing how values of y could be calculated from values of x?

Explain the reasons for your choice.

17 When there appears to be a relationship between values of two variables, how do you decide which should be considered the *independent variable* and which should be considered the *dependent variable*?

Extensions

These tasks provide opportunities for you to explore further or more deeply the mathematics you are learning.

18 Suppose that for a fund-raising event, your school can rent a climbing wall for $275. Complete the following tasks to help find the likely profit from using the climbing wall at the event.

16 Student preferences and explanations will vary.

17 Student responses should include whether or not the changing of one variable causes change in the other variable. Though, in general, it is not good practice to define a word using a form of the word, in this case, student use of the word *depend* may be an effective reinforcement of the terms in question.

Extensions

18 Answers will vary depending on the survey data reported in Part a. The general pattern of work should be similar to that of the Bungee Business problem.

a. Do a survey of your class to find out how many customers you might expect for various possible prices. Then use your data to estimate the number of students from your whole school who would try the climbing wall at various possible prices.

Climb Price (in dollars)	1	2	3	4	5	6	7	8	9	10
Number of Customers										

b. Plot a graph of the survey data and explain how it shows the pattern of change relating *number of customers* to *climb price*. Be sure to explain which number it makes sense to consider the independent variable and which the dependent variable in this situation.

c. Display the data relating *number of customers* to *climb price* in a table and a graph. Then use the pattern in the data to estimate the *income* that would be earned at various possible prices.

d. What do you recommend as the price that will maximize *profit* from the climbing wall rental? Explain how your decision is based on patterns in the data tables and graphs you've displayed.

19 One of the most important principles of physics is at work when two kids play on a teeter-totter. You probably know that for two weights on opposite sides of the *fulcrum* to balance, those weights need to be placed at just the right distances from the fulcrum.

a. Suppose that a 50-pound weight is placed at one end of a teeter-totter, 6 feet from the fulcrum. How far from the fulcrum should a person sit to balance the 50-pound weight if the person weighs:

   i. 50 pounds

  ii. 100 pounds

 iii. 150 pounds

(If you are unsure of the physical relationship required to make a balance, do some experiments with a meter stick as the teeter-totter and stacks of pennies as the weights.)

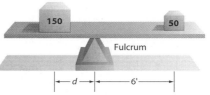

b. Sketch a graph showing the distance from the fulcrum required for various weights to balance a 50-pound weight that has been placed on the opposite side, 6 feet from the fulcrum. Describe the pattern relating distance from the fulcrum to the counter-balancing weight.

c. What rule relates distance from the fulcrum d (in feet) to weight w (in pounds) when the weight balances a 50-pound weight on the opposite side and 6 feet from the fulcrum?

19   **a.** The general lever principle involved says that the products of weights and distances from the fulcrum should be the same. For example, in this case:

    i. 50 pounds at 6 feet from the fulcrum will balance the same weight at the same distance on the other side of the fulcrum.

    ii. 100 pounds at 3 feet will balance 50 pounds at 6 feet from the fulcrum.

    iii. 150 pounds at 2 feet will balance 50 pounds at 6 feet from the fulcrum.

  b. As the weight on one side increases, its required distance decreases rapidly at first and then more slowly. The pattern is shown by the following plot of sample data pairs.

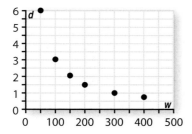

  c. The rule $d = \frac{300}{w}$ will give distance required by a weight w to balance a 50-pound weight positioned 6 feet from the fulcrum.

20 In many problems, it is helpful to express the relationship between dependent and independent variables with a symbolic rule that shows how values of one variable can be calculated from the values of the other.

    a. If number of customers n at a bungee jump is related to price per jump p by the rule $n = 50 - p$, what rule shows how to calculate income I from values of n and p? What rule shows how to calculate values of I from the value of p alone?

    b. What rule shows how to calculate Ethan and Anna's allowance on day n of a month if they receive 1 penny on day one, 2 pennies on day two, 4 pennies on day three, 8 pennies on day four, and so on?

    c. Devon and Kevin were offered a pay scheme for work at Fresh Fare Market that would earn each of them $0.10 for the first hour in a week, $0.20 for the second hour, $0.40 for the third hour, $0.80 for the fourth hour, and so on. What rule shows how to calculate their pay for the nth hour in a week?

Review

These tasks provide opportunities for you to review previously learned mathematics and to refine your skills in using that mathematics.

 21 Suppose a fair die is rolled.

    a. What is the probability that the top face is a 6?

    b. What is the probability that the top face is a 3?

    c. What is the probability that the top face is an even number?

    d. What is the probability that the top face is *not* a 6?

22 Micah and Keisha are renting a boat. The charge for the boat is $25 for the first hour and $12 for every hour (or portion of an hour) after the first.

    a. How much will it cost if they rent the boat at 1:00 P.M. and return it at 3:50 P.M.?

    b. They have been saving money all summer and have $80. What is the maximum amount of time that they can keep the boat?

23 The speed at which you travel, the length of time you travel, and the distance you travel are related in predictable ways. In particular, *speed · time = distance*. Use this relationship to help you answer the following questions.

    a. Dave rides his bike for 2 hours with an average speed of 8.6 miles per hour. How far does he travel?

    b. Kristen lives 4 miles from her friend's house. It is 2:30 P.M. and she needs to meet her friend at 3:00 P.M. How fast must she ride her bike in order to get to her friend's house on time?

    c. Jessie leaves home at 7:30 A.M. and rides his bike to school at a speed of 9 miles per hour. If his school is 3 miles from his house, what time will he get to school?

20 a. $I = pn$; $I = p(50 - p)$

 b. $a = 2^{n-1}$ pennies or $a = 0.5(2^n)$ pennies

 c. $w = \dfrac{2^{n-1}}{10} = 0.1(2^{n-1})$ or

 $w = 0.05(2^n)$ pennies

Review

 Just in Time

21 a. $\dfrac{1}{6}$ b. $\dfrac{1}{6}$

 c. $\dfrac{1}{2}$ d. $\dfrac{5}{6}$

22 a. \$49

 b. 5 hours

23 a. 17.2 miles

 b. 8 mph

 c. 7:50 A.M.

> **NOTE** See the information about the use of **just-in-time review** tasks in the Unit Overview. A clock icon will designate these tasks. Check the Unit Planning Guide for appropriate times to assign the tasks.

> **INSTRUCTIONAL NOTE** Review Task 23 offers an opportunity for students to recognize that rounding decisions are sometimes influenced by the context of the problem.

Unit 1

24 Consider this scale drawing of Mongoose Lake. Using the given scale, estimate the perimeter to the nearest 10 meters and the area to the nearest 100 square meters.

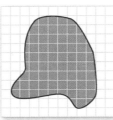

Mongoose Lake
Scale: ⊢—⊣ = **10 meters**

25 Convert each of these percents into equivalent decimals.

a. 75%

b. 5.4%

c. 0.8%

d. 0.93%

26 The table below gives some measurements associated with four different rectangles. Use the relationships between the lengths of the sides of a rectangle and the area and perimeter of a rectangle to complete the table.

Length (in cm)	Width (in cm)	Perimeter (in cm)	Area (in cm²)
25	10	?	?
15	?	42	?
?	25	?	150
?	?	28	40

27 Convert each of these decimals into equivalent percents.

a. 0.8

b. 0.25

c. 2.45

d. 0.075

28 Suppose that a student has $150 in a bank savings account at the start of the school year. Calculate the change in that savings account during the following year in case it

a. earns 5% interest over that year.

b. grows from monthly deposits of $10 throughout the year.

c. earns 6.5% interest over that year.

d. declines by 8.7% over the year because withdrawals exceed interest earned.

e. declines at an average rate of $2.50 per month.

LESSON 1 • Cause and Effect   **25**

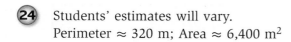

24 Students' estimates will vary.
Perimeter ≈ 320 m; Area ≈ 6,400 m²

Just in Time

25　**a.** 0.75　　　　**b.** 0.054　　　　**c.** 0.008　　　　**d.** 0.0093

26

Length (in cm)	Width (in cm)	Perimeter (in cm)	Area (in cm²)
25	10	**70**	**250**
15	**6**	42	**90**
6	25	**62**	150
10	**4**	28	40

27　**a.** 80%　　　　**b.** 25%
　　　c. 245%　　　　**d.** 7.5%

28 Assuming that the interest is paid only once per year (not a common interest payment scheme and one that will be refined in the next lesson and later in the *Exponential Functions* unit):

　a. The change will be 5% of $150 or $7.50, giving a new balance of $157.50.

　b. The change will be 12 × $10 or $120, giving a new balance of $270.

　c. The change will be 6.5% of $150 or $9.75, giving a new balance of $159.75.

　d. The change will be 8.7% of $150 or a loss of $13.05, giving a new balance of $136.95.

　e. The change will be a 12 × $2.50, or $30, decrease, giving a new balance of $120.

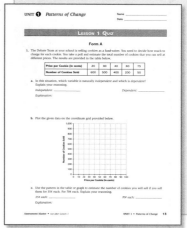

LESSON 2

Change Over Time

Every 10 years, the U.S. Census Bureau counts every American citizen and permanent resident. The 2000 census reported the U.S. population to be 281 million, with growth at a rate of about 1% each year. The world population is over 6 billion and growing at a rate that will cause it to exceed 9 billion by the year 2050.

Change Over Time

In many situations, our interest in change is focused on a single variable that changes in value as time passes. While there are often many factors contributing to the change in that variable, instead of trying to detect quantitative cause-and-effect relationships among those factors, we often focus simply on the change over time of the single variable. The most common examples of such focus on change over time are in various population studies and in economic analyses where interest or inflation rates cause bank balances or prices to grow as time passes. Throughout work on the problems of this lesson, students will be asked to use tables, graphs, and rules to describe, represent, and analyze patterns in variables that change with the passage of time.

This lesson is designed to develop students' understanding and skill in analyzing such "change over time" situations. It emphasizes an iterative or recursive perspective in which one compares the value of a variable at one point in time to the value of that same variable at successive, equally-spaced points in time. The primary vehicle for expressing such patterns of change is the *NOW-NEXT* rule. Two types of *NOW-NEXT* relationships are of particular interest:

NEXT = NOW ± C gives the pattern leading to linear functions, and
NEXT = C · NOW gives the pattern leading to exponential functions.

Each of these special types of functions will be studied in detail in subsequent Course 1 units, so the goal in this first unit is to sensitize students to the characteristic patterns as an intuitive foundation for more technical work ahead.

The combination of these patterns in the form *NEXT = C · NOW ± D* is also of considerable interest, but it does not lead to a simple closed form function rule.

Lesson Objectives

- Develop ability to recognize recursive patterns of change
- Develop ability to use calculators to iterate stages in a recursive pattern
- Develop ability to write *NOW-NEXT* rules to represent recursive patterns
- Develop ability to write and use spreadsheet formulas to explore recursive patterns of change (optional)
- Use iteration to solve problems about population and money change over time

National, state, and local governments and international agencies provide many services to people across our country and around the world. To match resources to needs, it is important to have accurate population counts more often than once every 10 years. However, complete and accurate census counts are very expensive.

World Population 1650–2050

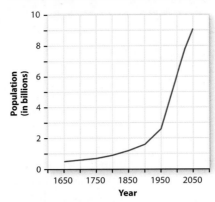

Source: www.census.gov/ipc/www/world.html

Think About This Situation

The population of the world and of individual countries, states, and cities changes over time.

a) How would you describe the pattern of change in world population from 1650 to 2050?

b) What do you think are some of the major factors that influence population change of a city, a region, or a country?

c) How could governments estimate year-to-year population changes without making a complete census?

Your work on investigations of this lesson will develop your understanding and skill in using algebra to solve problems involving variables like populations that change as time passes.

Investigation 1 — Predicting Population Change

If you study trends in population data over time, you will often find patterns that suggest ways to predict change in the future. There are several ways that algebraic rules can be used to explain and extend such patterns of change over time. As you work on the problems of this investigation, look for an answer to this question:

What data and calculations are needed to predict human and animal populations into the future?

Think About This Situation

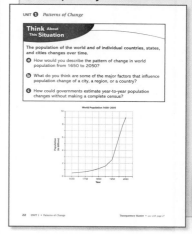

a Over fairly short periods of time, world population does not always grow exponentially or at a constant exponential rate. However, when considered over many centuries, it has followed such a pattern (though there are some indications that recent growth is at a faster exponential rate). The typical effect of exponential growth is shown in the graph. The point of this TATS is not to introduce exponential growth, but to get students thinking about new and nonlinear patterns of change.

b Population change of a region can be affected by war, fatal diseases, famines, people moving to cities for work, immigration, and many other factors.

c Estimates of population change between census counts can be based on samples of birth and death records and small-scale replication of census surveys in selected regions.

Investigation 1 Predicting Population Change

This investigation has two parts—the first focuses on population change in Brazil, without considering migration. That gives a simple *NOW-NEXT* relation in the general form *NEXT = NOW + X%NOW*. The second part of the investigation focuses on whale populations where hunting by indigenous people introduces a new consideration and a *NOW-NEXT* relation in the form *NEXT = NOW + X%NOW − C*.

Problems 1 and 2 can be done as a whole class using large sheets of chart paper to record the change, total population, and plot graphs with a few different vertical scales. Exponential growth with low growth rates is fairly linear for a long time. The point here is the iterative way of thinking. In Unit 5, *Exponential Functions*, students will learn much more about exponential growth and decay.

COLLABORATION SKILL
Keep track of time.

Population Change in Brazil Brazil is the largest country in South America. Its population in the year 2005 was about 186 million.

Census statisticians in Brazil can estimate change in that country's population from one year to the next using small surveys and these facts:

- Based on recent trends, births every year equal about 1.7% of the total population of the country.
- Deaths every year equal about 0.6% of the total population.

Source: *CIA—The World Factbook 2005*

① How much of the estimated change in Brazil's population from 2005 to 2006 was due to:

  a. births?   **b.** deaths?   **c.** both causes combined?

② Calculate estimates for the population of Brazil in 2006, 2007, 2008, 2009, and 2010. Record those estimates and the year-to-year changes in a table like the one below.

Population Estimates for Brazil

Year	Change (in millions)	Total Population (in millions)
2005	—	186
2006	?	?
2007	?	?
2008	?	?
2009	?	?
2010	?	?

  a. Make a plot of the (*year, total population*) data.

  b. Describe the pattern of change over time in population estimates for Brazil. Explain how the pattern you describe is shown in the table and in the plot.

③ Which of these strategies for estimating *change* in Brazil's population from one year to the next uses the growth rate data correctly? Be prepared to justify your answer in each case.

  a. 0.017(*current population*) − 0.006(*current population*) = *change in population*

  b. 0.011(*current population*) = *change in population*

  c. 0.17(*current population*) − 0.06(*current population*) = *change in population*

  d. 1.7%(*current population*) − 0.6% = *change in population*

④ Which of the following strategies correctly use the given growth rate data to estimate the *total* population of Brazil one year from now? Be prepared to justify your answer in each case.

  a. (*current population*) + 0.011(*current population*) = *next year's population*

(1) **a.** 3.16 million   **b.** −1.12 million   **c.** 2.04 million

(2)

Year	Change (in millions)	Total Population (in millions)
2005	—	186
2006	2.046	188.046
2007	2.0685	190.115
2008	2.0913	192.206
2009	2.1143	194.320
2010	2.1375	196.458

a–b. The table shows that the population change is increasing slowly from one year to the next. Eventually, this will produce noticeable effects in the total population. But for such a small percent growth rate and only a few years, the typical exponential up-surge will not be noticed in a table or a plot. The appearance of the plot of the total population data will depend on scales chosen and whether one wants to keep (0, 0) in the picture. (See the investigation introduction on page T27.)

(3) **a.** Correct use of growth data: 0.017 stands for 1.7% of current population (births) and minus 0.006 is subtracting 0.6% of the current population (deaths).

b. Correct use of growth data: The net increase is 1.1%, or 0.011 times the current population.

c. Incorrect: These decimals stand for 17% and 6%, not correct data.

d. Incorrect: "0.6%" is simply a number, 0.006. We want to subtract a percent *of* the current population, not a constant 0.006.

(4) **a.** Correct; This means adding 1.1% of the current population to the current population.

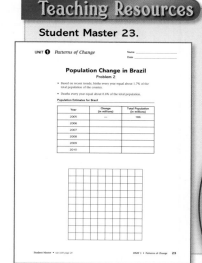

Unit 1

b. (*current population*) + 0.017(*current population*) − 0.006(*current population*) = *next year's population*

c. 1.011(*current population*) = *next year's population*

d. 186 million + 1.7 million − 0.6 million = *next year's population*

⑤ Use the word *NOW* to stand for the population of Brazil in any year and the word *NEXT* to stand for the population in the next year to write a rule that shows how to calculate *NEXT* from *NOW*. Your rule should begin "*NEXT* = ..." and then give directions for using *NOW* to calculate the value of *NEXT*.

The Whale Tale In 1986, the International Whaling Commission declared a ban on commercial whale hunting to protect the small remaining stocks of several whale types that had come close to extinction.

Scientists make census counts of whale populations to see if the numbers are increasing. While it's not easy to count whales accurately, research reports have suggested that one population, the bowhead whales of Alaska, was probably between 7,700 and 12,600 in 2001.

The difference between whale births and natural deaths leads to a natural increase of about 3% per year. However, Alaskan native people are allowed to hunt and kill about 50 bowhead whales each year for food, oil, and other whale products used in their daily lives.

⑥ Assume that the 2001 bowhead whale population in Alaska was the low estimate of 7,700.

a. What one-year change in that population would be due to the difference between births and natural deaths?

b. What one-year change in that population would be due to hunting?

c. What is the estimate of the 2002 population that results from the combination of birth, death, and hunting rates?

⑦ Use the word *NOW* to stand for the Alaskan bowhead whale population in any given year and write a rule that shows how to estimate the population in the *NEXT* year.

⑧ Which of the following changes in conditions would have the greater effect on the whale population over the next few years?

- decrease in the natural growth rate from 3% to 2%, or
- increase in the Alaskan hunting quota from 50 to 100 per year

b. Correct; The three parts combine to 1.1% of the current population.

c. Correct; 1.011 times current population

d. Incorrect; Using 1.7 and 0.6 as numbers, not percents

5 $NEXT = 1.011 \cdot NOW$

Other forms such as $NEXT = NOW + 0.011 \cdot NOW$ may also be correct.

COMMON CONCEPTUAL CHALLENGE The fact that a percent increase like 5% on a base of B can be expressed in two ways (as $B + 0.05B$ or as $1.05B$) is one of the most useful, but consistently puzzling, algebraic manipulations for students. Be sure to have students work through Problems 3 and 4 carefully and try to make sure that students are convinced that the basic identity $B + 0.05B = 1.05B$ is true. In some sense, it is a rather direct application of the distributive property of multiplication over addition. The implicit "1" in front of the first B seems to cause students difficulty.

INSTRUCTIONAL NOTE
You may wish to have a quick whole class discussion around Problems 3–5 before most groups begin Problem 6.

6 Starting from the low estimate of 7,700 whales:

a. +231 whales

b. −50 whales

c. +181, or 7,881 whales

7 $NEXT = 1.03 \cdot NOW - 50$ or $NEXT = NOW + 0.03 \cdot NOW - 50$

8 Changing the growth rate from 3% to 2% would have the greater effect on the whale population over the next few years.

Year	2001	2002	2003	2004	2005
$NEXT = 1.03 \cdot NOW - 50$	7,700	7,881	8,067	8,259	8,457
$NEXT = 1.02 \cdot NOW - 50$	7,700	7,804	7,910	8,018	8,128
$NEXT = 1.03 \cdot NOW - 100$	7,700	7,831	7,965	8,104	8,248

(Some students may think quantitatively as follows: In the first year, a 1% decrease in the growth rate for an initial population of 7,700 whales would result in 77 fewer whales; however, a change in the hunting quota from 50 to 100 would result in only 50 fewer whales. Since the *NEXT* whale population increases each year, the 2% growth rate will continue to outweigh the increase of 50 whales to the hunting quota.)

In studies of population increase and decrease, it is often important to predict change over many years, not simply from one year to the next. It is also interesting to see how changes in growth factors affect changes in populations. Calculators and computers can be very helpful in those kinds of studies.

For example, the following calculator procedure gives future estimates of the bowhead whale population with only a few keystrokes:

Calculator commands	Expected display

7700
ENTER
.03 × Answer + Answer − 50
ENTER
ENTER
ENTER
ENTER
ENTER
ENTER
ENTER
ENTER
ENTER
ENTER

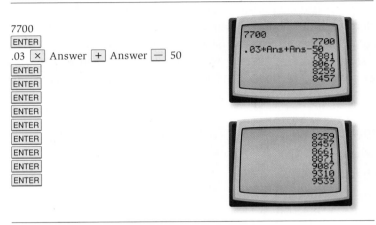

9. Examine the calculator procedure above.

   a. What seem to be the purposes of the various keystrokes and commands?

   b. How do the instructions implement a *NOW-NEXT* rule for predicting population change?

10. Modify the given calculator steps to find whale population predictions starting from the 2001 high figure of 12,600 and a natural increase of 3% per year.

   a. Find the predicted population for 2015 if the annual hunt takes 50 whales each year.

   b. Suppose that the hunt takes 200 whales each year instead of 50. What is the predicted population for 2015 in this case?

   c. Experiment to find a hunt number that will keep the whale population stable at 12,600.

9 **a.** Pressing **7700** ENTER places the value of 7,700 in the memory of the calculator under **ANS**. The second set of keystrokes calls up the 7,700 current population and multiplies by 0.03 for the 3% growth, adds the 7,700, and subtracts the 50 hunting amount. Repeatedly pressing ENTER continues to take the previously computed answer and recomputes the 3% growth and subtracts the 50 hunting amount.

b. The ANS represents the *NOW* value of the *NOW-NEXT* formula. Pressing ENTER computes the *NEXT* value defined by the formula.

10 **a.** The predicted 2015 population is around 18,204 whales.

b. With the change in the hunt amount, the 2015 projection is 15,641 whales.

c. If the number of whales hunted was increased to 378 (3% of 12,600), the population would stabilize.

Unit 1

Summarize
the Mathematics

In the studies of human and whale populations, you made estimates for several years based on growth trends from the past.

a What trend data and calculations were required to make these estimates:

   i. The change in the population of Brazil from one year to the next? The new total population of that country?

   ii. The change in number of Alaskan bowhead whales from one year to the next? The new total whale population?

b What does a *NOW-NEXT* rule like $NEXT = 1.03 \cdot NOW - 100$ tell about patterns of change in a variable over time?

c What calculator commands can be used to make population predictions for many years in the future? How do those commands implement *NOW-NEXT* rules?

Be prepared to share your thinking with the class.

✓Check Your Understanding

The 2000 United States Census reported a national population of about 281 million, with a birth rate of 1.4%, a death rate of 0.9%, and net migration of about 1.1 million people per year. The net migration of 1.1 million people is a result of about 1.3 million immigrants entering and about 0.2 million emigrants leaving each year.

a. Use the given data to estimate the U.S. population for years 2001, 2005, 2010, 2015, 2020.

b. Use the words *NOW* and *NEXT* to write a rule that shows how to use the U.S. population in one year to estimate the population in the next year.

c. Write calculator commands that automate calculations required by your rule in Part b to get the U.S. population estimates.

d. Modify the rule in Part b and the calculator procedure in Part c to estimate U.S. population for 2015 in case:

   i. The net migration rate increased to 1.5 million per year.

   ii. The net migration rate changed to −1.0 million people per year. That is, if the number of emigrants (people leaving the country) exceeded the number of immigrants (people entering the country) by 1 million per year.

Summarize
the Mathematics

(a)

i. We needed to know: birth rate, death rate, growth rate (calculated from birth and death rate), and the starting population. Calculations were: (1 + *growth rate*) × *starting population*.

ii. We needed to know the birth rate, natural death rate, (net growth rate), the starting population, and the annual number of whales hunted. Calculations were: (1 + *growth rate*) × *starting population* − *number of whales hunted*.

(b) The *NOW-NEXT* rule shows that the variable amount will both increase (by 3%) and decrease (by 100) over each unit of time. (Whether or not the values will be increasing or decreasing over the long run depends on the starting *NOW* value. Students have not yet seen a situation with a starting value that leads to a decrease in the long run.)

(c) Calculator commands enter the starting population and then generate answers using the ANS feature in a rule. Repeatedly pressing ENTER estimates for future years. The specific rule used involves the growth rate and other added or subtracted increases or decreases.

PROCESSING PROMPT Our group kept track of time by … and by … .

Teaching Resources

Transparency Master 24.

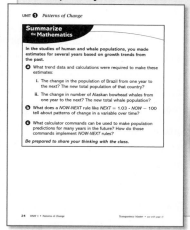

MATH TOOLKIT Some students may wish to add an example of a *NOW-NEXT* rule and the calculator procedure for using the ANS key to find values recursively.

✓ Check Your Understanding

a.

Year	U.S. Population (in millions)
2000	281
2001	283.505
2005	293.651
2010	306.621
2015	319.919
2020	333.553

b. $NEXT = 0.005 \cdot NOW + NOW + 1.1$, or $NEXT = 1.005 \cdot NOW + 1.1$, starting at 281

ASSIGNMENT NOTE If you omit Investigation 2 you may wish to assign A5 or A6.

c.

d.

i. $NEXT = 0.005 \cdot NOW + NOW + 1.5$, starting at 281
2015 estimate = 326.13 million

ii. $NEXT = 0.005 \cdot NOW + NOW - 1.0$, starting at 281
2015 estimate = 287.29 million

Promoting Mathematical Discourse

Summarize the Mathematics, *page 31*

Teacher: Let's summarize our thinking from Investigation 1. You made estimates of human and whale populations based on growth trends from the past. Take a look at Part a i. What trend data and calculations did you use to predict the population change in Brazil from one year to the next? And also the new total population?

Carley: There were births of 1.7% and deaths of 0.6% each year. You took the population and multiplied by 0.011 to get the next answer.

Teacher: What do the rest of you think?

Tony: Where did the 0.011 come from again? 1.7% − 0.6% is 1.1%. Oh, 1.1% is the same as 0.011. So, the next population is 0.011 times the previous population.

Teacher: What does the 1.1% represent?

Tony: That is the final growth rate made up of the birth and death rates.

Teacher: So, look again at Part a. What did we just answer?

Caitlyn: We were talking about the population change and not the new total population.

Ken: Yeah, you need to add in the current population to get the new total.

Teacher: What information were we using to get these results?

Chloe: We used the birth rate, death rate, and the current population.

Teacher: So, how did we express both the population change and the total population for each year in *NOW-NEXT* language?

Michael: The change was *NOW* times 0.011. And that was used to find the *NEXT* population. *NEXT* was equal to 0.011 times *NOW* plus *NOW*.

Teacher: *(Noticing a few furrowed brows)* Okay. *(Writes*
     Change =
     NEXT Pop. =
on the transparency next to Part a.) Michael, would you please write what you mean on the transparency here?

Michael: *(Writes on transparency.)*
     Change = *NOW* × 0.011
     NEXT Pop. = 0.011 × *NOW* + *NOW*

Teacher: Any comments?

Tanner: That's right! We have answered both questions now.

Teacher: But it seems that there may be an error to me. The first rule for change uses *NOW* times 0.011 and the second one uses 0.011 times *NOW*. Isn't that a problem?

Carley: Yes, we should have the same thing in both rules.

Thomas: No, it is okay this way. It is like 3 times 4 is the same as 4 times 3. It doesn't matter which order two numbers are multiplied.

Kyle: Well that is true, but I would still like to have them written the same way. Either way is fine, but both the same way.

Teacher: Okay, are we agreed that these rules are correct as written? *(Students agree.)*

Then you may choose the way that you would like to represent the yearly population change and the total population for your summary. As you finalize your answer to i of Part a, complete ii related to the whale population growth that you investigated. Since you used a variety of growth rates and hunting quotas for the whale population, look for a way to answer the questions in a more general form than we did for the Brazil population question.

(Students have two minutes to work.)

Teacher: Okay class. What trend data and calculations did you use to estimate the change in number of Alaskan bowhead whales each year and the new total population changes?

Leroy: We said that you multiplied 3% times the population of 7,700, then added that to 7,700, then subtracted 50. Sometimes the numbers were different for different problems though.

Teacher: Does everyone agree with the calculations described by Leroy? *(Students seem to agree.)* Well, then since we did use a variety of numbers, can we talk about the numbers and calculations in a more general way?

Zula: Our group said that we needed to multiply the growth rate and the starting population of whales to find the change each year. We then added that amount to the starting population and subtracted the hunting quota to get the total new whale population.

Stephanie: You asked us to write it more generally so we wrote … . Can I come up and write it on the transparency?

Teacher: Sure, anytime you think it would be better to write something out for the class, we can use the board or the overhead to display it.

Stephanie: *(Writes on transparency.)*
  Change = Growth Rate × Current Population
  New Population = Change + Current Population − Hunting Quota.
(Then speaks to class.) What do you guys think, is that okay?

Keisha: Sure, that's okay, but you could have written New Population = Growth Rate × Current Population + Current Population − Hunting Quota.

Stephanie: Right, I just thought it was shorter the way I wrote it.

Teacher: Why might someone wish to write the rule in the longer form offered by Keisha?

Tristen: Well, in the longer form, you can see all the pieces that make up the calculation.

Teacher: Okay, now think about Part b. What does a rule like $NEXT = 1.03 \cdot NOW - 100$ tell about patterns of change in a variable over time?

Joe: The variable is increasing by 3% each year, but 100 is also subtracted each year.

Teacher: The problems we did in this investigation all used a year as the time unit. Do you think NOW-NEXT rules only work for problems about yearly increases?

Elisa: No, the whale increases could have been measured monthly. But if the 3% increase was monthly, we would have a lot of whales in a few years.

Jon: Yeah, no more endangered species for whales.

Teacher: Let's move on to Part c. In general, what calculator commands can be used to make population predictions for many years in the future?

Joe: You can enter the current population and hit the enter button so that it is stored in the "answer" of the calculator. That way a rule can be written that updates the answer for each year. So, the rule would be Growth Rate × ANS + ANS − Hunting Quota (if there is one). Then you can press ENTER for each year after that.

Teacher: Would you please write that up here also? *(Joe writes on transparency.)* So, what do you notice?

Elisa: *(Pointing to the previous equation on the transparency—see Stephanie's comments.)* The general expression that we had for the whale problem is the same as the calculator equation if you think of ANS as the Current Population. The Change is the Growth Rate times the Current Population or ANS from the calculator.

Teacher: Good thinking!

One of the most useful tools for exploring relations among birth rates, death rates, migration rates, and population totals is a computer *spreadsheet*.

A spreadsheet is an electronic grid of cells in which numerical data or labels can be stored. The cells of a spreadsheet can be related by formulas, so that the numerical entry of one cell can be calculated from data in other cells.

The following table shows a piece of one spreadsheet that predicts growth of the Alaskan bowhead whale population.

Whale Population.xls

◇	A	B	C
1	Year	Population	Natural Growth Rate
2	2001	7700	1.03
3	2002	7881	Hunting Rate
4	2003	8067	50
5	2004	8259	
6	2005	8457	
7			

As you work on the problems in this investigation, think about the following question:

How do basic spreadsheet methods use the NOW-NEXT way of thinking to help solve problems about change over time?

1 From your earlier work with calculators, the numbers in column **B** of the preceding spreadsheet probably look familiar. However, you can't see how the spreadsheet actually produced those numbers. The next table shows the formulas used to calculate entries in columns **A** and **B** of the first display.

Whale Population.xls

A6 =A5+1

◇	A	B	C
1	Year	Population	Natural Growth Rate
2	2001	7700	1.03
3	=A2+1	=1.03*B2−50	Hunting Rate
4	=A3+1	=1.03*B3−50	50
5	=A4+1	=1.03*B4−50	
6	=A5+1	=1.03*B5−50	
7			

Compare the formula cell entries to the numerical cell values in the display above to help answer the next questions about how spreadsheets actually work.

a. How do you think the formulas in cells **A3**, **A4**, **A5**, and **A6** produce the pattern of entries 2002, 2003, 2004, and 2005 in the numerical form of the spreadsheet?

b. How do you think the formulas in cells **B3**, **B4**, **B5**, and **B6** produce the pattern of entries 7881, 8067, 8259, and 8457?

It is expected that students (and teachers) bring quite a variety of prior experiences with spreadsheets to the material in this investigation. While spreadsheets have an impressive array of mathematical capabilities, the problems here have been designed to introduce and begin developing students' skill in use of only a few key properties—especially those that connect with the *NOW-NEXT* way of tracking change over time. Students will need to learn the cell reference (row and column) conventions of spreadsheets (which unfortunately run opposite to the matrix convention in which row number comes before column number), the standard method of entering formulas for calculating cell entries from other cell entries (for example "=4*B2+C3"), the use of "fill down" and "fill across" to replicate formulas without tedious retyping of cell formulas, and (somewhat less important) the convention for fixing cell references by use of dollar signs before the column or row reference to be fixed (e.g., "$C$2" will not change even if it is part of a formula that is replicated by "fill down" or "fill across" in a sheet).

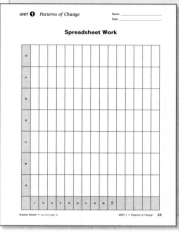

Teaching Resources

Student Masters 25–27.

Since spreadsheets are really only powerful if used on a computer, it will probably be essential to have some whole class work at the start of this investigation with the teacher displaying what actually happens in the sample spreadsheets of Problems 1–3 before turning students loose to try their own hands on the subsequent problems. Problems 1–3 have been written with the intention that even this whole class introduction need not be a lecture, but more of an interactive dialogue with problems posed, wait-time for student thought, and then testing of student ideas on actual spreadsheets. Some teachers have found it convenient to have one or more of the introductory sheets stored as files that students simply open in order to get started, since typing and navigating among cells might be quite time-consuming without compensatory illumination about how spreadsheets work.

TECHNOLOGY NOTE If students do not have access to spreadsheet software on their computer, you may wish to provide *CPMP-Tools*. The spreadsheet software is under the algebra menu.

a. The formulas in cells **A3**, **A4**, **A5**, and **A6** produce the pattern of entries 2002, 2003, 2004, and 2005 in the numerical form of the spreadsheet by adding one year to the value of the year in the preceding cell.

b. The formulas in cells **B3**, **B4**, **B5**, and **B6** produce the pattern of entries 7881, 8067, 8259, and 8457 in the numerical form of the spreadsheet by applying the natural growth rate of 3% to the previous year's population and subtracting the constant harvest of 50 per year from hunting by native people.

c. Why would it make sense to call the formulas in cells **A3–A6** and **B3–B6** *NOW-NEXT* formulas?

   d. What are the starting values for the formulas in columns **A** and **B**?

The real power of a spreadsheet comes from a feature not shown in this table of formulas. After entering the starting values in cells **A2** and **B2** and the *NOW-NEXT* formulas in cells **A3** and **B3**, the spreadsheet command "fill down" will automatically produce formulas for the cells below, changing the cell reference **A2** to **A3**, **B2** to **B3**, and so on.

2 Suppose that you were interested in studying population growth of the United States in 10-year intervals corresponding to the national census counts. With the 2000 population of 281 million, a natural 10-year growth rate of about 5%, and 10-year migration of about 11 million, a spreadsheet to make predictions for several decades might begin like the one below.

U.S. Population.xls

B3 =1.05*B2+11

	A	B	C
1	Year	Population	Natural Growth Rate
2	2000	281	1.05
3	=A2+10	=1.05*B2+11	Migration Rate
4			11
5			
6			

   a. What formula and numerical entries would you expect in cells **A3**, **A4**, **A5**, and **A6** if you use a fill down command in that column?

   b. What formula and numerical entries would you expect in cells **B3**, **B4**, **B5**, and **B6** if you use a fill down command in that column?

A second feature of spreadsheets makes exploratory work even more efficient. If you mark column and/or row labels with a dollar sign symbol, they will not change in response to fill down or fill across commands.

3 Suppose that you want to study the effects of change in both natural growth and migration rates for the U.S. population.

   a. What numerical value do you think will result from the formula "=C$2*B2+C$4" in cell **B3** of the spreadsheet below?

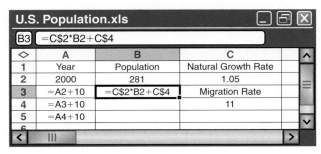

U.S. Population.xls

B3 =C$2*B2+C$4

	A	B	C
1	Year	Population	Natural Growth Rate
2	2000	281	1.05
3	=A2+10	=C$2*B2+C$4	Migration Rate
4	=A3+10		11
5	=A4+10		
6			

c. It makes sense to call the formulas in cells **A3–A6** and **B3–B6** *NOW-NEXT* formulas because they show how to obtain values in each cell from those in preceding cells.

d. The starting values for the formulas in columns **A** and **B** are 2001 and 7700, respectively.

2 Using the fill down command, the formulas will be as in this table.

U.S. Population.xls			

| B3 | =A2+10 | |

◇	A	B	C	
1	Year	Population	Natural Growth Rate	
2	2000	281	1.05	
3	=A2+10	=1.05*B2+11	Migration Rate	
4	=A3+10	=1.05*B3+11	11	
5	=A4+10	=1.05*B4+11		
6	=A5+10	=1.05*B5+11		
7				

a. The numerical entries in cells **A3**, **A4**, **A5**, and **A6** would be 2010, 2020, 2030, and 2040.

b. The numerical entries in cells **B3**, **B4**, **B5**, and **B6** would be 306, 332, 360, and 389.

3 **a.** The numerical value that results from the formula "=C$2*B2+C$4" in cell **B3** of the spreadsheet is still 306.

b. What formulas and numerical values will appear in cells **B4** and **B5** following a fill down command?

c. What formulas and numerical values will appear in cells **B4** and **B5** if the entry in cell **C2** is changed to 1.06 and the entry in cell **C4** is changed to 12?

d. What changes in natural growth and migration rates are implied by those changes in the spreadsheet?

4 When Robin got a summer job, she decided she could save $25 from her pay every week.

a. Construct a spreadsheet that will display Robin's total savings at the end of each week during the 10-week summer job.

b. If necessary, modify your spreadsheet so that the amount saved each week can be found by changing only one cell entry. Then use the new spreadsheet to display Robin's total savings at the end of each week if she actually saves only $17.50 per week.

5 Suppose that in September, Robin invests her summer savings of $250 in a bank account that pays interest at the rate of 0.5% per month (an annual rate of 6%).

a. Construct a spreadsheet that will display Robin's bank balance at the end of each month for the next year.

b. Modify your spreadsheet to account for Robin's habit of withdrawing $20 at the beginning of every month for extra spending money.

6 Modify the spreadsheet in Problem 5 to compare two possible savings plans.

Plan 1: Deposit $100 in September and add $10 per month thereafter.
Plan 2: Deposit $0 in September and add $20 per month thereafter.

a. How long will it take before Plan 2 gives a greater balance than Plan 1?

b. How will the answer to Part a change if the monthly interest rate decreases to 0.4%, 0.3%, 0.2%, or 0.1%?

7 When José was considering purchase of a $199 portable music player and ear phones, he was told that resale value of the gear would decline by about 5% per month after he bought it.

a. Construct a spreadsheet that will display the value of José's music gear at the start of each month over two years from its purchase.

b. Modify your spreadsheet to analyze the changing value of a PDA that would cost $499 to purchase and decline in value at about the same percent rate.

c. Explain why your spreadsheets in Parts a and b do not show loss of all value for the music player or the PDA in 20 months, even though $20 \cdot 5\% = 100\%$.

b. The formulas and numerical values that will appear in cells **B4** and **B5** following a fill down command are =C$2*B3+C$4 (332) and =C$2*B4+C$4 (360).

c. The formulas that will appear in cells **B4** and **B5** are unchanged if the entry in cell **C2** is changed to 1.06 and the entry in cell **C4** is changed to 12. But the numerical values change to 310 in **B3**, 340 in **B4**, and 373 in **B5**.

d. The changes implied by those changes in the spreadsheet are a natural 10-year growth rate of 6% and a 10-year net migration rate of 12 million people.

4 **a.** **INSTRUCTIONAL NOTE** If students decide to define column **B** as column **A** multiplied times 25, encourage them to find formulas that use *NOW-NEXT* thinking.

Robin's Savings1.xls

◇	A	B (Formulas)	B (Computations)
1	Week	Total Amount Saved	Total Amount Saved
2	1	=25	25
3	2	=B2+25	50
4	3	=B3+25	75
5	4	=B4+25	100
6	5	=B5+25	125
7	6	=B6+25	150
8	7	=B7+25	175
9	8	=B8+25	200
10	9	=B9+25	225
11	10	=B10+25	250

b. To display total savings with only one cell change, put the weekly savings in a cell (**B2** below). Then use the fixed cell reference **B2** in other formulas.

Robin's Savings2.xls

◇	A	B (Formulas)	B (Computations)
1		Weekly Savings	Weekly Savings
2		17.50	17.50
3	Week	Total Amount Saved	Total Amount Saved
4	1	=$B$2	17.5
5	2	=B4+$B$2	35.0
6	3	=B5+$B$2	52.5
7	4	=B6+$B$2	70.0
8	5	=B7+$B$2	87.5
9	6	=B8+$B$2	105.0
10	7	=B9+$B$2	122.5
11	8	=B10+$B$2	140.0
12	9	=B11+$B$2	157.5
13	10	=B12+$B$2	175.0

5 **a.**

Robin's Savings3.xls

◇	A	B (Formulas)	B (Computations)	C	D	
1	Month	Balance	Balance	Deposit=	250	
2	1	=D1*D$2	251.25	Rate+1=	1.005	
3	=A2+1	=B2*D$2	252.51			
4	=A3+1	=B3*D$2	253.77			
5	=A4+1	=B4*D$2	255.04			
⋮	⋮	⋮	⋮	⋮	⋮	
13	=A12+1	=B12*D$2	265.40			
14						

b. A spreadsheet incorporating a $20 withdrawal every month follows.

Robin's Savings4.xls

◇	A	B (Formulas)	B (Computations)	C	D	
1	Month	Balance	Balance	Deposit=	250	
2	1	=D1*D$2−D$3	231.25	Rate+1=	1.005	
3	=A2+1	=B2*D$2−D$3	212.41	Withdrawal=	20	
4	=A3+1	=B3*D$2−D$3	193.47			
5	=A4+1	=B4*D$2−D$3	174.44			
⋮	⋮	⋮	⋮	⋮	⋮	
13	=A12+1	=B12*D$2−D$3	18.71			
14						

6 **a.** Plan 2 will pass Plan 1 after 11 months.

Savings Plan1.xls

◇	A	B (Formulas)	B (Computations)	C	D	
1	Month	Balance	Balance	Deposit=	100	
2	1	=D1*D$2+D$3	110.50	Rate+1=	1.005	
3	=A2+1	=B2*D$2+D$3	121.05	Addition=	10	
4	=A3+1	=B3*D$2+D$3	131.66			
5	=A4+1	=B4*D$2+D$3	142.32			
⋮	⋮	⋮	⋮	⋮	⋮	
11	=A10+1	=B10*D$2+D$3	207.39			
12	=A11+1	=B11*D$2+D$3	218.43			
13	=A12+1	=B12*D$2+D$3	229.52			
14						

Savings Plan2.xls

◇	A	B (Formulas)	B (Computations)	C	D	
1	Month	Balance	Balance	Deposit=	0	
2	1	=D1*D$2+D$3	20.00	Rate+1=	1.005	
3	=A2+1	=B2*D$2+D$3	40.10	Addition=	20	
4	=A3+1	=B3*D$2+D$3	60.30			
5	=A4+1	=B4*D$2+D$3	80.60			
⋮	⋮	⋮	⋮	⋮	⋮	
11	=A10+1	=B10*D$2+D$3	204.56			
12	=A11+1	=B11*D$2+D$3	225.58			
13	=A12+1	=B12*D$2+D$3	246.71			
14						

b. If the interest rate is only 0.4% per month (4.8% APR), then Plan 2 will pass Plan 1 after 11 months. It turns out that it requires 11 months for Plan 2 to catch up with interest at 0.3% per month, 0.2% per month, and 0.1% per month as well.

   (This is because, relative to the amounts being deposited, the interest earned is very small. Thus, the gap between the plans is reduced primarily by the difference between $20 and $10 deposits. That means that Plan 2 requires at least 10 months to close the $100 initial gap. The 11th month is essentially catching up on the interest earned by the initial $100 deposit.)

7 Jose's music player will be declining in value each month, but not at a constant absolute rate. As the value gets smaller, the 5% decrease gets smaller in dollar terms.

   a. One spreadsheet that will track this situation might look like this:

José's Resale Values.xls			
◇	A	B (Formulas)	B (Computations)
1	Month	Resale Value	Resale Value
2	0	199	199
3	=A2+1	=B2−0.05*B2	189.05
4	=A3+1	=B3−0.05*B3	179.60
5	=A4+1	=B4−0.05*B4	170.62
6	=A5+1	=B5−0.05*B5	162.09
7	=A6+1	=B6−0.05*B6	153.98
⋮	⋮	⋮	⋮
26	=A25+1	=B25−0.05*B25	58.11
27			

   b. To track resale value of an item that starts at $499, simply change the entry in cell **B2** to 499. After 2 years, the value will be approximately $145.70.

   c. The resale value will not be gone in 20 months because although it loses a full 5% (or about $10) in the first month, when the value gets smaller, a 5% decline in value is fewer dollars. For instance, 5% of $100 is only $5.

COMMON CONCEPTUAL CHALLENGE Percent change is a topic that often confuses students and adults. The keys to any percent calculation are the rate (the percent) *and* the base. In Problem 7, students have to realize that although the percent decline is assumed constant at 5% per year, as the value of the year declines, that percent will be operating on a progressively smaller base. So, the absolute dollar decline becomes smaller each year.

In a somewhat different setting, this fact of life with percents means that giving every employee of a business a 5% raise will mean very different things to those who currently have large salaries than to those who have small salaries. This mathematical fact is compounded by the fact that those with larger salaries have probably already provided for basic living expenses and their raises will be applied to discretionary spending, while those with lower salaries might still be struggling to pay their rent and food bills.

Summarize
the Mathematics

In this investigation, you learned basic spreadsheet techniques for studying patterns of change.

a How are cells in a spreadsheet grid labeled and referenced by formulas?

b How are formulas used in spreadsheets to produce numbers from data in other cells?

c How is the "fill" command used to produce cell formulas rapidly?

d How are the cell formulas in a spreadsheet similar to the *NOW-NEXT* rules you used to predict population change?

Be prepared to share your ideas with other students.

✔ Check Your Understanding

The number pattern that begins 1, 1, 2, 3, 5, 8, 13, 21, 34, 55, … is known as the **Fibonacci sequence**. The pattern appears many places in nature. It also has been the subject of many mathematical investigations.

a. Study the pattern. What are the next five numbers in the sequence?

b. Write spreadsheet formulas that will produce columns **A** and **B** in the next table (and could be extended down to continue the pattern).

| Fibonacci Sequence.xls | ◻ ⊡ ☒ |
◇	A	B
1	1	1
2	2	1
3	3	2
4	4	3
5	5	5
6	6	8
⋮	⋮	⋮

c. Modify the spreadsheet of Part b to produce terms in the number pattern that begins 5, 5, 10, 15, 25, … and grows in the Fibonacci way. Use the spreadsheet to find the next 10 numbers in the pattern.

d. Compare the number patterns in Parts a and c. What explains the way the patterns are related?

LESSON 2 • Change Over Time   **35**

Summarize the Mathematics

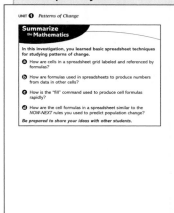

a Formulas call on cell values by referring to their column and row locations. A column is represented by a letter (or pair of letters in a larger sheet), and a row is represented by a number.

b Formulas guide calculations using inputs from cell locations that are indicated in the formula.

c The fill command allows us to copy a formula in new cells and change cell references as required.

d Cell formulas call upon the results in preceding cells, just like *NOW-NEXT* rules call upon *NOW* and operate on it to produce a new value.

MATH TOOLKIT Students may wish to record the spreadsheet commands that they have used for future reference.

✓ Check Your Understanding

INSTRUCTIONAL NOTE You might want to mention to your students that the person after whom the special sequence is named was an Italian mathematician who lived from 1180 to 1250 and is generally credited with bringing modern ideas of arithmetic from Hindu and Arabic cultures to the West as it emerged from the Dark Ages.

a. The pattern is to add two previous numbers together. The next five numbers are 89, 144, 233, 377, and 610.

b.

Fibonacci Sequence.xls

◇	A	B
1	1	1
2	=A1+1	1
3	=A2+1	=B1+B2
4	=A3+1	=B2+B3
5	=A4+1	=B3+B4
6	=A5+1	=B4+B5
⋮	⋮	⋮
7		

c.

Fibonacci-Like Seq.xls

◇	A	B
1	1	5
2	=A1+1	5
3	=A2+1	=B1+B2
4	=A3+1	=B2+B3
5	=A4+1	=B3+B4
6	=A5+1	=B4+B5
⋮	⋮	⋮
7		

The sequence will look like this: 5, 5, 10, 15, 25, 40, 65, 105, 170, 275, 445, 720, 1,165, 1,885, 3,050

d. Each number in the sequence that starts with 5, 5, … is 5 times the corresponding value in the sequence that starts 1, 1, … . Student explanations may cite specific examples such as: $1 + 1 = 2$ and $1 + 2 = 3$ and $5 + 5$ is $5(1 + 1)$ and $5 + 10$ is $5(1 + 2)$.

Unit 1

On Your Own

Applications

1 The People's Republic of China is the country with the largest population in the world. The population of China in 2005 was approximately 1.3 billion. Although families are encouraged to have only one child, the population is still growing at a rate of about 0.6% per year.

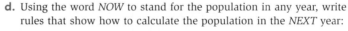

   a. Estimate the population of China for each of the next 5 years and record your estimates in a data table.

   b. When is it likely that the population of China will reach 1.5 billion?

   c. How would your prediction in Part b change if the growth rate were 1.2%, double the current rate?

   d. Using the word *NOW* to stand for the population in any year, write rules that show how to calculate the population in the *NEXT* year:

   i. if the growth rate stays at 0.6%.

   ii. if the growth rate doubles to 1.2%.

2 The country with the second largest population in the world is India, with about 1.1 billion people in 2005. The birth rate in India is about 2.2% per year and the death rate is about 0.8% per year.

   a. Estimate the population of India for each of the next 5 years and record your estimates in a data table.

   b. When is it likely that the population of India will reach 1.5 billion?

   c. How would your prediction in Part b change if the birth rate slows to 2.0%?

   d. Using the word *NOW* to stand for the population in any year, write rules that show how to calculate the population in the *NEXT* year:

   i. if the birth rate stays at 2.2%.

   ii. if the birth rate slows to 2.0%.

Applications

1 **a.**

Year	Population (in billions)
2005	1.3
2006	1.3078
2007	1.3156
2008	1.3235
2009	1.3315
2010	1.3395

b. In about 24 years, at the present growth rate, China's population is projected to reach 1.5 billion.

c. If the growth rate is doubled, it will take about 12 years.

d. i. $NEXT = 1.006 \cdot NOW$, starting at 1.3.

ii. $NEXT = 1.012 \cdot NOW$, starting at 1.3.

2 **a.**

Year	Population (in billions)
2006	1.1154
2007	1.1310
2008	1.1468
2009	1.1629
2010	1.1792

b. India's population will reach 1.5 billion in about 23 years.

c. If the birth rate slows to 2%, it will take about 26 years to reach 1.5 billion.

d. i. $NEXT = 1.014 \cdot NOW$, starting at 1.1.

ii. $NEXT = 1.012 \cdot NOW$, starting at 1.1.

3 Timber wolves were once very common in wild land across the northern United States. However, when the Endangered Species Act was passed in 1973, wolves were placed on the endangered list.

Thirty years later, the wolf populations have recovered in the northern Rockies and in the forests of Minnesota, Wisconsin, and Michigan.

In 2003, estimates placed the Midwest wolf population at more than 3,100 with an annual growth rate of 25% to 30%. (Source: "Timber Wolves Resurgent in Upper Midwest," *The Washington Post,* Monday, February 10, 2003.)

a. Use the given wolf population estimate and the 25% growth rate to predict populations for 10 years (from 2003 to 2013). Record your results in a data table.

b. Estimate the time when the Midwest wolf population will reach 30,000 (the number believed to have lived in the Great Lakes region 500 years ago).

c. How does your answer to Part b change if you use the higher growth rate estimate of 30%?

d. Using the word *NOW* to stand for the Midwest wolf population in any year, write rules that show how to calculate the population in the *NEXT* year:

  i. if the growth rate stays at 25%.

  ii. if the growth rate increases to 30%.

4 Midwestern farmers who raise dairy cattle are concerned that growing wolf populations described in Task 3 above threaten the safety of their herds. They want permission to eliminate wolves that kill livestock.

a. Make a table showing how the Midwest wolf population of 3,100 would change over the next 10 years if an annual harvest of 250 animals were allowed, but the natural growth rate continued at 25% per year.

b. When is it likely that the Midwest wolf population would reach 30,000 if the annual harvest of 250 animals were permitted?

c. How would your answer to Part b change if the annual harvest were increased to 500?

d. Using the word *NOW* to stand for the population in any year, write rules that show how to calculate the population in the *NEXT* year:

  i. if the natural growth rate stays at 25% and 250 wolves are killed each year.

  ii. if the growth rate stays at 25% but the annual harvest increases to 500 wolves per year.

INSTRUCTIONAL NOTE For Tasks 3 and 4, you may wish to have students record every other year or only do 5 years out.

 a.

Year	2003	2004	2005	2006	2007	2008	2009	2010	2011	2012
Pop. (in billions)	3,100	3,875	4,844	6,055	7,568	9,460	11,826	14,782	18,477	23,097

b. Sometime during 2013, the wolf population is projected to reach 30,000.

c. The wolf population would reach 30,000 in 2012 with the 30% growth rate.

d. **i.** *NEXT* = 1.25 • *NOW*, starting at 3,100.

　　ii. *NEXT* = 1.30 • *NOW*, starting at 3,100.

4 **a.**

Year	2003	2004	2005	2006	2007	2008	2009	2010	2011	2012
Pop. (in billions)	3,100	3,625	4,281	5,102	6,127	7,409	9,011	11,014	13,517	16,646

b. Sometime during 2015, the wolf population is projected to reach 30,000.

c. The wolf population would reach 30,000 in 2018 with an annual harvest of 500.

d. **i.** *NEXT* = 1.25 • *NOW* − 250, starting at 3,100.

　　ii. *NEXT* = 1.25 • *NOW* − 500, starting at 3,100.

Unit 1

5 China experiences annual negative net migration of its population. People leave for other countries of the world in large numbers.

   a. How would the current 1.3 billion population of China change in 10 years in case of natural growth rate of 0.6% and net migration of about −500,000 people per year? (Remember to use uniform units.)

   b. What net migration would have to occur for China to reach *zero population growth,* assuming that the natural growth rate remained at 0.6% per year?

   c. Using *NOW* to stand for the population of China in any year, write a rule that shows how to calculate the population in the *NEXT* year if the natural growth rate is 0.6% and the net migration is about −500,000 people per year.

6 India has an annual negative migration to somewhat offset its natural population growth.

   a. How would the current 1.1 billion population of India change in 10 years in case of a natural growth rate of 1.4% and net migration of about only −80,000 people per year? (Use uniform units.)

   b. What net migration would have to occur for India to reach *zero population growth,* assuming that the natural growth rate remained at 1.4% per year?

   c. Using *NOW* to stand for the population of India in any year, write a rule that shows how to calculate the population in the *NEXT* year if the natural growth rate is 1.4%, and the net migration is about −80,000 people per year.

7 If money is invested in a savings account, a business, or real estate, its value usually increases each year by some percent. For example, investment in common stocks yields growth in value of about 10% per year in the long run. Suppose that when a child is born, the parents invest $1,000 in a mutual fund account.

   a. If that fund actually grows in value at a rate of 10% per year, what will its value be after 1 year? After 2 years? After 5 years? After 18 years when the child is ready to go to college?

   b. Using *NOW* to stand for the investment value at the end of any year, write a rule showing how to calculate the value at the end of the *NEXT* year.

   c. How will your answers to Parts a and b change if:

   i. the initial investment is only $500?

   ii. the initial investment is $1,000, but the growth rate is only 5% per year?

   d. How will your answers to Parts a and b change if, in addition to the percent growth of the investment, the parents add $500 per year to the account?

8 Select one of Applications Tasks 1–3 and develop a spreadsheet that could be used to answer the population growth questions asked in those items. Use the spreadsheet to answer those questions.

5 **a.** China's population would grow to about 1.375 billion in the next ten years.

b. The net migration would have to equal the natural increase of 0.6%, so it would have to be 0.006 · 1.3 billion or 7.8 million people.

c. $NEXT = 1.006 · NOW - 0.5$, starting at 1,300 million people. (Rules will depend on units used.)

6 **a.** In the next ten years, India's population would increase to about 1,263,220,904 people.

b. To get zero population growth in India, net migration would have to equal the natural increase of 15.4 million people.

c. $NEXT = 1.014 · NOW - 0.08$, starting at 1,100 million people. (Rules will depend on units used.)

7 **a.**

Year	0	1	2	5	18
Fund Value (in $)	1,000	1,100	1,210	1,611	5,560

b. $NEXT = 1.10 · NOW$, starting at 1,000

c. **i.** If the initial investment was only $500, each answer in Part a would be half as large.

ii. If the percent growth rate is cut in half to 5%, the investment would grow as follows:

Year	0	1	2	5	18
Fund Value (in $)	1,000	1,050	1,103	1,276	2,407

d. $NEXT = 1.10 · NOW + 500$, starting at 1,000

Year	0	1	2	5	18
Fund Value (in $)	1,000	1,600	2,260	4,663	28,360

8 Spreadsheets will vary, but the basic code will include something like the *NOW-NEXT* rules in each task. Here is a sample spreadsheet that could be used to begin analysis of factors in the population growth of China as described in Task 1.

China Population.xls

◇	A	B (Formulas)	B (Computations)	C	D	
1	Year	Population	Population	Start=	1.3	
2	2006	=D1*D$2	1.3078	Rate=	1.006	
3	=A2+1	=B2*D$2	1.316			
4	=A3+1	=B3*D$2	1.324			
5	=A4+1	=B4*D$2	1.331			
⋮	⋮	⋮	⋮	⋮	⋮	

(9) Select one of Applications Tasks 4–7 and develop a spreadsheet that could be used to answer the questions about population or investment growth over time. Use the spreadsheet to answer those questions.

Connections

Data in the next table show population (in thousands) of some major U.S. cities in 1990 and in 2000. Use the data to complete Connections Tasks 10–13 that follow.

Major U.S. Cities: 1990 and 2000 Population (in 1,000s)

U.S. City	1990	2000	U.S. City	1990	2000
Atlanta, GA	394	416	Independence, MO	112	113
Aurora, CO	222	276	Milwaukee, WI	628	597
Berkeley, CA	103	103	Newark, NJ	275	274
Boise, ID	127	186	Portland, OR	437	529
El Paso, TX	515	564	St. Louis, MO	397	348
Hartford, CT	140	122	Washington, DC	607	572

(10) The population of Berkeley, California, changed by fewer than 1,000 people. Among the remaining cities in the list, which cities had:

   a. the greatest absolute decrease in population?

   b. the greatest absolute increase in population?

   c. the greatest percent decrease in population?

   d. the greatest percent increase in population?

(11) What were the mean and median population change for the listed cities?

(12) Suppose that the population of Aurora, Colorado, continues increasing at the rate it changed between 1990 and 2000.

   a. What population for Aurora would be predicted for 2010, 2020, 2030, 2040, and 2050 if population increases by the same number of people in each decade?

   b. What *NOW-NEXT* rule describes the pattern of change in Part a?

   c. What was the percent change in the Aurora population between 1990 and 2000?

   d. What *NOW-NEXT* rule describes the pattern of change in Aurora's population each decade, if the percent rate of change from Part c is used?

   e. What population is predicted for Aurora in 2010, 2020, 2030, 2040, and 2050 if growth occurs at the percent rate of Part c?

9 Spreadsheets will vary. Here is a sample spreadsheet that could be used to begin analysis of factors in the investment plans of Task 7.

Investment.xls ⬜▢✖

◇	A	B (Formulas)	B (Computations)	C	D	
1	Year	Balance	Balance	Deposit=	1000	
2	1	=D1*D$2+D$3	1600	Rate=	1.10	
3	=A2+1	=B2*D$2+D$3	2260	Addition=	500	
4	=A3+1	=B3*D$2+D$3	2986			
5	=A4+1	=B4*D$2+D$3	3785			
⋮	⋮	⋮	⋮	⋮	⋮	

Connections

10 **a.** Greatest absolute decline was St. Louis, Missouri, down 49,000.

b. Greatest absolute increase was Portland, Oregon, up 92,000.

c. Greatest percent decline was Hartford, Connecticut, down 13%.

d. Greatest percent increase was Boise, Idaho, up 46%.

> **TECHNOLOGY NOTE**
> The U.S. City Population Data is in *CPMP-Tools* under Statistics, Data Analysis, Unit 1.

11 The mean change for the listed cities was about 11.9 thousand or 11,900; the median change was 0.5 thousand or 500.

12 **a.** If the population continues to increase by 54,000 per decade, its population would be as follows:

Year	2010	2020	2030	2040	2050
Pop. (in 1,000s)	330	384	438	492	546

b. $NEXT = NOW + 54$, starting at 276.

c. $\frac{54}{222} = 24.3\%$

d. $NEXT = 1.243 \cdot NOW$, starting at 276.

e.

Year	2010	2020	2030	2040	2050
Pop. (in 1,000s)	343	426	530	659	819

f. How are the predicted change patterns in Parts a and e similar, and how are they different? Why are they not the same?

g. What reasons could you have to doubt the predictions of Parts a or e?

13 Suppose that the population of Washington, D.C., continues decreasing at the rate it changed between 1990 and 2000.

a. What population for Washington, D.C., would be predicted for 2010, 2020, 2030, 2040, and 2050 if population decreases by the same number of people in each decade?

b. What *NOW-NEXT* rule describes the pattern of change in Part a?

c. What was the percent change in the Washington, D.C., population between 1990 and 2000?

d. What *NOW-NEXT* rule describes the pattern of change in the Washington, D.C., population each decade, if the percent rate of change from Part c is used?

e. What population is predicted for Washington, D.C., in 2010, 2020, 2030, 2040, and 2050 if growth occurs at the percent rate of Part c?

f. How are the predicted change patterns in Parts a and e similar, and how are they different? Why are they not the same?

g. What reasons could you have to doubt the predictions of Parts a or e?

14 Sketch graphs that match each of the following stories about quantities changing over time. On each graph, label the axes to indicate reasonable scale units for the independent variable and the dependent variable. For example, use "time in hours" and "temperature in degrees Fahrenheit" for Part a.

a. On a typical summer day where you live, how does the temperature change from midnight to midnight?

b. When a popular movie first appears in video rental stores, demand for rentals changes as time passes.

c. The temperature of a cold drink in a glass placed on a kitchen counter changes as time passes.

d. The number of people in the school gymnasium changes before, during, and after a basketball game.

f. Both growth projections show rapid growth prospects, however the percent growth projections are much greater because of the compounding factor.

g. There are probably many reasons to doubt the projections far into the future, including limitations of space, jobs, water, and so on.

13 **a.**

Year	2010	2020	2030	2040	2050
Pop. (in 1,000s)	537	502	467	432	397

b. $NEXT = NOW - 35$, starting at 572.

c. $\frac{-35}{607} = -5.8\%$

d. $NEXT = NOW - 0.058 \cdot NOW$, starting at 572.

e.

Year	2010	2020	2030	2040	2050
Pop. (in 1,000s)	539	508	478	450	424

f. Both predict decline, but the percent decline is slower because a constant percent factor operates on progressively smaller populations.

g. As populations decline it might become cheaper to buy houses, more space opens up to make the city attractive, jobs might become available, and so on.

14 Answers will vary, but here are some plausible graphs.

a. Temperature change on a typical 24-hour day might oscillate something like this graph, from midnight to midnight.

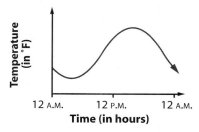

b. Demand for a new movie in video rental stores might decline like this graph as time passes since its release.

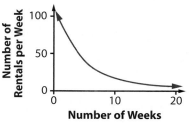

c. A graph of the temperature of a cold drink that is taken out of the refrigerator will rise rapidly at first and then more slowly as time goes on until the drink reaches room temperature.

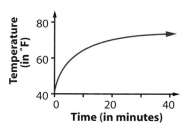

d. A graph of the number of people in a school gymnasium before, during, and after a basketball game might look something like this. Scales on the vertical axis will depend on the size of the school.

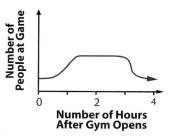

15 Each part below gives a pair of *NOW-NEXT* rules. For each rule in each pair, produce a table of values showing how the quantities change from the start through 5 stages of change. Then compare the patterns of change produced by each rule in the pair and explain how differences are related to differences in the *NOW-NEXT* rules.

a. Rule 1: *NEXT = NOW + 10*, starting at 5
Rule 2: *NEXT = NOW + 8*, starting at 5

Sample Table:

Stage	0	1	2	3	4	5
Rule 1	5	15	25			
Rule 2	5	13	...			

b. Rule 1: *NEXT = 2 · NOW*, starting at 5
Rule 2: *NEXT = 1.5 · NOW*, starting at 10

c. Rule 1: *NEXT = 0.5 · NOW*, starting at 100
Rule 2: *NEXT = 0.9 · NOW*, starting at 50

d. Rule 1: *NEXT = 2 · NOW + 10*, starting at 8
Rule 2: *NEXT = 3 · NOW − 10*, starting at 8

16 The graph below shows how the amount of water in a city's reservoir changed during one recent year.

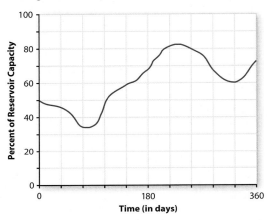

On a copy of the graph, mark points that show when the reservoir's water supply is:

a. increasing at the fastest rate—label the point(s) with the letter "A".

b. decreasing at the fastest rate—label the point(s) with the letter "B".

c. increasing at a constant rate—label the point(s) with the letter "C".

d. decreasing at a constant rate—label the point(s) with the letter "D".

e. neither increasing nor decreasing—label the point(s) with the letter "E".

15 a.

Stage	0	1	2	3	4	5
Rule 1	5	15	25	35	45	55
Rule 2	5	13	21	29	37	45

Rule 1 adds two more than Rule 2 at each stage and thus the results for Rule 1 are 2, 4, 6, 8, etc. more than the results for Rule 2 at corresponding stages.

b.

Stage	0	1	2	3	4	5
Rule 1	5	10	20	40	80	160
Rule 2	10	15	22.5	33.8	50.6	75.9

Because Rule 2 starts off at an initial value of 10, its values are greater for a short while. Because Rule 1 multiplies each previous term by 2 (doubles) and Rule 2 only multiplies current values by 1.5, values produced by Rule 1 soon pass Rule 2 values.

c.

Stage	0	1	2	3	4	5
Rule 1	100	50	25	12.5	6.3	3.2
Rule 2	50	45	40.5	36.5	32.8	29.5

Over time, Rule 2 will produce larger values. The rule is *NEXT* = 0.9 · *NOW*. Think of it as keeping 90% of the previous value, whereas Rule 1, or *NEXT* = 0.5 · *NOW*, only keeps 50% of the previous value. So, even though Rule 1 starts at 100 rather than at 50, the results from Rule 1 will quickly become less than the same-stage results for Rule 2.

d.

Stage	0	1	2	3	4	5
Rule 1	8	26	62	134	278	566
Rule 2	8	14	32	86	248	734

Students should recognize that multiplying by 3 rather than by 2 will produce a larger effect than the addition or subtraction of 10. Thus, in the long run, Rule 2 will have greater results. As a general rule, multiplicative effects are usually ultimately stronger than additive effects.

16 a–e. A reasonable range for student placement of points or intervals is shown by the thick sections on the graph below.

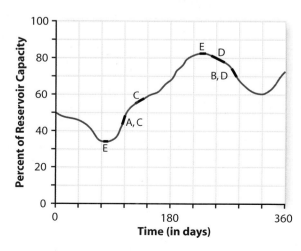

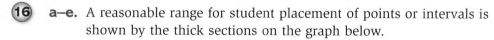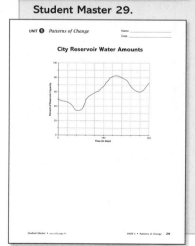

Teaching Resources

Student Master 29.

Reflections

17. How are patterns in the data tables and graphs arising in the studies of human and whale populations similar to or different from those that related:

   a. *weight* and *stretched length* of a bungee cord (page 5)?

   b. *price per jump* and *number of customers* for a bungee jump (page 6)?

   c. *price per jump* and *daily income* for operation of the bungee jump (page 6)?

   d. *number of plays* and fund-raiser *cumulative profit* in the *Take a Chance* die-tossing game (pages 8–9)?

   e. *average speed* and *race time* for a 500-mile NASCAR race (pages 11–12)?

   f. *hours worked* and *earnings* at Fresh Fare Market (page 12)?

18. In what ways are the methods used to describe "change over time" patterns similar to or different from the methods used to study "cause and effect" patterns?

19. Consider the *NOW-NEXT* rules:

   $$NEXT = NOW + 0.05 \cdot NOW \quad \text{and} \quad NEXT = 1.05 \cdot NOW$$

   a. Find several values produced by these *NOW-NEXT* rules, starting from *NOW* = 10.

   b. Then explore the patterns produced by each rule for some other common starting values.

   c. Explain why the results of the explorations in Parts a and b are not surprising.

20. Do the ideas of independent and dependent variables have useful meaning in the study of "change over time" patterns? If so, how? If not, why not?

21. Both animal and human population growth rates commonly change as the years pass.

   a. What factors might cause change in the percent growth rates of a population?

   b. Why, if growth rates change, does it still make sense to use current growth rates for predictions of future populations?

Unit 1

Reflections

17 **a.** *Similarities*: Both population growth situations and the stretch of the bungee cord situation are increasing functions.
Differences: The stretched length of the bungee cord increases at a constant rate (linear) as attached weight increases, but the populations increase at a non-constant rate (nonlinear) over time.

b. *Similarities*: No obvious similarities.
Differences: The number of customers decreases at a constant rate (linear) as price increases, but the populations increase at non-constant rates over time.

c. *Similarities*: Both the bungee jump daily income function and the population growth over time are nonlinear patterns of change.
Differences: The bungee jump income will increase and then decrease as jump price increases, whereas the populations are always increasing.

d. *Similarities*: Both profit from the die-tossing game and the various population functions involve factors that could make them either increase (winning and births or migration) or decrease (losing and deaths or emigration).
Differences: The Take a Chance game will produce profit values that can be summarized as a roughly linear trend. However, that trend will be marked by random variations up and down. Unless the population growth occurs only from constant migration or emigration (controlled by quotas, for example) it will not generally be linear.

e. *Similarities*: Both the NASCAR time/speed function and population growth functions are nonlinear.
Differences: In the NASCAR situation, the time decreases as speed increases, whereas the population situations are frequently increasing functions. The time for a 500-mile race at 0 miles per hour is not defined, whereas population at time 0 is generally interpretable as the population when analysis is begun.

f. *Similarities*: Both the Fresh Fare Market situation and the population growth situations are modeled by non-linear increasing functions.
Differences: The Fresh Fare Market pay options tend to involve increases that are more rapid than those in the population growth situations.

18 *Similarities*: In both kinds of relational situations, tables and graphs of values and (where feasible) algebraic rules are useful tools for studying patterns of change. It usually helps to look for increasing or decreasing change patterns as values of the independent variable increase steadily and, more precisely, to ask whether the rate of change is constant or not.
Differences: In "cause-and-effect" change situations, one can generally imagine some sort of operational connection between the variables that explains why the dependent variable changes when the independent variable changes. In "change-over-time" situations, the time variable itself is not a cause of change, only a marker that helps to see the rate of change that results from a variety of situational factors.

19 **a–c.** With common starting values, the rules produce the same sequences of subsequent values since *NOW* + 0.05 · *NOW* is the same as calculating 1.05 · *NOW*.

NOTE The answers to Problems 20 and 21 can be found on page T43.

Unit 1

Extensions

22 The amusement park ride test team took their radar gun for a ride on the Ferris wheel. They aimed the gun at the ground during two nonstop trips around on the wheel, giving a graph relating height above the ground to time into the trip.

a. The total time for the ride was 100 seconds. Sketch a graph showing how you think height will change over time during the ride. Then write an explanation of the pattern in your graph. (*Hint:* You might experiment with a bicycle wheel as a model of a Ferris wheel; as you turn the wheel, how does the height of the air valve stem change?)

b. Given next is the graph of (*time into ride, height of rider*) data for one Ferris wheel test ride. Write an explanation of what the graph tells about that test ride.

First Test Ride

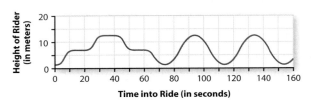

c. Given next are some (*time, height*) data from a second test ride. Write a short description of the pattern of change in height over time during this ride.

Second Test Ride

Time (in seconds)	0	2	5	10	15	20	22.5	25	30	35	40	42.5	45	50	55	60	62.5	65
Height (in meters)	1	1	3	3	11	11	13	11	11	3	3	1	3	3	11	11	13	11

d. Plot the data from the second test ride on a coordinate graph. Connect the points if it seems to make sense to do so. Then explain whether you think the graph or the table better shows the pattern of change in height during the ride.

20 With regard to "change-over-time" patterns, time is most often the independent variable. One way to think of this idea is that population change can only happen if time passes; however, time can pass whether whale or human populations change. Passage of time does not itself cause change in a population or an investment account.

21 **a.** Students might suggest a variety of issues, including environmental, health, and social factors like regulation of hunting for animals or public policy initiatives to encourage or discourage potential parents.

b. Students may suggest that the reliability of certain models over time would make it reasonable to use current growth rates for predictions. Others may note that the current rates are all that we have to work with, and that predictions are just that—predictions. They tell us what will happen if things continue as they are now.

Extensions

22 **a.** Responses will vary, but should show some movement up and down. Without stops, the pattern of height versus time (moving at a constant rotational velocity) will generate a sinusoid. What will be hard for students to detect without very careful measurement is the fact that the motion is not a pair of semicircles, one concave up and the other concave down.

b. Stories will vary when interpreting the given graph. Flat points will in general indicate times when the wheel is stopped to load new passengers. This trip had three such stops. The graph shows that the wheel had a diameter of approximately 10 meters (the difference between highest and lowest heights). When the wheel was in continuous motion, it made a complete rotation in about 40 seconds.

c. The given data suggest a ride on a wheel with diameter about 12 meters since the position of the rider varied from 1 meter above the ground to 13 meters above. One complete turn takes at most 42 seconds, perhaps less if the points of repeated height represent stops. The time when the rider was rising most rapidly involved lift of about 8 meters in 5 seconds, with similar speed on the descent.

d.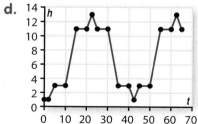

Students may say that the table better shows the pattern of change in height since it shows exact values. Or they may prefer the graph because you can quickly see the similarities and patterns over time.

Connecting the dots may help get a sense for the pattern, but curves such as in the graph in Part b more accurately depict the slowing down and speeding up process at stops.

A manatee is a large sea mammal native to Florida waters that is listed as endangered. The chart below gives the number of manatees killed in watercraft collisions near the Gulf Coast of Florida every year from 1985 through 2004.

Manatee/Watercraft Mortalities

Year	Number of Manatees Killed	Year	Number of Manatees Killed
1985	33	1995	42
1986	33	1996	60
1987	39	1997	54
1988	43	1998	66
1989	50	1999	82
1990	47	2000	78
1991	53	2001	81
1992	38	2002	95
1993	35	2003	73
1994	49	2004	69

Source: www.savethemanatee.org/mortalitychart.htm

a. Prepare a plot of the number of manatees killed in watercraft collisions between 1985 and 2004. Connect the points in that plot to help you study trends in manatee/watercraft mortalities.

b. Describe the pattern of change in mortalities that you see in the table and the *plot over time.*

c. During what one-year period was there the greatest change in manatee deaths if one measures change by:

   i. difference?

   ii. percent change?

d. How is the time of greatest change in manatee deaths shown in the table? In the graph?

e. What factors in the marine life and boating activity of Florida might be causing the increase in manatee deaths? What actions could be taken by government to reduce the number of deaths?

a. Although the segments connecting the data points do not represent manatee mortalities, drawing such connecting segments often highlights a trend in time-series data that is not so evident in the individual points.

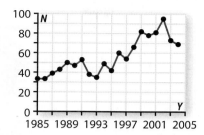

TECHNOLOGY NOTE
These data and an extended data set are included in *CPMP-Tools* under Statistics, Data Analysis, Unit 1.

b. The number of manatee deaths due to collisions with watercraft oscillates some from year to year, but there is an increasing trend, particularly after 1993.

c. i. The greatest absolute change in manatee deaths was from 2002 to 2003 with an increase of 19.

  ii. The greatest percent change was from 1995 to 1996 when there was about a 43% increase in manatee deaths.

INSTRUCTIONAL NOTE
You may wish to provide students an opportunity to ask and answer their own questions using the Manatee data sets.

d. The time of greatest change in deaths is shown by the largest increase or decrease from one value in the deaths column to the next value in the deaths column. On the graph, it is a big jump up or down between consecutive points.

e. The number of motorboats in action is an obvious explanatory factor for the increase in deaths. Greater speed of newer boats might be a factor too. It is also possible that there has been an increase in the number of manatees in the area because of migration pattern changes, changes in water temperature, or the extinction of a manatee predator. Thus, there could be more manatees for boats to hit. Furthermore, manatees themselves may have become accustomed to boat traffic and so seem to disregard it.

The government could first research the causes of the increased deaths to make reasonable and effective decisions. They could choose to be more stringent on the speed of boats, have additional regulations placed on boat structure, or increase regulations on where boaters can operate in certain waterways where manatees are known to exist.

Unit 1

24 The Fibonacci sequence has many interesting and important properties. One of the most significant is revealed by studying the ratios of successive terms in the sequence. Consider the Fibonacci sequence 1, 1, 2, 3, 5, 8, 13, ...

a. Modify the spreadsheet you wrote to generate terms of the Fibonacci sequence to include a new column **C**. In cell **C2**, enter the formula "=B2/B1" and then repeat this formula (with cell references changing automatically down the column **C**). Record the sequence of terms generated in that column.

b. What pattern of numerical values do you notice as you look farther and farther down column **C**?

Leonardo Fibonacci
1180–1250

25 In an earlier problem, you explored the rate at which the allowance paid to Ethan and Anna would increase if it began with only 1 penny on the first day of the month but doubled each day thereafter.

a. Write a spreadsheet with three columns: "Day of the Month" in column **A**, "Daily Allowance" in column **B**, and "Cumulative Allowance" in column **C**, with rows for up to 31 days.

b. Use the spreadsheet to find the total allowance paid to Ethan and Anna in a month of 31 days.

Review

26 Find the value of each expression.

a. $4 \cdot 2 - 3$ b. $2(-5) + 2(3)$ c. $-5^2 - (3 - 5)$

d. $(-3)(2)(-5)$ e. $-5 + 2 + 10 + (-5)^2$ f. $|-5| + 15 - |5 - 3|$

27 In figures A and B, squares are built on each side of a right triangle.

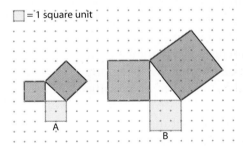

$\square$ = 1 square unit

a. For figure A:

i. Find the area of the triangle.

ii. Find the area of each square. How are the areas related?

iii. Find the perimeter of the triangle.

b. For figure B:

i. Find the area of the triangle.

24 **a.** Making the suggested change in the spreadsheet will generate a
column of ratios like these: 1, 2, 1.5, 1.67, 1.6, 1.625, 1.61538, …

b. It should be fairly clear that these ratios seem to be converging on a
value a bit more than 1.6. That is, in fact, the *golden ratio*, which is
officially $\frac{1 + \sqrt{5}}{2}$.

25 **a.**

Allowance.xls			▢ ▣ ☒
B3	=2*B2		

◇	A	B	C	^
1	Day	Daily Payment	Total to Date	
2	1	0.01	0.01	☰
3	=A2+1	**=2*B2**	=C2+B3	
⋮	⋮	⋮	⋮	
32	=A31+1	=2*B31	=C31+B32	∨
<	III		>	

b. The total allowance paid to each child in a month of 31 days is
$21,474,836.47.

Review

26 **a.** 5   **b.** −4   **c.** −23

    d. 30   **e.** 32   **f.** 18

 Just in Time

27 **a.** **i.** $\frac{1}{2}(2)(2) = 2$ square units

ii. The areas from smallest to largest are 4 square units, 4 square
units, and 8 square units. The area of the larger square is the sum
of the areas of the smaller squares.

iii. The perimeter of the triangle is $2 + 2 + 2\sqrt{2} \approx 6.83$ units.

b. **i.** $\frac{1}{2}(3)(4) = 6$ square units

> **INSTRUCTIONAL NOTE**
> Review Task 26 should be
> done without calculators. You
> may wish to discuss students'
> methods since these tasks
> offer a variety of approaches,
> including working right to
> left in Part e and choosing
> to combine numbers in
> convenient ways to reduce
> the possibility of errors.
> So, Part e could be
> $25 + 10 − 5 + 2 = 32$.

ii. Find the area of each of the squares. How are the areas of the squares related in this case?

iii. Find the perimeter of the triangle.

c. How is the work you did in Parts a and b related to the Pythagorean Theorem?

28 Consider the circle drawn below.

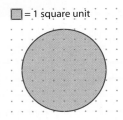

□ = 1 square unit

a. Use the dot grid to find the approximate area of the circle.

b. Use the formula $C = 2\pi r$ or $C = \pi d$ to find the circumference of the circle.

c. Use the formula $A = \pi r^2$ to find the area of the circle.

d. In what kind of unit is area measured? How can you use this fact to avoid confusing the formulas $2\pi r$ and πr^2 when computing the area of a circle?

29 The population of India is about 1.1 billion people. Suppose the population of country X is 1.1 million, and the population of country Y is 11 million.

a. How many times larger is the population of India than that of country Y? Than that of country X?

b. What percent of the Indian population is the population of country Y? Is the population of country X?

30 Consider the three parallelograms shown below.

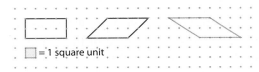

□ = 1 square unit

a. Rachel thinks that all three parallelograms have the same area. Is she correct? Explain your reasoning.

b. Sketch a parallelogram, different from those above, that has an area of 8 square units.

31 Place the following numbers in order from smallest to largest.

2.25   2.05   −2.35   −2.75   0   2.075

ii. The areas from smallest to largest are 9 square units, 16 square units, and 25 square units. The area of the large square is the sum of the areas of the two smaller squares.

iii. The perimeter of the triangle is $3 + 4 + 5 = 12$ units.

c. Both examples illustrate the theorem that for any right triangle, the area of the square on the hypotenuse is equal to the sum of the area of the squares on the legs.

28 a. Student approximations should be around 50 square units.

b. $C = 2\pi(4) = 8\pi \approx 25.12$ units

c. $A = \pi(4)^2 = 16\pi \approx 50.27$ square units

d. Area is measured in square units and the formula for computing the area of a circle contains r^2.

29 a. India has a population 100 times larger than country Y because $11,000,000 \cdot 100 = 1,100,000,000$. India has a population 1,000 times larger than country X because $1,100,000 \cdot 1,000 = 1,100,000,000$.

b. Since $\dfrac{11,000,000}{1,100,000,000} = 0.01$, the population of country Y is 1% of the population of India. Since $\dfrac{1,100,000}{1,100,000,000} = 0.001$, the population of country X is 0.1% of the population of India.

30 a. The parallelograms all have an area of 8 square units since they each have a base of 4 units and a height of 2 units.

b. Student sketches will vary.

31 $-2.75, -2.35, 0, 2.05, 2.075, 2.25$

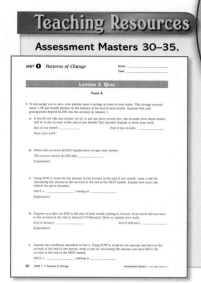

Teaching Resources

Assessment Masters 30–35.

LESSON 3

Tools for Studying Patterns of Change

In your work on problems of Lesson 1, you studied a variety of relationships between dependent and independent variables. In many cases, those relationships can be expressed by calculating rules that use letter names for the variables. For example,

The *stretched length L* of a simulated bungee cord depends on the *attached weight w* in a way that is expressed by the rule $L = 30 + 0.5w$.

The *number of customers n* for a bungee jump depends on the *price per jump p* in a way that is expressed by the rule $n = 50 - p$.

The *time t* of a 500-mile NASCAR race depends on the *average speed s* of the winning car in a way that is expressed by the rule $t = \frac{500}{s}$.

These symbolic rules give directions for calculating values of dependent variables from given values of related independent variables. They also enable use of calculator and computer tools for solving problems involving the relationships.

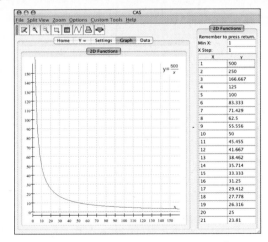

Tools for Studying Patterns of Change

The main goals of this lesson are to develop student ability to write and solve equations that answer questions in situations modeled by several basic patterns of change. The first investigation focuses on developing students' informal abilities to translate data patterns, verbal conditions, and geometric patterns into algebraic rules and formulas. Then the second investigation focuses on use of calculator and computer tools to study those rules and to solve equations. The third investigation is an exploratory study of patterns in tables and graphs associated with linear, quadratic, inverse, and exponential variation. It sets the stage for future units that examine the special properties of each family of functions.

The central idea of this lesson is that when one is able to express a relationship between two variables in the form of an algebraic rule or equation, there are powerful tools (including thinking) available for answering further questions about the relationship.

Lesson Objectives

- Develop skill in writing rules that express problem conditions
- Review perimeter and area formulas for triangles, parallelograms, and circles and the Pythagorean Theorem
- Develop skill in producing tables and graphs for functions
- Develop skill in using function tables, graphs, and computer algebra manipulations to solve problems that involve functional relationships, especially solving equations in one variable
- Develop informal knowledge about connections among function rules, tables, and graphs for linear, inverse, exponential, and quadratic functions

Lesson Launch

This TATS asks students to think about and report ideas that they have about relationships between algebraic forms and corresponding table and graph patterns. It also asks them to describe any strategies they already have for developing equations that relate dependent and independent variables and for using calculator or computer tools to analyze those relationships. The questions given are intended to be used for diagnostic purposes—to see what knowledge and dispositions students have about using algebraic rules and calculating tools. The problems of the lesson will develop further understanding and skill in each area.

Think About This Situation

If you were asked to solve problems in situations similar to those described on the previous page:

a How would you go about finding algebraic rules to model the relationships between dependent and independent variables in any particular case?

b What ideas do you have about how the forms of algebraic rules are connected to patterns in the tables and graphs of the relationships that they produce?

c How could you use calculator or computer tools to answer questions about the variables and relationships expressed in rules?

Your work in this lesson will help you develop skills in writing algebraic rules to express relationships between variables. You will also use calculator and computer strategies to determine relationships expressed by those rules.

Investigation 1 Communicating with Symbols

The first challenge in using algebraic expressions and rules to study a relationship between variables is to write the relationship in symbolic form. There are several ways information about such relationships occur and several strategies for translating information into symbolic form. As you work on the problems of this investigation, look for answers to this question:

What are some effective strategies for finding symbolic expressions that represent relationships between variables?

Translating Words to Symbols In many problems, important information about a relationship between variables comes in the form of written words. Sometimes it is easy to translate those words directly into algebraic expressions.

For example, if a restaurant adds a 15% gratuity to every food bill, the *total bill T* is related to the *food charges F* by the rule:

$$T = F + 0.15F.$$

In other cases, you might need to calculate the value of the dependent variable for several specific values of the independent variable to see how the two are related in general. Suppose that a library loans books free for a week, but charges a fine of $0.50 each day the book is kept beyond the first week. To find a rule relating *library fines* for books to the *number of days* the book is kept, you might begin by calculating some specific fines, like these:

Book Kept 10 Days: Fine = 0.50(10 − 7)
Book Kept 21 Days: Fine = 0.50(21 − 7)

Think About This Situation

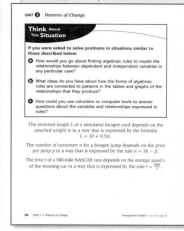

(a) You might launch discussion of this question by pointing to the three function rules described in the lesson introduction and noting that in much previous work of the unit rules like these have been provided for students. The questions so far have mainly asked students to use given rules and see how they do (or do not) accurately capture the relationships represented by data tables or graphs. Then ask students to share their ideas about how they might go about developing the rules from given data. There is, of course, no "right answer" to this question. Its purpose is to see what ideas students already know about tackling this key challenge of algebra.

(b) You might next ask students to give quick sketches (or "air graphs") to illustrate their ideas about the shapes of graphs that they expect for each rule given in the lesson introduction. Then ask them if they can explain why (other than remembering the examples from earlier work) they connect particular rule forms with particular graph shapes. Again, the purpose of this questioning would be primarily to see how comfortable students already are with connections between symbolic, table, and graph forms.

(c) By this time in the unit, you will have some good ideas about how comfortable students are with graphing calculators, though little prompting has been used to encourage the use of graphing and table features of the calculator in Lessons 1 and 2. The idea of this question is to see whether students have the knowledge and disposition to scan tables and trace graphs in search of specific pieces of information about a relationship between variables. If they do, they're going to have a head start on this lesson. If they do not, assure them that they will develop ideas and technology skills while working on the problems of the lesson.

Investigation 1 — Communicating with Symbols

The problems in this investigation pose the classic algebra word problem challenge, and there is no magic procedure for helping students to deal with it. Many teachers like to use a "word-by-word" translation strategy that relies on training students in recognition of "key words." While this strategy often works in situations that have been carefully designed to cater to it (i.e., school textbooks, but not real-life problems), we do not recommend it.

Instead, students are encouraged to make sense of the problem situations and the relationships involved. The most effective way to get started on that process is to try some calculations involving specific values of the variables involved in a problem and then to look for a generalization of that calculation process.

COLLABORATION SKILL
Help group check thinking or solutions.

Unit 1

(1) Can you create a rule relating *library fines* for new books to the *number of days* the book is kept? Write your rule in symbolic form, using F for the fine and d for number of days the book is kept.

(2) Midwest Amusement Park charges $25 for each daily admission. The park has daily operating expenses of $35,000.

   a. What is the operating profit (or loss) of the park on a day when 1,000 admission tickets are sold? On a day when 2,000 admission tickets are sold?

   b. Write a symbolic rule showing how daily profit P for the park depends on the number of paying visitors n.

(3) A large jet airplane carries 150,000 pounds of fuel at takeoff. It burns approximately 17,000 pounds of fuel per hour of flight.

   a. What is the approximate amount of fuel left in the airplane after 3 hours of flight? After 7 hours of flight?

   b. Write a rule showing how the amount of fuel F remaining in the plane's tanks depends on the elapsed time t in the flight.

(4) The costs for a large family reunion party include $250 for renting the shelter at a local park and $15 per person for food and drink.

   a. Write a rule showing how the total cost C for the reunion party depends on the number of people n who will attend.

   b. Write another rule showing how the cost per person c (including food, drink, and a share of the shelter rent) depends on the number of people n who plan to attend.

Measurement Formulas Many of the most useful symbolic rules are those that give directions for calculating measurements of geometric figures. You probably know several such formulas from prior mathematics studies.

(5) Figure *BCDE* below is a rectangle.

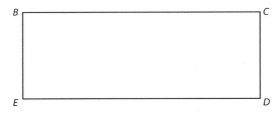

   a. Use a ruler to make measurements from which you can estimate the perimeter and area of rectangle *BCDE*. Then calculate those estimates.

1 $F = 0.50(d - 7)$ with the condition that the fine is 0 for $d < 8$.

2 **a.** If 1,000 tickets were sold, the park would have a loss of $10,000. A profit of $15,000 would occur if 2,000 tickets were sold.

   b. $P = 25n - 35,000$

3 **a.** After 3 hours, the airplane would have about 99,000 pounds of fuel left. After 7 hours, 31,000 pounds would remain.

   b. $F = 150,000 - 17,000t$

4 **a.** $C = 250 + 15n$

   b. $C = \dfrac{250}{n} + 15$ or $C = \dfrac{250 + 15n}{n}$

5 **a.** The measurements are approximately $BE = 3$ cm $\left(1\frac{3}{16} \text{ in.}\right)$ and $BC = 8$ cm $\left(3\frac{1}{8} \text{ in.}\right)$.

   Based on these measurements:
   $$P = 22 \text{ cm } \left(8\frac{5}{8} \text{ in.}\right)$$
   $$A = 24 \text{ cm}^2 \ (3.7 \text{ in}^2)$$

b. For any given rectangle, what is the minimum number of ruler measurements you would need in order to find both its perimeter and area? What set(s) of measurements will meet that condition?

c. What formulas show how to calculate perimeter P and area A of a rectangle from the measurements described in Part b?

6 Figure $QRST$ below is a parallelogram.

a. Use a ruler to make measurements from which you can estimate the perimeter and the area of $QRST$. Then calculate those estimates.

b. For any given parallelogram, what is the minimum number of measurements you would need in order to find both the perimeter and area? What measurements will meet that condition?

c. What formulas show how to calculate perimeter P and area A of a parallelogram from the measurements you described in Part b?

7 The two figures below are triangles—one a right triangle and one an obtuse triangle.

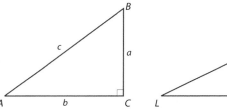

a. Use a ruler to make measurements from which you can estimate the perimeter and the area of each triangle. Then calculate those estimates.

b. If the lengths of the sides of a right triangle are a, b, and c, with the side of length c opposite the right angle, the **Pythagorean Theorem** guarantees that $a^2 + b^2 = c^2$. Using this fact, what is the minimum number of ruler measurements you would need in order to find both the perimeter and area of any right triangle? What set(s) of measurements will meet that condition?

c. What formulas show how to calculate perimeter P and area A of a right triangle from the measurements you described in Part b?

b. Two ruler measurements are required. Measuring the length and width of the rectangle will provide enough information for calculating both perimeter and area. However, one could also measure a diagonal and one side and then use the Pythagorean Theorem (probably the hard way to get what is needed).

c. Students may have a variety of formulas to express perimeter and area. At the Summarize the Mathematics class discussion, it will be important to have discussions around advantages and disadvantages of different forms and identifying what the variables represent. Using the most likely choices of measurements, the formulas for perimeter could be:

$$P = 2\ell + 2w$$
$$P = \ell + \ell + w + w$$
$$P = 2b + 2h$$
$$P = 2(b + h)$$

where ℓ and w or b and h represent the lengths of two adjacent sides. For area, the most familiar formulas would be:

$$A = bh$$
$$A = \ell w$$

6 **a.** The measurements are approximately $TQ = 8$ cm $\left(3\frac{1}{8} \text{ in.}\right)$, $ST = 4.3$ cm $\left(1\frac{11}{16} \text{ in.}\right)$, and $height = 3$ cm $\left(1\frac{3}{16} \text{ in.}\right)$. Based on these measurements:

$$P = 24.6 \text{ cm} \left(9\frac{5}{8} \text{ in.}\right)$$
$$A = 24 \text{ cm}^2 \ (3.7 \text{ in}^2)$$

b. At least three ruler measurements are required for calculating both perimeter and area (because the angles involved affect the shape of the parallelogram and thus the area). For calculating perimeter, the length of any two adjacent sides is necessary and sufficient. Calculating area requires the length of one of the bases and the height of the parallelogram to the base to be measured (in general a parallelogram's height will not be identical to one of the sides).

While the most familiar ruler measurements for finding perimeter and area would be something like segments *TS*, *SR*, and *TB* on the following sketch, one could also use the Pythagorean Theorem to derive the familiar lengths from measures of segments *BS*, *SR*, and *TR*, for example. No fewer than 3 segment lengths will do.

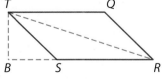

c. The most familiar formulas for perimeter and area will probably be $P = 2a + 2b$, where a and b are the lengths of any two adjacent sides, and $A = bh$, where b is the length of a base and h is the height of the parallelogram to the base b. There are, of course, many other equivalent formulas.

NOTE The answers to Problem 7 can be found on page T51.

d. What is the minimum number of measurements you would need in order to find both the perimeter and the area of any nonright triangle? What measurements will meet that condition?

e. What formulas show how to calculate perimeter *P* and area *A* of a nonright triangle from the measurements you described in Part d?

8 The figure below is a circle with center *O*.

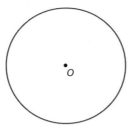

a. Use a ruler to make measurements from which you can estimate the circumference and area of the circle. Then calculate those estimates.

b. For any given circle, what is the minimum number of measurements you would need in order to find both the circumference and the area? What measurements will meet that condition?

c. What formulas show how to calculate circumference *C* and area *A* of a circle from the measurements you described in Part b?

Summarize
the Mathematics

In this investigation, you developed your skill in finding symbolic rules for patterns that relate dependent and independent variables.

a What strategies for finding algebraic rules do you find helpful when information about the pattern comes in the form of words describing the relationship of the variables?

b In general, what information is needed to calculate perimeter and area for:

   i. a rectangle?   **ii.** a parallelogram that is not a rectangle?

   iii. a right triangle?   **iv.** a nonright triangle?

   v. a circle?

c What formulas guide calculations of perimeter and area for each figure listed in Part b?

Be prepared to share your strategies and results with the class.

7 **a.** The measurements for the right triangle are approximately
$a = 3$ cm $\left(1\frac{3}{16}\text{ in.}\right)$, $b = 4$ cm $\left(1\frac{9}{16}\text{ in.}\right)$, and $c = 5$ cm $\left(1\frac{15}{16}\text{ in.}\right)$.
Based on these measurements:
$$P = 12 \text{ cm } \left(4\frac{11}{16}\text{ in.}\right)$$
$$A = 6 \text{ cm}^2 \ (0.93 \text{ in}^2)$$

The measurements for the obtuse triangle are approximately
$LM = 4$ cm $\left(1\frac{9}{16}\text{ in.}\right)$, $LN = 6.5$ cm $\left(2\frac{9}{16}\text{ in.}\right)$, $MN = 3.7$ cm $\left(1\frac{7}{16}\text{ in.}\right)$,
and the height from N to LM is 3 cm $\left(1\frac{3}{16}\text{ in.}\right)$. Based on these
measurements:
$$P = 14.2 \text{ cm } \left(5\frac{9}{16}\text{ in.}\right)$$
$$A = 6 \text{ cm}^2 \ (0.93 \text{ in}^2)$$

b. In a right triangle, if any two of the side lengths are known, the third can be calculated using the Pythagorean Theorem. That means only two ruler measurements will be required to find perimeter and area.

c. $P = a + b + c$
$A = 0.5ab$

d. In general, three ruler measurements are needed to find the perimeter and area of a triangle that is not some special type (like right, equilateral, or isosceles triangles). That might not be so obvious on the given drawing of triangle *LMN*, since students might argue that you need to measure all three sides and an altitude. Since the first point of this problem is to review formulas for finding perimeter and area of familiar figures, the point will have been made even if no student recognizes a more efficient 3-measurement strategy (using the Pythagorean Theorem for some intermediate calculations).

The following sketch shows how 3 measurements will be sufficient. From knowledge of *LM, MB,* and *NB* one can deduce the other side lengths; the same result can be derived from knowledge of *LM, MN,* and *NB* or from several other combinations of three relevant segment lengths.

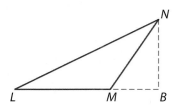

e. The most familiar formulas will probably be something like
$P = \ell + m + n$, where ℓ, m, and n are the three side lengths, and
$A = \frac{1}{2}bh$, where b is one of the side lengths and h is the height from
point N to side *LM*.

a. The radius is approximately 2 cm $\left(\frac{13}{16}\text{ in.}\right)$. Based on that measurement:

$$C \approx 4\pi \text{ cm} \left(1\tfrac{5}{8}\pi \text{ in.}\right)$$
$$A \approx 4\pi \text{ cm}^2 \ (0.66 \text{ in}^2)$$

b. For both the circumference and area, the radius (or diameter) is the only ruler measurement required.

c. $C = 2\pi r$, when r is the radius, and $C = \pi d$ when d is the diameter. $A = \pi r^2$, when r is the radius of the circle, and $A = \pi\left(\frac{d}{2}\right)^2$ when d is the diameter of the circle.

Summary

Students need not write a solution to this Summarize the Mathematics until after the class discussion. See Part c. You might ask groups presenting particular problems to be prepared to respond to particular questions.

Problem(s)	Summary Item
1–4	a
5	bi
6	bii
7	biii and biv
8	bv

Summarize
the Mathematics

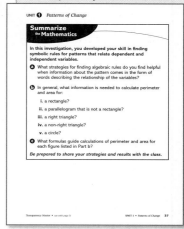

(a) There aren't well-defined and easily learned algorithms for the processes involved in this sort of problem modeling, so the summary discussion should encourage students to share their struggles with the tasks openly. Responses will vary as students report how they approached the problems of this type. They might report strategies like looking at some sample related pairs to see what arithmetic operations would derive the second number from the first. The second step may be to try those operations on some other related numbers. They might look for the pattern of change in the y values and try to link that to *NOW-NEXT* thinking. Students might also report looking for some fixed amounts and some rates per person or per item.

(b)
  i. The length and width of the rectangle are the most common measurements used for calculating perimeter and area of rectangles.

  ii. For parallelograms the lengths of any two adjacent sides are the most common measurements used to find perimeter. The length of one side and the altitude to that side are the most common measurements used to find area.

  iii. The most common measurements used to find perimeter of a right triangle are the lengths of the three sides. However, if one uses the Pythagorean Theorem, it is only necessary to measure two of those sides and derive the length of the third. To find the area of a right triangle, the most common approach uses the lengths of the two legs (not the hypotenuse).

  iv. For triangles that are not right, equilateral, or isosceles, one needs to make three measurements in order to find perimeter and area. At this point, students will likely not know this. They will indicate the need to make four measurements—all three side lengths and an altitude.

  v. Circumference and area of a circle can be calculated after measuring only the radius or the diameter.

(c) Students' perimeter and area formulas may vary. Class discussion about which formulas are most informative and the importance of defining variables should occur at this point. Class agreed-upon formulas can be written on the Unit Summary template.

  i. $P = 2\ell + 2w$ and $A = \ell w$, where ℓ and w represent the lengths of two adjacent sides.

  ii. $P = 2a + 2b$, where a and b are the lengths of any two adjacent sides. $A = bh$, where b is the length of a base and h is the height of the parallelogram to the base b.

  iii. $P = a + b + c$ and $A = 0.5ab$, where a and b are the lengths of the legs and c is the length of the hypotenuse.

  iv. $P = \ell + m + n$, where ℓ, m, and n are the three side lengths. $A = bh$, where b is one of the side lengths and h is the height to b.

  v. $C = 2\pi r$ and $A = \pi r^2$, where r is the radius of the circle.

> **MATH TOOLKIT** Class agreed-upon formulas for perimeter and area can be recorded if students themselves think it would be helpful.

Unit 1

✓ Check Your Understanding

Write algebraic rules expressing the relationships in these situations.

a. Students and parents who attend the Banneker High School *Take a Chance* carnival night spend an average of $12 per person playing the various games. Operation of the event costs the student government $200. What is the relationship between profit *P* of the carnival night and number of people who attend *n*?

b. The figure drawn below is an isosceles triangle with *KL* = *LM*.

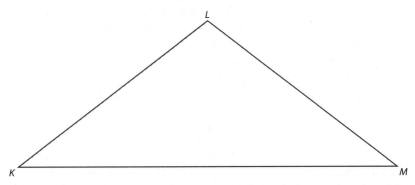

  i. Use a ruler to make measurements from which you can estimate the perimeter and area of triangle *KLM*.

  ii. For any isosceles triangle, what is the minimum number of measurements you would need in order to estimate both its perimeter and its area? What measurements will meet that condition?

  iii. Write formulas showing how the measurements you described in part ii can be used to calculate perimeter *P* and area *A* of an isosceles triangle.

 **Quick Tables, Graphs, and Solutions**

The rule $I = p(50 - p)$ predicts daily bungee jump income at Five Star Amusement Park. This rule arises from the fact that income is computed by multiplying price by the number of customers. In this case, *p* is the price per jump and $(50 - p)$ is the number of customers expected at that price. In this investigation, you will use rules to produce tables, graphs, and symbolic manipulations that help to answer questions such as:

- What income is expected if the price is set at $10 per jump?

- What should the price be in order to get income of at least $500 per day?

- What price per jump will produce maximum daily income?

✓Check Your Understanding

a. $P = 12n - 200$, where P is profit of the carnival night and n is the number of people who attend.

b. **i.** $KL \approx 3\frac{3}{16}$", $KM = 5$", and height from L to $\overline{KM}$ is 2".

ii. Two ruler measurements are good enough to find the perimeter and area of the isosceles triangle, if one knows how to use the Pythagorean Theorem. For the given drawing, one could use a measurement of the base and one of the congruent sides—applying Pythagoras to calculate the height from L to KM—or the base KM and one of the congruent sides—again using the Pythagorean Theorem to find the height.

iii. One natural formula for perimeter would be $P = \ell_1 + 2\ell_2$, where ℓ_1 is the base of the isosceles triangle and ℓ_2 is the length of the two equal sides.

For area, the most common formula would be $A = 0.5\ell_1 a_1$, where ℓ_1 is the length of the base and a_1 is the length of the altitude from L to KM. If one wanted to get by with only the side length measurements ℓ_1 and ℓ_2 for area as well, it would be necessary to replace a_1 by the expression $\sqrt{\ell_2^2 - \left(\frac{1}{2}\ell_1\right)^2}$.

Investigation 2 — Quick Tables, Graphs, and Solutions

The purpose of this investigation is to help students develop skill in searching through calculator- or computer-generated tables of function values, graphs of functions, and computer symbol manipulation tools to answer the kinds of questions that come up so often when two variables are related by a rule or an equation. The questions often fit one of these generic problem types:

- Find the output of a rule for a given input.
- Find the input that will give a specified output.
- Find inputs that keep an output greater than or less than some specified value.

Many such questions, for simple functions, can be solved without use of fancy calculating, graphic, or symbol manipulation tools. However, as the algebraic expressions involved get more complex, the tools are very helpful.

In this investigation, we follow a single rule that students have worked with before—the dependence of *daily income* from an amusement park bungee jump on price per jump given by the rule $I = p(50 - p)$—in order to demonstrate use of tables, graphs, and computer symbol manipulation to answer questions about that relationship. The basic demand function $n = 50 - p$ is, of course, much simpler than what one might find from realistic analysis of careful market research data. However, it has some of the reasonable properties of such relationships (e.g., as price increases, sales decrease), and it does not disguise the underlying algebraic issues with contextual complexity.

Sometimes you can answer questions like these by doing some simple arithmetic calculations. In other cases, calculators and computers provide useful tools for the work. As you work through the investigation, look for answers to this question:

How can you use calculator or computer tools to produce tables, graphs, and symbolic manipulations, which can help you to study relationships between variables?

1 **Using Tables** You can use computer software or a graphing calculator to produce tables of related values for the independent and dependent variables. For example, examine the table of sample (*price per jump*, *daily income*) data below.

Producing a Table

Enter Rule	Set Up Table	Display Table

Scanning the table you can see, for example, that with the price set at $10, Five Star expects a daily bungee jump income of $400.

Use the software or calculator you have to produce and scan tables for the rule $I = p(50 - p)$ in order to estimate answers for these questions:

 a. What daily income will result if the price is set at $19?

 b. To reach a daily income of at least $500, why should the price be at least $14, but not more than $36?

 c. What price(s) will yield a daily income of at least $300?

 d. What price will yield the maximum possible daily income?

 e. How would you describe the pattern of change in income as price increases from $0 to $50 in steps of $1?

2 **Using Graphs** Computer software and graphing calculators can also be used to produce graphs of relationships between variables. For example, see the graph below for $I = p(50 - p)$ relating *price per jump* and *daily income* for the Five Star bungee jump.

Producing a Graph

Enter Rule	Set Viewing Window	Display Graph
		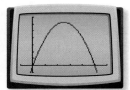

LESSON 3 • Tools for Studying Patterns of Change **53**

Investigation Launch

While it might be somewhat natural to us that one can calculate income from a commercial venture by finding the product of *price* and *number of sales*, experience has taught us that this key concept is puzzling to students. As you launch students into Investigation 2, you might start with reintroducing the Five Star Amusement Park context and the information that this investigation will focus on the income produced by the bungee attraction. Then ask, "If the price for a jump is $10, how much income will the park get?" Students should recognize that they need more information to know how many customers bought tickets. Recognizing that *Income* is related to price of tickets and that the number of customers is related to the price of tickets before students read the investigation introduction should help them understand the text. Note that students need not answer the bulleted questions in the introduction. The questions are listed as the types of questions students will encounter in the investigation.

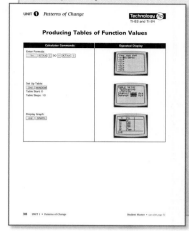
COLLABORATION COMMUNICATION SKILL Disagree in an agreeable way.

 a. $I = \$589$ when $p = 19$ is found in the table for $Y1 = x(50 - x)$.

b. Looking at the table, you see that ticket prices of $14, $36, and any prices between $14 and $36 give an income greater than $500. You also see that $x < \$14$ or $x > \$36$ gives an income less than $500.

c. Any price between $7 and $43 including $7 and $43 will give daily income of at least $300. Symbolically, $7 \leq p \leq 43$.

d. A price of $25 will yield $I = 625$. That appears to be the maximum daily income in dollars.

e. Income increases quickly at first, then more slowly when approaching the maximum point. It then decreases slowly at first and then more quickly. Change from increase to decrease happens at $x = 25$. This can be seen by scrolling through the table from $p = 1$ to $p = 50$ and observing how successive income values change.

TECHNOLOGY NOTE
Encourage students to change the values for TblStart and ΔTbl in order to see helpful values in the table.

Use the software or calculator you have to produce and trace a graph for $I = p(50 - p)$ and estimate answers to the following questions. In each case, report your results with a sketch that shows how the answer is displayed on the calculator or computer screen.

a. What income is expected if the price is set at $17?

b. What price(s) will lead to a daily income of about $550?

c. How does the predicted income change as the price increases from $0 to $50?

d. What price will lead to maximum daily income from the bungee jump attraction?

3 **Using Computer Algebra Systems** When you can express the connection between two variables with a symbolic rule, many important questions can be written as equations to be solved. For example, to find the price per bungee jump that will give daily income of $500, you have to solve the equation

$$p(50 - p) = 500.$$

As you've seen, it is possible to estimate values of p satisfying this equation by scanning values in a table or tracing points on the graph of $I = p(50 - p)$. Computers and calculators are often programmed with computer algebra systems that solve automatically and exactly. One common form of the required instructions looks like this:

solve(p•(50−p)=500,p)

When you execute the command (often by simply pressing ENTER), you will see the solution(s) displayed in a form similar to that shown below.

Solving an Equation

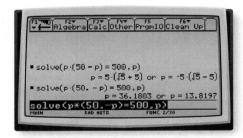

This display shows a special feature of computer algebra systems— they can operate in both *approximate* mode like graphing calculators or *exact* mode. (When some calculators with computer algebra systems are set in AUTO mode, they use exact form where possible. But they use approximate mode when an entry contains a decimal point.)

You can check both solutions with commands that substitute the values for p in the expression $p(50 - p)$. The screen will look something like the following display.

a. $I \approx 561$ when $p \approx 17$ can be seen by tracing points on the graph.

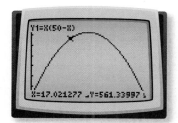

b. $p \approx 16.5$ and $p \approx 33.5$ make $I \approx 550$, as can be seen by tracing the graph.

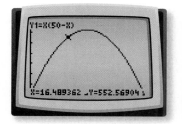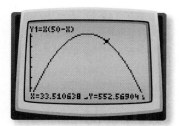

c. Starting at $p = 0$, income increases quickly at first and then more slowly to $625 when $p = 25$. Then income decreases slowly at first and then more quickly to zero again when $p = 50$. This numerical pattern can be seen by the shape of the graph.

d. A price of $25 will yield maximum income of $625. This can be seen to be the highest point on the graph.

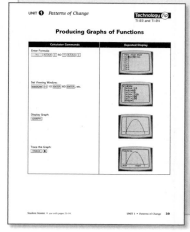
INSTRUCTIONAL NOTE
This is an opportunity to have a class discussion about how the information in tables can help decide on a good viewing window for the corresponding graph.

Unit 1

Evaluating an Expression

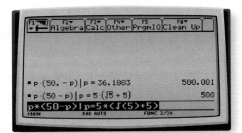

Computer algebra systems can do many other algebraic operations that you will learn about in future study. To get started, modify the instructions illustrated above to answer the following questions. In each case, check your results by using the same computer algebra system, scans of graphing calculator tables or traces of graphs, or arithmetic calculations.

a. What bungee jump price will give a predicted daily income of $450? An income of $0?

b. What daily income is predicted for a jump price of $23? For a jump price of $42?

c. What question will be answered by solving the equation $p(50 - p) = 225$? What is the answer?

d. How could you solve the equation $p(50 - p) = 0$ just by thinking about the question, "What values of p will make the expression $p(50 - p)$ equal to zero?"

Summarize
the Mathematics

In this investigation, you developed skill in use of calculator or computer tools to study relations between variables. You learned how to construct tables and graphs of pairs of values and how to use a computer algebra system to solve equations.

a Suppose that you were given the algebraic rule $y = 5x + \dfrac{10}{x}$ relating two variables. How could you use that rule to find:

- the value of y when $x = 4$
- the value(s) of x that give $y = 15$

  i. using a table of (x, y) values?

  ii. using a graph of (x, y) values?

  iii. using a computer algebra system?

b What seem to be the strengths and limitations of each tool—table, graph, and computer algebra system—in answering questions about related variables? What do these tools offer that makes problem solving easier than it would be without them?

Be prepared to share your thinking with the class.

TECHNOLOGY NOTE You may choose to use a one-computer interactive discussion using the *CPMP-Tools* CAS under Algebra, or other CAS tools. See page T55B.

a. To find prices that will give income of $450, we need to solve $p(50 - p) = 450$.

To find prices that will give income of $0, we need to solve $p(50 - p) = 0$.

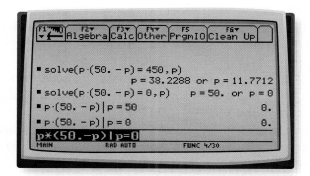

b. To find the predicted income for prices of $23 and $42, we need to evaluate the expression $p(50 - p)$ at those values of p.

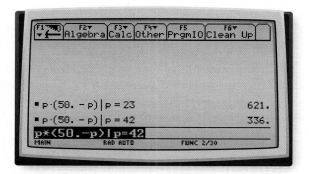

c. To find the price that will yield a daily income of $225 we need to solve the equation $p(50 - p) = 225$.

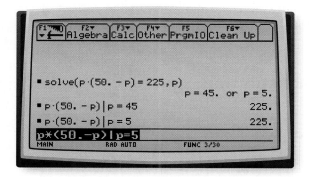

d. This equation can be solved if one realizes that the product will be zero if $p = 0$ or if $p = 50$. That does not require a CAS. However, only a small change in the question and the related equation makes access to a CAS very helpful.

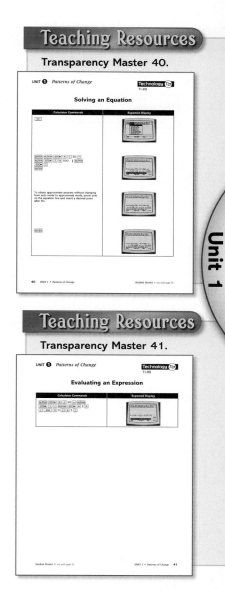
NOTE One important goal of the algebra and functions strand in *Core-Plus Mathematics* is to help students develop good judgment about choice of tools that are well-suited to the problems that are presented as in this lesson.

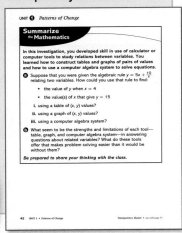

Summarize
the Mathematics

a i. Using a table:
  - Scroll to the given *x* value and look at the corresponding *y* value.
  - Scroll to the given *y* value (approximately) and look at the corresponding *x* value.

ii. Using a graph:
  - You can use the cursor keys to place the trace mark over the point with the *x*-coordinate of interest and read off the *y*-coordinate.
  - Using "trace," find the point(s) with approximate given *y* value, and read off the corresponding *x*-coordinates to get as close as possible.

iii. Using a CAS:
  - Type **5x+10/x|x=4** in the command line and press ENTER.
  - Type **solve(5x+10/x=15,x)** in the command line and press ENTER. Alternatively, select "Solve" from the algebra pull down menu (F2) and follow with typing in the equation to be solved and the variable to solve for, followed by pressing ENTER.

b Using the table may take a long time, it is not always easy to see the overall pattern of change, and if there are two corresponding *x* values for a given *y* you might miss one of them. However, the table does give numerical information directly.

The graph gives an overall view of the pattern of change involved in the situation, assuming you find an appropriate viewing window. Tracing the graph allows you to see approximate *x* values and *y* values.

Using the computer algebra system makes it easy to find exact solution of equations. However, it is also easy to overlook typing errors and the CAS does not give any overall view of the pattern of change involved in the situation.

MATH TOOLKIT Summarize how you can use a table, graph, or CAS to answer questions about an algebraic rule.

PROCESSING PROMPT In any group, it is helpful to disagree in an agreeable way because …

1. _____   2. _____

TECHNOLOGY AND DIFFERENTIATION NOTE *CPMP-Tools* algebra software includes a CAS that allows you to solve equations as on page 54.

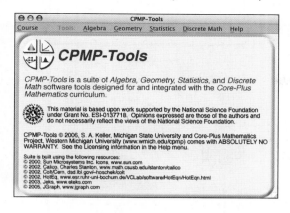

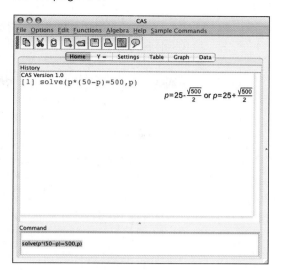

The *CPMP-Tools* CAS also allows you to define functions with parameters as coefficients and adjust those coefficients dynamically. Investigation 3, The Shapes of Algebra, has the focus question: "How do the forms of algebraic rules give useful information about the patterns in tables and graphs produced by those graphs?" This question could be investigated using the CAS slider feature and the split screen as shown in the screens below. One way to facilitate the investigation would be to have each group of students use a single computer to complete one of the experiments or explore one of the forms of algebraic rules. Then have students demonstrate their findings using a projection system. Another option would be to begin the investigation in class and allow students to continue seeking an answer to this question using *CPMP-Tools* at home or on a school computer following the class period. This would allow students who process more slowly some individual time to explore these ideas. Alternatively, those students who pick up quickly on the information from the rules suggested in the text may wish to explore other algebraic rules of their own design. Placing the choice of tool and how far to extend the investigation in the hands of students may increase the motivation of some students.

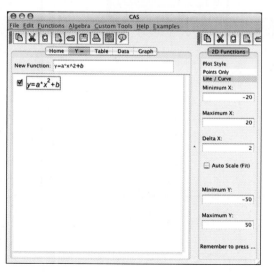

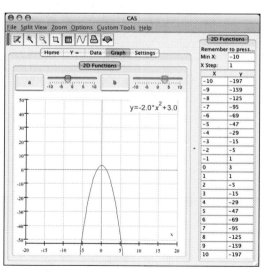

Unit 1

✔Check Your Understanding

Weekly profit at the Starlight Cinema theater depends on the number of theater customers according to the rule $P = 6.5n - 2,500$. Use table, graph, and computer algebra system methods to complete Parts a–c. For each question:

- Report the setups you use to answer the questions by making and studying tables of (n, P) values. In each case, give the starting value and step size for the table that shows a satisfactory estimate of the answer.

- Report the window setups used to answer the questions by tracing a graph of the rule $P = 6.5n - 2,500$.

- Report the computer algebra system commands used to answer the questions and the results in approximate and exact modes.

a. To find the **break-even point** for the business, you need to find the value of n that produces a value of P equal to 0. That means you have to solve the equation $0 = 6.5n - 2,500$. What values of n satisfy that equation?

b. What profit is predicted if the theater has 750 customers in a week?

c. What number of customers will be needed to make a profit of $1,000 in a week?

d. How could you answer the questions in Parts a–c if the only "tool" you had was your own arithmetic skills or a calculator that could only do the basic operations of arithmetic $(+, -, \times, \div)$?

Investigation 3 The Shapes of Algebra

The patterns you discovered while working on problems of earlier investigations illustrate only a few of the many ways that tables, graphs, and algebraic rules are useful in studying relations among variables. To find and use rules that relate independent and dependent variables or that predict change in one variable over time, it helps to be familiar with the table and graph patterns associated with various symbolic forms.

✓ Check Your Understanding

INSTRUCTIONAL NOTE
Before assigning the Check Your Understanding, you might ask students to explain what is meant by a break-even point.

Using a calculator or computer table tool, setup and result screens for $y = 6.5x - 2500$ might look like this:

Using a calculator or computer graphing tool, the setup and result screens might look like this:

Using a computer algebra system, the screens will look like this:

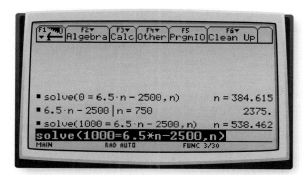

a. Break-even with about 385 customers

b. Profit of $2,375 with 750 customers

c. 539 customers needed to make $1,000 profit

d. To find the break-even point you only need to calculate $2,500 \div 6.5$; to find the profit from 750 customers, you only need to calculate $6.5(750) - 2,500$; to find the price that will give $1,000 profit you only need to calculate $(1,000 + 2,500) \div 6.5$.

While for many students, these problems might be easy to solve with just arithmetic reasoning and mental or paper and pencil calculation, the main point of the investigation and this CYU problem is to develop technology skills and the associated function and equation concepts that will be useful when the algebraic tasks are not so simple.

As you work on the explorations of this investigation, look for answers to this question:

How do the forms of algebraic rules give useful information about the patterns in tables and graphs produced by those rules?

You can get ideas about connections between symbolic rules and table and graph patterns by exploration with a graphing calculator or a computer tool. You might find it efficient to share the following explorations among groups in your class and share examples within an exploration among individuals in a group.

In each exploration, you are given several symbolic rules to compare and contrast. To discover similarities and differences among the examples of each exploration:

- For each rule in the set, produce a table of (x, y) values with integer values of x and graphs of (x, y) values for x between −5 and 5.

- Record the table patterns and sketches of the graphs in your notes as shown here for the example $y = 0.5x - 1$.

x		−5	−4	−3	−2	−1	0	1	2	3	4	5
$y = 0.5x - 1$	−3.5	−3.0	...									

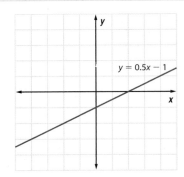

- Then compare the tables, graphs, and symbolic rules in the exploration. Note similarities, differences, and connections between the symbolic rules and the table and graph patterns. Explore some other similar rules to test your ideas.

- Try to explain why the observed connection between rules and table/graph patterns makes sense.

Exploration 1. Compare the patterns of change in tables and graphs for these rules.

a. $y = 2x - 4$ **b.** $y = -0.5x + 2$ **c.** $y = 0.5x + 2$ **d.** $y = \dfrac{2}{x} - 4$

Exploration 2. Compare the patterns of change in tables and graphs for these rules.

a. $y = x^2$ **b.** $y = 2^x$ **c.** $y = -x^2$ **d.** $y = -x^2 + 2$

Investigation 3 · The Shapes of Algebra

This investigation continues the spirit of exploring a range of common algebraic functions, to build students' intuition about the connections between numerical patterns, graphs, rules, and problem conditions. Specifically, this investigation does two things. First, it gives students further practice in use of the calculator or computer graphing and table tools. Second, it engages students in systematic comparison of table and graph patterns associated with some of the basic function rule types.

The idea behind this particular investigation is to give students some initial ideas about the important function families they will study in detail in later *Core-Plus Mathematics* units. There is no need to linger over this investigation until students have gotten everything possible from it. Furthermore, we envision a classroom operating environment in which different groups tackle different explorations and prepare reports to the class on their particular set of function examples.

INSTRUCTIONAL NOTE You might assign one exploration to each group so that every exploration is dealt with by at least one group. Groups could record the following information on chart paper for their group report to the class.

1. Graph one of the three similar rules.
2. Record their observations about similarities in the (1) graphs, (2) tables, and (3) algebraic rules.

These summaries could be extended as a class discussion takes place after each group presentation. The charts could be left up in the classroom and referred to as students explore these functions throughout the year. If you do a Google search for "getting out of line CPMP," you will find this lesson on PBS TeacherSource. The printable lesson plan includes other resources. "Tips from Ellen" might give additional ideas for presenting group work.

Exploration 1—The examples here are, with only one exception, linear functions with the types of table and graph patterns one would expect (though students won't necessarily know what to expect). Students should notice that Part d is the exception and that the coefficient of x tells whether the linear graph is increasing or decreasing and roughly whether the graph slope is steep or flat. They might notice that the constant term tells the y-intercept. However, at this point all of these observations should be viewed as conjectures. When students are presenting their ideas, you might want to ask them if they can explain *why* things happen the way they do by analyzing the form of the function rule. For example, they might notice that the difference in $y = \frac{2}{x} - 4$ is largely due to the fact that when x approaches 0, the values of $\frac{2}{x}$ get very large and when the values of x get large (positive), the values of $\frac{2}{x}$ get small (positive). All of this is related to the way division behaves.

Teaching Resources

Students should record their work on the student master. They will need one sheet for each exploration.

Student Master 43.

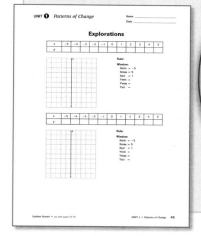

TECHNOLOGY NOTE
CPMP-Tools CAS can be incorporated into this investigation. See page T55B for options.

a. $y = 2x - 4$

x	−5	−4	−3	−2	−1	0	1	2	3	4	5
y	−14	−12	−10	−8	−6	−4	−2	0	2	4	6

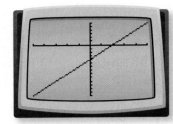 

b. $y = -0.5x + 2$

x	−5	−4	−3	−2	−1	0	1	2	3	4	5
y	4.5	4	3.5	3	2.5	2	1.5	1	0.5	0	−0.5

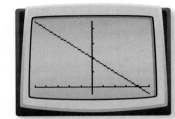 

c. $y = 0.5x + 2$

x	−5	−4	−3	−2	−1	0	1	2	3	4	5
y	−0.5	0	0.5	1	1.5	2	2.5	3	3.5	4	4.5

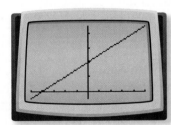 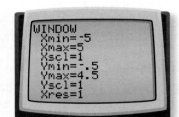

d. $y = \frac{2}{x} - 4$

x	−5	−4	−3	−2	−1	0	1	2	3	4	5
y	−4.4	−4.5	−4.667	−5	−6	undefined	−2	−3	−3.333	−3.5	−3.6

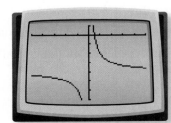 

Exploration 2—All but one of these functions are quadratics, the exception being the item in Part b, which is exponential. Students might note that all have graphs that are either hill- or valley-shaped. Values in the tables rise to a maximum and then fall or vice versa. The quadratic rules all involve an x^2 term, and the coefficient of that term (positive or negative) tells whether one has a hill or a valley graph. The fact that for Part b the variable is in the exponent is the distinguishing feature, making the power rather than the base grow as x increases.

a. $y = x^2$

x	−5	−4	−3	−2	−1	0	1	2	3	4	5
y	25	16	9	4	1	0	1	4	9	16	25

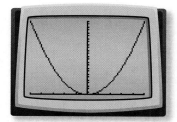 

b. $y = 2^x$

x	−5	−4	−3	−2	−1	0	1	2	3	4	5
y	0.031	0.063	0.125	0.25	0.5	1	2	4	8	16	32

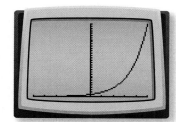 

c. $y = -x^2$

x	−5	−4	−3	−2	−1	0	1	2	3	4	5
y	−25	−16	−9	−4	−1	0	−1	−4	−9	−16	−25

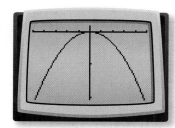 

d. $y = -x^2 + 2$

x	−5	−4	−3	−2	−1	0	1	2	3	4	5
y	−23	−14	−7	−2	1	2	1	−2	−7	−14	−23

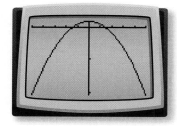 

Exploration 3. Compare the patterns of change in tables and graphs for these rules.

a. $y = \frac{1}{x}$ **b.** $y = \frac{x}{3}$ **c.** $y = \frac{3}{x}$ **d.** $y = -\frac{5}{x}$

Exploration 4. Compare the patterns of change in tables and graphs for these rules.

a. $y = 3^x$ **b.** $y = x^3$ **c.** $y = 1.5^x$ **d.** $y = 4^x$

Summarize the Mathematics

As a result of the explorations, you probably have some ideas about the patterns in tables of (x, y) values and the shapes of graphs that can be expected for various symbolic rules. Summarize your conjectures in statements like these:

ⓐ If we see a rule like ... , we expect to get a table like ... .

ⓑ If we see a rule like ... , we expect to get a graph like ... .

ⓒ If we see a graph pattern like ... , we expect to get a table like ... .

Be prepared to share your ideas with others in your class.

✔Check Your Understanding

Each item here gives three algebraic rules—one of which will have quite different table and graph patterns than the other two. In each case, spot the "alien" rule and explain how and why its graph and/or table pattern will look different from the other two.

a. $y = \frac{10}{x}$
$y = 10x$
$y = x + 10$

b. $y = x^2 + 1$
$y = x + 1$
$y = 1 - x^2$

c. $y = 1.5x - 4$
$y = (1.5^x) - 4$
$y = 2^x$

d. $y = 1.5x - 4$
$y = 0.5x - 4$
$y = -1.5x - 4$

Exploration 3—All but one of the functions in this set are examples of inverse variation. The exception is in Part b, which is a linear rule but in a form that students seem to have a great deal of trouble recognizing.

For the inverse variation examples (a, c, and d), students may notice two symmetric hyperbola wings, an undefined point wherever the denominator is zero, and curved graphs that approach the *x*- and *y*-axes without intercepting them.

The pattern of change for equations with variables in the denominator is not a constant rate of change.

a. $y = \frac{1}{x}$

x	−5	−4	−3	−2	−1	0	1	2	3	4	5
y	−0.2	−0.25	−0.333	−0.5	−1	undefined	1	0.5	0.333	0.25	0.2

b. $y = \frac{x}{3}$

x	−5	−4	−3	−2	−1	0	1	2	3	4	5
y	−1.667	−1.333	−1	−0.667	−0.333	0	0.333	0.667	1	1.333	1.667

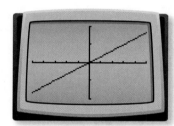 

c. $y = \frac{3}{x}$

x	−5	−4	−3	−2	−1	0	1	2	3	4	5
y	−0.6	−0.75	−1	−1.5	−3	undefined	3	1.5	1	0.75	0.6

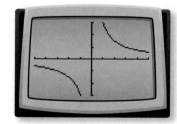 

d. $y = -\frac{5}{x}$

x	−5	−4	−3	−2	−1	0	1	2	3	4	5
y	1	1.25	1.667	2.5	5	undefined	−5	−2.5	−1.667	−1.25	−1

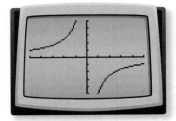 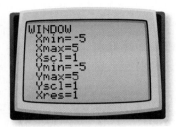

Exploration 4—All but one of the functions in this set are examples of exponential functions. The exception is in Part b because the variable is not in the exponent in that case. Exponential growth curves look similar to half a parabola. The differences between those exponential curves and parabolic curves are more subtle than we expect students to notice or be able to understand at this point. Students should describe patterns of change for each graph as increasing quickly, slowly, etc. They will examine each type in more detail in later units.

a. $y = 3^x$

x	−5	−4	−3	−2	−1	0	1	2	3	4	5
y	0.004	0.012	0.037	0.111	0.333	1	3	9	27	81	243

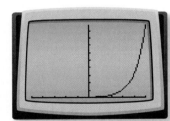 

b. $y = x^3$

x	−5	−4	−3	−2	−1	0	1	2	3	4	5
y	−125	−64	−27	−8	−1	0	1	8	27	64	125

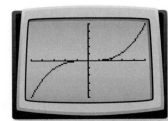 

c. $y = (1.5^x)$

x	−5	−4	−3	−2	−1	0	1	2	3	4	5
y	0.132	0.198	0.296	0.444	0.667	1	1.5	2.25	3.375	5.063	7.594

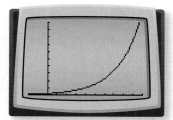

d. $y = 4^x$

x	−5	−4	−3	−2	−1	0	1	2	3	4	5
y	0.00098	0.004	0.0156	0.0625	0.25	1	4	16	64	256	1,024

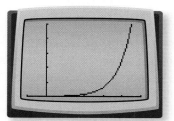

INSTRUCTIONAL NOTE
Groups doing Part d should report how they interpreted the calculator display for 4^{-5}. This is an opportunity to introduce or revisit the "E" (scientific notation on the calculator).

Summary

The group presentations suggested for the explorations are designed to include these summary ideas. Use the notes here to help guide your class discussion and your questions for the groups of the class as presentations are made.

Summarize
the Mathematics

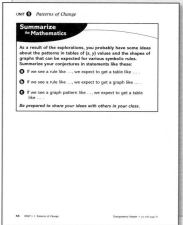
(a) If you see a rule like $y = 3x + 4$, you expect to get a table that has a y value of 4 when $x = 0$, and a pattern that sees the y values increase by 3 for every increase of 1 in the x values.

Rules like $y = x^2 + 2$ will give tables in which y values decrease for a while and then increase from $y = 2$ when $x = 0$; if the rule is $y = -x^2 + 2$, the table values of y will increase for a while and then decrease.

Rules that have the variable in the denominator of a fraction will produce tables that have very large (negative or positive) values of y as x nears 0 and very small (positive or negative) values of y for large (negative or positive) values of x. For $x = 0$, the calculator will report "error" for the corresponding y value.

Rules that have the variable in an exponent position and a base greater than 1 will produce table patterns in which y values start out small and grow more and more rapidly as x values increase. If the base is between 0 and 1, the y values start out large and approach 0 as x values increase.

b If you see a rule like $y = 3x + 4$, you expect to get a straight line graph that crosses the y-axis at 4 and slopes upward from left to right in a straight line. If the coefficient of x is negative, the graph will slope downward from left to right.

If you see a rule like $y = x^2$ or $y = -x^2$, you expect to get graphs that look like valleys or hills, respectively.

If you see a rule with x in the denominator of a fraction, you expect to see a two-part graph with symmetric bowl shapes in opposite quadrants. Depending on how the graphing mode is set, one might see a line connecting the left and right parts of the graph. Since the limit as x approaches 0 from the left is $-\infty$, and the limit as x approaches 0 from the right is ∞, there might be a line drawn from the bottom of the screen, just left of the y-axis, to the top of the screen, just right of the y-axis.

If you see a rule with x in the exponent, you expect to get a curve that either starts along the x-axis rising slowly and then more and more rapidly (base greater than 1), or starts quite high and then descends in a curve to run closer and closer to the x-axis (base less than 1).

c If you see a straight-line graph, you expect to see a table pattern in which y values increase at a steady rate as x values increase.

If you see a valley- or hill-shaped graph, you expect to see a table in which y values decrease to a minimum and then increase or y values that increase to a maximum and then decrease.

If you see a graph with bowl-like curved parts in opposite quadrants, you expect to see table values of y that are close to 0 for large (positive or negative) values of x and growing very large (negative or positive) for values of x near 0.

If you see the exponential shape of a curved graph, you expect values of y in a table to grow slowly at first and then more and more rapidly as x increases (base greater than 1) or to fall rapidly at first and then more and more slowly approaching 0 as x increases (base less than 1).

MATH TOOLKIT Students should record samples of each of the patterns of change studied in this lesson.

✓ Check Your Understanding

a. The first rule is the "alien," as it is an inverse variation and the other two are linear functions. Students should note that the inverse variation has a "jump" at 0, while the linear rules are continuous. Most students will probably note that the rate of change is constant in both of the linear rules, while in the inverse variation rule the rate of change is not constant.

b. The second rule is linear while the other two have the variable squared. Students should note the very differently shaped graphs of the rules. Also, the rule with the variable squared has values that decrease and then increase (or vice versa) while the linear rule's values always increase.

c. The first rule is linear while the second and third are exponential. Although all three are both continuous and always increasing, students should point out the great difference in the shape of their graphs, as well as the constant rate of change in the linear rule.

d. While all three rules are linear, the third might be considered "alien" because it has a negative rate of change. This results in a graph that is "slanted" a different way than the other two and a table in which values are decreasing instead of increasing. Some students could appropriately reason that the second rule is "alien" because of its 0.5 rate of change.

Applications

① Members of the LaPorte High School football team have decided to hold a one-day car wash to raise money for trophies and helmet decals. They plan to charge $7.50 per car, but they need to pay $55 for water and cleaning supplies. Write a rule that shows how car wash profit is related to the number of car wash customers.

② Juan and Tiffany work for their town's park department cutting grass in the summer. They can usually cut an acre of grass in about 2 hours. They have to allow 30 minutes for round-trip travel time from the department equipment shop to a job and back. What rule tells the time required by any job as a function of the number of acres of grass to be cut on that job?

③ When a summer thunder-and-lightning storm is within several miles of your home, you will see the lightning and then hear the thunder produced by that lightning. The lightning travels 300,000 kilometers per second, but the sound of the thunder travels only 330 meters per second. That means that the lightning arrives almost instantly, while the thunder takes measurable time to travel from where the lightning strikes to where you are when you hear it.

You can estimate your distance from a storm center by counting the time between seeing the lightning and hearing the thunder. What formula calculates your distance from the lightning strike as a function of the time gap between lightning and thunder arrival?

④ Rush Computer Repair makes service calls to solve computer problems. They charge $40 for technician travel to the work site and $55 per hour for time spent working on the problem itself. What symbolic rule shows how the cost of a computer repair depends on actual time required to solve the problem?

⑤ The freshman class officers at Interlake High School ordered 1,200 fruit bars to sell as a fund-raising project. They paid $0.30 per bar at the time the order was placed. They plan to sell the fruit bars at school games and concerts for $0.75 apiece. No returns of unsold bars are possible. What rule shows how project profit depends on the number of bars sold?

On Your Own

Applications

1 $p = 7.5n - 55$, where n represents the number of car washes and p represents the profit in dollars.

2 $t = 0.5 + 2a$, where a represents the area of the grass and t represents the time in hours required to do the job.

3 $d = 330t$, where t is the time in seconds and d is the distance away in meters of the lightning strike. The rule assumes that the sight of lightning arrives instantly.

4 $c = 40 + 55t$, where t represents the time spent on the job and c represents the total cost in dollars for the repair job.

5 $p = 0.75n - 360$, where n represents the number of bars sold and p represents the profit in dollars.

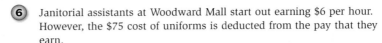

6 Janitorial assistants at Woodward Mall start out earning $6 per hour. However, the $75 cost of uniforms is deducted from the pay that they earn.

  a. Explain how the rule $E = 6.00h - 75$ shows how a new employee's earnings depend on the number of hours worked.

  b. How many hours will a new employee have to work before receiving a paycheck for some positive amount?

  c. How many hours will a new employee have to work to earn pay of $100 before taxes and other withholdings?

  d. Sketch a graph of the rule relating pay earned to hours worked, and label points with coordinates that provide answers to Parts b and c.

7 Experiments with a bungee jump suggested the rule $L = 30 + 0.2w$ relating stretched length of the cord (in feet) to weight of the jumper (in pounds).

  a. What will be the stretched cord length for a jumper weighing 140 pounds?

  b. What jumper weights will stretch the cord to a length of at most 65 feet?

  c. Sketch a graph of the cord length relationship and label points with coordinates that give answers to Parts a and b.

  d. Study entries in a table of (w, L) values for $w = 0$ to $w = 300$ in steps of 10. Try to figure out what the values 30 and 0.2 tell about the bungee jump experience.

8 When promoters of a special Bruce Springsteen Labor Day concert did some market research, they came up with a rule $N = 15,000 - 75p$ relating number of tickets that would be sold to the ticket price.

  a. Income from ticket sales is found by multiplying the number of tickets sold by the price of each ticket. The rule $I = p(15,000 - 75p)$ shows how *income* depends on *ticket price*.

  i. What do the terms p and $(15,000 - 75p)$ each tell about how ticket price affects the concert business?

  ii. Why does the product give income as a function of ticket price?

  b. What ticket price(s) is likely to produce concert income of at least $550,000?

  c. What is the predicted concert income if the ticket price is set at $30?

  d. What ticket price is likely to lead to the greatest concert income?

  e. What ticket price(s) will lead to 0 income?

  f. Sketch a graph of the relationship between concert income and ticket price. Then label the points with coordinates that provide answers to Parts b, c, and d.

6 **a.** $E = 6.00h - 75$, represents the earnings E because the hourly rate of $6 is multiplied times the number of hours h and then the $75 uniform cost is deducted.

b. More than 12.5 hours

c. 29.17 hours

d.

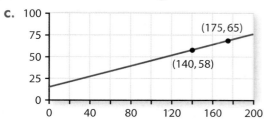

7 **a.** 58 feet   **b.** Weight less than 175 pounds

c.

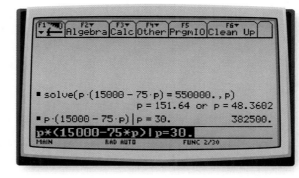

(graph: points (140, 58) and (175, 65))

d. 30 tells length of unstretched cord and 0.2 tells that for every 10 pounds of weight added, the cord stretches an additional 2 feet (or 0.2 feet per pound).

8 **a.** **i.** p is the ticket price and $15{,}000 - 75p$ is the number of tickets sold at price p.

ii. The product is the income I as a function of ticket price because the amount of money taken in (I) can be computed knowing only the ticket price p. Income is found by multiplying the price of each ticket times the number of tickets sold.

b. $48 < p < 152$; Ticket prices more than $48 and less than $152 will give income of at least $550,000.

c. $I = 382{,}500$

d. A ticket price of $100 gives a maximum income of $750,000.

e. Income is 0 when $p = 0$ (free admission) or when $p = 200$.

NOTE The answer to Problem 8, Part f can be found on page T61.

9 When members of the LaPorte High School football team ran their fund-raising car wash, they expected profit to be related to number of cars washed by $P = 7.50n - 55$.

  a. If their goal was to earn a $500 profit, how many cars would the team have to wash?

  b. How many cars would the team need to wash to break even?

10 Without use of your graphing calculator or computer software, sketch graphs you would expect from these rules. Explain your reasoning in each case.

  a. $y = 7x^2 + 4$

  b. $y = 7 - \frac{1}{4}x$

  c. $y = 4^x - 7$

11 Without use of your graphing calculator or computer software, match the following four rule types to the tables below. Explain your reasoning in each case.

  a. $y = ax + b$ **b.** $y = ax^2 + b$ **c.** $y = \frac{a}{x}$ **d.** $y = a^x$

I

x	−4	−3	−2	−1	0	1	2	3	4	5
y	18	11	6	3	2	3	6	11	18	27

II

x	−4	−3	−2	−1	0	1	2	3	4	5
y	16	14	12	10	8	6	4	2	0	−2

III

x	−4	−3	−2	−1	0	1	2	3	4	5
y	0.0625	0.125	0.25	0.5	1	2	4	8	16	32

IV

x	−4	−3	−2	−1	0	1	2	3	4	5
y	−1.5	−2	−3	−6	error	6	3	2	1.5	1.2

12 Without use of your graphing calculator or computer software, match the following four rule types to the graph sketches below. Explain your reasoning in each case.

  a. $y = ax + b$ **b.** $y = ax^2 + b$ **c.** $y = \frac{a}{x}$ **d.** $y = a^x$

I
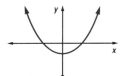

II
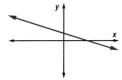

III
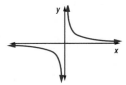

IV
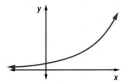

f.

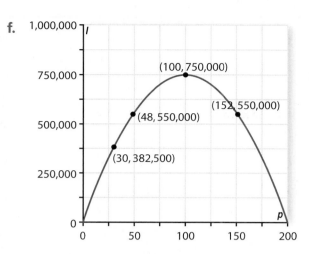

(9) **a.** $n = 74$ gives profit of $500.

b. $n = 8$ gives profit of $5, n = 7$ gives loss of $2.50.

Both answers can be obtained by scanning tables or graphs for
$p = 7.5n - 55$ or by use of a computer algebra system as follows:

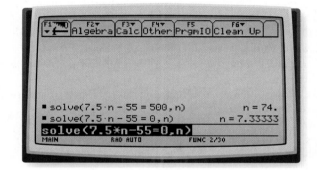

(10) **a.**

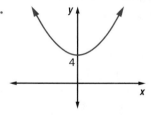

The graph is valley-shaped
because the x^2 term is
positive. It crosses the
y-axis at 4.

b.

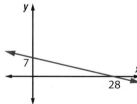

The graph is linear and
crosses the y-axis at 7 and
the x-axis at 28.

c.

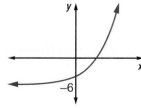

The 4^x means that the
function is exponential,
so it goes up quickly. The
y-intercept is -6 since
$4^0 - 7 = -6$.

(11) **a.** $y = ax + b$: II **b.** $y = ax^2 + b$: I **c.** $y = \frac{a}{x}$: IV **d.** $y = a^x$: III

(12) **a.** $y = ax + b$: II **b.** $y = ax^2 + b$: I **c.** $y = \frac{a}{x}$: III **d.** $y = a^x$: IV

Connections

13 Three familiar formulas relate circumference and area of any circle to the radius or diameter of the circle. All three involve the number π, which is approximately 3.14.

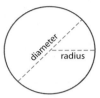

Circumference: $C = \pi d$ and $C = 2\pi r$
Area: $A = \pi r^2$

a. Complete a table like the one below to show the pattern of change in circumference and area of a circle as the radius increases.

Radius r	0	1	2	3	4	5	10	20
Circumference C								
Area A								

b. Compare the pattern of change in area to the pattern of change in circumference as radius increases. Explain differences in the patterns of change by comparing the formulas.

c. How will the area change if the radius is doubled? If it is tripled?

d. How will the circumference change if the radius is doubled? If it is tripled?

e. Which change in the size of a circle will cause the greater increase in circumference—doubling the radius or doubling the diameter? Which of those changes will cause the greater increase in area?

f. Tony's Pizza Place advertises 2-item, 10-inch pizzas for $7.95 and 2-item, 12-inch pizzas for $9.95. Which pizza is the better buy?

14 For polygons like triangles and rectangles, the formulas for perimeter and area often involve two variables—usually *base* and *height*.

Triangle Area: $A = \frac{1}{2}bh$
Rectangle Area: $A = bh$
Rectangle Perimeter: $P = 2b + 2h$

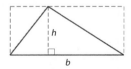

a. Complete entries in a table like the following to give a sample of triangle areas for different base and height values. The base values are in column **A**; the height values are in row **1**; the areas go in cell **B2** through **J10**. Then use the table patterns to answer questions in Parts b and c.

You might find it helpful to write a spreadsheet program to do the calculations.

(13) a.

Radius r	0	1	2	3	4	5	10	20
Circumference C	0	2π	4π	6π	8π	10π	20π	40π
Area A	0	π	4π	9π	16π	25π	100π	400π

b. Circumference grows at a steady rate—as radius increases by 1, circumference increases by 2π; area grows at an increasing rate due to the squaring of the radius.

c. If radius is doubled, the area is multiplied by 4; tripling the radius multiplies the area by 9.

d. If the radius is doubled, the circumference is also doubled. If the radius is tripled the circumference is also tripled.

e. Doubling the radius and doubling the diameter have the same effect on both circumference and area, since the radius and diameter are directly proportional to each other. Doubling one essentially doubles the other also.

f. Figuring the pizza value should be done by comparing cost per unit of area, you get $\frac{7.95}{25\pi}$ for the 10-inch pizza and $\frac{9.95}{36\pi}$ for the 12-inch pizza. The rates are 0.10 dollars per square inch and 0.09 dollars per square inch, respectively; so the larger pizza is the better buy (if you are actually hungry enough to eat it all).

(14) a.

Polygon Areas.xls

◇	A	B	C	D	E	F	G	H	I	J
1		1	2	3	4	5	6	7	8	9
2	1	0.5	1	1.5	2	2.5	3	3.5	4	4.5
3	2	1	2	3	4	5	6	7	8	9
4	3	1.5	3	4.5	6	7.5	9	10.5	12	13.5
5	4	2	4	6	8	10	12	14	16	18
6	5	2.5	5	7.5	10	12.5	15	17.5	20	22.5
7	6	3	6	9	12	15	18	21	24	27
8	7	3.5	7	10.5	14	17.5	21	24.5	28	31.5
9	8	4	8	12	16	20	24	28	32	36
10	9	4.5	9	13.5	18	22.5	27	31.5	36	40.5
11										

Triangle Areas.xls

◇	A	B	C	D	E	F	G	H	I	J
1		1	2	3	4	5	6	7	8	9
2	1	0.5	1							
3	2	1	2							
4	3	1.5								
5	4									
6	5									
7	6									
8	7									
9	8									
10	9									
11										

b. Which change in the size of a triangle causes the greater increase in area—doubling the base or doubling the height?

c. How will the area of a triangle change if both the base and the height are doubled? What if both are tripled?

15 Create a table like that in Connections Task 14 to explore patterns of change in area of rectangles for base and height values from 1 to 9. Answer the same questions about the effects of doubling base and height for a rectangle.

16 Create a table like that in Connections Task 14 to explore patterns of change in perimeter of rectangles for base and height values from 1 to 9. Answer similar questions about the effects on perimeter of doubling base and height for a rectangle.

17 To answer Connections Task 14 with a spreadsheet, Mr. Conklin wrote some formulas for a few cells and then used "fill down" and "fill right" to get the rest of the sheet. Check his ideas in Parts a–c and explain why each is correct or not.

a. In cell **B1**, he entered "1". Then in cell **C1**, he wrote "=B1+1" and did "fill right" to complete row **1** of the table.

b. In cell **A2**, he entered "1". Then in cell **A3**, he wrote "=A2+1" and did "fill down."

c. In cell **B2**, he wrote "=0.5*$A2*B$1" and then did "fill down" and "fill right."

18 How could the instructions in Connections Task 17 be modified to produce the tables for

a. rectangle area?

b. rectangle perimeter?

19 For each algebraic rule below, use your calculator or computer software to produce a table and then write a rule relating *NOW* and *NEXT* values of the *y* variable.

a. $y = 5x + 2$ **b.** $y = 10x - 3$

c. $y = 2^x$ **d.** $y = 4^x$

LESSON 3 • Tools for Studying Patterns of Change   **63**

b. Doubling the base and doubling the height have the same effect on area of triangles.

c. If both base and height are doubled, the area will be multiplied by 4; if both are tripled, the area will be multiplied by 9. See, for example, in the table 2 × 3 has area 3, but 4 × 6 has area 12.

15 The rectangle table will have entries that are double those of the triangle table. It matters not whether one doubles base or doubles height, the effect on area is the same. Doubling both base and height multiplies area by 4. If both are tripled, the area is multiplied by 9.

16 The perimeter table is given below, for rectangles. Doubling only one dimension does not double perimeter. Doubling both dimensions does double the perimeter.

Polygon Perimeters.xls ⬜ ⬛ ❌

◇	A	B	C	D	E	F	G	H	I	J	
1		1	2	3	4	5	6	7	8	9	
2	1	4	6	8	10	12	14	16	18	20	
3	2	6	8	10	12	14	16	18	20	22	
4	3	8	10	12	14	16	18	20	22	24	
5	4	10	12	14	16	18	20	22	24	26	
6	5	12	14	16	18	20	22	24	26	28	
7	6	14	16	18	20	22	24	26	28	30	
8	7	16	18	20	22	24	26	28	30	32	
9	8	18	20	22	24	26	28	30	32	34	
10	9	20	22	24	26	28	30	32	34	36	
11											

17 a. Correct, because each new cell to the right has an entry one greater than its predecessor to the left.

b. Correct, because each new cell down the **A** column has an entry one greater than its predecessor above.

c. Correct, because you want the entry in any cell to be one-half the product of the entries in the corresponding cells at the top of the column and the left of the row. The dollar signs fix the letter A to make sure one factor comes from column **A** and the number 1 to make sure the other factor comes from row **1**.

18 a. To find area, change cell **B2** instruction to remove the factor of 0.5.

b. To find perimeter, change cell **B2** instruction to "=2*$A2+2*B$1" or, alternatively, "=2*($A2+B$1)."

NOTE The answers to Problem 19 can be found on page T64.

20 A cube is a three-dimensional shape with square faces.

   a. If the length of an edge of a cube is L, write an expression for the area of one of its faces.

   b. Write a rule that gives the total surface area A of a cube as a function of the length L of an edge.

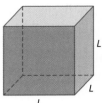

   c. Suppose you wished to design a cube with surface area of 1,000 square centimeters. To the nearest 0.1 centimeter, what should be the length of the edge of the cube?

Reflections

21 If you are asked to write a rule or formula relating variables in a problem, how would you decide:

   a. what the variables are?

   b. which of the variables seems most natural to be considered the independent variable and which the dependent variable?

   c. what symbols should be used as shorthand names for the variables?

   d. whether to express the relationship with "$y = \ldots$" or *NOW-NEXT* form?

22 If you enter the rule $y = 5x + 100$ in your calculator and press the `GRAPH` key, you might at first find no part of the graph on your screen. The plotted points may not appear in your graphing window. Talk with others in your class about strategies for making good window choices. Write down good ideas as a reminder to yourself and as a help to others.

23 Look back at your work for Part c of Connections Task 20.

   a. What technology tool, if any, did you use in answering that question? How did you decide to use that tool?

   b. How could you answer Part c using only the arithmetic capabilities of your calculator?

24 Suppose that you were asked to answer the following questions about a relationship between variables given by $y = 3.4x + 5$. Explain the tool *you* would choose for answering each question—calculation in your head, arithmetic with a calculator, study of a calculator- or computer-produced table of (x, y) values, study of a calculator- or computer-produced graph, or use of a computer algebra system command. Also, explain how you would use the tool.

   a. Do the values of y increase or decrease as values of x increase?

   b. How rapidly do the values of y change as the values of x increase?

   c. What is the value of y when $x = 7.5$?

   d. What is the value of x when $y = 23.8$?

19 **a.**

x	0	1	2	3	4	5	6
y	2	7	12	17	22	27	32

NEXT = NOW + 5, starting at 2

b.

x	0	1	2	3	4	5	6
y	−3	7	17	27	37	47	57

NEXT = NOW + 10, starting at −3

c.

x	0	1	2	3	4	5	6
y	1	2	4	8	16	32	64

NEXT = 2 · *NOW*, starting at 1

d.

x	0	1	2	3	4	5	6
y	1	4	16	64	256	1,024	4,096

NEXT = 4 · *NOW*, starting at 1

20 **a.** L^2

b. $A = 6L^2$

c. $1,000 = 6L^2$, so $L = \sqrt{\dfrac{1,000}{6}} \approx 12.9$ cm.

Students may find the necessary length by looking at a table of $6L^2$ values to find the L value that gives a surface area of 1,000 cm^2.

Reflections

21 **a–d.** Student strategies will vary from student to student, as well as from item to item.

22 Student responses will vary.

23 **a.** Student responses will vary.

b. Enter $\sqrt{(1000/6)}$ into a calculator to answer Part c.

24 **a–d.** Student responses will vary.

Extensions

25 The following sketches show the first four stages in a geometric pattern of rectangular grids made up of unit squares.

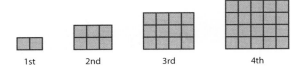

1st   2nd   3rd   4th

    a. Describe geometrically how the grids change from one stage to the next.

    b. What is the perimeter of the 5th rectangle?

    c. What is the perimeter of the nth rectangle?

    d. What is the area of the 5th rectangle?

    e. What is the area of the nth rectangle?

26 Two different civic groups operate concession stands during games at the local minor-league baseball stadium. Group A sells hot dogs and soft drinks. Their profit P_A depends on the number of customers m and is given by $P_A = 3m - 100$. Group B sells ice cream. Their profit P_B depends on the number of customers n and is given by $P_B = 2n - 40$.

    a. What are the break-even numbers of customers for each concession stand?

    b. Is there any number of customers for which both stands make the same profit?

    c. Which stand is likely to make the greater profit when the game draws a small crowd? When the game draws a large crowd?

27 Metro Cab Company charges a base price of $1.50 plus 80¢ per mile. A competitor, Tack See Inc., charges a base price of $2.50 plus 60¢ per mile.

    a. What rules give the charge for a trip with each company as a function of the length of the trip?

    b. If you need to travel 3 miles, which cab company is the least expensive?

    c. If you need to travel 15 miles, which cab company is the least expensive?

    d. For what trip length are the costs the same for the two cab companies?

28 Suppose, as part of an agreement with her father to do some work for him during the summer, Tanya will receive 2¢ for the first day of work, but every day after that her pay will double.

    a. What rule shows how to calculate Tanya's daily pay p on work day n.

    b. What rule using *NOW* and *NEXT* shows how Tanya's pay grows as each additional day of work passes?

Extensions

25
a. The grids increase in size by 1 unit horizontally and 1 unit vertically.

b. 22 units

c. $P = 4n + 2$, where n represents the stage of the pattern and P represents the perimeter of the rectangle.

d. 30 square units

e. $A = n(n + 1)$, where n represents the stage of the pattern and A represents the area of the rectangle.

26
a. Break-even for Group A is 34 customers $\left(\text{actually } \frac{100}{3}\right)$; for Group B it is 20 customers.

b. At 60 customers, both groups make $80 profit.

c. Group B makes greater profit per customer if there are fewer than 60 customers. (If there are 19 or fewer customers, neither group makes a profit, but Group B will not lose as much as Group A.)

   When the game draws a large crowd, Group A will make the greater profit per customer, with more than 60 customers.

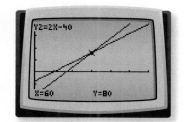

27
a. If d represents distance of the trip and C represents cost of the trip:
Metro Cab: $C_M = 1.50 + 0.80d$
Tack See Inc.: $C_T = 2.50 + 0.60d$

b. For 3 miles, Metro Cab costs less ($3.90 rather than $4.30 with Tack See Inc.).

c. For 15 miles, Tack See Inc. costs less ($11.50 rather than $13.50 with Metro Cab).

d. For 5 miles, both cost $5.50.

28
a. $p = 0.02(2^{n-1})$, where n is the number of days.

b. $NEXT = 2 \cdot NOW$, starting at 0.02

c. If Tanya's pay for a day is $10.24, how many days has she worked?

d. Find Tanya's pay for a day after she has worked 20 days.

e. For how many days will she earn less than $20 per day?

29 One car rental company charges $35 per day, gives 100 free miles per day, and then charges 35¢ per mile for any miles beyond the first 100 miles per day.

a. What rule gives the charge for renting for one day from this company as a function of the number of miles m driven that day?

b. What rule gives the charge for renting from this company as a function of both miles driven m and number of days d?

c. A business person plans a trip of 300 miles that could be made in one day. However, she would arrive home late and is considering keeping the rental car until the next morning. What would you suggest? Explain your reasoning.

30 At the start of a match race for two late-model stock cars, one stalls and has to be pushed to the pits for repairs. The other car roars off at an average speed of 2.5 miles per minute. After 5 minutes of repair work, the second car hits the track and maintains an average speed of 2.8 miles per minute.

a. How far apart in the race are the two cars 5 minutes after the start? How far apart are they 10 minutes after the start?

b. What three rules can be used to calculate the distance traveled by each car and the distance between the two cars at any time after the start of the race?

c. On the same coordinate axes, make graphs displaying the distances traveled by each car as a function of time. Use a horizontal scale that allows you to see the first 60 minutes of the race.

d. On a different set of axes, make another graph showing the distance between the two cars as a function of time since the start of the race.

e. Explain what the patterns of the graphs in Parts c and d show about the progress of the race.

f. Write and solve equations that will answer each of these questions about the race:

  i. How long after the start of the race will it take the first car to travel 75 miles? The second car?

  ii. At what time after the start of the race will the second car catch up to the first car?

c. On the 10th day she earns $10.24.

d. Tanya's pay is $10,485.76 for the 20th day of work.

e. Her pay per day is less than $20 until day 11, when it becomes $20.48.

 29 a. If m represents the number of miles driven that day and c represents the charge for renting that day, then $c = 35 + 0.35(m - 100)$ when $m \geq 100$. When $0 < m < 100$, it is $35.

b. Here m represents the miles driven, d represents the number of days rented, and c represents the total rental charge.
$c = 35d + 0.35(m - 100d)$ when $m \geq 100d$. When $0 < m < 100$, it is $35d$.

c. For a day trip of 300 miles, the rental charge will be $105. For a two-day trip of the same distance, the charge will be the same.

30 a. Five minutes after the start, the cars are 12.5 miles apart. After ten minutes, they are 11 miles apart because the second car is gaining 0.3 miles per minute.

b. The first car distance (in miles) is $d_1 = 2.5t$ and the second car distance is $d_2 = 2.8(t - 5)$, where t represents the number of minutes after the start of the race.

The distance between the two cars is $d_2 - d_1 = 2.8(t - 5) - 2.5t$.

c.

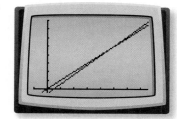 

d. $y = 2.8(x - 5) - 2.5x$

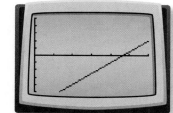 

e. The graphs show that the second car catches up to and passes the first car about 47 minutes into the race. This can be seen by the intersection point in the graph in Part c and the x-intercept in the graph in Part d.

f. i. For d_1: $2.5t = 75$ implies $t = 30$ minutes.

   For d_2: $2.8(t - 5) = 75$ implies $t = 31.8$ minutes.

   ii. Catch-up time: $2.5t = 2.8(t - 5)$ implies $t = 46.7$ minutes.

Review

31 Evaluate each expression if $x = 1$, $y = 3$, $a = -1$, and $b = 2$.

a. $a^2x + b^3y$

b. $a^2(x + by)$

c. $\dfrac{x^3(y + 1)}{by + a^3}$

32 A random sample of 100 students is chosen to survey about lunch preferences.

25 say their first choice is pizza.

30 say their first choice is chicken nuggets.

15 say their first choice is salad bar.

20 say their first choice is tacos.

10 say their first choice is subs.

If the entire school population is 1,500 students, how many students can you predict will have pizza as a first choice?

33 Estimate the measure of each angle. Check your estimates with a protractor.

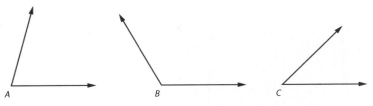

34 The dot plot below indicates the number of students in the 40 first-hour classes at Lincoln High School.

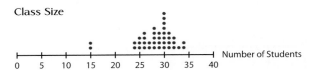

a. What was the smallest class size?

b. What was the largest class size?

c. What percent of the classes had 30 students in them?

d. What percent of the students had fewer than 25 students in them?

Review

31 **a.** 25

b. 7

c. 0.8

32 Twenty-five out of 100 students, or $\frac{1}{4}$ of the sample, prefer pizza. You would predict that $\frac{1}{4} \cdot 1{,}500 = 375$ students would have pizza as their first choice.

33 Student estimates may vary slightly. Actual angle measures are approximately as follows:

$m\angle A = 75°$
$m\angle B = 120°$
$m\angle C = 45°$

Just in Time

34 **a.** 15 students

b. 34 students

c. 20%

d. 10%

35 Consider the triangles drawn below. Assume that angles that look like right angles are right angles and that segments that appear to be the same length are the same length.

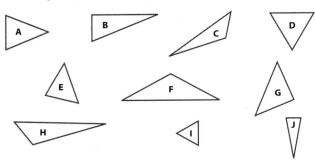

a. Identify all acute triangles.

b. Identify all obtuse triangles.

c. Identify all isosceles triangles.

d. Identify all scalene triangles.

e. Identify all equilateral triangles.

f. Identify all right triangles.

36 The lengths of the sides of a triangle are 4, 5, and 6 inches. These sides are scaled up by multiplying by a factor so that the length of the longest side of the new triangle is 10 inches.

a. What is the scale factor?

b. What are the lengths of the two shorter sides of the new triangle?

35 **a.** A, D, E, I, J

   b. C, F, H

   c. A, D, F, G, I, J

   d. B, C, E, H

   e. D, I

   f. B, G

36 **a.** $\frac{10}{6}$

   b. $4\left(\frac{10}{6}\right) = 6\frac{2}{3}$ inches

   $5\left(\frac{10}{6}\right) = 8\frac{1}{3}$ inches

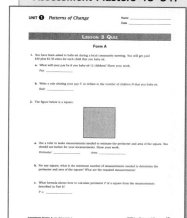
Unit 1

LESSON
4

Looking Back

In your work on problems and explorations of this unit, you studied many different patterns of change in variables. In some cases, the aim was to describe and predict patterns of change in a dependent variable that are caused by change in values of an independent variable. In other cases, the goal was to describe and predict patterns of change in values of a single variable with the passage of time. For example:

> *For each weight attached to a bungee cord, there was a predicted stretched length for the cord.*

> *For each year after the census in 2001, there was a predicted population of Alaskan bowhead whales.*

For each possible price for a bungee jump at Five Star Amusement Park, there was a predicted daily income from the attraction.

In mathematics, relations like these—where each possible value of one variable is associated with exactly one value of another variable—are called **functions**. The use of the word "function" comes from the common English phrase that appears in statements like "cord stretch *is a function of* attached weight" or "average speed for the Iditarod Sled Race *is a function of* time to complete the race."

Many functions of interest to mathematicians have no particular cause-and-effect or change-over-time story attached. The only condition required for a relationship to be called a function is that each possible value of the independent variable is paired with one value of the dependent variable.

As a result of your work on Lessons 1–3, you should be better able to:

- recognize situations in which variables are related in predictable ways,
- use data tables and graphs to display patterns in those relationships,
- use symbolic rules to describe and reason about functions, and
- use spreadsheets, computer algebra systems, and graphing calculators to answer questions about functions.

The tasks in this final lesson of the *Patterns of Change* unit will help you review, pull together, and apply your new knowledge as you work to solve several new problems.

LESSON 4 • Looking Back **69**

Looking Back

This lesson includes tasks intended to provide review and practice of key ideas developed throughout the unit. Summary questions are designed to stimulate student articulation of the key principles and techniques.

Five Star Swimming In addition to bungee jumping and rides like roller coasters and a Ferris wheel, Five Star Amusement Park has a large lake with a swimming beach and picnic tables.

Every spring when the park is preparing to open, lifeguards at the beach put out a rope with buoys outlining the swimming space in the lake. They have 1,000 feet of rope, and they generally outline a rectangular swimming space like that shown below.

When working on this task one year, the lifeguards wondered whether there was a way to choose dimensions of the rectangular swimming space that would provide maximum area for swimmers.

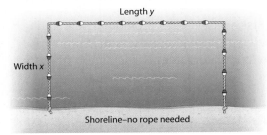

Shoreline–no rope needed

a. Complete entries in a table like this, showing how dimensions of the swimming space are related to each other. Then write a rule giving y as a function of x.

Width x (in feet)	50	100	150	200	250	300	350	400	450
Length y (in feet)									

b. One of the lifeguards claimed that the rule in Part a can be used to write another rule that shows how area A of the swimming space depends on choice of the width x. She said that $A = x(1,000 - 2x)$ would do the job. Is she right? How do you think she arrived at this area rule?

c. Use the area function in Part b and strategies you have for reasoning about such relationships to answer the following questions. To show what you've learned about using different tools for studying functions:

- Answer one question by producing and scanning entries in a table of values for the area function.

- Answer another question by producing and tracing coordinates of points on a graph of the function.

- Then answer another question using a computer algebra system equation solver.

When you report your results, explain your strategies as well.

i. What dimensions of the swimming space will give maximum area? What is that area?

ii. What dimensions will give a swimming area of 100,000 square feet?

iii. What dimensions will give a swimming area of 50,000 square feet?

INSTRUCTIONAL NOTE Students have been calculating areas of rectangles since early in middle school, so they will generally be quite comfortable with the basic $A = bh$ formula. What will not be so comfortable is thinking about how a fixed perimeter can be associated with rectangles of wildly different area. There seems to be a natural instinct to believe that once the perimeter of a rectangle is known, the area must be determined as well.

Since the goal of this Looking Back task is to focus on properties of a simple quadratic function, we would not want students to be stalled by inability to recognize that varying x directly affects variation in y and in the area of the swimming region. You might want to launch this investigation by a physical demonstration of the situation. This could be done using a rope made into a loop. Four students could hold the fixed perimeter corners of various rectangles. Areas could be compared visually. Be prepared to monitor student work to be sure they realize this critical aspect of the task.

   a.

Width (in feet) x	50	100	150	200	250	300	350	400	450
Length (in feet) y	900	800	700	600	500	400	300	200	100

Rule: $y = 1{,}000 - 2x$

b. She is correct. The area of a rectangle is the product of its length and width. In this case, $A = xy$. However, in Part a it was established that $y = 1{,}000 - 2x$. Therefore, by substitution, $A = x(1{,}000 - 2x)$.

c. **i.** The maximum area of 125,000 square feet can be made using a length of 500 feet and a width of 250 feet. This can be found by scanning tables or graphs of the area function $A = x(1{,}000 - 2x)$.

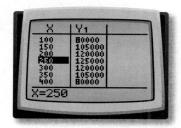   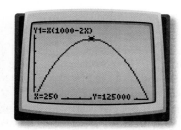

ii. The areas can be found by scanning tables or graphs of the area function or by solving $100{,}000 = x(1{,}000 - 2x)$.

Width (in feet)	Length (in feet)	Area (in ft²)
361.8	276.4	100,000
138.2	723.6	100,000

iii.

Width (in feet)	Length (in feet)	Area (in ft²)
443.65	112.7	50,000
56.35	887.3	50,000

2 **Borrowing to Expand** When the Five Star Amusement Park owners decided to expand park attractions by adding a new giant roller coaster, they borrowed $600,000 from a local bank. Terms of the bank loan said that each month interest of 0.5% would be added to the outstanding balance, and the park would have to make monthly payments of $10,000. For example, at the end of the first month of the loan period, the park would owe $600,000 + 0.005(600,000) - 10,000 = \$593,000$.

  a. Make a table showing what the park owes the bank at the end of each of the first 12 months.

  b. Write a *NOW-NEXT* rule that shows how the loan balance changes from one month to the next.

  c. Use a calculator or spreadsheet strategy to find out how long it will take to pay off the loan.

  d. Plot a graph showing the amount owed on the loan at the end of months 0, 6, 12, 18, … until it is paid off. Describe the pattern of change in loan balance over that time.

3 **Setting the Price** Because Five Star managers expected the new roller coaster to be a big attraction, they planned to set a high price for riders. They were unsure about just what that price should be. They decided to do some market research to get data about the relationship between *price per ride* and *number of riders* that would be expected each day.

  a. Complete a table that shows how you believe the *number of riders* will depend on the *price per ride*. Explain the pattern of entries you make and your reasons for choosing that pattern.

Price per Ride (in dollars)	0	5	10	15	20	25	30	35
Number of Riders								

  b. Add a third row to the table in Part a to give the predicted *income* from the new roller coaster for each possible *price per ride*. Then plot the (*price per ride, income*) data and describe the pattern of change relating those variables.

  c. Estimate the price per ride that will give maximum daily income.

  d. What factors other than price are likely to affect daily income from the roller coaster ride? How do you think each factor will affect income?

2 It would be efficient to use a spreadsheet for this task.

a.

Month	Amount Owed	Month	Amount Owed
1	$593,000.00	10	$528,403.82
2	$585,965.00	12	$513,651.06
4	$571,789.30	⋮	⋮
6	$557,471.49	71	$5,112.45
8	$543,010.14		

b. $NEXT = NOW + 0.005 \cdot NOW - 10{,}000$ or
$NEXT = 1.005 \cdot NOW - 10{,}000$, both starting at $600,000.

c. One final payment of only $5,112.45 at the end of month 71 should pay off the loan.

d. A plot of the loan balance amounts at the end of six-month periods will show a rather steady decline in the outstanding balance, with some acceleration near the end of the loan period.

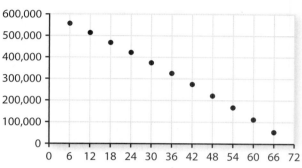

3 Responses to Part a will determine the remaining results. The sample responses below are used to answer the other questions.

a.

Price per Ride (in dollars)	0	5	10	15	20	25	30	35
Number of Riders	500	430	360	290	220	150	80	10

The pattern shows a decrease in the number of riders at a constant rate—about 70 for every $5 increase in price per ride. It seemed logical to conclude that the higher the price, the fewer the number of riders. (Some students may argue that to a certain extent, a higher price may attract riders because they think an expensive ride must be worth the price.)

b.

Price per Ride (in dollars)	0	5	10	15	20	25	30	35
Number of Riders	500	430	360	290	220	150	80	10
Income (in dollars)	0	2,150	3,600	4,350	4,400	3,750	2,400	350

The income seems to rise at a decreasing rate to a certain point and then decrease at an increasing rate. It appears to be a similar shape as the $y = -x^2 + b$ family of graphs studied earlier.

c. Maximum income seems to occur at a price per ride of about $15–$20.

d. Other factors affecting daily income may include weather, advertising of the attraction, and other marketing issues. One important factor will be whether or not people are enjoying the ride. If people are enjoying the ride, others will want to take part in the fun, sometimes regardless of the price. The opposite can happen, as well; if people are not enjoying the ride, then others will not want to attempt it, even though it may be inexpensive to participate.

Unit 1

(4) Without using a graphing calculator or doing any calculation of (x, y) values, match each of the following functions with the graph that best represents it.

a. $y = -0.5x - 4$ **b.** $y = x^2 - 4$ **c.** $y = \dfrac{4}{x}$ **d.** $y = (1.5^x)$

I
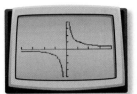

II
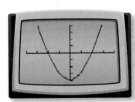

III
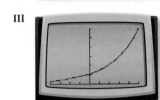

IV
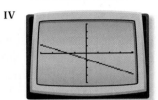

Summarize
the Mathematics

When two variables change in relation to each other, the pattern of change often fits one of several common forms. These patterns can be recognized in tables and graphs of (x, y) data, in the rules that show how to calculate values of one variable from given values of the other, and in the conditions of problem situations.

a Sketch at least four graphs showing different patterns relating change in two variables or change in one variable over time. For each graph, write a brief explanation of the pattern shown in the graph and describe a problem situation that involves the pattern.

b Suppose that you develop or discover a rule that shows how a variable y is a function of another variable x. Describe the different strategies you could use to:

i. Find the value of y associated with a specific given value of x.

ii. Find the value of x that gives a specific target value of y.

iii. Describe the way that the value of y changes as the value of x increases or decreases.

iv. Find values of x that give maximum or minimum values of y.

Be prepared to share your ideas and reasoning with the class.

✓ Check Your Understanding

Write, in outline form, a summary of the important mathematical concepts and methods developed in this unit. Organize your summary so that it can be used as a quick reference in future units and courses.

4 **a.** Graph IV

    b. Graph II

    c. Graph I

    d. Graph III

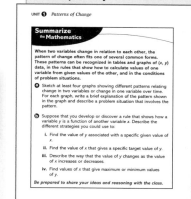
Summarize
the Mathematics

Student responses will vary, but it is important that key mathematical concepts are discussed and recorded by each student. The following is one possible set of responses.

a   Here are some of the patterns encountered in the unit, with typical graph shapes and stories of the sort that led to those graph patterns.

  i. This graph increases at a constant rate. Joe receives a $10 per month base allowance plus $0.50 for every chore he does. So, his total monthly allowance is a function of, or depends on, the number of chores he does.

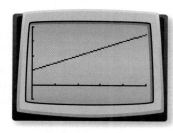

  ii. This graph increases at an increasing rate. A stockbroker, Chris, has found a system that doubles a $2,000 investment every year. The graph shows the dollar value of that investment as a function of the number of years since the initial investment.

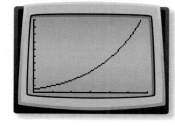

  iii. This graph decreases at a decreasing rate. The amount of time it takes to finish the Kingsbury 500 Scooter Race depends on the racer's speed.

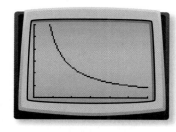

  iv. This graph increases at a decreasing rate, reaches a maximum value and then decreases indefinitely at an increasing rate. The graph could represent the income in dollars from the sales of notebooks in a school store as a function of the price charged per notebook.

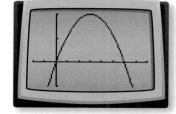

i. Substitute the given x value in the rule and evaluate it. The result will be the y value. One could also go to a table of values and find the y value that corresponds with the given x value. One could also trace a graph of the function to the point where the specified x value is the approximate coordinate for a point with the y value you are looking for. In a computer algebra system, the evaluation of an expression for given value of the variables involved will look something like this: **$(3x\char`\^2-5x)|x=2$.**

ii. You could substitute the y value and solve the resulting equation for x. A table of values could also be used by finding the given y value in the table and viewing the corresponding x value(s). A similar strategy could be used in tracing a graph, looking for points with y-coordinates of interest and reading off the corresponding x-coordinate.

Using a computer algebra system, the required equation can be solved by entering instructions like this: **solve $(3x\char`\^2-5x=8,x)$.**

iii. One could view a graph of the rule and decide whether the rate of change is constant. It is also important to note whether the graph is increasing or decreasing on certain intervals. Lastly, it might be possible to tell whether the rates of change themselves are increasing or decreasing. This may be evident on the graph if the graph is increasing or decreasing more quickly as you move out from the y-axis. Similar information can be obtained by scanning the pattern of x and y values in a table of values for the function.

iv. One could use the "trace" or "maximum" tools on a graphing calculator. A detailed table of values might also be used to decide which x values give the largest y value(s).

✓Check Your Understanding

You may wish to have students use the Teaching Master, *Patterns of Change* Unit Summary, to help them organize the information. Above all, this should be something that is useful to the individual student.

Practicing for Standardized Tests

Each Practicing for Standardized Tests teaching master presents ten questions that draw on all content strands. The questions are presented in the form of test items similar to those that often appear in standardized tests such as state assessment tests, the Preliminary Scholastic Aptitude Test (PSAT), or the ACT PLAN. We suggest using these practice sets following the unit assessment so students can become familiar with the formats of standardized tests and develop effective test-taking strategies for performing well on such tests. Answers are provided below.

Answers to Practice Set 1

1. (a)   **2.** (b)   **3.** (d)   **4.** (c)   **5.** (b)
6. (d)   **7.** (b)   **8.** (d)   **9.** (c)   **10.** (e)

Teaching Resources

Student Masters 53–54.

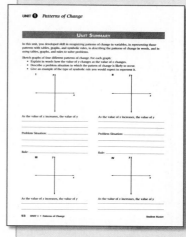

Student Masters 73–74.

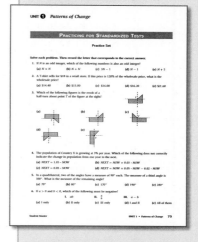

Assessment Masters 55–72.

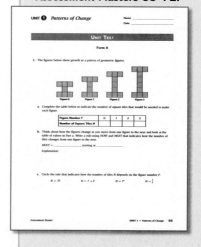

UNIT 2

PATTERNS IN DATA

In this unit of *Core-Plus Mathematics*, you will explore principles and techniques for organizing and summarizing data. Whether the data are the results of a science experiment, from a test of a new medical procedure, from a political poll, or from a survey of what consumers prefer, the basic principles and techniques of analyzing data are much the same: make a plot of the data; describe its shape, center, and spread with numbers and words; and interpret your results in the context of the situation. If you have more than one distribution, compare them.

Key ideas of data analysis will be developed through your work in two lessons.

Lessons

1 Exploring Distributions

Plot single-variable data using dot plots, histograms, and relative frequency histograms. Describe the shape and center of distributions.

2 Measuring Variability

Calculate and interpret percentiles, quartiles, deviations from the mean, and standard deviation. Calculate and interpret the five-number summary and interquartile range and construct and interpret box plots. Predict the effect of linear transformations on the shape, center, and spread of a distribution.

PATTERNS IN DATA

Unit Overview

Patterns in Data is an introduction to the analysis of univariate (one variable) data. In Unit 3, students will learn some basics of handling bivariate (two variables) data: first, plot the data on a scatterplot and, if there is a linear pattern, summarize by fitting a regression line. Throughout this unit, students will be developing tools and strategies that will help them make sense of data and communicate their conclusions. The focus will be on displaying data (to observe shape, center, and variability/spread) and then computing and interpreting summary statistics such as measures of center (mean, median, and mode) and measures of variability (range, interquartile range, and standard deviation).

Data analysis has been called the art of letting the data speak for themselves. This means that there is an emphasis on constructing graphical displays (plots) of the data that reveal the shape of the distribution and any patterns that might not be visible in a numerical listing or from summary statistics. Useful graphical displays included in this unit are dot plots, stemplots, histograms, and box plots. (Stemplots are examined in Extensions Tasks 19 and 20 of Lesson 1.)

Data Analysis and Graphical Displays When doing data analysis, summary statistics are computed after examination of the graphical displays. The graphical display may help determine which summary statistics are most appropriate. For example, the graphical display may reveal an outlier that will have a great effect on the mean, but not on the median. This forces the data analyst to reconsider why he or she needs a measure of center and whether the mean or the median will be most useful.

Becoming a good data analyst takes practice on sets of data that are interesting and important to the analyst. Data analysis should not be done without any knowledge of the situation from which the data came. It isn't just a matter of making a plot or computing a mean. It is largely a matter of interpreting the plots and summary statistics and asking the right questions. Why is there a gap there? Why is the mean so much larger for these countries than for others? To ask and answer such questions means that the analyst must have some knowledge of the situation that goes beyond the numbers collected. In this course, developers have tried to provide data for situations about which students care and have some knowledge.

The major themes of univariate data analysis are summarized below.

I. *First, plot the data.* Plots to use include a dot plot (easiest to make by hand), box plot (for comparing several distributions when there are many values), histogram (when there are many values), and stemplot (for a single distribution when there are few values or for comparing two distributions).

II. *Summarize the distribution using shape, center, and spread.* The basic shapes are approximately normal, skewed right, skewed left, rectangular (rare in the wild), and bimodal. If a distribution is bimodal, examine it to see if it is the result of the mixture of two populations (see Reflections Task 15 of Lesson 1).

Typically, use the median and quartiles (or interquartile range) to measure center and spread in a skewed distribution. The median is the value that divides the area of the histogram in half. In any distribution, the first and third quartiles enclose the middle one-half of the values.

For approximately normal distributions, typically use the mean and standard deviation to measure center and spread. The mean is the balance point of the histogram. In a normal distribution, one standard deviation either side of the mean encloses the middle two-thirds of the values.

III. *If helpful, transform the data.* (Students will learn to perform log transformations in Course 3.) Sliding the distribution by adding the same constant d to each value doesn't change the shape, adds d to the measures of center, and doesn't change the spread.

Stretching the distribution by multiplying each value by the same positive constant c doesn't change the shape, changes the measures of center by a factor of c, and changes the measures of spread by a factor of c.

IV. *Identify potential outliers using the 1.5 • IQR rule.* Examine outliers to determine if they are a mistake or are fundamentally different from the other cases. If so, remove them from the analysis. If not, either use summary statistics that are resistant to outliers or do the analysis with and without them and report both analyses. If the distribution is skewed, the "outliers" simply may be the tail of the distribution (and a log transformation may be appropriate).

Unit Objectives

- Use various graphical displays of data to reveal important patterns in a data set and interpret those patterns in the context of the data
- Compute measures of center and variability for sets of data and interpret the meaning of those statistics
- Transform distributions by adding a constant or by multiplying by a positive constant and recognize how those transformations affect the shape, center, and spread of distributions

Access and Equity Matters

Research by Jo Boaler (Boaler, J. 1998, 2000, 2002) and by the Quasar Project (Brown, C. A., Stein, M. K. and Favar, E. A., 1996) have identified particular teaching practices with curricula such as Core-Plus Mathematics that promote greater access and equity in mathematics classrooms. These practices include:

- introducing activities through discussion,
- teaching students to explain and justify, and
- making real-world contexts accessible.

Additional information on access and equity and research sources is in the front matter of this text on page xvi.

The *Core-Plus Mathematics* curriculum offers many opportunities for teachers to incorporate these practices into daily routines. The Think About This Situation is one built-in opportunity to introduce investigations through discussion. You may wish to begin investigations in a similar way. Since much of the mathematical content is based in real-world contexts, it is important that all students understand the contexts and draw on their own or a classmate's background knowledge when possible.

Built into all curriculum features are opportunities for students to explain and justify their thinking. Look for opportunities to encourage the habit of mind of justifying their thinking, individually and in small group or class discussions.

Technology Tools

CPMP-Tools is a suite of Java-based mathematical software, specifically designed to support student learning and problem solving in each *Core-Plus Mathematics* course. The *CPMP-Tools* software includes four families of programs: algebra (spreadsheet and CAS), geometry, statistics, and discrete mathematics. Each content area includes a general purpose tool and specific custom tools for use in investigations and/or homework. Additional information about the course-specific software for Course 1 is included in the front matter of this book on page xix.

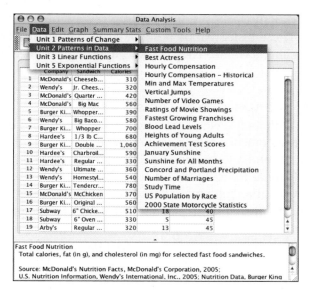

In Course 1, the use of general tool software is limited. General tools and custom tools are offered as an opportunity to integrate technology into the investigations and provide technology tools for student use outside the classroom. As students progress to other courses, the use of the general tools will be increased.

Relevant to this unit are the general data analysis software and the custom tools "Estimating Center" and "Estimating Center and Spread." Many data sets are included in *CPMP-Tools* to allow flexibility for homework tasks and accommodations and extensions for some students. Suggestions to integrate this technology are included in the student text and teaching notes at point of use.

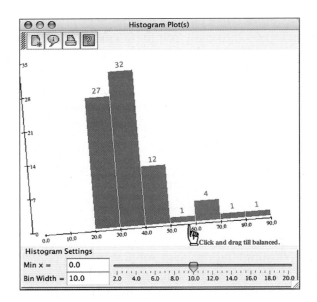

Review and Practice

One of the features of the Core-Plus Mathematics curriculum is the inclusion of review tasks in the homework sets. The purpose of the review tasks is two-fold. Most tasks are meant as **distributed practice** of mathematical skills to maintain procedural fluency. Some tasks are **just-in-time review** of skills needed in the following lesson. These tasks will be designated by a clock icon near the task solution in the Teacher's Guide. These tasks should be assigned as outside of class work.

Practicing for Standardized Tests

Opportunities for additional review and practice are provided in eight Preparing for Standardized Tests practice sets. Each Practicing for Standardized Tests master presents 10 questions and a test-taking tip. The questions are presented in the form of test items similar to how they often appear in standardized tests such as state assessment tests, the Preliminary Scholastic Aptitude Test (PSAT), or the ACT PLAN. We suggest using these practice sets following the unit assessment so students can become familiar with the formats of standardized tests and develop effective test-taking strategies for performing well on such tests.

Promoting Mathematical Discourse

Periodically, you will find sample class discussions for selected Think About This Situation (TATS) and Summarize the Mathematics (STM) in the Teacher's Resources. These sample dialogues may provide some ideas for your class discussions. In this unit, *Promoting Mathematical Discourse* scenarios are written for the TATS on page 75 and the STM on page 122.

Lesson Objectives	On Your Own Assignments*	Suggested Pacing	Materials
Lesson 1 *Exploring Distributions* • Construct dot plots, histograms, and relative frequency histograms • Describe the shape of a distribution • Compute and interpret the mean, median, and mode (from a list of values and from a frequency table) • Estimate the mean and median from a histogram • Use the relationship between the mean, total, and number of values to find a missing value given the mean and the other values	**After Investigation 1:** A1 or A2, A3, C8, R14, R15, Rv26, Rv30 **After Investigation 2:** A4 or A5, A6 or A7, C9–C13, R17, E19, choice of one other Extensions task, Rv31, Rv32	7 days (including assessments)	• Rulers with inch scale • *CPMP-Tools* custom tool, "Estimating Center" • *Optional:* Yardstick, set of identical weights such as small cubes or plastic interlocking blocks • Teaching Resources • Assessment Resources
Lesson 2 *Variability* • Find and interpret percentiles and quartiles as measures of the position of a value in a distribution • Find the five-number summary and the interquartile range (IQR) and interpret the IQR as a measure of variability • Determine if a value is an outlier • Construct and interpret a box plot • Compute and interpret deviations from the mean • Compute or estimate and interpret the standard deviation as a measure of spread • Predict the effect on the shape, center, and spread of a distribution when the same number is added to each value or when each value is multiplied by the same number	**After Investigation 1:** A1, A2, E23, E24, Rv29, Rv30 **After Investigation 2:** A3, A4, C12, R16, R17, Rv31, Rv32 **After Investigation 3:** A5, R18–R20, E25, Rv33, Rv34 **After Investigation 4:** Choose two of A6–A8, C13, C14, R23, E26, E27 or E28, Rv35, Rv36 **After Investigation 5:** A9, A10, C15, R21, R22, Rv37, Rv38	11 days (including assessments)	• Watch with a second hand or stopwatch • *CPMP-Tools* custom tool, "Estimating Center and Spread" • Rulers with millimeter scale • Teaching Resources • Assessment Resources
Lesson 3 *Looking Back* • Review and synthesize the major objectives of the unit		2 days (including assessments)	• Teaching Resources • Assessment Resources

* When choice is indicated, it is important to leave the choice to the student.

Note: *It is best if Connections tasks are discussed as a whole class after they have been assigned as homework.*

Exploring Distributions

The statistical approach to problem solving includes refining the question you want to answer, designing a study, collecting the data, analyzing the data collected, and reporting your conclusions in the context of the original question. For example, consider the problem described below.

A Core-Plus Mathematics teacher in Traverse City, Michigan, was interested in whether eye-hand coordination is better when students use their dominant hand than when they use their nondominant hand. She refined this problem to the specific question of whether students can stack more pennies when they use their dominant hand than when they use their nondominant hand. In her first-hour class, she posed the question:

How many pennies can you stack using your dominant hand?

In her second-hour class, she posed this question:

How many pennies can you stack using your nondominant hand?

Exploring Distributions

In this lesson, students will learn how to use various graphical displays to uncover important patterns in a set of data and will practice interpreting these patterns in the context of the situation. They will review measures of center (mean and median) of a distribution and explore some of their properties. The *CPMP-Tools* custom tool "Estimating Center" can be used to help students understand and develop their skill at estimating the mean from a histogram. Data sets included from this lesson are Fast Food Nutrition (page 82), Best Actress (page 85), Hourly Compensation (page 90), Hourly Compensation-Historical (includes extra information), Minimum and Maximum Temperatures (page 91), Vertical Jumps (page 92), Number of Video Games (page 92), Ratings of Movie Showings (page 92), and Fastest Growing Franchises (page 99).

In Lesson 2, students will learn about the various summary statistics used to describe the spread of the data.

Lesson Objectives

- Construct dot plots, histograms, and relative frequency histograms
- Describe the shape of a distribution
- Compute and interpret the mean and median (from a list of values and from a frequency table)
- Estimate the mean and median from a histogram
- Use the relationship between the mean, total, and number of values to find a missing value when given the mean and the other values

Lesson Launch

For Part c of the TATS, you may want to make a living histogram. Write a scale on the ground in chalk or make individual cards that give appropriate intervals for the number of pennies stacked. The first card might say 0–4 pennies, the next 5–9 pennies, and so on. Have the students line up behind the appropriate card. Be sure to have your camera ready. Another option is to have *CPMP-Tools*, data analysis software available on a class computer for students to enter their own numbers of pennies stacked. Histograms can be displayed and compared to results from other classes when they complete the penny-stacking task.

A sample TATS dialogue is included on pages T75A and T75B.

PROMOTING MATHEMATICAL DISCOURSE Periodically when this icon appears you will find a sample discussion offering possible teacher-student discourse around Think About This Situation and Summarize the Mathematics questions at point of use.

In both classes, students were told: "You can touch pennies only with the one hand you are using; you have to place each penny on the stack without touching others; and once you let go of a penny, it cannot be moved. Your score is the number of pennies you had stacked before a penny falls."

Students in each class counted the number of pennies they stacked and prepared a plot of their data. The plot from the first-hour class is shown below. A value on the line between two bars (such as stacking 24 pennies) goes into the bar on the right.

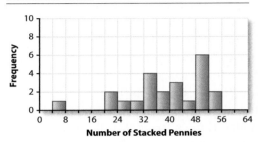

Dominant Hand

Think About This Situation

Examine the distribution of the number of pennies stacked by students in the first-hour class using their dominant hand.

a How many students were in the first-hour class? What percentage of the students stacked 40 or more pennies using their dominant hand?

b What do you think the plot for the second-hour class might look like?

c Check your conjecture in Part b by having your class stack pennies using your nondominant hands. Make a plot of the numbers stacked by your class using the same scale as that for the dominant hand plot above.

d Compare the shape, center, and spread of the plot from your class with the plot of the first-hour class on the previous page. What conclusions, if any, can you draw?

e Why might comparing the results of first- and second-hour students not give a good answer to this teacher's question? Can you suggest a better design for her study?

In this lesson, you will learn how to make and interpret graphical displays of data so they can help you make decisions involving data.

The data for dominant hand stacking displayed in the histogram is:

6, 21, 22, 25, 30, 33, 33, 34, 38, 39, 41,
42, 42, 46, 48, 49, 50, 50, 51, 51, 55, 55

By entering the data into the *CPMP-Tools* data analysis software, your students can easily compare the numbers of pennies they stacked using their non-dominant hand with the numbers stacked by the Traverse City students using their dominant hand.

Think About This Situation

a) There were 23 students in the first-hour class. Twelve of 23 students, or about 52% of the students, stacked 40 or more pennies.

b) A reasonable conjecture is that the plot may look about the same in shape and spread but be centered at a smaller number of pennies.

c) Each student should do the penny stacking using his or her nondominant hand. Collect the number of pennies stacked from each student and make a plot.

d) If students don't compare the distributions using ideas of shape, measures of center such as mean or median, and measures of spread such as range or interquartile range, inquire about these ideas to determine what students know from middle school math.

e) The first-hour and second-hour students may not be in the same grade or may be different in other ways. For example, if older students were in the second-hour class, there might not be any difference in the two distributions. (Older students may be just as good with their nondominant hand as the younger students are with their dominant hand.)

   Commonly, such studies are done using *paired comparisons:* have each student stack pennies twice, using one hand and then the other, and compute the difference *dominant hand – nondominant hand*. Because people get better with practice, half of the students should use their dominant hand first and their nondominant hand second and the other half should do the opposite. Which students use their dominant hand first should be decided in a random way.

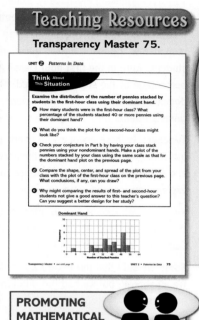

Teaching Resources

Transparency Master 75.

PROMOTING MATHEMATICAL DISCOURSE

Unit 2

INSTRUCTIONAL NOTE
Retain your nondominant hand data for Investigation 2.

ELL TIP To aid English Language Learners in performing the penny-stacking task, consider the underlying actions that the students will need to do. For this TATS, demonstrate the following words as you launch the lesson: *stack, touch, place, move, fall.*

Promoting Mathematical Discourse

Think About This Situation, *page 75*

Teacher: Thinking individually, examine the distribution of the number of pennies stacked by students in the first-hour class using their dominant hand. Then, on a scrap piece of paper, jot down your response to the following two questions. Question one, how many students were in the first hour class? And question two, what percentage of the students stacked 40 or more pennies using their dominant hand? *(The teacher repeats the two questions and gives students time to consider and record their responses.)*

Teacher: Is there anyone who needs more time? *(No one indicates that they do.)* Okay, then compare with others around you and reach consensus on a response to both questions. Be ready to explain your agreed upon answers.

Teacher: Who would like to offer an answer to the first question? *(Several students raise their hands. The teacher selects one.)* Sam, what did your group decide?

Sam: We said that there were 23 students in the first-hour class. We all agreed, but we had two different ways that we got our answers.

Teacher: Tell us more about that Sam.

Sam: Well, Julie counted by ones and Jodi used the frequency numbers to count.

Teacher: Julie, can you tell us more about what Sam means when he says you counted by ones?

Julie: You can see that the frequency goes by twos; so a column that is half of one unit high will represent pennies stacked by one person. So, I counted one for the stack that was between 4 and 8 pennies high, then two for the stack that was between 20 and 24 pennies high and just kept going like that. So, I went one, then two, three, then four, then five, then six, seven, eight, nine, then ten, eleven, then twelve, thirteen, fourteen, then fifteen, then sixteen, seventeen, eighteen, nineteen, twenty, and twenty-one, then twenty-two, twenty-three. So, I get 23 students in the class.

Teacher: How many of you used Julie's strategy to determine the number of students in the first-hour class? *(The teacher notices that eight students also thought about the question as Julie did.)*

Teacher: Jodi, how did you think about this question?

Jodi: I just added up the frequencies. So, I did one plus two plus one plus one plus four plus two plus three plus one plus six plus two. I got 23.

Teacher: Did anyone use a strategy different than the ones used by Julie or Jodi? (No other strategies are offered.) What about the second question? What percentage of the students stacked 40 or more pennies using their dominant hand? Sierra, how did your group think about this question?

Sierra: Well, we did what Jodi did. We added the frequencies of the columns where more than 40 pennies were stacked. So, we had three plus one plus six plus two or 12 students.

Pedro: Then we just found the percent by taking 12 and dividing by 23. We got about 52%.

Teacher: What do the rest of you think? Did you have the same solution, and did you think about the percentage in the same way?

Jaclyn: We also said that there were twelve students who stacked 40 or more pennies but we just called that a little more than 50%, since 12 is a little more than half of 23.

Teacher: Are there other ideas anyone would like to share? *(None are offered.)*

Teacher: The teacher in Traverse City asked her second-hour class to stack pennies using their nondominant hand. I would like you to think individually again. How might the plot for the second-hour class look? *(The teacher gives students time to think individually.)*

Teacher: Page, what do you think?

Page: Um, I think that the second hour class will not be able to stack as many pennies with their nondominant hand so maybe the highest stack will only be about 40 pennies.

Hachi: I agree with Page. I also think that there will be more students at the low end. Like, maybe, six students who only stack between 4 and 8 pennies.

Danika: Maybe the plot will be reversed.

Teacher: Can you tell us more about what you mean by "reversed"?

Danika: I just mean that the taller bars in the plot will be at the start and the short bars will be at the end. It is like Hachi is saying—more students will be at the low end.

Sani: Someone might be really good at stacking pennies with both hands so there might be one or two people at the high end, say maybe 50 or 52 pennies.

Teacher: Any other ideas?

Vern: I'm not sure it will be much different than the dominant hand plot. Some people had high stacks and some had low stacks. I don't see why that would be any different.

Teacher: Well, let's test our conjectures by stacking pennies with our nondominant hands. Then we can add these results to the results from other classes that I have saved.

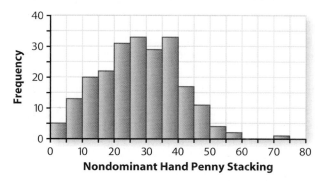

Teacher: Let's compare the shape, center, and spread of our class plot with the plot of the Traverse City teacher's first-hour class on page 2. What can you say about the shapes of the two plots.

Trina: Our shape is more symmetric. We have some small stacks of pennies and a few tall stacks of pennies but lots of middle-sized stacks of pennies.

Teacher: What can we say about the centers of the two distributions?

Juan: The middle of our data seems to be around 30. The middle of the data in the book seems to be around 36.

Teacher: Juan, describe what you are thinking when you say "middle of the data."

Juan: Half of the values are above 30 and half are below. Kinda like the average number of pennies stacked. (The teacher recognizes that Juan is talking about two different measures of center. She makes a mental note of this prior knowledge but is aware that Investigation 2 will help students be more clear about when and how to use different measures of center.)

Teacher: Does anyone recall mathematical terms you may have used in middle school to describe centers?

Rachael: We used some "m" words: "mean" was one of them. I can't remember the other ones.

Teacher: That is okay. We will be reviewing and extending your formal understanding of "centers" of sets of numbers in the second investigation of this lesson. What can we say about the spread of the two distributions?

Marlo: Our data has a greater spread than the data from the class in the book. Our class had stacks of pennies as short as 3 and as tall as 61. The other class had stacks maybe as high as 56 and as low as 4.

Teacher: Why might comparing the results of first- and second-hour students not give a good answer to the teacher's question? Is there anything else you might suggest as a better design for her study?

Sam: There are different students in the classes. If she wants to know if students can stack more pennies with their dominant hand than with their nondominant hand, then she should use the same students. Can we try with our dominant hand now?

Teacher: We do not want to take any additional class time for this task, but you are welcome to try it at home to compare your own results with both hands. Maybe you could report back to us tomorrow.

Investigation 1 — Shapes of Distributions

Every day, people are bombarded by data on television, on the Internet, in newspapers, and in magazines. For example, states release report cards for schools and statistics on crime and unemployment, and sports writers report batting averages and shooting percentages. Making sense of data is important in everyday life and in most professions today. Often a first step to understanding data is to analyze a plot of the data. As you work on the problems in this investigation, look for answers to this question:

How can you produce and interpret plots of data and use those plots to compare distributions?

1 As part of an effort to study the wild black bear population in Minnesota, Department of Natural Resources staff anesthetized and then measured the lengths of 143 black bears. (The length of a bear is measured from the tip of its nose to the tip of its tail.) The following **dot plots** (or *number line plots*) show the distributions of the lengths of the male and the female bears.

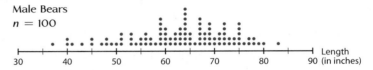

Source: Minitab Statistical Software Data Set

a. Compare the shapes of the two distributions. When asked to *compare*, you should discuss the similarities and differences between the two distributions, not just describe each one separately.

  i. Are the shapes of the two distributions fundamentally alike or fundamentally different?

  ii. How would you describe the shapes?

b. Are there any lengths that fall outside the overall pattern of either distribution?

c. Compare the centers of the two distributions.

d. Compare the spreads of the two distributions.

2 When describing a distribution, it is important to include information about its *shape*, its *center*, and its *spread*.

In this investigation, students will learn to describe the shape of a distribution as approximately normal, symmetric, or skewed to the right or left. They will interpret dot plots and histograms and estimate centers of distributions. Relative frequency histograms are introduced. Instead of a count of frequency of values on the vertical axis, they have a proportion or percentage of values.

If your students already know how to use their calculators to make a histogram, you can skip Problems 7 and 8. Problem 8 is optional in any case.

You might ask students to bring to class any histograms (or other plots) that they find in the media. Often it is instructive to ask students to redraw plots from the media so they are more understandable.

COMMUNICATION SKILL Thoughtful listening to group members in order to provide input or ask questions to make discussion deeper

 1

a. i–ii. The shapes are fundamentally alike, with most of the data clustered in a mound, but with a long tail towards the smaller values. (This shape is sometimes called "skewed left" or "skewed toward the smaller values.")

b. The smallest length for female bears is the only length that seems to fall outside the overall pattern. (However, if there were more lengths, this length might look like part of the tail of the distribution.) The longest bear, a male, is 83 inches long. (He was given the name Eddie and he weighed 396 pounds.) He doesn't appear to fall outside the overall pattern, but is part of the short tail at the upper end.

c. The distribution of male lengths is centered about 5 inches higher, in the mid 60s, than the distribution of female lengths, which is centered at a bit less than 60 inches. Students may compare the medians, which are about 64 inches for the male bears and 59 inches for the female bears, by counting values. If students know that the mean is the balance point of a distribution, they may compare the means (which are about 63 inches and 58 inches, respectively).

d. There is more than twice as much spread (variability) in the distribution of male lengths. All but one female bear are in the interval from 44 to 70 inches, with the bulk between 55 and 65 inches. All but two male bears are in the interval from 40 to 80 inches, with the bulk between 55 and 75 inches.

> **INSTRUCTIONAL NOTE**
> This problem provides an opportunity to assess students' prior knowledge of shapes of distributions, measures of center, and measures of spread.

a. *Describing shape.* Some distributions are **approximately normal** or *mound-shaped*, where the distribution has one peak and tapers off on both sides. Normal distributions are **symmetric**—the two halves look like mirror images of each other. Some distributions have a **tail** stretching towards the larger values. These distributions are called **skewed to the right** or **skewed toward the larger values**. Distributions that have a tail stretching toward the smaller values are called **skewed to the left** or **skewed toward the smaller values**.

Approximately normal	**Skewed to the right**	**Skewed to the left**

A description of shape should include whether there are two or more *clusters* separated by gaps and whether there are *outliers*. **Outliers** are unusually large or small values that fall outside the overall pattern.

   • How would you use the ideas of skewness and outliers to describe the shape of the distribution of lengths of female black bears in Problem 1?

b. *Describing center.* The measure of center that you are most familiar with is the *mean* (or average).

   • How could you estimate the mean length of the female black bears?

c. *Describing spread.* You may also already know one measure of spread, the **range**, which is the difference between the maximum value and the minimum value:

   $$range = maximum\ value - minimum\ value$$

   • What is the range of lengths of the female black bears?

d. Use these ideas of shape, center, and spread to describe the distribution of lengths of the male black bears.

Measures of center (mean and median) and measures of spread (such as the range) are called **summary statistics** because they help to summarize the information in a distribution.

3 In the late 1940s, scientists discovered how to create rain in times of drought. The technique, dropping chemicals into clouds, is called "cloud seeding." The chemicals cause ice particles to form, which become heavy enough to fall out of the clouds as rain.

To test how well silver nitrate works in causing rain, 25 out of 50 clouds were selected at random to be seeded with silver nitrate. The remaining 25 clouds were not seeded. The amount of rainfall from each cloud was measured and recorded in acre-feet (the amount of water to cover an acre 1 foot deep). The results are given in the following dot plots.

2

a. The distribution of female lengths is skewed to the left with what appears to be an outlier at 36 inches. (Using the rule that students will learn in Lesson 2, the female bear population actually has outliers at 36, 44, 46, 48, and 70.)

b. Students may not yet know that you can estimate the mean by estimating the balance point of the distribution. They may suggest estimating the lengths from the plot, adding them all up, and dividing by the number of bears.

c. The range is $70 - 36 = 34$ inches.

d. The shape of the male bear distribution is skewed to the left with a center of about 64 inches. There do not appear to be any outliers. The range is $83 - 37 = 46$ inches.

Unit 2

Seeded Clouds

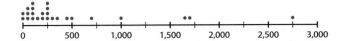

Unseeded Clouds

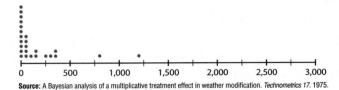

Source: A Bayesian analysis of a multiplicative treatment effect in weather modification. *Technometrics 17.* 1975.

a. Describe the shapes of these two distributions.

b. Which distribution has the larger mean?

c. Which distribution has the larger spread in the values?

d. Does it appear that the silver nitrate was effective in causing more rain? Explain.

Dot plots can be used to get quick visual displays of data. They enable you to see patterns or unusual features in the data. They are most useful when working with small sets of data. **Histograms** can be used with data sets of any size. In a histogram, the horizontal axis is marked with a numerical scale. The height of each bar represents the **frequency** (count of how many values are in that bar). A value on the line between two bars (such as 100 on the following histogram) is counted in the bar on the right.

④ *Pollstar* estimates that revenue from all major North American concerts in 2005 was about $3.1 billion. The histogram below shows the average ticket price for the top 20 North American concert tours.

Concert Tours

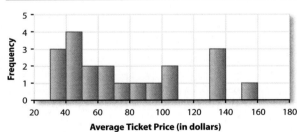

Source: www.pollstaronline.com

a. For how many of the concert tours was the average price $100 or more?

b. Barry Manilow had the highest average ticket price.

    i. In what interval does that price fall?

3 **a.** Both distributions are skewed right. The distribution of rainfall for the seeded clouds is so strongly skewed right and there are so few values that it is difficult to decide if the higher values are outliers or part of the general pattern. There are no separate clusters. It is reasonable to identify the three largest values, at about 1,600, 1,650, and 2,700 acre-feet, as possible outliers. The distribution for the unseeded clouds appears to have two outliers, at about 800 and 1,200 acre-feet. (In Lesson 2, students will learn a rule for identifying possible outliers.)

b. The seeded clouds have the higher mean rainfall.

c. Using the range as a measure of spread, the seeded clouds have a much greater range, about 2,750 acre-feet rather than about a 1,200 acre-feet range for the unseeded clouds. In addition, the bulk of the seeded clouds lie in the interval from 0 to 500 acre-feet. The bulk of the unseeded clouds lie in the interval from 0 to about 250 acre-feet.

d. Yes, the seeded clouds produced more than twice the amount of rainfall, on average. (Notice, however, that there is a large overlap in the two distributions and this must be taken into account when deciding whether the silver nitrate is effective. The difference in the two means is not as impressive as it would be if there weren't so much overlap in the two distributions. In fact, the difference in the two means is just barely statistically significant.)

4 **a.** 6

b. **i.** The Barry Manilow ticket price is in the interval from $150 up to $160.

> **INSTRUCTIONAL NOTE**
> This context of cloud seeding and the use of acre-feet as a unit of measure may not be familiar to your students. Introducing this problem with a short class discussion will help promote access and equity (see the Unit Overview page T73A) in your classroom. There are 325,851 gallons in an acre-foot.

    ii. The 147,470 people who went to Barry Manilow concerts paid an average ticket price of $153.93. What was the total amount paid (*gross*) for all of the tickets?

  c. The lowest average ticket price was for Rascal Flatts.

    i. In what interval does that price fall?

    ii. Their concert tour sold 807,560 tickets and had a gross of $28,199,995. What was the average price of a ticket to one of their concerts?

  d. Describe the distribution of these average concert ticket prices.

5 Sometimes it is useful to display data showing the percentage or proportion of the data values that fall into each category. A **relative frequency histogram** has the proportion or percentage that fall into each bar on the vertical axis rather than the frequency or count. Shown below is the start of a relative frequency histogram for the average concert ticket prices in Problem 4.

  a. Since prices between $30 and $40 happened 3 out of 20 times, the relative frequency for the first bar is $\frac{3}{20}$ or 0.15. Complete a copy of the table and relative frequency histogram. Just as with the histogram, an average price of $50 goes into the interval 50–60 in the table.

Average Price (in $)	Frequency	Relative Frequency
30–40	3	$\frac{3}{20} = 0.15$
40–50		
50–60		
60–70		
70–80		
80–90		
90–100		
100–110		
110–120		
120–130		
130–140		
140–150		
150–160		
Total		

Concert Tours

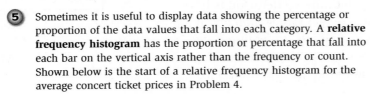

LESSON 1 • Exploring Distributions   **79**

ii. The gross was 147,470(153.93), or about $22,700,057.

c. **i.** In the interval from 30 up to 40

   ii. The average price was $\frac{28,199,995}{807,560}$, or about $34.92.

d. This distribution is skewed to the right (although it is difficult to determine shape when there are only 20 values) and is centered at about $70 to $80. The average ticket prices all fall within a range of approximately $153 - 33$, or $120.

5 **a.**

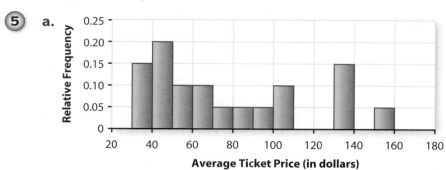

Average Ticket Price (in dollars)

Average Price (in $)	Frequency	Relative Frequency
30–40	3	$\frac{3}{20} = 0.15$
40–50	4	$\frac{4}{20} = 0.20$
50–60	2	$\frac{2}{20} = 0.10$
60–70	2	$\frac{2}{20} = 0.10$
70–80	1	$\frac{1}{20} = 0.05$
80–90	1	$\frac{1}{20} = 0.05$
90–100	1	$\frac{1}{20} = 0.05$
100–110	2	$\frac{2}{20} = 0.10$
110–120	0	$\frac{0}{20} = 0$
120–130	0	$\frac{0}{20} = 0$
130–140	3	$\frac{3}{20} = 0.15$
140–150	0	$\frac{0}{20} = 0$
150–160	1	$\frac{1}{20} = 0.05$
Total	20	$\frac{20}{20} = 1.00$

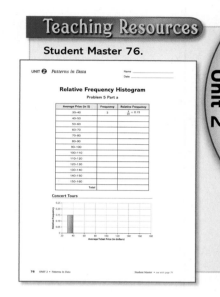

b. When would it be better to use a relative frequency histogram for the average concert ticket prices rather than a histogram?

6 To study connections between a histogram and the corresponding relative frequency histogram, consider the histogram below showing Kyle's 20 homework grades for a semester. Notice that since each bar represents a single whole number (6, 7, 8, 9, or 10), those numbers are best placed in the middle of the bars on the horizontal axis. In this case, Kyle has one grade of 6 and five grades of 7.

a. Make a relative frequency histogram of these grades by copying the histogram but making a scale that shows proportion of all grades on the vertical axis rather than frequency.

b. Compare the shape, center, and spread of the two histograms.

Homework Grades

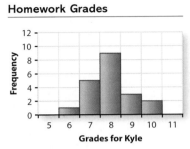

7 The relative frequency histograms below show the heights (rounded to the nearest inch) of large samples of young adult men and women in the United States.

Heights of Young Adult Men

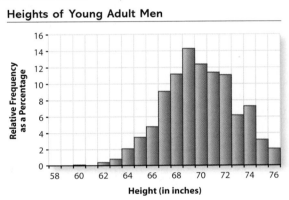

Heights of Young Adult Women

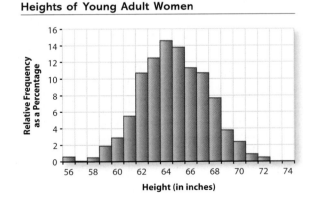

b. It's better to use a relative frequency histogram when it is more important to know about what proportion of the entire sample falls in each bar than it is to know how many fall into each bar. (This is almost always the case if the sample is very large.) For example, if you were writing a newspaper article, you might want to say something like almost half of the average ticket prices are under $60. It is easier to see that from a relative frequency histogram.

6   **a.** This histogram shows $1 + 5 + 9 + 3 + 2 = 20$ grades. To change the frequency scale to relative frequency, divide each number on the scale by 20.

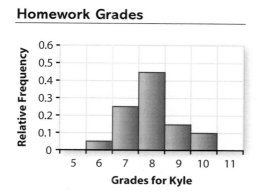

Homework Grades

Grades for Kyle

b. The shape, center, and spread of the two histograms are the same: mound-shaped, center at 8, range of 4.

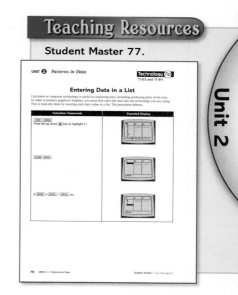

a. About what percentage of these young men are 6 feet tall? About what percentage are at least 6 feet tall?

b. About what percentage of these young women are 6 feet tall? About what percentage are 5 feet tall or less?

c. If there are 5,000 young men in this sample, how many are 5 feet, 9 inches tall? If there are 5,000 young women in this sample, how many are 5 feet, 9 inches tall?

d. Walt Disney World recently advertised for singers to perform in *Beauty and the Beast—Live on Stage*. Two positions were Belle, with height 5'5"–5'8", and Gaston, with height 6'1" or taller. What percentage of these young women would meet the height requirements for Belle? What percentage of these young men would meet the height requirements for Gaston? (Source: corporate.disney.go.com/auditions/disneyworld/roles_dancersinger.html)

Producing a graphical display is the first step toward understanding data. You can use data analysis software or a graphing calculator to produce histograms and other plots of data. This generally requires the following three steps.

- After clearing any unwanted data, enter your data into a list or lists.
- Select the type of plot desired.
- Set a *viewing window* for the plot. This is usually done by specifying the minimum and maximum values and scale on the horizontal (x) axis. Depending on the type of plot, you may also need to specify the minimum and maximum values and scale on the vertical (y) axis. Some calculators and statistical software will do this automatically, or you can use a command such as **ZoomStat**.

Examples of the screens involved are shown here. Your calculator or software may look different.

Producing a Plot

Enter Data	Select Plot	Set Window

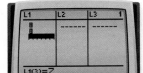  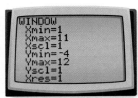

Choosing the width of the bars (Xscl) for a histogram determines the number of bars. In the next problem, you will examine several possible histograms of the same set of data and decide which you think is best.

a. About 11% are 72 inches (six feet) tall. About
11 + 6 + 7 + 3 + 2 = 29% are 6 feet tall or taller.

b. Fewer than 1% are 6 feet tall. About 0.75 + 0 + 0.5 + 2 + 3 = 6.25% are 60 inches (5 feet) tall or less.

c. About 14% of 5,000, or 700, young men in this sample are 5 feet, 9 inches tall. About 4% of 5,000 or 200 young women in this sample are 5 feet, 9 inches tall.

d. About 44% (14 + 11 + 11 + 8) of the women and about 18% (6 + 7 + 3 + 2) of the men.

8 The following table gives nutritional information about some fast-food sandwiches: total calories, amount of fat in grams, and amount of cholesterol in milligrams.

a. Use your calculator or data analysis software to make a histogram of the total calories for the sandwiches listed. Use the values Xmin = 300, Xmax = 1100, Xscl = 100, Ymin = −2, Ymax = 10, and Yscl = 1. Experiment with different choices of Xscl. Which values of Xscl give a good picture of the distribution?

b. Describe the shape, center, and spread of the distribution.

c. If your calculator or software has a "Trace" feature, use it to display values as you move the cursor along the histogram. What information is given for each bar?

d. Investigate if your calculator or data analysis software can create a relative frequency histogram.

How Fast-Food Sandwiches Compare

Company	Sandwich	Total Calories	Fat (in grams)	Cholesterol (in mg)
McDonald's	Cheeseburger	310	12	40
Wendy's	Jr. Cheeseburger	320	13	40
McDonald's	Quarter Pounder	420	18	70
McDonald's	Big Mac	560	30	80
Burger King	Whopper Jr.	390	22	45
Wendy's	Big Bacon Classic	580	29	95
Burger King	Whopper	700	42	85
Hardee's	1/3 lb Cheeseburger	680	39	90
Burger King	Double Whopper w/Cheese	1,060	69	185
Hardee's	Charbroiled Chicken Sandwich	590	26	80
Hardee's	Regular Roast Beef	330	16	40
Wendy's	Ultimate Chicken Grill	360	7	75
Wendy's	Homestyle Chicken Fillet	540	22	55
Burger King	Tendercrisp Chicken Sandwich	780	45	55
McDonald's	McChicken	370	16	50
Burger King	Original Chicken Sandwich	560	28	60
Subway	6" Chicken Parmesan	510	18	40
Subway	6" Oven Roasted Chicken Breast	330	5	45
Arby's	Regular Roast Beef	320	13	45
Arby's	Super Roast beef	440	19	45

Source: *McDonald's Nutrition Facts*, McDonald's Corporation, 2005; *U.S. Nutrition Information*, Wendy's International, Inc., 2005; *Nutrition Data*, Burger King Corp., 2005; *Nutrition*, Hardee's Food Systems, Inc., 2005; *Subway Nutrition Facts-US*, Subway, 2005; *Arby's Nutrition Information*, Arby's, Inc., 2005.

8 **a. TECHNOLOGY NOTE** The data for Problems 8 and 9 are in *CPMP-Tools* under Statistics, Data Analysis, Data, Unit 2.

The histograms below with Xscl = 50 and Xscl = 100 are very readable. The histogram with Xscl = 100 does not show the information that there are no values between 450 and 500. You don't want to have too many bars or it is hard to see the general shape of the distribution. But you don't want to have so few of them that details of the distribution are lost. Using 25 bars or fewer often will produce a good picture.

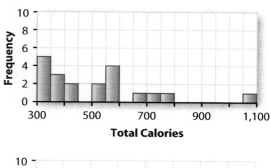

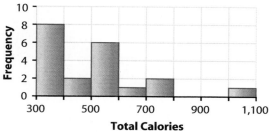

b. The distribution of calories in the fast food items has an outlier. The Burger King Double Whopper with Cheese has 1,060 calories, which is far more than any other item. The distribution is skewed right. There isn't any obvious split between chicken and beef sandwiches. The center appears to be around 500 calories. There is a large range of 750 calories in the sandwiches. However, all but one sandwich has between 300 calories and 800 calories.

c. The "Trace" feature on the TI-84 shows the minimum value in the bar, the border with the next bar, and the number of values that actually appear in the bar.

d. Students should note whether or not their calculator or statistical software can create a relative frequency histogram and, if so, what steps are necessary to create it.

TECHNOLOGY NOTE If students choose too small of an Xscl, the calculator will display **ERR: STAT1:Quit**. Also, students should recognize that sometimes it is necessary or helpful to adjust the Ymax when the Xscl is changed.

Teaching Resources

Student Masters 78–81.

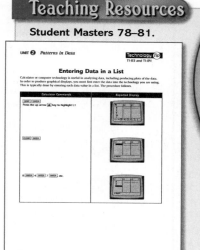

TECHNOLOGY NOTE On the TI-84, the command **ZOOM 9:ZoomStat** is a quick way to set the window for a histogram, but you may wish to hold off alerting students to this option so that they develop a sense for appropriate windows.

Unit 2

(9) Now consider the amounts of cholesterol in the fast-food sandwiches.

   a. Make a histogram of the amounts. Experiment with setting a viewing window to get a good picture of the distribution.

   b. Describe the distribution of the amount of cholesterol in these sandwiches.

   c. What stands out as the most important thing to know for someone who is watching cholesterol intake?

Summarize the Mathematics

In this investigation, you explored how dot plots and histograms can help you see the shape of a distribution and to estimate its center and spread.

a What is important to include in any description of a distribution?

b Describe some important shapes of distributions and, for each, give a data set that would likely have that shape.

c Under what circumstances is it best to make a histogram rather than a dot plot? A relative frequency histogram rather than a histogram?

Be prepared to share your ideas and reasoning with the class.

✓Check Your Understanding

Consider the amount of fat in the fast-food sandwiches listed in the table on page 82.

   a. Make a dot plot of these data.

   b. Make a histogram and then a relative frequency histogram of these data.

   c. Write a short description of the distribution so that a person who had not seen the distribution could draw an approximately correct sketch of it.

Investigation 2 · Measures of Center

In the previous investigation, you learned how to describe the shape of a distribution. In this investigation, you will review how to compute the two most important measures of the center of a distribution—the mean and the median—and explore some of their properties. As you work on this investigation, think about this question:

How do you decide whether to use the mean or median in summarizing a set of data?

9 **a.**

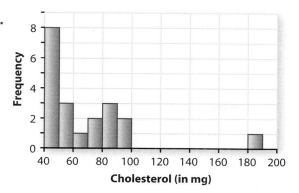

b. This distribution has two peaks, from 40 to 50 and from 80 to 90. It is centered around 60. The maximum and an outlier is again the Burger King Double Whopper with Cheese with 185 mg of cholesterol. The range is 145 mg. However, all but one sandwich are between 40 and 95 mg of cholesterol.

c. The most important thing to know is the wide spread in the amounts of cholesterol. It's possible to get a reasonable amount from both chicken and beef fast-food sandwiches, but it's also possible to get a huge amount.

Summarize
the Mathematics

a Any description of a distribution should discuss its shape (including any outliers and clusters), center, and spread.

b An approximately *normal distribution* is mounded in the center and tapers off on each side. This shape is typical of measurements such as height or scores of students on standardized tests.

  A distribution that is *skewed to the right* has values that are clustered at the low end with a long tail towards larger values. This often means that there is some lower limit to the values, usually zero, as with the grams of fat data.

  A distribution that is *skewed to the left* has values that are clustered at the high end, and the longer tail stretches towards the smaller values. This often means that there is some upper limit to the values, as on an easy test where the maximum is 100%.

c Make a histogram rather than a dot plot when there are many values. Make a relative frequency histogram rather than a histogram when you are more interested in the percentage or proportion of values that fall into each bar than in the number of values.

PROCESSING PROMPT We listened to _____ talk about
(person)
_____ and were then able to make our discussion deeper by ... .
(topic)

MATH TOOLKIT Students should include information from the class in their toolkit. It will be helpful to include a sketch of the following distributions: normal, skewed to the right, and skewed to the left distributions.

✓ *Check Your Understanding*

a. Fast-Food Sandwiches

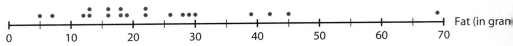

b.

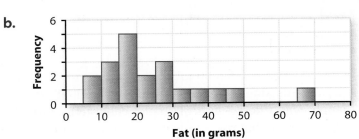

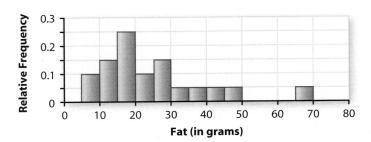

c. This distribution is skewed right. The distribution is centered between 20 and 25 and has a peak between 15 and 20. The minimum is 5 and the maximum is a whopping 69 grams. There are no values between 50 and 65.

In this investigation, students review the measures of the center of a distribution—mean and median—which they should have encountered in middle-school mathematics courses. You may wish to launch this investigation by asking students to discuss in pairs what they know about the mean and median as measures of the center of a distribution. Once a quick class discussion occurs, students should be able to connect their understandings to the formal definitions in the text.

Students learn that the mean tends to be farther out in the tail of a skewed distribution than the median and learn to estimate the mean and median from histograms. They will also learn to compute the mean and median from frequency tables and develop their understanding of which measure of center to use for particular situations.

Unit 2

Here, for your reference, are the definitions of the median and the mean.

- The **median** is the midpoint of an *ordered* list of data—at least half the values are at or below the median and at least half are at or above it. When there are an odd number of values, the median is the one in the middle. When there are an even number of values, the median is the average of the two in the middle.

- The **mean**, or arithmetic average, is the sum of the values divided by the number of values. When there are n values, $x_1, x_2, \ldots, x_n$, the formula for the mean $\bar{x}$ is

$$\bar{x} = \frac{x_1 + x_2 + \cdots + x_n}{n}, \text{ or } \bar{x} = \frac{\Sigma x}{n}.$$

The second formula is written using the Greek letter *sigma*, Σ, meaning "sum up." So Σx means to add up all of the values of x. Writing Σx is a shortcut so you don't have to write out all of the xs as in the first formula.

1 Refer back to the penny-stacking experiment described on pages 74–75. The table below gives the number of pennies stacked by the first-hour class in Traverse City with their dominant hand.

Dominant Hand

27	35	41	36	34	6	42	20
47	41	51	48	49	32	29	21
50	51	49	35	36	53	54	

  a. Compute the median and the mean for these data. Why does it make sense that the mean is smaller than the median?

  b. Now enter into a list in your calculator or statistical software the data your class collected on stacking pennies with your nondominant hand. Learn to use your calculator or statistical software to calculate the mean and median.

  c. Compare the mean and median of the dominant hand and nondominant hand distributions. When stacking pennies, does it appear that use of the dominant or nondominant hand may make a difference? Explain your reasoning.

  d. In what circumstances would you give the mean when asked to summarize the numbers of stacked pennies in the two experiments? The median?

2 Without using your calculator, find the median of these sets of consecutive whole numbers.

  a. 1, 2, 3, … , 7, 8, 9

  b. 1, 2, 3, … , 8, 9, 10

  c. 1, 2, 3, … , 97, 98, 99

  d. 1, 2, 3, … , 98, 99, 100

  e. Suppose n numbers are listed in order from smallest to largest. Which of these expressions gives the *position* of the median in the list?

$$\frac{n}{2} \qquad \frac{n}{2} + 1 \qquad \frac{n + 1}{2}$$

TECHNOLOGY NOTE You may wish to have students use the custom tool "Estimate Center" in *CPMP-Tools* under statistics to help develop the ability to estimate means and medians and check their estimates. One computer in the classroom would allow groups to check Problem 5.

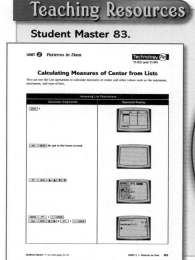

 a. Median: 41

Mean: 38.6

The value of 6, an exceptionally small number of pennies, doesn't make the median any smaller than if the number had been larger (say 30). However, this exceptionally small value does "pull down" the mean somewhat.

b. On the TI-84, the mean and median may be found under STAT, CALC, 1-Var Stats. In addition, you may wish to have students use the LIST MATH functions here so that they also become familiar with this menu. On the TI-84, the **SortA(** command is found under LIST, OPS.

c. The comparison will depend on the nondominant hand data collected in your classroom.

d. You probably would give the mean when asked for the average. You would give the median if you want to emphasize that about half of the students stacked more pennies than the median and about half stacked fewer pennies than the median.

2 **a.** 5

b. 5.5

c. 50

d. 50.5

e. $\dfrac{n + 1}{2}$

3 Now examine this histogram, which shows a set of 40 integer values.

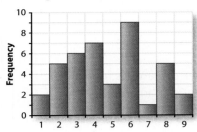

a. What is the position of the median when there are 40 values? Find the median of this set of values. Locate the median on the horizontal axis of the histogram.

b. Find the area of the bars to the left of the median. Find the area of the bars to the right of the median. How can you use area to estimate the median from a histogram?

4 The mean lies at the "balance point" of the plot. That is, if the histogram were made of blocks stacked on a lightweight tray, the mean is where you would place one finger to balance the tray. Is the median of the distribution below to the left of the mean, to the right, or at the same place? Explain.

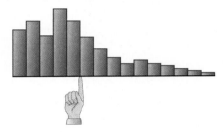

5 The histogram at the right shows the ages of the 78 actresses whose performances won in the Best Leading Role category at the annual Academy Awards (Oscars) 1929–2005. (Ages were calculated by subtracting the birth year of the actress from the year of her award.)

Age of Best Actress

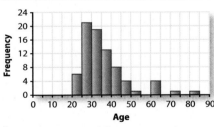

Source: www.oscars.com; www.imdb.com

a. Describe the shape of this distribution.

b. Estimate the mean age and the median age of the winners. Write a sentence describing what each tells about the ages.

c. Use the "Estimate Center" custom tool to check your estimate of the mean.

6 Find the mean and median of the following set of values: 1, 2, 3, 4, 5, 6, 70.

a. Remove the outlier of 70. Then find the mean and median of the new set of values. Which changed more, the mean or the median?

LESSON 1 • Exploring Distributions   **85**

3 **a.** There are 40 values, so the median occurs at position $\frac{40 + 1}{2}$, or halfway between the 20th and 21st values, which are 4 and 5. The median is 4.5 and is located on the boundary between the 4 bar and the 5 bar.

b. The area of the bars to the left of the median is 20. The area of the bars to the right of the median is 20. Estimate the value that divides the total area of the bars in half. (Note that histograms don't always divide so easily into two equal areas. So sometimes it is difficult to estimate the median this way.)

4 Students may think in terms of frequency in bars. More than half of the data are left of the hand, so the median is to the left of the hand. Alternatively, the total area of the bars to the left of the hand is greater than the total area of the bars to the right of the hand, so the median is to the left of the hand.

5 **a.** The distribution of ages is skewed right.

b. The mean (balance point of the histogram) is approximately 35.5 and the median (age that divides the area in half) is 33. Good estimates from the histogram are 35–40 and 30–35, respectively.

   If you add up all of the ages and divide by the number of actresses, (78) you get the mean.

   The median of 33 tells you that about half of the women were under 33 when they won their Oscar and about half were older.

c. See Technology Note.

6 The mean of the original set of values is 13, and the median is 4.

a. The mean decreased from 13 to 3.5 while the median decreased from 4 to 3.5. The mean changed much more.

TECHNOLOGY NOTE
CPMP-Tools contains the data from Problem 5 as well as some data from homework tasks. Students can check their work in class, at the library, or from home using the custom tool "Estimate Center."

b. Working with others, create three different sets of values with one or more outliers. For each set of values, find the mean and median. Then remove the outlier(s) and find the mean and median of the new set of values. Which changed more in these cases?

c. In general, is the mean or the median more **resistant to outliers** (or, less **sensitive to outliers**)? That is, which measure of center tends to change less if an outlier is removed from a set of values? Explain your reasoning.

d. The median typically is reported as the measure of center for house prices in a region and also for family incomes. For example, you may see statements like this: "The *Seattle Times* analyzed county assessor's data on 83 neighborhoods in King County and found that last year a household with median income could afford a median-priced home in 49 of them." Why do you think medians are used in this story rather than means? (Source: seattletimes. nwsource.com/homes/html/affo05.html)

7 Make a copy of each of the distributions below. For each distribution, indicate the relationship you would expect between the mean and median by marking and labeling their approximate positions on the distribution.

a.

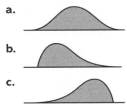

b.

c.

8 In a competitive candy sale, the six students in the Drama Club at Sparta High School sold a mean of 14 bars each; the eight students in the Math Club sold a mean of 11 bars each.

a. The winner of the competition is the club that sells more candy bars. Which club was the winner?

b. Construct an example, giving the number of bars sold by each student, where the median for the six students in the Drama Club is 14 bars, the median for the eight students in the Math Club is 11 bars, and the Drama Club wins the competition.

c. Now construct an example where the median for the six students in the Drama Club is 14 bars, the median for the eight students in the Math Club is 11 bars, but the Math Club is the winner this time.

b. Students should find that the mean changes more than the median for each set of data. (There can be exceptions when there is a large gap in the middle of a set of numbers.)

c. The median is more resistant to outliers. This is because if you order an odd number of values the median changes only by half of the size of the gap between the current median and the next smallest value (assuming the outlier is on the high end). If there were originally an even number of values, the median changes by the size of the gap between it and the next smallest value. In contrast, the total, and so the mean, can decrease quite a bit if a very large value is removed.

d. The two distributions of income and housing prices are strongly skewed to the right. In most communities, the bulk of the housing prices and incomes are moderate while a few of them are much, much larger than the others. The median is resistant to these very large values. Further, the median has the easily understood interpretation that about half of the prices or incomes are larger than the median and about half are smaller.

7 **a.** They would be equal and lie right beneath the peak.

b. The mean will be larger than the median.

c. The mean will be smaller than the median.

8 **a.** The total number of bars sold by students in the Drama Club was $6 \cdot 14 = 84$ and by students in the Math Club was $8 \cdot 11 = 88$, so the Math Club won by 4 bars.

b. One possible example: The six students in the Drama Club each sell 14 bars, for a total of 84 bars. The eight students in the Math Club sell 2, 2, 2, 11, 11, 12, 12, and 12 bars for a total of 64 bars. The Drama Club wins.

c. One possible example: The six students in the Drama Club sell 2, 2, 14, 14, 15, and 15 bars, for a total of 62 bars. The eight students in the Math Club sell 2, 2, 2, 11, 11, 12, 12, and 12 bars for a total of 64 bars. The Math Club wins this time.

d. Does knowing only the two medians let you determine which club won? Does knowing only the two means?

e. Which of the following formulas would you use to find the *total* (or *sum*) of a set of numbers if you know the mean $\bar{x}$ and the number of values n?

$$total = \frac{\bar{x}}{n} \qquad total = n \cdot \bar{x} \qquad total = \bar{x} + n \qquad total = \bar{x} - n \cdot \bar{x}$$

⑨ When a distribution has many identical values, it is helpful to record them in a **frequency table**, which shows each value and the number of times (*frequency* or *count*) that it occurs. The following frequency table gives the number of goals scored per game during a season of 81 soccer matches. For example, the first line means that there were 5 matches with no goals scored.

Goals per Match

Goals Scored	Number of Matches (frequency)	Goals Scored	Number of Matches (frequency)
0	5	5	8
1	7	6	5
2	28	7	1
3	10	8	1
4	15	9	1

a. What is the median number of goals scored per match?

b. What is the total number of goals scored in all matches?

c. What is the mean number of goals scored per match?

d. Think about how you computed the mean number of goals per match in Part c. Which of the following formulas summarizes your method?

$$\frac{\Sigma \text{ goals scored}}{10} = \frac{0 + 1 + 2 + \cdots + 8 + 9}{10}$$

$$\frac{\Sigma \text{ number of matches}}{10} = \frac{5 + 7 + 28 + \cdots + 1 + 1}{10}$$

$$\frac{\Sigma(\text{goals scored})(\text{number of matches})}{\Sigma \text{ number of matches}} = \frac{0 \cdot 5 + 1 \cdot 7 + 2 \cdot 28 + \cdots + 8 \cdot 1 + 9 \cdot 1}{5 + 7 + 28 + \cdots + 1 + 1}$$

$$\frac{\Sigma \text{ goals scored}}{\Sigma \text{ number of matches}} = \frac{0 + 1 + 2 + \cdots + 8 + 9}{5 + 7 + 28 + \cdots + 1 + 1}$$

d. Knowing the two medians does not tell you the winner because, for example, the medians were the same in Parts b and c, but the club that won was different. Knowing the two means (and the number of students in each club) does let you know the winner because the total is equal to the number of students in the club times the mean for that club.

e. $total = n \cdot \bar{x}$

a. There were 81 matches, so the median occurs in location $\frac{81 + 1}{2} = 41$. The median is 3 goals.

b. $0 \cdot 5 + 1 \cdot 7 + 2 \cdot 28 + \cdots + 8 \cdot 1 + 9 \cdot 1 = 247$ total goals

c. $\bar{x} = \frac{247}{81} \approx 3.05$

d. $\bar{x} = \dfrac{\Sigma \, (goals \; scored)(number \; of \; matches)}{\Sigma \; number \; of \; matches}$

10 Suppose that, to estimate the mean number of children per household in a community, a survey was taken of 114 randomly selected households. The results are summarized in this frequency table.

Household Size

Number of Children	Number of Households
0	15
1	22
2	36
3	21
4	12
5	6
7	1
10	1

a. How many of the households had exactly 2 children?

b. Make a histogram of the distribution. Estimate the mean number of children per household from the histogram.

c. Calculate the mean number of children per household. You can do this on some calculators and spreadsheet software by entering the number of children in one list and the number of households in another list. The following instructions work with some calculators.

  • Enter the number of children in L1 and the number of households in L2.

  • Position the cursor on top of L3 and type L1 $\boxed{\times}$ L2. Then press $\boxed{\text{ENTER}}$. What appears in list L3?

  • Using the sum of list L3, and the sum of list L2, find the mean number of children per household.

d. How will a frequency table of the number of children in the households of the students in your class be different from the one above? To check your answer, make a frequency table and describe how it differs from the one from the community survey. Would your class be a good sample to use to estimate the mean number of children per household in your community?

10 **a.** 36

b. The balance point of the histogram below is towards the right side of the 2 bar. A good estimate of the mean would be between 2.0 and 2.5.

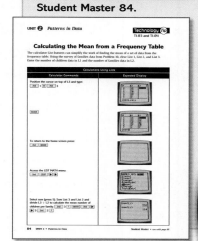
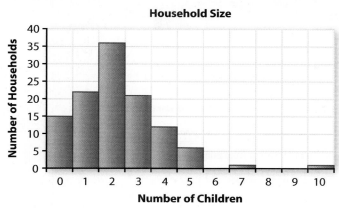

c. The mean is about 2.21.

d. Since every student in the class is a child in their own household, the frequency table will have a frequency of 0 for a household with no children. Thus, the distribution will have no bar at 0 and will likely have a higher mean value.

Thus, a classroom of students wouldn't be a good sample to use to estimate the mean number of children per household in a given community. Households with no children could not possibly be represented in such a sample.

Unit 2

Summarize the Mathematics

Whether you use the mean or median depends on the reason that you are computing a measure of center and whether you want the measure to be resistant to outliers.

a In what situations would you use the mean to summarize a set of data? The median?

b Describe how to estimate the mean and median from a histogram.

c Describe how to find the mean and median from a frequency table.

d What is the relationship between the sum of the values and their mean?

Be prepared to share your examples and ideas with the class.

✓Check Your Understanding

Leslie, a recent high school graduate seeking a job at United Tool and Die, was told that "the mean salary is over $31,000." Upon further inquiry, she obtained the following information about the number of employees at various salary levels.

Type of Job	Number Employed	Individual Salary
President/Owner	1	$210,000
Business Manager	1	70,000
Supervisor	2	55,000
Foreman	5	36,000
Machine Operator	50	26,000
Clerk	2	24,000
Custodian	1	19,000

a. What percentage of employees earn over $31,000?

b. What is the median salary? Write a sentence interpreting this median.

c. Verify whether the reported mean salary is correct.

d. Suppose that the company decides not to include the owner's salary. How will deleting the owner's salary affect the mean? The median?

e. In a different company of 54 employees, the median salary is $24,000 and the mean is $26,000. Can you determine the total payroll?

LESSON 1 • Exploring Distributions **89**

Summarize the Mathematics

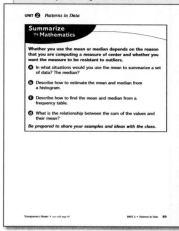

a Which of the two is the most appropriate to use in a given situation ultimately depends on the reason for wanting a measure of center.

Mean—The mean, or average, is the measure of center most commonly used. People are comfortable with it. It is very easy to compute and to estimate from a histogram. The mean typically is the preferred measure of center when you want to compute a final grade from test scores or a typical June 4th maximum temperature for a city. It is used even if there is an outlier if you want the outlier's effect to be retained. An example would be if someone had many grades between 75 and 85 and then received a 100.

Median—The median is easy to understand. It also tells you something very specific about the values. About half of the values are above the median and about half are below. Nothing so simple can be said about the mean. Because the median is resistant to outliers and the mean isn't, the median often is preferred to the mean with a data set that is strongly skewed or has outliers. You would use the median when you want to say something like, "Half of the houses cost more than $250,000."

b The mean is the "balance point" of the histogram. The median is the point where half of the values lie to the left and half to the right. The median can be estimated visually by identifying the location where half the area of the histogram is above and half below that value.

c To find the mean, multiply each value by its frequency, add up these products, and divide by the total of the frequencies. To find the median, count down the frequency column until you reach the frequency numbered $\frac{n+1}{2}$. The value associated with that frequency (or the two surrounding frequencies if it is a fraction) is the median.

d The sum of the values is equal to the mean times the number of values. For example, if you knew the mean housing price in a community, you could get the total value by multiplying the mean by the number of houses.

MATH TOOLKIT This is an opportunity for students to articulate the difference between the two measures of center, median and mean. Including situations in which each are used will be a helpful reference for them as they continue their work with statistical analysis. Descriptions of how to find both measures of center from a histogram and from a frequency table will also provide a helpful reference for future investigations of data.

✓ Check Your Understanding

a. Nine employees out of 62, or about 14.5%.

b. The median is $26,000. About half of the employees earn $26,000 or less, and about half earn $26,000 or more.

c. The total payroll is $1(210,000) + 1(70,000) + 2(55,000) + 5(36,000) + 50(26,000) + 2(24,000) + 1(19,000) = \$1,937,000$. So, the mean is $\frac{1,937,000}{62} \approx \$31,242$. The reported mean salary is correct.

d. The mean will decrease while the median will not change. Without the owner's salary the mean is $28,311, but the median remains $26,000.

e. Yes, the total payroll is $54 \cdot \$26,000$, or $1,404,000.

Unit 2

On Your Own

Applications

1. The following table gives average hourly compensation costs for production workers from 24 countries. Hourly compensation costs include hourly salary, vacation, holidays, benefits, and other costs to the employer.

Average Hourly Compensation Costs for Production Workers
(in U.S. dollars for selected countries, 2004)

Country	Cost	Country	Cost	Country	Cost	Country	Cost
Australia	23.09	Finland	30.67	Japan	21.90	Spain	17.10
Austria	28.29	France	23.89	Mexico	2.50	Sweden	28.42
Belgium	29.98	Germany	32.53	Netherlands	30.76	Switzerland	30.26
Brazil	3.03	Hong Kong	5.51	New Zealand	12.89	Taiwan	5.97
Canada	21.42	Ireland	21.94	Norway	34.64	United Kingdom	24.71
Denmark	33.75	Italy	20.48	Singapore	7.45	United States	23.17

Source: U.S. Bureau of Labor Statistics, www.bls.gov/news.release/ichcc.t02.htm

a. What is the average yearly compensation cost for a Japanese worker who gets paid for a 40-hour week, 52 weeks a year?

b. Make a dot plot of the costs. Describe how U.S. average hourly compensation costs compare to those of the other countries.

c. Make a histogram of the average hourly compensation costs. Write a summary of the information conveyed by the histogram.

2. In 2004, a family of four was considered to be living in poverty if it had income less than $18,850 per year. The percentage of persons who live below the poverty level varies from state to state. The histogram shows these percentages for the fifty states in 2004.

Percentage of Persons Under Poverty Level, by State

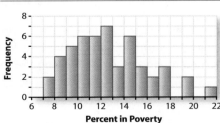

Source: U.S. Census Bureau, *2004 American Community Survey* at www.factfinder.census.gov

On Your Own

Applications

 a. The average yearly compensation cost is $(40)(52)(\$21.90) = \$45,552$.

b. Average Hourly Compensation Costs

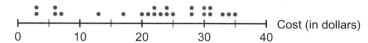

In the dot plot above, the average hourly compensation costs for the United States, $23.17, lies right about at the median (23.13) of the costs for the 24 countries and has costs similar to those of quite a few other countries.

c.

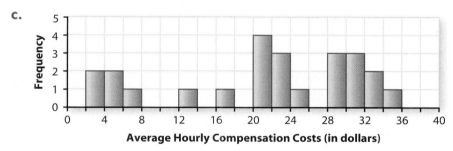

A student's summary might include the following points:

• The distribution appears to be made up of three clusters. (It would be interesting to get more countries to see if the gaps fill in.)

• The distribution is skewed to the left, but does not have a very regular shape.

• The distribution is centered at $20 to $25.

• No country is an outlier or has an unusual value.

(The clusters in this distribution are interesting. The upper cluster consists entirely of central and northern European countries. The lower cluster includes Latin American and small Asian countries: Brazil, Hong Kong, Mexico, Singapore, and Taiwan.)

The following graphs show the hourly compensation data using different-sized intervals. The graph with Xscl of $5.00 obscures the major clusters somewhat because their intervals are so wide. The graph with Xscl of $1.00 appears to show additional gaps and multiple clusters, which are bound to occur with only 24 countries and so aren't worth mentioning.

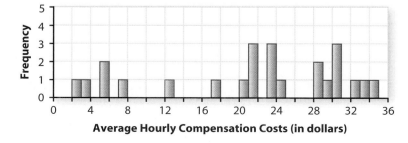

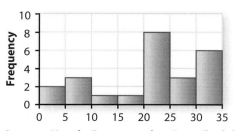

TECHNOLOGY NOTE
The data for this task are found in *CPMP-Tools* under Statistics Data Analysis. An additional data set for other years is also included. Students can use the expanded data to ask and answer their own questions.

a. In how many states do at least 17% of the people live in poverty? In how many states do 15% or more of the people live in poverty?

b. The highest poverty rate is in Mississippi. In what interval does that rate fall? The population of Mississippi is about 2,794,925, and 603,954 live in poverty. Compute the poverty rate for Mississippi. Is this consistent with the interval you selected?

c. The lowest poverty rate is 7.6%, in New Hampshire. About 94,924 people live in poverty in New Hampshire. About how many people live in New Hampshire?

d. About 37,161,510 people in the United States, or 13.1%, are in poverty. Where would this rate fall on the histogram? About how many people live in the United States?

e. Describe the distribution of these percentages.

3 Make a rough sketch of what you think each of the following distributions would look like. Describe the shape, center, and spread you would expect.

a. the last digits of the phone numbers of students in your school

b. the heights of all five-year-olds in the United States (*Hint:* the mean is about 44 inches)

c. the weights of all dogs in the United States

d. the ages of all people who died last week in the United States

4 The two distributions below show the highest and the lowest temperatures on record at 289 major U.S. weather-observing stations in all 50 states, Puerto Rico, and the Pacific Islands.

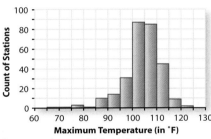

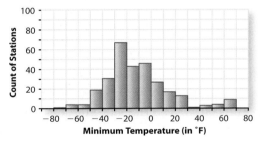

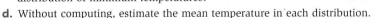
Source: www.ncdc.noaa.gov/oa/climate/online/ccd/

a. Yuma, Arizona, has the highest maximum temperature ever recorded at any of these stations. In what interval does that temperature fall? The coldest ever temperature was recorded at McGrath, Alaska. What can you say about that temperature?

b. About how many stations had a record minimum temperature from −40°F up to −30°F? About how many had a record maximum temperature less than 90°F?

c. Describe the shapes of the two distributions. What might account for the cluster in the tail on the right side of the distribution of minimum temperatures?

d. Without computing, estimate the mean temperature in each distribution.

e. Which distribution has the greater spread of temperatures?

LESSON 1 • Exploring Distributions   **91**

2 **a.** 6 states; 11 states

b. Mississippi's rate falls in the interval from 21% up to 22%. The poverty rate is $\frac{603,954}{2,794,925} \approx 21.6\%$. Yes, this is in the interval.

c. Let N be the number of people in New Hampshire. Then $\frac{94,924}{N} = 0.076$, so $N \approx 1,249,000$ people.

d. A rate of 13.1% would fall in the bar with height 3 right before the 14 on the x-axis. Let N be the number of people in the United States. Then $\frac{37,161,510}{N} = 0.131$, so $N \approx 283,675,649$ people.

e. The distribution is skewed right with no outliers. About half of the states have poverty rates under 12%, and about half have rates higher than this. The percentages range from about 8% to almost 22%.

3 **a.** The shape would be rectangular (or *uniform*), but not perfectly so, centered at about 4.5 and likely with a minimum of 0 and maximum of 9. A histogram for a class of 27 students appears below. Your school probably has many more than 27 students, and thus the histograms should be more uniform than the one below.

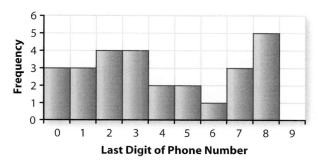

Last Digit of Phone Number

b. The heights are approximately normal, centered at 44 inches with almost all five-year olds between 40 inches and 48 inches tall. (Source: www.cdc. gov/nchs/data/nhanes/growthcharts/zscore/zstatage.txt) The distribution would look about like the first image below.

Students might sketch a histogram with approximately normal distribution centered at about 44 similar to the one at the right below.

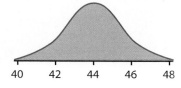 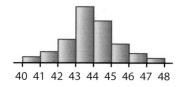

c. The distribution probably is a bit skewed right, as most dogs nowadays are on the smaller side. The center might be around 20 or 25 pounds, with a range from about 3 pounds up to about 115 pounds.

Information on breeds and weights of dogs can be found at electron.cs.uwindsor.ca/~kasinad/table.html.

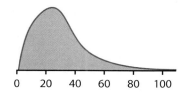

> **NOTE** The solutions to Problem 3, Part d and Problem 4 can be found on page T92.

Unit 2

5 For each of the following two distributions:

  i. Describe the shape of the distribution.

  ii. Estimate the median and write a sentence describing what the median tells about the data.

  iii. Estimate the mean and write a sentence describing what the mean tells about the data.

a. This histogram displays the vertical jump, in inches, of 27 basketball players in an NBA draft.

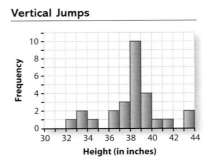

Vertical Jumps

b. This histogram displays the number of video games that are available for each of 43 different platforms (computer operating systems, console systems, and handhelds). The platform with the largest number of games has 3,762. (Source: www.mobygames.com/moby_stats)

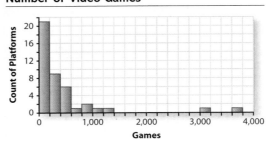

Number of Video Games

Ratings of Movie Showings

Points Deducted	Frequency
0	38
1	14
2	14
3	9
4	7
5	3
6	3
7	1
8	1
9	0
10	0
11	0
12	2

Source: hsvmovies.com/generated_subpages/
ratings_table/ratings_table.html

6 As a hobby, a student at the University of Alabama, Huntsville, rated the projection quality of nearby movie theaters. For each showing, a point was deducted for such things as misalignment, misframing, or an audio problem. He visited one theater in Huntsville 92 times in the first $5\frac{1}{2}$ years it was open. A frequency table of the number of points deducted per showing is at the left.

d. This distribution is very strongly skewed left with a rise at the left because of infant deaths. The center is more than 65. The minimum is 0 and the maximum is over 100.

NOTE Information on all deaths in the United States for 2003 can be found at the U.S. National Center for Health Statistics (www.cdc. gov/nchs/data/nvsr/nvsr54/ nvsr54_13.pdf).

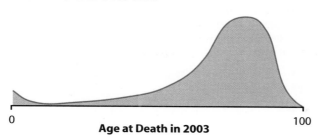

Age at Death in 2003

4 **a.** The highest maximum temperature falls in the interval from 120° up to 125°F, or [120, 125). (The temperature in Yuma actually was 124°F.) The lowest falls in the interval from −80° up to −70°F, or [−80, −70). (The temperature in McGrath actually was −75°F.)

TECHNOLOGY NOTE The data for Tasks 4 and 5 are included in the *CPMP-Tools* under Statistics, Data Analysis.

Unit 2

b. 31 stations had a record minimum from −40° up to −30°F. About $1 + 1 + 3 + 1 + 10 = 16$ had a record maximum less than 90°F.

c. The distribution of maximums is skewed to the left. The distribution of minimums is more symmetric, but has a cluster in the right tail. This cluster consists of stations on various Pacific Islands such as Pago Pago and Guam, where it never gets very cold.

d. The means are about 103°F for the maximum temperature and −12°F for the minimum temperature.

e. The minimum temperatures have the greater spread. The minimum temperatures fall between about −80°F and 69°F for a range of about 149°F. The range for the maximums is only about 60°F.

5 **a.** **i.** The shape is fairly symmetric, mound-shaped with irregular tails on both sides.

 ii. The median is between 38 and 39 inches. About half of the players in this draft jumped higher than 38–39 inches, and about half jumped lower.

 iii. The mean of about 38.2 is the balance point of the distribution. Mean is another word for the average jump by a player in the draft.

b. **i.** The shape is skewed right with two outliers.

 ii. The median falls just about between the first and second bars, or at about 200 games. About half of the 43 platforms have fewer than 200 games written for them, and about half have more.

 iii. The mean is the balance point of the distribution and is another word for the average number of games per platform. Students should estimate that it falls to the left of the bar between 400 and 600. (The mean, in fact, is about 425.)

a. Without sketching it, describe the shape of this distribution.

b. Find the median number and the mean number of points deducted for this theater (which was a relatively good one and given an A rating). Is the mean typical of the experience you would expect to have in this theater? Explain your answer.

(7) Suppose your teacher grades homework on a scale of 0 to 4. Your grades for the semester are given in the following table.

Homework Grades

Grade	Frequency
0	5
1	7
2	9
3	10
4	16

a. What is your mean homework grade?

b. When computing your final grade in the course, would you rather have the teacher use your median grade? Explain.

c. Suppose that your teacher forgot to record one of your grades in the table above. After it is added to the table, your new mean is 2.50. What was that missing grade?

Connections

(8) The two histograms below display the heights of two groups of tenth-graders.

Heights of Group I

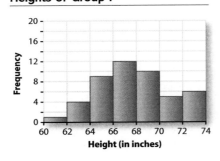

Heights of Group II

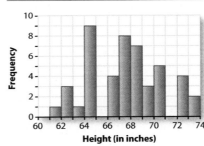

a. Compare their shapes, centers, and spreads.

b. Remake the histogram on the right so that the bars have the same 2-inch width as the one on the left. Now compare the two histograms once again.

6 **a.** The distribution is strongly skewed to the right.

b. The median is 1, and the mean is about 1.84. The mean, which is close to 2, is not typical in the sense that the most common experience is 0 points deducted (which happens in about 41% of the showings), and more than half of the time you would experience only 1 or 0 points deducted. The two times when 12 points were deducted make the mean higher than "typical."

7 **a.** The mean is $\frac{110}{47}$, or about 2.53.

b. The median is 3 and is larger than the mean, so it would be better for you if the teacher uses the median rather than the mean.

c. The missing grade is a 1. This can be found by noticing that the new total is equal to the new number of grades, 48, times the new mean of 2.5. So, the new total must be 120. The old total was 119. So, the new grade is a 1. Alternatively, you solve the equation below where x represents the missing grade.

$$2.5 = \frac{119 + x}{47 + 1}$$

$$2.5 = \frac{119 + x}{48}$$

$$2.5(48) = \frac{119 + x}{48}(48)$$

$$120 = 119 + x$$

$$x = 1$$

Connections

8 **a.** The two distributions have about the same mound shape, except that you can see from the second histogram in the Student Edition that there are no heights between 60 and 61 inches, between 65 and 66 inches, or between 71 and 72 inches in the second group of tenth-graders. Both distributions are centered at about 67 inches and have about the same spread.

b. The new histogram will look exactly like the one on the left in the Student Edition when they are constructed with the same bar width and frequency scale. This shows that large bar widths may disguise gaps. (Further, you shouldn't make too much of gaps in distributions when there aren't a large number of values.)

9 Another measure of center that you may have previously learned is the **mode**. It is the value or category that occurs the most frequently. The mode is most useful with **categorical data**, data that is grouped into categories. The following table is from a study of the passwords people use. For example, only 2.3% of all passwords that people generate refer to a friend.

Entity Referred to	Percentage of All Passwords
Self	66.5
Relative	7.0
Animal	4.7
Lover	3.4
Friend	2.3
Product	2.2
Location	1.4
Organization	1.2
Activity	0.9
Celebrity	0.1
Not specified	4.3
Random	5.7

Source: "Generating and remembering passwords," *Applied Cognitive Psychology 18.* 2004.

a. What is the *modal* category?

b. Use this category in a sentence describing this distribution of types of passwords.

c. When someone says that a typical family has two children, is he or she probably referring to the mean, median, or mode? Explain your reasoning.

10 Suppose that $x_1 = 2$, $x_2 = 10$, $x_3 = 5$, and $x_4 = 6$. Compute:

a. Σx

b. Σx^2

c. $\Sigma(x - 2)$

d. $\Sigma \frac{1}{x}$

11 Matt received an 81 and an 83 on his first two English tests.

a. If a grade of B requires a mean of at least 80, what must he get on his next test to have a grade of B?

b. Suppose, on the other hand, that a grade of B requires a median of at least 80. What would Matt need on his next test to have a grade of B?

(9) **a.** Passwords that refer to oneself.

b. More passwords (66.5%) refer to the people who generated them than refer to any other entity, by far.

c. They probably are referring to the mode—the number of children they see most often. (It's unlikely that the mean would be a whole number.)

(10) **a.** $\Sigma x = 23$

b. $\Sigma x^2 = 165$

c. $\Sigma(x - 2) = 15$

d. $\Sigma\frac{1}{x} = \frac{29}{30}$, or about 0.967

(11) **a.** The sum of the three grades must be at least $80(3) = 240$. So far, Matt has $81 + 83 = 164$ points. He must get $240 - 164 = 76$ on the next test.

b. Any grade will do.

12 The scatterplot below shows the maximum and minimum record temperatures for the 289 stations from Applications Task 4. What information is lost when you see only the histograms? What information is lost when you see only the scatterplot?

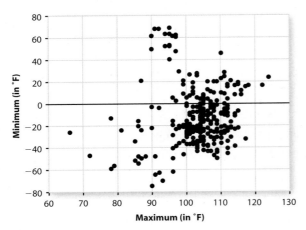

13 The term *median* is also used in geometry. A **median of a triangle** is the line segment joining a vertex to the midpoint of the opposite side. The diagram below shows one median of △*ABC*.

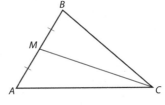

a. On a copy of the diagram, draw the other medians of this triangle.

b. On a sheet of posterboard, draw and cut out a right triangle and a triangle with an obtuse angle. Then draw the three medians of each triangle.

c. What appears to be true about the medians of a triangle?

d. Try balancing each posterboard triangle on the tip of a pencil. What do you notice?

e. Under what condition(s) will the median of a set of data be the balance point for a histogram of that data? Give an example.

Reflections

14 Distributions of real data tend to follow predictable patterns.

a. Most distributions of real data that you will see are skewed right rather than skewed left. Why? Give an example of a distribution not in this lesson that is skewed left.

b. If one distribution of real data has a larger mean than a second distribution of similar data, the first distribution tends also to have the larger spread. Find examples in this lesson where that is the case.

12 From the individual histograms, you don't see the fact that the positive relationship between maximum and minimum temperatures is very weak. One might expect a fairly strong relationship: stations that have higher maximums would also tend to be the stations with higher minimums, and stations that have lower maximums would also tend to be the ones with the lower minimums. That is, there are "colder" stations and "warmer" stations. That is true to some extent, but the relationship is weak. Also, the scatterplot shows a cluster in the upper center that consists of the Pacific Islands.

If you see only the scatterplot, you might miss noticing the shapes of the individual distributions, including the skewness in the shape of the distribution of maximums and the lump in the right tail of the distribution of minimums.

13 **a.**

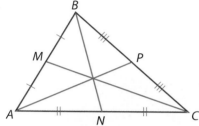

b. Students should create the triangles described.

c. The medians always intersect at a single point inside the triangle.

d. The triangle should balance when the tip of the pencil is placed at the point where the medians intersect (the centroid or center of mass).

e. The median for a histogram will be the balance point when it is also the mean of the distribution. In a symmetric distribution, such as 1, 2, 4, 4, 5, 6, 6, 8, 9, the mean and median are the same value.

Reflections

14 **a.** It is more difficult to find examples of data skewed to the left than to the right because a left skew requires most values to be near some maximum value. This is less common than the situation where most values are near a minimum value, typically 0. Gas mileage, weights, income, calories consumed, and retail prices, for example, can go only so low, and certainly not below 0, but there may be no limit (wall) on the high end.

Here are some examples of distributions that are skewed to the left: the test scores of an "easy" exam or for a class that studied hard; ages of people who were diagnosed with Alzheimer's disease in the United States last year; winning points in a blackjack game, where the maximum is 21.

b. Examples include the cloud-seeding data on page 78 in Investigation 1, the lengths of male and female bears on page 76 in Investigation 1, and young adult men's and women's heights on page 80 in Investigation 1. Another example is that the mean and spread in the heights of 3-year-old people are less than the mean and spread in the heights of 30-year olds.

15 Sometimes a distribution has two distinct peaks. Such a distribution is said to be **bimodal**. Bimodal distributions often result from the mixture of two populations, such as adults and children or men and women. Some distributions have no peaks. These distributions are called **rectangular** distributions.

a. Give an example of a bimodal distribution from your work in this lesson.

b. Describe a different situation that would yield data with a bimodal distribution.

c. Describe a situation that would yield data with a rectangular distribution.

d. The following photo shows a "living histogram" of the heights of students in a course on a college campus. How would you describe the shape of this distribution? Why might this be the case?

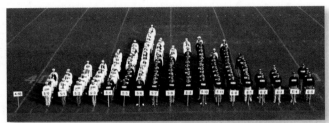

Source: *The Hartford Courant,* "Reaching New Heights," November 23, 1996. Photo by K. Hanley.

16 Suppose that you want to estimate the total weekly allowance received by students in your class.

a. Should you start by estimating the mean or the median of the weekly allowances?

b. Make a reasonable estimate of the measure of center that you selected in Part a and use it to estimate the total weekly allowance received by students in your class.

17 A soccer goalie's statistics for the last three matches are: saved 9 out of 10 shots on goal, saved 8 out of 9 shots on goal, and saved 3 out of 5 shots on goal.

a. Which of the following computations gives the mean percentage saved per match?

$$\frac{20}{24} = 83\% \qquad \frac{\frac{9}{10} + \frac{8}{9} + \frac{3}{5}}{3} \approx 79.6\%$$

b. What does the other computation tell you?

15 **a.** Students might suggest the female bear, seeded clouds, or the cholesterol in fast-food sandwiches as examples of bimodal distributions. In the cholesterol distribution, the chicken and beef sandwiches have separate peaks.

b. One example of a bimodal distribution would be the amount of weight that could be bench-pressed by a large group consisting of approximately the same number of males and females.

c. Rectangular distributions would occur for equally-likely probabilistic situations such as the number on a die when rolled many times or (as seen in Applications Task 3, Part a) with random assignment of numbers such as the last digit of phone numbers.

d. The shape is bimodal—with two peaks in the center and sloping down symmetrically on both sides. This distribution, like many distributions, is a mixture of two different groups, males and females. (However, if there were more students, the distribution probably wouldn't be bimodal. There isn't enough separation in the heights of young men and young women to produce bimodality.

16 **a.** Start by estimating the mean allowance, because by multiplying the mean by the number of students, you will get the total.

b. For example, if there are 32 students in the class and a good estimate of the mean allowance is $10, then the total would be $320.

17 **a.** The second computation gives the mean percentage saved per game. This computation lets all three games count equally.

b. The first computation is the percentage saved over all three games. This computation lets all 24 shots on goal count equally.

> **INSTRUCTIONAL NOTE**
> Task 17 provides an opportunity to discuss fractions and order of operations.

Extensions

18 To test the statement, "The mean of a set of data is the balance point of the distribution," first get a yardstick and a set of equal weights, such as children's cubical blocks or small packets of sugar.

a. Place two weights at 4 inches from one end and two weights at 31 inches. If you try to balance the yardstick with one finger, where should you place your finger?

b. What if you place one weight at 4 inches and two weights at 31 inches?

c. Experiment by placing more than three weights at various positions on the yardstick and finding the balance point.

d. What rule gives you the balance point?

19 In this lesson, you saw that for small data sets, dot plots provide a quick way to get a visual display of the data. **Stemplots** (or *stem-and-leaf plots*) provide another way of seeing patterns or unusual features in small data sets. The following stemplot shows the amount of money in cents that each student in one class of 25 students carried in coins. The stems are the hundreds and tens digits and the leaves are the ones digits.

Amount of Money in Coins (in cents)

```
 0 | 0  0  0  0  0
 1 | 2  7  8  9
 2 | 0  5  5  8
 3 | 4  4  7
 4 | 5  6  6  9
 5 |
 6 | 7
 7 | 3
 8 |
 9 | 0
10 |
11 | 4
12 |
13 |
14 |
15 | 2            11 | 4 represents 114¢
```

a. How many students had less than 30¢ in coins?

b. Where would you record the amount for another student who had $1.37 in coins? Who had 12¢?

c. Stemplots make it easy to find the median. What was the median amount of change?

Extensions

18 **a.** For weights placed at 4, 4, 31, and 31 inches, the yardstick will balance if you place your finger at $\frac{4 + 4 + 31 + 31}{4} = 17.5$ inches.

b. For weights placed at 4, 31, and 31 inches, place your finger at 22 inches.

c. Students should experiment with various placements of weights.

d. $\frac{d_1 + d_2 + \cdots + d_n}{n}$ is the balance point, where d_n represents the distance from zero on the yardstick for each weight and n represents the number of weights.

19 **a.** 13 students

b. Place a 7 on the stem of 13 so it looks like $13 \mid 7$. Place another 2 on the stem of 1 so it looks like $1 \mid 2\ 2\ 7\ 8\ 9$.

c. 28¢

NOTE To keep blocks from falling, use plastic interlocking blocks or you can attach binder clips to the yardstick. The weights must be heavy compared to the weight of the yardstick.

Unit 2

20 Sometimes a **back-to-back stemplot** is useful when comparing two distributions. The back-to-back stemplot below shows the ages of the 78 actors and 78 actresses who have won an Academy Award for best performance. The tens digit of the age is given in the middle column and the ones digit is given in the left column for actors and in the right column for actresses. The youngest actor to win an Academy Award was 29, and the youngest actress was 21. This stemplot has **split stems** where, for example, the ages from 20 through 24 are put on the first stem, and the ages from 25 through 29 are put on the second stem. (Source: www.oscars.com; www.imdb.com)

Ages of Academy Award Winners

Age of Actor		Age of Actress
	2	1 2 4 4 4 4
9	2	5 5 6 6 6 6 6 6 6 7 7 7 7 8 8 8 9 9 9 9 9
4 4 3 2 2 1 1 0 0	3	0 0 0 1 1 1 1 2 3 3 3 3 3 4 4 4 4 4 4
9 8 8 8 8 8 7 7 7 6 6 6 5 5 5 5	3	5 5 5 5 5 7 7 7 8 8 8 8 9
4 4 4 3 3 3 3 3 3 2 2 2 2 1 1 1 1 1 0 0 0 0 0 0 0	4	0 1 1 1 1 1 2 2
9 9 8 8 8 7 7 6 6 6 6 5	4	5 7 9 9
4 3 3 2 2 2 1 1	5	4
6 6 6	5	
2 2 1 0 0	6	0 1 1 3
	6	
	7	4
6	7	
	8	0

| 2 | 1 means 21 years of age

a. What would have happened if the stems hadn't been split?

b. An article on salon.com in March 2000 reported a study that was published in the journal *Psychological Reports*. The article discusses only the difference in the mean ages. For example,

> "The study, from the journal *Psychological Reports,* says the average age of a best actress winner in the past 25 years is 40.3. The average age for men is 45.6—a five-year difference.

> "While the gap isn't enormous, it is significant, and for actors it grew even larger when nominees, rather than just winners, were analyzed."

Do you think the means are the best ways to compare the ages? If not, explain what measure of center would be better to use and why.

c. Write a paragraph giving your interpretation of the data. (The stemplot includes all winners, not just those from 1975 to 2000, so you will get different values for the means than those reported.)

20 **a.** The lines for actors and actresses in their thirties and forties would no longer fit on the page.

b. The means aren't the best way to compare the distributions because the distribution for the age of actresses, but not for the actors, is skewed right, and the mean is sensitive to skewness. It would be better to compare the medians.

c. The shape of the distribution of ages of the actors is approximately normal, while the shape of the ages of actresses is skewed to the right (toward the larger values). In general, the actresses are much younger. The median age of the actors who have won an Academy Award for best performance is 42. The median age of the actresses is only 33. This is a nine-year difference. While this gap isn't enormous, it is pretty large. The means of 43.6 and 35.6, for men and women, respectively, are eight years apart. Even though two women won while in their 70s or 80s and only one man older than 62 has ever won, the majority of women winners were in their 20s and 30s while men were in their 30s and 40s, causing the mean and median for women to be significantly lower than for the men. The spread of the distributions for men and women are almost the same, with an IQR of 11.5 for men and 12 for women.

Unit 2

Read the following table about characteristics of public high schools in the United States.

National Public High School Characteristics 2002–2003

Characteristic	Mean	Median
Enrollment size	754	493
Percent minority	31.0	17.9

Source: Pew Hispanic Center analysis of U.S. Department of Education, Common Core of Data (CCD), Public Elementary/Secondary School Universe Survey, 2002–03. *The High Schools Hispanics Attend: Size and Other Key Characteristics*, Pew Hispanic Center Report, November 1, 2005.

a. The mean high school size is larger than the median. What does this tell you about the distribution of the sizes of high schools?

b. There are about 17,505 public high schools in the United States. About how many high school students are there in these schools?

c. A footnote to the table above says, "The mean school characteristics are the simple average over all high schools. These are not enrollment weighted. A small high school receives the same weight as a large high school." Suppose that there are four high schools in a district, with the following enrollments and percent minority.

High School	Enrollment	Percent Minority
Alpha	1,000	14
Beta	1,500	20
Gamma	2,000	15
Delta	3,500	35

i. What is the median percent minority if computed as described above? Interpret this percent in a sentence.

ii. What is the mean percent minority if computed as described above? Interpret this percent in a sentence.

iii. What percentage of students in the district are minority? Interpret this percent in a sentence.

d. From the information in the first table and in Part b, can you determine the percentage of U.S. public high school students who are minority? Explain.

 Examine the Fastest-Growing Franchise data set in your data analysis software. That data set includes the rank, franchise name, type of service, and minimum startup costs for the 100 fastest growing franchises in the United States. (Source: www.entrepreneur.com)

21 **a.** The fact that the mean is larger than the median suggests that the distribution is skewed to the right (towards the larger numbers). In fact, that is the case. For your information, here is the distribution.

Enrollment of High School	Number of Public High Schools
Fewer than 172 students	4,425
172 to 493	4,394
494 to 1,144	4,321
1,145 to 1,838	2,603
More than 1,838 students	1,762

(As an additional task, you might ask students to use this table to estimate the mean high school enrollment.)

b. $17,505(754) = 13,198,770$ students in public high schools

c. **i.** The median percent minority is $\frac{15 + 20}{2}$, or 17.5%. In half of these high schools, more than 17.5% of the students are minority, and in half of the high schools, less than 17.5% of the students are minority.

ii. $\frac{14 + 20 + 15 + 35}{4} = 21\%$. That is, if you average the percents from the four high schools, the mean percent of minority in a high school is 21%. (This is not the same as the overall percentage of minority in the district because the high schools have different enrollments.)

iii. The percentage of all students in the district who are minority is about 24.6%, as shown by the computation below.

$$\frac{0.14(1,000) + 0.20(1,500) + 0.15(2,000) + 0.35(3,500)}{1,000 + 1,500 + 2,000 + 3,500} = \frac{1,965}{8,000} \approx 0.246$$

d. No. Note that in Part c, the answer to part ii is different from that in part iii. This question asks for the equivalent of part iii, but you do not have the enrollment numbers and percent minority for each high school building in the United States.

22 **a.** Fast-food franchises occur most often. Student answers may vary, including: daily need to eat, advertising, and low startup costs (for some).

b.
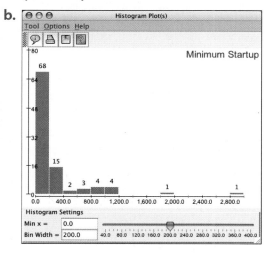

TECHNOLOGY NOTE These data are in *CPMP-Tools* under Statistics, Data Analysis, Data, Unit 2, Fastest Growing Franchises.

a. What kinds of businesses occur most often in that list? What are some possible reasons for their popularity?

b. Use data analysis software to make an appropriate graph for displaying the distribution of minimum startup costs.

c. Describe the shape, center, and spread of the distribution. Use the "Estimate Center" custom tool.

d. Why might a measure of center of minimum startup costs be somewhat misleading to a person who wanted to start a franchise?

23 The **relative frequency table** below shows (roughly) the distribution of the proportion of U.S. households that own various numbers of televisions.

Household Televisions

Number of Televisions, x	Proportion of Households, p
1	0.2
2	0.3
3	0.3
4	0.1
5	0.1

a. What is the median of this distribution?

b. To compute the mean of this distribution, first imagine that there are only 10 households in the United States. Convert the relative frequency table to a frequency table and compute the mean.

c. Now imagine that there are only 20 households in the United States. Convert the relative frequency table to a frequency table and compute the mean.

d. Use the following formula to compute the mean directly from the relative frequency table.

$$\bar{x} = x_1 \cdot p_1 + x_2 \cdot p_2 + x_3 \cdot p_3 + \cdots + x_k \cdot p_k \text{ or } \bar{x} = \Sigma x_i \cdot p_i$$

e. Explain why this formula works.

24 Suppose your grade is based 50% on tests, 30% on homework, and 20% on the final exam. So far in the class you have 82% on the tests and 90% on homework.

a. Compute your overall percentage (called a **weighted mean**) if you get 65% on the final exam. If you get 100% on the final exam.

b. Your teacher wants to use a spreadsheet to calculate weighted means for the students in your class in order to assign grades. She uses column **A** for names, column **B** for test score, column **C** for homework percentage, column **D** for final exam, and column **E** for the weighted mean. Give the function she would use to calculate the values in column **E**.

c. Using the display on the previous page, this distribution is skewed right, with a high peak at $0 to $200,000. Since it is skewed right the mean (approximately $256,930) will be larger than the median (approximately $105,550). There is a lot of variability in the startup costs with a minimum startup price of $25 for a Results Travel franchise and a maximum cost of $2,800,000 for a Pizza Hut, Inc. franchise. Most of the variability is in the upper quartile because three-fourths of the values are between $0 and $269,380.

d. These franchises are the fastest growing franchises. Any measure of center of the top 100 franchises would not convey much information to a person interested in starting any franchise. If someone wanted to enter into a particular type of business, it would be more helpful to know the mean or median for that particular type of business.

23 a. The median is 2.5 televisions.

b. The frequency table below is for the case of only 10 households in the United States. The mean is $\bar{x} = \dfrac{x_1 \cdot f_1 + x_2 \cdot f_2 + x_3 \cdot f_3 + \cdots + x_k \cdot f_k}{f_1 + f_2 + f_3 + \cdots + f_k} =$

$\dfrac{1(2) + 2(3) + 3(3) + 4(1) + 5(1)}{10} = 2.6.$

Number of Televisions	Count of Households
1	2
2	3
3	3
4	1
5	1

c. If there were 20 households, the frequency table would be

The mean is unchanged; $\bar{x} = \dfrac{1(4) + 2(6) + 3(6) + 4(2) + 5(2)}{20} = 2.6.$

Number of Televisions	Count of Households
1	4
2	6
3	6
4	2
5	2

d. The mean is $\bar{x} = x_1 \cdot p_1 + x_2 \cdot p_2 + x_3 \cdot p_3 + \cdots + x_k \cdot p_k =$
$1(0.2) + 2(0.3) + 3(0.3) + 4(0.1) + 5(0.1) = 2.6$

e. To show why this formula works, you can go through the following reasoning, either algebraically or in words:

$$\bar{x} = \frac{x_1 \cdot f_1 + x_2 \cdot f_2 + x_3 \cdot f_3 + \cdots + x_k \cdot f_k}{f_1 + f_2 + f_3 + \cdots + f_k}$$
$$= \frac{x_1 \cdot f_1 + x_2 \cdot f_2 + x_3 \cdot f_3 + \cdots + x_k \cdot f_k}{\Sigma f}$$
$$= x_1 \cdot \frac{f_1}{\Sigma f} + x_2 \cdot \frac{f_2}{\Sigma f} + x_3 \cdot \frac{f_3}{\Sigma f} + \cdots + x_k \cdot \frac{f_k}{\Sigma f}$$
$$= x_1 \cdot p_1 + x_2 \cdot p_2 + x_3 \cdot p_3 + \cdots + x_k \cdot p_k$$

24 a. $0.50(82) + 0.30(90) + 0.20(65) = 81\%$
$0.50(82) + 0.30(90) + 0.20(100) = 88\%$

b. Type the formula "=0.5*B1+0.3*C1+0.2*D1" and then paste it into all cells in column **E**.

NOTE The computations here are like those for computing a mean from a relative frequency table in Extensions Task 21.

25. Many people who have dropped out of the traditional school setting earn an equivalent to a high school diploma. A GED (General Educational Development Credential) is given to a person who passes a test for a course to complete high school credits.

    There were 501,000 people in the United States and its territories who received GEDs in 2000. The following table gives the breakdown by age of those taking the test.

Taking the GED

Age	19 yrs and under	20–24 yrs	25–29 yrs	30–34 yrs	35 yrs and over
% of GED Takers	42%	26%	11%	8%	14%

Source: American Council on Education, General Educational Development Testing Service, *Who took the GED?* Statistical Report, August 2001.

   a. Estimate the median age of someone who takes the test and explain how you arrived at your estimate.

   b. Estimate the mean age of someone who takes the test and explain how you arrived at your estimate.

Review

26. Given that $4.2 \cdot 5.5 = 23.1$, use mental computation to evaluate each of the following.

   a. $-4.2 \cdot 5.5$ b. $-4.2(-5.5)$ c. $\dfrac{23.1}{-5.5}$

   d. $4.2(-55)$ e. $\dfrac{-23.1}{2.1}$

27. When an object is dropped from some high spot, the distance it falls is related to the time it has been falling by the formula $d = 4.9t^2$, where t is time in seconds and d is distance in meters. Suppose a ball falls 250 meters down a mineshaft. To estimate the time, to the nearest second, it takes for the ball to fall this distance:

   a. What possible calculator or computer tools could you use?

   b. Could you answer this question without the aid of technology tools? Explain.

   c. What solution method *would* you use? Why?

   d. What is your estimate of the time it takes for the ball to fall the 250 meters?

   e. How could you check your estimate?

25 **a.** The median is between 20 and 24 years of age. The median is the age where half of those receiving a GED are below that age and half are above, which happens in the 20–24 age range.

b. The mean is approximately 25 years.

   Students have to find some way to summarize the age categories by a single number. Answers can vary depending on the age chosen to represent each age bracket. One way might be to use the center of the age interval: 18.5 years old (GEDs usually do not apply to people under age 17), 22 years, 27 years, 32 years, and then make an estimate of maybe 45 years for the final category. Then the mean age is
$$\bar{x} \approx 18.5(0.42) + 22(0.26) + 27(0.11) + 32(0.08) + 45(0.14)$$
$$= 25.32 \text{ years.}$$

Review

 26 **a.** -23.1 **b.** 23.1 **c.** -4.2

       d. -231 **e.** -11

 27 **a.** You might use the tables or graphs on a graphing calculator, a calculator to compute $\sqrt{\frac{250}{4.9}}$, or a CAS or spreadsheet application to solve $4.9t^2 = 250$.

b. Since the solution only needs to be given in seconds, students might approximate the solution by rounding 4.9 to 5, resulting in $t^2 = 50$. This is very close to $t^2 = 49$, giving a solution of $t = 7$ seconds.

c. Methods may vary. Graphs allow you to get an overall visual of the range of solutions. Some students may use tables to help them find an appropriate window, and then a graph to find the solutions.

d. $t \approx 7$ seconds

e. The best way to check the estimate is by substituting 7 seconds into the rule for t. The distance should be approximately 250 meters.

28 Consider the square shown at the right.

   a. Find the area of square *ABCD*.

   b. Find the length of $\overline{BD}$.

   c. Find the area of △*BDC*.

29 Evaluate each expression when $x = 3$.

   a. 2^x **b.** $5 \cdot 2^x$ **c.** $(5 \cdot 2)^x$

   d. $(-x)^2$ **e.** $(-2)^{x+1}$ **f.** -2^{x+1}

30 If the price of an item that costs $90 in 2005 increases to $108 by 2006, we say that the percent increase is 20%.

   a. Assuming that the percent increase is the same from 2006 to 2007, what will be the cost of this same item in 2007?

   b. If this percent increase continues, how long will it take for the price to double?

   c. Use the words *NOW* and *NEXT* to write a rule that shows how to use the price of the item in one year to find the price of the item in the next year.

31 Trace each diagram onto your paper and then complete each shape so the indicated line is a symmetry line for the shape.

   a.   **b.**   **c.**

32 The temperature in Phoenix, Arizona, on one October day is shown in the graph below.

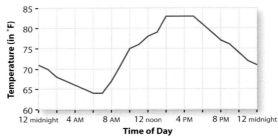

   a. What was the high temperature on this day and approximately when did it occur?

   b. What was the low temperature on this day and approximately when did it occur?

   c. During what part(s) of the day was the temperature less than 75°?

   d. During what time period(s) was the temperature increasing? Decreasing? How is this reflected in the graph?

28 **a.** $AB = \sqrt{3^2 + 2^2} = \sqrt{13}$

Area of square
$ABCD = \sqrt{13}\sqrt{13} = 13$ square units

Also, *area of square*
$ABCD = 4\left(\frac{1}{2}(3)(2)\right) + 1 = 13$ square units

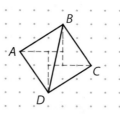

b. $BD = \sqrt{1^2 + 5^2} = \sqrt{26}$

c. *Area of* $\triangle BDC = \frac{1}{2}\sqrt{13}\sqrt{13} = 6.5$ square units

29 **a.** $2^3 = 8$ **b.** $5 \cdot 2^3 = 40$
c. $(5 \cdot 2)^3 = (10)^3 = 1{,}000$ **d.** $(-3)^2 = 9$
e. $(-2)^4 = 16$ **f.** $-2^4 = -16$

> **INSTRUCTIONAL NOTE**
> Task 29 provides an opportunity to review order of operations.

30 **a.** Students might figure 20% of $108 to get $21.60, for a total of $129.60. Or they might figure $(1.20)(108) = \$129.60$.

b. In 2008, the price is 120% of 129.60 = $155.52. In 2009, the price is 120% of 155.52 = $186.62, more than double the original $90. So it takes 4 years. (Students who do not continue the calculation may be misled into thinking it will take 5 years since the increase every year is $\frac{1}{5}$.)

c. $NEXT = 1.20 \cdot NOW$, starting at $90

31 **a.**   **b.**   **c.**

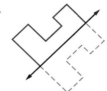

32 **a.** The high temperature was 83°F between 2:00 PM and 5:00 PM.

b. The low temperature was approximately 64°F between 6:00 AM and 7:00 AM.

c. The temperature was less than 75°F between midnight and 10 AM, and then again between about 9:30 PM and midnight.

d. The temperature was increasing between 7 AM and 2 PM.

The temperature was decreasing between midnight and 6 AM, and then again between 5 PM and midnight.

An increasing temperature is shown in the graph by line segments with positive slopes.

A decreasing temperature is shown in the graph by line segments with negative slopes.

Assessment Masters 86–94.

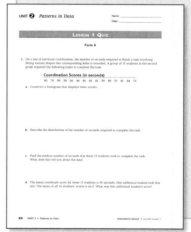

LESSON
2

Measuring Variability

The observation that no two snowflakes are alike is somewhat amazing. But in fact, there is *variability* in nearly everything. When a car part is manufactured, each part will differ slightly from the others. If many people measure the length of a room to the nearest millimeter, there will be many slightly different measurements. If you conduct the same experiment several times, you will get slightly different results. Because variability is everywhere, it is important to understand how variability can be measured and interpreted.

People vary too and height is one of the more obvious variables. The growth charts on page 105 come from a handbook for doctors. The plot *on the left* gives the mean height of boys at ages 0 through 14 and the plot *on the right* gives the mean height for girls at the same ages.

LESSON 2 • Measuring Variability **103**

Measuring Variability

Variability is present in all processes and in all physical things. Measures of variability tell us how spread out a distribution is. Examples of people for whom the variability in a distribution is important are doctors who must decide if a test result is abnormal, engineers who need to know how far off measurements are likely to be, educators who need to know how many items to put on a standardized test to get a precise measure of a student's achievement, and machine operators who must know how much variability is normal in the output of their machine.

Students should understand by now that the range is not sufficient as a measure of variability. The range is computed using only the minimum and the maximum, so is too sensitive to outliers. Further, the maximum and minimum tend to get farther apart with larger samples.

In this lesson, students will learn how to measure the position of a value in a distribution using percentiles and deviations from the mean. They will quantify variability using the five-number summary (minimum, lower quartile, median, upper quartile, and maximum), and the standard deviation. They will learn to use a box plot to display variability.

For approximately normal distributions, students will estimate the mean and standard deviation from a histogram of the distribution. The *CPMP-Tools* data analysis software contains some of the data sets in this lesson. Students can check their estimates using the "Estimate Center and Spread" custom tool or by entering the data into a graphing calculator or other computer application. Data included in the data analysis software are Blood Lead Levels (page 112), Heights of Young Adults (page 117), Achievement Test Scores (page 118), January Sunshine (page 123) (extra sunshine data), Concord and Portland Precipitation (page 123), Number of Marriages (page 130), Study Time (page 134), and U.S. Population by Race (page 139).

Transformations are basic to data analysis. You transform to get the unit of measurement that you want, for convenience in computations, or to make a highly skewed distribution into one that is approximately normal. Students already are quite familiar with transformations like converting from feet to inches and from counts to percents. Students will examine the effect of linear transformations on the shape of the distribution, on measures of center, and on measures of spread.

Heights from Birth to 14 Years of Age

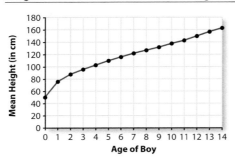

Think About This Situation

Use the plots above to answer the following questions.

a Is it reasonable to call a 14-year-old boy "taller than average" if his height is 170 cm? Is it reasonable to call a 14-year-old boy "tall" if his height is 170 cm? What additional information about 14-year-old boys would you need to know to be able to say that he is "tall"?

b From what you know about people's heights, is there as much variability in the heights of 2-year-old girls as in the heights of 14-year-old girls? Can you use this chart to answer this question?

c During which year do children grow most rapidly in height?

In this lesson, you will learn how to find and interpret measures of position and measures of variability in a distribution.

Investigation 1 Measuring Position

If you are at the 40th **percentile** of height for your age, that means that 40% of people your age are your height or shorter than you are and 60% are taller. Percentiles, like the median, describe the position of a value in a distribution. Your work in this investigation will help you answer this question:

How do you find and interpret percentiles and quartiles?

The physical growth charts on page 105 display two sets of curved lines. The curved lines at the top give height percentiles, while the curved lines at the bottom give weight percentiles. The percentiles are the small numbers 5, 10, 25, 50, 75, 90, and 95 on the right ends of the curved lines.

Lesson Objectives

- Find and interpret percentiles and quartiles as measures of the position of a value in a distribution
- Find the five-number summary and the interquartile range (IQR) and interpret the IQR as a measure of variability
- Determine if a value is an outlier using a common rule
- Construct and interpret a box plot
- Compute and interpret deviations from the mean
- Compute or estimate and interpret the standard deviation as a measure of spread
- Predict the effect on the shape, center, and spread of a distribution when the same number is added to each value or when each value is multiplied by the same number

Lesson Launch

Students may be interested that the average height of boys and girls are so close for ages 0 to 14. Boys are slightly taller at ages 5 and 6. For Part c, ask students how the graphs help them to answer this question.

Think About This Situation

a Yes, a 14-year-old boy who is 170 cm tall is taller than average. (The average height for a 14-year-old boy is 163 cm.) You can't say whether or not he is "tall" unless you know something about the spread of heights for 14-year-old boys.

b Experience suggests that the heights of 14-year-old girls vary more than the heights of 2-year-old girls, but you don't have enough information from the chart alone to make this judgment. This is because the charts represent the mean heights based on many children.

c During their first year, children grow about 25 cm, more than any other year. This year also has the largest percentage change, about a 50% increase.

Teaching Resources

Transparency Master 95.

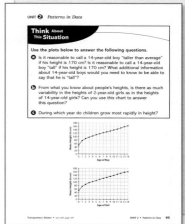

Investigation 1 Measuring Position

In this investigation, students explore the concept of percentile, and quartile.

Defining percentiles. Percentiles typically are used only when there are a very large or infinite number of possible values, such as with heights. When there are a small number of possible values we get into difficulty trying to define percentiles. For example, with the values 1, 2, 3, 4, 5, the value 3 is the median, and so should be at the 50th percentile, but it isn't true that half of the numbers are less than or equal to 3.

INSTRUCTIONAL NOTE The *n*th percentile is the value at which *n*% of the data are less than or equal to that value. For example, 40% of the data are at or below the 40th percentile and about 60% are above.

Boys' Physical Growth Percentiles,
(2 to 20 Years)

Girls' Physical Growth Percentiles,
(2 to 20 Years)

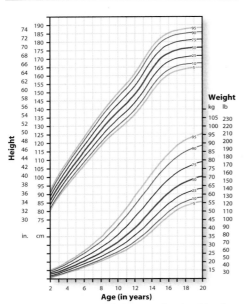

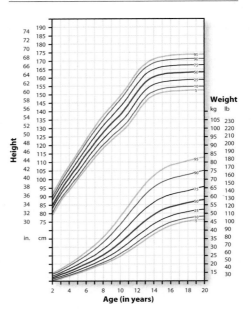

Source: National Center for Health Statistics, www.cdc.gov/growthcharts/

1. Suppose John is a 14-year-old boy who weighs 45 kg (100 pounds). John is at the 25th percentile of weight for his age. Twenty-five percent of 14-year-old boys weigh the same or less than John and 75% weigh more than John. If John's height is 170 cm (almost 5'7"), he is at the 75th percentile of height for his age. Based on the information given about John, how would you describe John's general appearance?

2. Growth charts contain an amazing amount of information. Use the growth charts to help you answer the following questions.

   a. What is the approximate percentile for a 9-year-old girl who is 128 cm tall?

   b. What is the 25th percentile of height for 4-year-old boys? The 50th percentile? The 75th percentile?

   c. About how tall does a 12-year-old girl have to be so that she is as tall or taller than 75% of the girls her age? How tall does a 12-year-old boy have to be?

   d. How tall would a 14-year-old boy have to be so that you would consider him "tall" for his age? How did you make this decision?

   e. According to the chart, is there more variability in the heights of 2-year-old girls or 14-year-old girls?

   f. How can you tell from the height and weight chart when children are growing the fastest? When is the increase in weight the greatest for girls? For boys?

Percentiles and standardized tests. You may want to bring to class booklets about standardized tests that your students have taken or will be taking (such as the preACT PLAN or the PSAT). You may be able to get these booklets from the counseling office. They describe what a given score means in terms of percentiles. This information is also available on the College Board's Web site for counselors: www.collegeboard.com/toc/html/toccounselors000.html. Students need to understand that their percentile on these tests is not the same as the percentage of questions that they answered correctly.

Quartiles versus quarters. The first quartile, for example, is a number. So, it isn't correct for very short students to say that their height is "in the first quartile." Their height is said to be "below the first quartile," or, "in the bottom quarter of the population." That is, "quartile" isn't a synonym for "quarter," but is rather a point on the number line that divides the data into quarters.

Various rules for finding quartiles. The TI-83 and TI-84 calculators and some statistical software use the same rule as in the Student book for finding the quartiles when there are an odd number of values (Problem 6 Part c, page 107). That is, when finding the first and third quartiles, don't consider the value that is at the median position a part of either "half." However, be aware that there are other definitions used by some statistical software.

For example, the value in the median position may be included in *both* halves. The latter definition will result in quartiles closer together and may result in identifying more values being identified as outliers, especially when the number of values is small.

The growth charts and sensitivity. Students should spend some time becoming comfortable with the growth charts. They will certainly want to start by finding their own percentile.

It is best not to ask them to reveal their percentiles to the rest of the class since their own heights and weights can be sensitive issues to teenagers. You might use for illustration the heights and weights of school athletes, which many schools make available.

INSTRUCTIONAL NOTE
You may wish to use this information about quartiles to stress the importance of having clear workable definitions and that definitions in different texts may not be identical.

COMMUNICATION SKILL
Ask questions when I am not sure I understand what we are doing

① John is somewhat tall and quite thin since he is taller than three-fourths of the boys his age but weighs less than three-fourths of the boys his age.

② **a.** About the 25th percentile

b. 25th percentile: 39.5 inches, or 100 cm
50th percentile: 40.5 inches, or 103 cm
75th percentile: 42 inches, or 106 cm

c. Girl: about 61.5 inches, or 156 cm
Boy: about 60.5 inches, or 154 cm

d. If, for example, students decide that he should be at the 90th percentile or above, he would be at least 68 inches, or 173 cm.

e. There is almost twice as much variability in the heights of 14-year-old girls. For example, the middle 90% of 14-year-old girls are in the 22-cm range between 150 and 172 cm. The middle 90% of 2-year-old girls are in the 13-cm range between 80 and 93 cm.

f. The greatest increase in growth occurs where the lines are the steepest. That occurs with weight for girls around age 12 and for boys around age 14.

Teaching Resources

Student Masters 96–97.

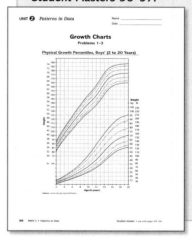

3 Some percentiles have special names. The 25th percentile is called the **lower** or **first quartile**. The 75th percentile is called the **upper** or **third quartile**. Find the heights of 6-year-old girls on the growth charts.

   a. Estimate and interpret the lower quartile.

   b. Estimate and interpret the upper quartile.

   c. What would the *middle* or *second quartile* be called? What is its percentile?

4 The histogram below displays the results of a survey filled out by 460 varsity athletes in football and women's and men's basketball from schools around Detroit, Michigan. These results were reported in a school newspaper.

Hours Spent on Homework per Day

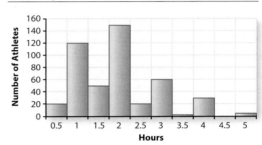

   a. What is an unusual feature of this distribution? What do you think is the reason for this?

   b. Estimate the median and the quartiles. Use the upper quartile in a sentence that describes this distribution.

   c. Estimate the percentile for an athlete who studied 3.5 hours.

5 Suppose you get 40 points out of 50 on your next math test. Can you determine your percentage correct? Your percentile in your class? If so, calculate them. If not, explain why not.

6 The math homework grades for two ninth-grade students at Lakeview High School are given below.

Susan's Homework Grades

8, 8, 7, 9, 7, 8, 8, 6, 8, 7,
8, 8, 8, 7, 8, 8, 10, 9, 9, 9

Jack's Homework Grades

10, 7, 7, 9, 5, 8, 7, 4, 7,
5, 8, 8, 8, 4, 5, 6, 5, 8, 7

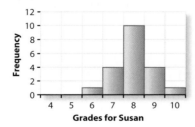

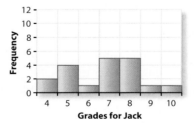

3　**a.** The lower quartile is about 44 inches, or 111 cm. About 25% of 6-year-old girls are 44 inches tall or shorter.

　　b. The upper quartile is about 46.5 inches, or 118 cm. About 75% of 6-year-old girls are 46.5 inches tall or shorter.

　　c. For 6-year-old girls, the second quartile in height is 115 cm, or about 45 inches. The second or middle quartile is the median. It is at the 50th percentile.

4　**a.** The unusual feature is that the taller bars occur at whole numbers. Many athletes must be estimating the number of hours to the nearest hour. Another unusual feature is that apparently all athletes reported doing some homework that week.

　　b. Students are to estimate the measures, not calculate them. The median is about 2. The lower quartile is about 1. The upper quartile is about 2.5. About 25% of the athletes reported that they spent more than 2.5 hours per day on homework.

　　c. All but about 27 of the 460 athletes spent the same or fewer hours than this athlete on homework. Because $\frac{433}{470} \approx 0.92$, he or she is at about the 92nd percentile.

5　Yes, your percentage correct is $\frac{40}{50}$, or 80%.

　　No. If everyone else in the class had a score lower than 40 points, you would be at the 100th percentile. If almost everyone else scored more points than you did, you would be near the 0th percentile.

a. Which of the students has greater variability in his or her grades?

b. Put the 20 grades for Susan in an ordered list and find the median.

    i. Find the quartiles by finding the medians of the lower and upper halves.

    ii. Mark the positions of the median and quartiles on your ordered list of grades.

c. Jack has 19 grades. Put them in an ordered list and find the median.

    i. To find the first and third quartiles when there are an odd number of values, one strategy is to leave out the median and then find the median of the lower values and the median of the upper values. Use this strategy to find the quartiles of Jack's grades.

    ii. Mark the positions of the median and quartiles on your ordered list of Jack's grades.

d. For which student are the lower and upper quartiles farther apart? What does this tell you about the variability of the grades of the two students?

Summarize
the Mathematics

In this investigation, you learned how percentiles and quartiles are used to locate a value in a distribution.

a What information does a percentile tell you? Give an example of when you would want to be at the 10th percentile rather than at the 90th. At the 90th percentile rather than at the 10th percentile.

b What does the lower quartile tell you? The upper quartile? The middle quartile?

Be prepared to share your ideas and reasoning with the class.

✓Check Your Understanding

The table on page 108 gives the price per ounce of each of the 16 sunscreens rated as giving excellent protection by *Consumer Reports*.

a. Find the median and quartiles of the distribution. Explain what the median and quartiles tell you about the distribution.

b. Which sunscreen is at about the 70th percentile in price per ounce?

6 **a.** Jack's grades are more spread out. His grades vary from 4 through 10, while Susan's grades only vary from 6 through 10. But aside from looking at just the extreme values, most of the grades for Jack are away from the center of his distribution, while those for Susan tend to be lumped in the middle.

b. **i.** Susan's median is 8, lower quartile is 7.5, and upper quartile is 8.5.

   ii. Ordered list: 6, 7, 7, 7, 7 | 8, 8, 8, 8, 8 | 8, 8, 8, 8, 8 | 9, 9, 9, 9, 10

   $Q_1 = 7.5$ Median = 8 $Q_3 = 8.5$

c. **i.** Jack's median is 7, lower quartile is 5, and upper quartile is 8.

   ii. Ordered list: 4, 4, 5, 5, <u>5</u>, 5, 6, 7, 7, <u>7</u>, 7, 7, 8, 8, <u>8</u>, 8, 8, 9, 10

   $Q_1 = 5$ Median = 7 $Q_3 = 8$

d. Susan's quartiles are only 1 unit apart while Jack's quartiles are 3 units apart. There is more variability in the middle half of Jack's grades than in Susan's.

Summarize
the Mathematics

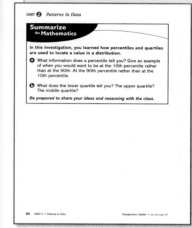

Teaching Resources

Transparency Master 98.

a Some examples where students would want to be at the 10th percentile include blood pressure, number of homework assignments missed, price paid for a new CD, and number of colds in a year. Some examples where students would want to be at the 90th percentile include score on academic test, income as an adult, and number of friends.

b The lower quartile is the number that divides the lower quarter of the values from the upper three-quarters. The upper quartile is the number that divides the lower three-quarters of the values from the upper quarter. The middle quartile, or median, is the number at which half of the values are larger and half are smaller.

PROCESSING PROMPT When I did not understand _____,
I asked … .   *(topic/problem)*

✓ Check Your Understanding

a. The ordered values are 0.50, 0.68, 0.81, 0.90, 0.90, 0.91, 0.92, 1.13, 1.17, 1.25, 1.59, 2.02, 2.17, 2.17, 4.79, 4.91. The median is $1.15 and the quartiles are $0.90 and $2.095. About a quarter of the sunscreens that provide excellent protection cost less than 90 cents per ounce. About half cost less than $1.15 per ounce. Only a quarter cost more than $2.095 per ounce.

b. This would be the sunscreen at about 0.7(16) = 11.2, or 11th from the bottom. This is Olay Complete UV Protective Moisture.

Best Sunscreens

Brand	Price Per Ounce
Banana Boat Baby Block Sunblock	$1.13
Banana Boat Kids Sunblock	0.90
Banana Boat Sport Sunblock	0.92
Banana Boat Sport Sunscreen	4.91
Banana Boat Ultra Sunblock	0.91
Coppertone Kids Sunblock With Parsol 1789	1.25
Coppertone Sport Sunblock	4.79
Coppertone Sport Ultra Sweatproof Dry	2.02
Coppertone Water Babies Sunblock	1.17
Hawaiian Tropic 15 Plus Sunblock	0.81
Hawaiian Tropic 30 Plus Sunblock	0.90
Neutrogena UVA/UVB Sunblock	2.17
Olay Complete UV Protective Moisture	1.59
Ombrelle Sunscreen	2.17
Rite Aid Sunblock	0.50
Walgreens Ultra Sunblock	0.68

Source: www.consumerreports.org

 **Investigation 2**

Measuring and Displaying Variability: The Five-Number Summary and Box Plots

The quartiles together with the median give a good indication of the center and variability (spread) of a set of data. A more complete picture of the distribution is given by the **five-number summary**, the **minimum value**, the **lower quartile** (Q_1), the **median** (Q_2), the **upper quartile** (Q_3), and the **maximum value**. The distance between the first and third quartiles is called the **interquartile range** (IQR = $Q_3 - Q_1$).

As you work on the following problems, look for answers to these questions:

How can you use the interquartile range to measure variability?

How can you use plots of the five-number summary to compare distributions?

1. Refer back to the growth charts on page 105.

   a. Estimate the five-number summary for 13-year-old girls' heights. For 13-year-old boys' heights.

   b. Estimate the interquartile range of the heights of 13-year-old girls. Of 13-year-old boys. What do these IQRs tell you about heights of 13-year-old girls and boys?

Measuring and Displaying Variability: The Five-Number Summary and Box Plots

In this investigation, students will use their knowledge about quartiles to describe distributions using the five-number summary and to understand the interquartile range (IQR) as a measure of variability. Box plots are used to display the five-number summaries.

Students sometimes have trouble interpreting box plots, confusing the length of a whisker or section of the box with the number of values. For example, students may think that because the lower whisker is longer than the upper whisker, there are more values in the lower whisker. In fact, each whisker contains about 25% of the values.

Students should be aware that some software makes box plots so that they appear vertically, usually with the scale on the left. See the example below from *Data Desk*.

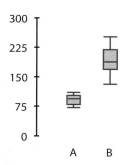

POSSIBLE MISCONCEPTION
Sometimes students incorrectly assume that the longer the whisker, the more values in that whisker.

1 a. The maximum and minimum cannot be read directly from the graph. Students will have to make a reasonable choice. For the maximum, for example, students may decide to go another jump beyond the 95th percentile that is as big as the jump from the 90th to 95th percentiles. That won't be big enough, but it is a reasonable maximum for almost all children. Using that reasoning, they should get the following five-number summaries.

INSTRUCTIONAL NOTE
The transparencies of growth charts for boys and girls made from the Teaching Masters 96 and 97 can be placed on top of each other to illustrate the answer to Problem 1, Part c.

	Min	Q_1	Q_2	Q_3	Max
Girls' height (in cm)	142	153	157	161	171
Boys' height (in cm)	140	150	156	161	172

b. Girls: $161 - 153 = 8$ cm
Boys: $161 - 150 = 11$ cm
The middle half of the girls' heights fall within an 8-cm interval. The middle half of the boys' heights fall within an 11-cm interval. Thus, there is more variation in the heights of the 13-year-old boys than in the heights of the 13-year-old girls.

c. What happens to the interquartile range of heights as children get older? In general, do boys' heights or girls' heights have the larger interquartile range, or are they about the same?

d. What happens to the interquartile range of weights as children get older? In general, do boys' weights or girls' weights have the larger interquartile range, or are they about the same?

(2) Find the range and interquartile range of the following set of values.

1, 2, 3, 4, 5, 6, 70

a. Remove the outlier of 70. Find the range and interquartile range of the new set of values. Which changed more, the range or the interquartile range?

b. In general, is the range or interquartile range more resistant to outliers? In other words, which measure of spread tends to change less if an outlier is removed from a set of values? Explain your reasoning.

c. Why is the interquartile range more informative than the range as a measure of variability for many sets of data?

The five-number summary can be displayed in a **box plot**. To make a box plot, first make a number line. Above this line draw a narrow box from the lower quartile to the upper quartile; then draw line segments connecting the ends of the box to each **extreme value** (the maximum and minimum). Draw a vertical line in the box to indicate the location of the median. The segments at either end are often called **whiskers**, and the plot is sometimes called a **box-and-whiskers plot**.

(3) The following box plot shows the distribution of hot dog prices at Major League Baseball parks.

Hot Dog Prices (in dollars)
Source: www.teammarketing.com/fci.cfm?page=fci_mlb2004.cfm

a. Is the distribution skewed to the left or to the right, or is it symmetric? Explain your reasoning.

b. Estimate the five-number summary. Explain what each value tells you about hot dog prices.

(4) Box plots are most useful when the distribution is skewed or has outliers or if you want to compare two or more distributions. The math homework grades for five ninth-grade students at Lakeview High School—Maria (M), Tran (T), Gia (G), Jack (J), and Susan (S)—are shown with corresponding box plots.

c. The interquartile range of heights increases as children get older. The IQRs of boys and girls are about the same at younger ages, but that of the boys is slightly larger than that of the girls at older ages.

d. As children get older, the interquartile range of weights increases. It increases more than for heights. The IQR for weights is a bit larger for girls than for boys up to around age 14, after which it is larger for boys.

2 The five-number summary is 1, 2, 4, 6, 70.
The range is $70 - 1 = 69$ and the IQR is $6 - 2 = 4$.

a. The range is now $6 - 1 = 5$ while the IQR is relatively unchanged at $5 - 2 = 3$. The range certainly changed more.

b. The IQR is resistant to outliers, but the range is not. In other words, the range is sensitive to outliers, but the interquartile range is not.

c. The range is computed using only the minimum and the maximum and thus is too sensitive to outliers. Further, the maximum and minimum tend to get farther apart with larger samples. The IQR doesn't have either of these drawbacks.

For example, in examining heights of 18-year-old boys, a small sample probably would have all boys between about 5 feet, 4 inches and 6 feet, 2 inches for a range of about 10 inches. However, a very large sample might have a 7-foot-tall and a 4-foot-tall 18-year-old boy, for a range of 24 inches. You do not expect the interquartile range to increase as the sample gets bigger. It would be about 3.5 inches with either sample size.

3 **a.** The distribution is skewed to the right.

b. The five-number summary is about $2.20, $2.60, $3.00, $3.50, $4.50.

The lowest price for a hot dog at a Major League Baseball park is about $2.20. Twenty-five percent of the parks have prices for hot dogs less than or equal to about $2.60. Half of the parks charge more than $3.00 and half charge less. Seventy-five percent of the parks have hot dog prices less than or equal to $3.50. The highest price charged is $4.50.

Maria's Grades

8, 9, 6, 7, 9, 8, 8, 6, 9, 9,
8, 7, 8, 7, 9, 9, 7, 7, 8, 9

Tran's Grades

9, 8, 6, 9, 7, 9, 8, 4, 8, 5,
9, 9, 9, 6, 4, 6, 5, 8, 8, 8

Gia's Grades

8, 9, 9, 9, 6, 9, 8, 6, 8, 6,
8, 8, 8, 6, 6, 6, 3, 8, 8, 9

Jack's Grades

10, 7, 7, 9, 5, 8, 7, 4, 7,
5, 8, 8, 8, 4, 5, 6, 5, 8, 7

Susan's Grades

8, 8, 7, 9, 7, 8, 8, 6, 8, 7,
8, 8, 8, 7, 8, 8, 10, 9, 9, 9

Math Homework Grades

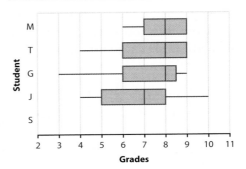

a. On a copy of the plot, make a box plot for Susan's homework grades.

b. Why do the plots for Maria and Tran have no whisker at the upper end?

c. Why is the lower whisker on Gia's box plot so long? Does this mean there are more grades for Gia in that whisker than in the shorter whisker?

d. Which distribution is the most symmetric? Which distributions are skewed to the left?

e. Use the box plots to determine which of the five students has the lowest median grade.

f. Use the box plots to determine which students have the smallest and largest interquartile ranges.

   i. Does the student with the smallest interquartile range also have the smallest range?

   ii. Does the student with the largest interquartile range also have the largest range?

g. Based on the box plots, which of the five students seems to have the best record?

5 You can produce box plots on your calculator by following a procedure similar to that for making histograms. After entering the data in a list and specifying the viewing window, select the box plot as the type of plot desired.

a. Use your calculator to make a box plot of Susan's grades from Problem 4.

b. Use the Trace feature to find the five-number summary for Susan's grades. Compare the results with your computations in the previous problem.

a. The five-number summary for Susan is 6, 7.5, 8, 8.5, 10 (from Problem 6 of the previous investigation), and the box plot is given below.

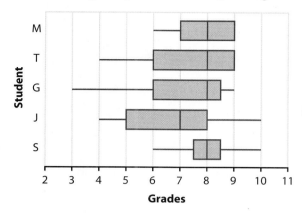

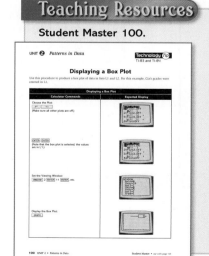

b. The upper quartiles (Q_3) and the maximums are both 9. This means that about 25% of the grades are 9s.

c. The lower whisker is so long because she had an unusually low grade of 3. It doesn't mean there are more grades in a longer whisker than in a shorter whisker; both include about 25% of the grades.

d. The grades for Susan are symmetric. The grades for Tran and Gia are skewed to the left.

e. Jack has the lowest median grade, 7. The rest of the students are all tied with medians of 8.

f. Jack and Tran have the largest IQR, 3, and Susan the smallest, 1.

   i. No, Susan has the smallest IQR, 1, but Maria has the smallest range, 3.

   ii. No, Jack and Tran have the largest IQR, 3, but Gia has the largest range, 6.

g. Susan has the best, and most consistent, record. Although her minimum, median, and maximum are the same as those of other students, overall she does the best. Students might also make a case for Maria, who has the most grades of 9 or above, a higher upper quartile than Susan, the same median, and almost as high a mean.

> **INSTRUCTIONAL NOTE**
> Many distributions do not have a standard shape and so it is not necessary or desirable to try to assign a shape to them. This is especially true when the distribution has only a small number of values. Maria's distribution is an example of such a distribution and should not be assigned a shape.

5 **a.**

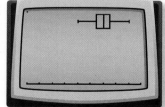 

TECHNOLOGY NOTE A Technology Tip for how to use the one-variable statistics (1-Var Stats) function on the TI-calculators is not provided at this point in the lesson. Even though this one command will calculate the mean, standard deviation, and five-number summary, at this stage students should become familiar with the LIST MATH menu.

b. Susan's minimum is 6, lower quartile is 7.5, median is 8, upper quartile is 8.5, and maximum is 10.

(6) Resting pulse rates have a lot of variability from person to person. In fact, rates between 60 and 100 are considered normal. For a highly conditioned athlete, "normal" can be as low as 40 beats per minute. Pulse rates also can vary quite a bit from time to time for the same person. (Source: www.nlm.nih.gov/medlineplus/ency/article/003399.htm)

a. Take your pulse for 20 seconds, triple it, and record your pulse rate (in number of beats per minute).

b. If you are able, do some mild exercise for 3 or 4 minutes as your teacher times you. Then take your pulse for 20 seconds, triple it, and record this exercising pulse rate (in number of beats per minute). Collect the results from all students in your class, keeping the data paired (*resting*, *exercising*) for each student.

c. Find the five-number summary of resting pulse rates for your class. Repeat this for the exercising pulse rates.

d. Above the same scale, draw box plots of the resting and exercising pulse rates for your class.

e. Compare the shapes, centers, and variability of the two distributions.

f. What information is lost when you make two box plots for the resting and exercising pulse rates for the same people?

g. Make a scatterplot that displays each person's two pulse rates as a single point. Can you see anything interesting that you could not see from the box plots?

h. Make a box plot of the differences in pulse rates, (*exercising − resting*). Do you see anything you didn't see before?

Summarize the Mathematics

In this investigation, you learned how to use the five-number summary and box plots to describe and compare distributions.

a) What is the five-number summary and what does it tell you?

b) Why does the interquartile range tend to be a more useful measure of variability than the range?

c) How does a box plot convey the shape of a distribution?

d) What does a box plot tell you that a histogram does not? What does a histogram tell you that a box plot does not?

Be prepared to share your ideas and reasoning with the class.

LESSON 2 • Measuring Variability **111**

6 **INSTRUCTIONAL NOTE** Be aware that you might have students who cannot or should not do even the mildest exercise. Make it easy for them to excuse themselves.

Students should start counting their pulse when you say "go." Say "stop" after 20 seconds. (If you go much longer than 20 seconds, students tend to lose count.) Then have students multiply their count by 3 to get the number of beats per minute.

INSTRUCTIONAL NOTE
Save these data for use in the next investigation.
---

a. Results will vary. The stemplot below shows the resting pulse rates from a class of 38 students. The data for your class should be similar, with a slight skew to the right and centered in the low 70s, perhaps with rates slightly higher than these older students.

Sample Class Pulse Rates

5	9
6	0 1 2 4 4
6	5 6 6 7 7 7 8 8 8 9 9 9
7	0 1 1 1 2 2 2 2 4
7	5 6 6 7 8 8 8
8	0 4
8	6 9

6|5 represents 65 beats per minute

b. You might have students run or march in place for three or four minutes, climb stairs, or walk quickly around the building.

c. The five-number summary of resting pulse rates for the students in Part a is:

minimum = 59, Q_1 = 67, median = 70.5, Q_3 = 76, maximum = 89

The IQR is $76 - 67 = 9$.

Exercising pulse rates will be higher.

d. Exercising pulse rate box plots will vary. A box plot for the students in Part a follows:

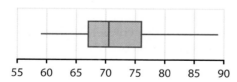

e. The distribution of exercising pulse rates probably will have more skewness to the right, a higher median, and a greater spread.

f. You can't see how much an individual's pulse rate changed. The data naturally are paired and you lose the connection if you make separate box plots.

Unit 2

g. Students should make a scatterplot with *resting pulse rate* on the *x*-axis and *exercising pulse rate* on the *y*-axis. There probably will be a positive trend in the scatterplot. Students who had higher pulse rates before exercising will tend to be the ones with higher pulse rates after exercising, and students who had lower pulse rates before exercising will tend to be the ones with lower pulse rates after exercising. Further, most or all points will be above the line $y = x$, indicating that each student's exercising pulse rate was higher than his or her resting pulse rate.

h. Box plots will vary. It probably will be the case that all differences are positive.

Teaching Resources

Transparency Master 101.

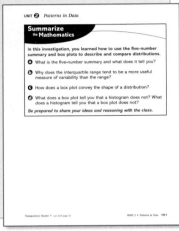

INSTRUCTIONAL NOTE
During the discussion of these items, help students recognize that the five-number summary and box plots are particularly useful with a skewed distribution or a distribution with outliers. Also, ask students to consider whether identical ranges for two data sets mean that the IQRs will be identical.

Summarize
the Mathematics

a The five-number summary consists of the minimum, the three quartiles, and the maximum, which divide the set of data into quarters of approximately the same number of values. From the five-number summary, you can get a good indication of the shape, center, and spread of the distribution.

b The range typically is not useful as a measure of variability because it is so sensitive to outliers. The range is computed using only the minimum and maximum, which often tend to get farther apart with a larger sample size. The interquartile range is resistant to outliers and tends to stay about the same size with a larger sample size as with a smaller one.

c If the distribution is symmetric, the two parts of the box will be about the same length and the two whiskers will also be about the same length. If any one of the four parts of a box plot is much shorter than the others, then the values tend to be closely clustered in that quarter. If one whisker and its adjacent part of the box are longer than the others, then the distribution is skewed in that direction.

d From a box plot, you clearly can see the upper and lower quartiles, the median, and the extremes. (In the next investigation, students will see how to identify outliers on a box plot.) Box plots make it easier to compare several distributions. From a histogram you can see the shape more exactly, including gaps that don't show up in a box plot. Also, you can see how many values there are from a histogram, but not from a box plot.

MATH TOOLKIT Students should write descriptions of how to locate the five-number summary in an ordered data set in their toolkit notes. They might use an example data set and also show how to compute the range and IQR. A discussion of how the range and IQR describe variability should also be included.

INSTRUCTIONAL NOTE The data set for the Check Your Understanding on the next page is included in *CPMP-Tools*. Students can produce two box plots on the same grid for this task by selecting both columns. The "i" button will display the statistics.

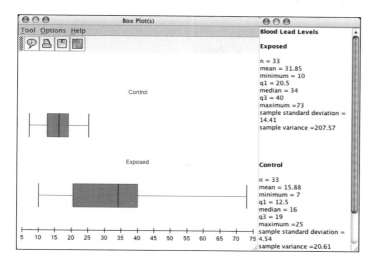

✔Check Your Understanding

People whose work exposes them to lead might inadvertently bring lead dust home on their clothes and skin. If their child breathes the dust, it can increase the level of lead in the child's blood. Lead poisoning in a child can lead to learning disabilities, decreased growth, hyperactivity, and impaired hearing. A study compared the level of lead in the blood of two groups of children—those who were exposed to lead dust from a parent's workplace and those who were not exposed in this way.

The 33 children of workers at a battery factory were the "exposed" group. For each "exposed" child, a "matching" child was found of the same age and living in the same area, but whose parents did not work around lead. These 33 children were the "control" group. Each child had his or her blood lead level measured (in micrograms per deciliter).

Blood Lead Level (in micrograms per deciliter)

Exposed	Control	Exposed	Control
10	13	34	25
13	16	35	12
14	13	35	19
15	24	36	11
16	16	37	19
17	10	38	16
18	24	39	14
20	16	39	22
21	19	41	18
22	21	43	11
23	10	44	19
23	18	45	9
24	18	48	18
25	11	49	7
27	13	62	15
31	16	73	13
34	18		

Source: "Lead Absorption in children of employees in a lead-related industry," *American Journal of Epidemiology 155.* 1982.

a. On the same scale, produce box plots of the lead levels for each group of children. Describe the shape of each distribution.

b. Find and interpret the median and the interquartile range for each distribution.

c. What conclusion can you draw from this study?

✓ Check Your Understanding

INSTRUCTIONAL NOTE Students will come back to this study in Reflections Task 19.

TECHNOLOGY NOTE The data for this task are in *CPMP-Tools* under Statistics. See the note on page T111B.

a. The distribution for the exposed group has a long whisker on the upper end. The distribution for the control group is quite symmetric.

For the exposed group:
  minimum = 10, Q_1 = 20.5, median = 34, Q_3 = 40, maximum = 73.

For the control group:
  minimum = 7, Q_1 = 12.5, median = 16, Q_3 = 19, maximum = 25.

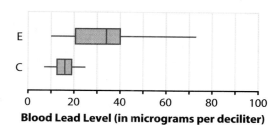

Blood Lead Level (in micrograms per deciliter)

b. The median for the exposed group is 34 micrograms per deciliter, meaning that half of the children had lead levels this low or lower. The median for the control group was only 16 micrograms per deciliter, meaning that half of the children had lead levels this low or lower.

The IQR for the exposed group is $40 - 20.5 = 19.5$. The middle half of the blood lead levels are within 19.5 micrograms per deciliter of each other. (Or, the middle half of the blood lead levels are within an interval of length 19.5.)

The IQR for the control group is $19 - 12.5 = 6.5$. The middle half of the blood lead levels are within 6.5 micrograms per deciliter of each other. (Or, the middle half of the blood lead levels are within an interval of length 6.5.)

c. The level of lead in the blood of exposed children tends to be quite a bit higher than that of children who weren't exposed. The median is more than twice as high and so is the upper quartile. The spread is also much larger for the exposed children. One of them has a level of only 10, but the highest is 73, almost three times as high as that of any of the control children. (The exposed children's levels of lead may vary depending on how much lead the parent is exposed to at work and whether the parent hugs or plays with the child while still in work clothes.)

Unit 2

Identifying Outliers

When describing distributions in Lesson 1, you identified any **outliers**— values that lie far away from the bulk of the values in a distribution. You should pay special attention to outliers when analyzing data.

As you work on this investigation, look for answers to this question:

*What should you do when you identify
one or more outliers in a set of data?*

1. Use the algorithm below to determine if there are any outliers in the resting pulse rates of your class from Problem 6 (page 111) of the previous investigation.

   Step 1: Find the quartiles and then subtract them to get the interquartile range, IQR.

   Step 2: Multiply the IQR by 1.5.

   Step 3: Add the value in Step 2 to the third quartile.

   Step 4: Check if any pulse rates are larger than the value in Step 3. If so, these are outliers.

   Step 5: Subtract the value in Step 2 from the first quartile.

   Step 6: Check if any pulse rates are smaller than the value in Step 5. If so, these are outliers.

2. Reproduced below is the dot plot of lengths of female bears from Lesson 1.

   Female Bears
   $n = 43$

   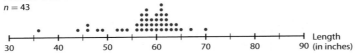

   Length (in inches)

   a. Do there appear to be any outliers in the data?

   b. The five-number summary for the lengths of female bears is:

   minimum = 36, Q_1 = 56.5, median = 59, Q_3 = 61.5, maximum = 70.

      i. Use the steps above to identify any outliers on the high end.

      ii. Are there any outliers on the low end?

   c. The box plot below (often referred to as a **modified box plot**) shows how the outliers in the distribution of the lengths of female bears may be indicated by a dot. The whiskers end at the last length that is not an outlier. What lengths of female bears are outliers?

   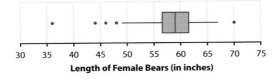

   Length of Female Bears (in inches)

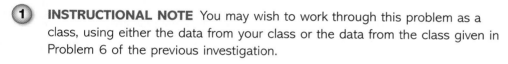

Investigation 3 — Identifying Outliers

In this investigation, students will identify outliers for data sets and consider whether to leave the outliers in the analysis.

The rule given here is the most common elementary rule for identifying outliers in a distribution, but there are others. The number 1.5 for the multiplier was proposed by John Tukey, who invented stemplots and box plots and is perhaps the most important data analyst of recent years. When asked why 1.5 and not some other number, Tukey replied 1 was too small and 2 was too big. (See Reflections Task 18.) Tukey had found that using 1.5 as the multiplier tended to identify the same values as outliers that he would have identified using his own judgment developed through his vast experience with data.

Any values identified by this rule should be examined to see why they appear. Perhaps they were a mistake and should be thrown out; perhaps they rightly belong to another set of data and should be moved there; or perhaps they simply are unusually large or small values. In the latter case, a data analyst has several choices. Often an outlier is simply part of the tail of a skewed distribution. In that case, the analyst can use a log or other transformation on the data to make the distribution more approximately normal and "bring in" the tail. Alternatively, a statistical analysis may be done both with and without the outlier. If the analysis doesn't change much, the analyst is in luck and reports it including the outlier. If it does change, then either both analyses must be reported or the analyst must use summary statistics that are resistant to outliers.

(1) **INSTRUCTIONAL NOTE** You may wish to work through this problem as a class, using either the data from your class or the data from the class given in Problem 6 of the previous investigation.

Step 1: For the data for the class given in Problem 6 of the previous investigation, the five-number summary is minimum = 59, $Q_1 = 67$, median = 70.5, $Q_3 = 76$, maximum = 89. The interquartile range is $76 - 67 = 9$.

Step 2: $1.5 \cdot IQR = 1.5(9) = 13.5$

Step 3: $Q_3 + 1.5 \cdot IQR = 76 + 13.5 = 89.5$

Step 4: No value lies above 89.5 beats per minute.

Step 5: $Q_1 - 1.5 \cdot IQR = 67 - 13.5 = 53.5$

Step 6: No value lies below 53.5 beats per minute. So, there are no outliers in these pulse rates.

(2) **a.** Students will likely select only 36 as an outlier. However, as they will see in Part b, the five lowest values (those below 49) and the largest value 70 (above 69) are outliers.

   b. **i.** Any outlier on the high end must be larger than 69 inches, so 70 inches is the only high outlier.

      ii. Any outlier on the low end must be smaller than 49 inches. There are five outliers on the low end, 36, 44, 46, 46, and 48 inches.

   c. The outliers are 36, 44, 46, 46, 48, and 70 inches.

3 In the Check Your Understanding of Investigation 1 (page 107), you found that the quartiles for the price per ounce of sunscreens with excellent protection were $Q_1 = \$0.90$ and $Q_3 = \$2.095$.

  a. Identify any outliers in the distribution of price per ounce of these sunscreens.

  b. Make a modified box plot of the data, showing any outliers.

  c. Here is the box plot of the prices per ounce for the sunscreens that offered less than excellent protection. Compare this distribution with the distribution from Part b.

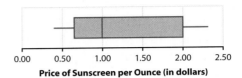

Price of Sunscreen per Ounce (in dollars)

  i. Do you tend to get better protection when you pay more?

  ii. Do you always get better protection when you pay more?

4 Jolaina found outliers by using a box plot. She measured the length of the box and marked off 1 box length to the right of the original box and 1 box length to the left of the original box. If any of the values extended beyond these new boxes, these points were considered outliers.

  a. Jolaina had a good idea but made one mistake. What was it? How can Jolaina correct her mistake?

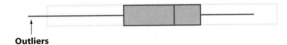

Outliers

  b. Using the corrected version of Jolaina's method, determine if there should be any outliers displayed by these box plots.

  i.

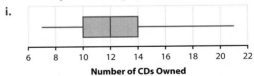

Number of CDs Owned

  ii.

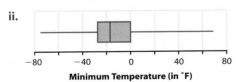

Minimum Temperature (in °F)

3 **a.** The quartiles are 0.90 and 2.095 so the interquartile range is $1.195 per ounce. Any outlier lies above $Q_3 + 1.5 \cdot IQR = 2.095 + 1.5(1.195) = 3.8875$ or below $Q_1 - 1.5 \cdot IQR = 0.90 - 1.5(1.195) = -0.8925$. There are two outliers on the high end, $4.79 and $4.91 per ounce.

b. In the box plot below, the upper whisker ends at 2.17.

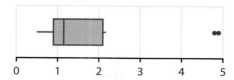

c. **i.** The sunscreens with better protection generally cost more. The minimum, lower quartile, median, upper quartile, and maximum are all larger for the sunscreens with excellent protection than for the sunscreens with less than excellent protection. So, yes, you tend to get better protection when you pay more.

ii. You don't always get better protection when you pay more. You can buy a sunscreen with excellent protection for only 50¢ an ounce and you can pay as much as about $2.30 an ounce for a sunscreen with less than excellent protection.

4 **a.** The length of the box is the same as the interquartile range. Jolaina graphically adds the interquartile range to the upper quartile by marking off one box length above the original box. She subtracts the interquartile range from the lower quartile by marking off one box length below the original box. However, to identify outliers using the rule given, she should mark off 1.5 times the interquartile range. That is, she would have to mark off an additional half-box in each direction in order for her method to work.

b. **i.** There is at least one outlier in these data on the upper end. The upper quartile whisker is longer than one-and-a-half boxes.

ii. There are outliers in these data on both the upper and lower ends as both whiskers are longer than one-and-a-half boxes.

> **INSTRUCTIONAL NOTE**
> Students might mark the length of one box on a sticky note or other paper to use as a measuring tool rather than using a ruler to approximate 1.5 boxes. They should be able to correctly respond to Part bi without measuring.

Unit 2

c. Jolaina then made symbolic rules for finding possible outliers in a data set. She says that outliers are values that are

larger than $Q_3 + 1.5 \cdot (Q_3 - Q_1) = Q_3 + 1.5 \cdot IQR$

or smaller than $Q_1 - 1.5 \cdot (Q_3 - Q_1) = Q_1 - 1.5 \cdot IQR$.

Are Jolaina's formulas correct? If so, use them to determine if there are any outliers in the data on lengths of female bears in Problem 2. If not, correct the formulas and then use them to find if there are any outliers in these data.

Whether to leave an outlier in the analysis depends on close inspection of the reason it occurred. If it was the result of an error in data collection or if it is fundamentally unlike the other values, it should be removed from the data set. If it is simply an unusually large or small value, you have two choices:

- Report measures of center and measures of variability that are resistant to outliers, such as the median, quartiles, and interquartile range.
- Do the analysis twice, with and without the outlier, and report both.

5 Decide what you would do about possible outliers in each of these situations.

a. The District of Columbia has a far higher number of physicians per 100,000 residents than does any state. That rate, shown on the box plot below, is 683 physicians per 100,000 residents. Why might you not want to include the District of Columbia in this data set of the 50 states?

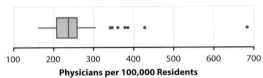

Physicians per 100,000 Residents

Source: U.S. Census Bureau, *Statistical Abstract of the United States: 2004–2005*

b. The box plots below show the number of grams of fat in chicken (C) and beef (B) sandwiches. Check the table of data on page 82 and identify the sandwich that is the outlier.

  i. Do you know of any reason to exclude it from the analysis?

  ii. Compute the mean and median of the grams of fat in the beef sandwiches only. Now compute them excluding the outlier. How much does the outlier affect them?

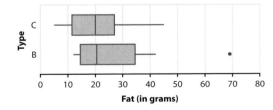

Fat (in grams)

LESSON 2 • Measuring Variability **115**

c. Jolaina's formulas are correct as they summarize the description of how to find outliers in Problem 1. For the female bear lengths,

$$Q_3 + 1.5 \cdot IQR = 61.5 + 1.5(5) = 69$$
$$Q_1 - 1.5 \cdot IQR = 56.5 - 1.5(5) = 49$$

Outliers are any values above 69 or below 49. Thus, as students found in Problem 2, the lengths 36, 44, 46, 46, and 48 inches are outliers on the low end since they are all less than 49, and 70 is the only outlier on the high end since it is the only length greater than 69.

5 **a.** The District of Columbia consists only of the city of Washington, DC. It is completely urban and so is different from the fifty states. Its rate would best be compared by removing it here and including it in a distribution of the rates of large cities in the United States.

b. **i.** The outlier is Burger King's Double Whopper with Cheese, with 69 grams of fat. It has two patties, but so does McDonald's Big Mac, so it is not different from the other hamburgers listed and there doesn't appear to be any reason to exclude it.

ii. The mean fat content of the beef sandwiches with and without the Burger King Double Whopper with Cheese are about 26.8 and 23, respectively. The medians with and without the Burger King Double Whopper with Cheese are 20.5 and 19. The mean, being more sensitive to outliers, changed by 3.8 grams, while the median changed by only 1.5 grams. You might go ahead and do the analysis including the Burger King Double Whopper with Cheese, using summary statistics that are resistant to outliers such as the median and the IQR.

(Students may note that this sandwich also has 1,060 calories, far more than any other sandwich. When calories are taken into account, typically fat content is measured by percentage of calories from fat. There are 9 calories per gram of fat, so the Burger King Double Whopper with Cheese has $\frac{(9)(69)}{1,060} \approx 59\%$ of its calories from fat. In contrast, Subway's 6-inch Oven Roasted Chicken Breast Sub has only $\frac{(9)(5)}{330} \approx 14\%$ of its calories from fat.

Summarize the Mathematics

Most calculators and statistical software show outliers on modified box plots with a dot.

a Describe in words the rule for identifying outliers. Describe it geometrically. Finally, write the formula.

b How do you decide what to do when you find an outlier in a set of data?

Be prepared to share your ideas and reasoning with the class.

✔ Check Your Understanding

Refer back to the data on lead levels in the two groups of children on page 112. Use the five-number summary you calculated to complete the following tasks.

a. Identify any outliers in these two distributions. What should you do about them?

b. Make a box plot that shows any outliers.

Investigation 4 | Measuring Variability: The Standard Deviation

In the previous investigation, you learned how to use the five-number summary and interquartile range (IQR) to describe the variability in a set of data. The IQR is based on the fact that half of the values fall between the upper and lower quartiles. Because it ignores the tails of the distribution, the IQR is very useful if the distribution is skewed or has outliers.

For data that are approximately normal—symmetric, mound-shaped, without outliers—a different measure of spread called the *standard deviation* is typically used. As you work on the problems of this investigation, keep track of answers to this question:

> *How can you determine and interpret the standard deviation of an approximately normal distribution?*

The **standard deviation** s is a distance that is used to describe the variability in a distribution. In the case of an approximately normal distribution, if you start at the mean and go the distance of one standard deviation to the left and one standard deviation to the right, you will enclose the middle 68% (about two-thirds) of the values. That is, in a distribution that is approximately normal, about two-thirds of the values lie between $\bar{x} - s$ and $\bar{x} + s$.

Summarize
the Mathematics

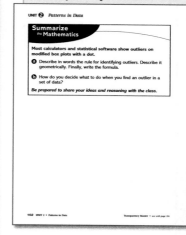
a Add $1\frac{1}{2}$ IQRs to the upper quartile and subtract $1\frac{1}{2}$ IQRs from the lower quartile. Any values outside those limits are outliers. Any value on a box plot that lies more than one-and-a-half box lengths outside of the box is an outlier. Outliers are values that are

larger than $\quad Q_3 + 1.5 \cdot (Q_3 - Q_1) = Q_3 + 1.5 \cdot \text{IQR}$
or smaller than $\quad Q_1 - 1.5 \cdot (Q_3 - Q_1) = Q_1 - 1.5 \cdot \text{IQR}.$

b Don't throw out outliers automatically. Perhaps they were a mistake and should indeed be thrown out; perhaps they rightly belong to another set of data and should be moved there; or perhaps they simply are unusually large or small values. In the latter case, you have a couple of choices. Often an outlier is simply part of the tail of a skewed distribution. In that case, the statistical analysis may be done both with and without the outlier. If the analysis doesn't change much, you are in luck and can report it including the outlier. If it does change, then either report both analyses or report only summary statistics that are resistant to outliers. (In Course 3, students will learn to transform such data using logs.)

> **MATH TOOLKIT** Students may wish to record the rule for identifying outliers in their Math Toolkit.

PROCESSING PROMPT Today I acted as an initiator by _____ .

✔️ Check Your Understanding

a. Here are the five-number summaries from the previous Check Your Understanding:

Exposed group: $\quad$ min $= 10$, $Q_1 = 20.5$, median $= 34$, $Q_3 = 40$, max $= 73$

Control group: $\quad$ min $= 7$, $Q_1 = 12.5$, median $= 16$, $Q_3 = 19$, max $= 25$

For the exposed group, the IQR is $40 - 20.5 = 19.5$. Any outliers lie below $20.5 - 1.5(19.5) = -8.25$, or above $40 + 1.5(19.5) = 69.25$. The only outlier is the measurement of 73. This child's lead level should be re-checked to be sure the original reading wasn't an error.

There are no outliers in the control group as no measurements fall below $12.5 - 1.5(19 - 12.5) = 2.75$, or above $19 + 1.5(19 - 12.5) = 28.75$.

> **ASSESSMENT NOTE** You may wish to use Lesson 2 Form A Quiz Task 1 or Form B Tasks 1 and 2 as a short quiz after this investigation.

b.

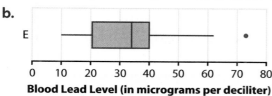

Blood Lead Level (in micrograms per deciliter)

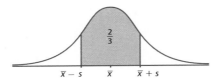

$$\frac{2}{3}$$

$\overline{x} - s \qquad \overline{x} \qquad \overline{x} + s$

1 On each of the following distributions, the arrows enclose the middle two-thirds of the values. For each distribution:

   i. Estimate the mean $\overline{x}$.

   ii. Estimate the distance from the mean to one of the two arrows. This distance is (roughly) the standard deviation.

a. Heights of a large sample of young adult women in the United States

Heights of Young Adult Women

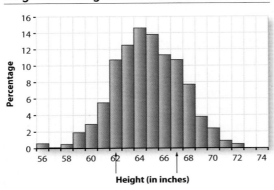

b. Heights of a large sample of young adult men in the United States

Heights of Young Adult Men

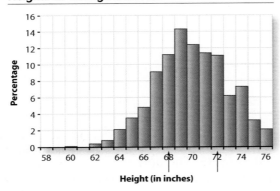

Measuring Variability: The Standard Deviation

The previous two investigations dealt with center as summarized by the median and variability as measured by the interquartile range. This investigation returns to the idea of variability around the mean, using the deviations from the mean to define another measure of spread.

The distance between two points in the plane, (x_1, y_1) and (x_2, y_2), is given by

$$d = \sqrt{(x_2 - x_1)^2 + (y_2 - y_1)^2}.$$

If your students have seen this formula in their middle school program, it is easy to motivate the formula for the standard deviation. First, ignore the division by $(n - 1)$ in the formula for the standard deviation, which is about the same as dividing by the sample size to make the standard deviation a kind of average. Then, both formulas are the square root of a sum of squared differences. For example, suppose you have only two data values, v_1 and v_2. Let the point (x_1, y_1) be $(\bar{x}, \bar{x})$ and the point (x_2, y_2) be (v_1, v_2). Then the two formulas have exactly the same form. That is, the standard deviation is a formula that measures the distance from (v_1, v_2) to the mean point $(\bar{x}, \bar{x})$. If there are more than two values, the standard deviation generalizes just like the distance formula generalizes to more than two dimensions.

1 **TECHNOLOGY NOTE** The data for this task are in *CPMP-Tools* under Statistics. Students will use these data in Part c. If you have a few computers avaliable in the classroom, groups can check the estimates when they reach Part c. Under the information button you will find the summary statistics. Note that the distance between the hands is providing boundaries for various percentages of data above and below the mean. The distance between the hands usually is not a good estimate of the standard deviation unless the distribution is approximately normal.

a. **i.** A good estimate of the mean height is 64 or 65 inches.

   ii. The middle two-thirds of the heights lie roughly in the interval between 62 and 67 inches, each of which is 2.5 inches from the mean. Thus, the standard deviation is about 2.5 inches.

b. **i.** A good estimate of the mean height is 70 inches.

   ii. About two-thirds of the heights lie in the interval between 68 and 72 inches. Each of these is 2 inches from the mean. Thus, the standard deviation is about 2 inches.

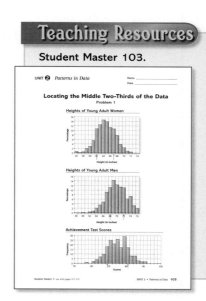

Teaching Resources

Student Master 103.

UNIT **2** *Patterns in Data* Name _____
  Date _____

Locating the Middle Two-Thirds of the Data
Problem 1

Heights of Young Adult Women

Heights of Young Adult Men

Achievement Test Scores

Student Master • *use with pages 117–119* UNIT 2 • *Patterns in Data* **103**

c. Achievement test scores for all ninth graders in one high school

Achievement Test Scores

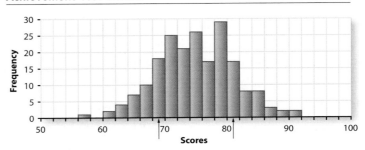

d. Use the "Estimate Center and Spread" custom tool to check your estimates of the mean and standard deviation in Parts a–c.

2 The sophomores who took the PSAT/NMSQT test in 2004 had a mean score of 44.2 on the mathematics section, with a standard deviation of 11.1. The distribution of scores was approximately normal. The highest possible score was 80 and the lowest was 20.
(Source: www.collegeboard.com/researchdocs/2004_psat.html)

a. Sketch the shape of the histogram of the distribution of scores, including a scale on the x-axis.

b. A sophomore who scored 44 on this exam would be at about what percentile?

c. A sophomore who scored 33 on this exam would be at about what percentile?

d. A sophomore who scored 55 on this exam would be at about what percentile?

Another measure of where a value x lies in a distribution is its **deviation from the mean**.

$$\textit{deviation from mean} = \textit{value} - \textit{mean} = x - \bar{x}$$

3 In 2003, LeBron James was a first-round draft pick and NBA Rookie of the Year. The following table gives the number of points he scored in the seven games he played in the first month of his freshman season at St. Vincent-St. Mary High School in Akron, Ohio. That season he led his high school team to a perfect 27-0 record and the Division III state title.

c. **i.** A good estimate of the mean is about 75.

   ii. About two-thirds of the scores lie in the interval between 69 and 81. Each of these scores lies 6 points from the mean. Thus, the standard deviation is about 6.

d. Use the "Estimate Center and Spread" custom tool to visually estimate and check the mean and standard deviation as shown below using the women's height data. The standard deviation is approximately 2.75. This can be found from the information ("I" bubble) button in the software.

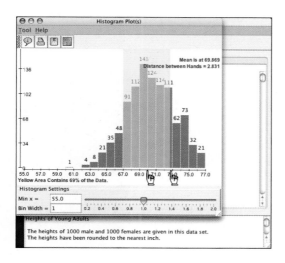

2 **a.**

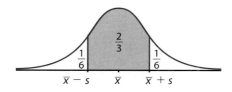

b. This score is at about the mean so the student is at about the 50th percentile.

c. This score is about 1 standard deviation below the mean. If two-thirds of the values are within one standard deviation of the mean, then one-third are farther away, or one-sixth are in the tail on each side:

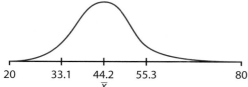

INSTRUCTIONAL NOTE
Watch for opportunities to help students recognize that the $\frac{2}{3}$ rule of thumb applies to approximately normal distributions.

Since $\frac{1}{6} \approx 0.17$, the student is at about the 17th percentile.

d. This score is about 1 standard deviation above the mean and $\frac{1}{6} + \frac{2}{3} \approx 0.83$, so the student is at about the 83rd percentile.

Points Scored by LeBron James in His First Month

Date	Opponent	Total Points
Dec. 3	Cuyahoga Falls	15
Dec. 4	Cleveland Central Catholic	21
Dec. 7	Garfield	11
Dec. 17	Benedictine	27
Dec. 18	Detroit Redford	18
Dec. 28	Mansfield Temple Christian	20
Dec. 30	Mapleton	21

Source: www.cleveland.com/hssports/lebron/agate.ssf?/hssports/lebron/lebron_stats.html

a. Find the mean number of points scored per game.

   i. For each game, find the deviation from the mean.

   ii. For which game(s) is James's total points farthest from the mean?

   iii. For which game(s) is James's total points closest to the mean?

b. For which game would you say that he has the most "typical" deviation (not unusually far or unusually close to the mean)?

c. In James's rookie season with the Cleveland Cavaliers, he averaged 20.9 points per game.

   i. The highest number of points he scored in a game that season was 20.1 points above his season average. How many points did he score in that game?

   ii. In his first game in his rookie season for the Cavaliers, he scored 25 points. What was the deviation from his season average for that game?

   iii. In one game that season, James had a deviation from his season average of −12.9 points. How many points did he score in that game?

4 The fact that the mean is the balance point of the distribution is related to a fact about the sum of all of the deviations from the mean.

a. Find the sum of the deviations in Problem 3.

b. Make a set of values with at least five different values. Find the mean and the deviations from the mean. Then find the sum of the deviations from the mean.

c. Check with classmates to see if they found answers similar to yours in Parts a and b. Then make a conjecture about the sum of the deviations from the mean for any set of values.

d. Complete the rule below. (Recall that the symbol Σ means to add up all of the following values. In this case, you are adding up all of the deviations from the mean.)

$$\Sigma(x - \bar{x}) =$$

e. Using the data sets from Parts a and b, do you think there is a rule about the sum of the deviations from the median? Explain your reasoning.

3 **a.** The mean is 19.

　i. The deviations from the mean of 19 are given in the table below.

Points Scored by LeBron James in His First Month

Date	Opponent	Total Points	Deviation
Dec. 3	Cuyahoga Falls	15	−4
Dec. 4	Cleveland Central Catholic	21	2
Dec. 7	Garfield	11	−8
Dec. 17	Benedictine	27	8
Dec. 18	Detroit Redford	18	−1
Dec. 28	Mansfield Temple Christian	20	1
Dec. 30	Mapleton	21	2

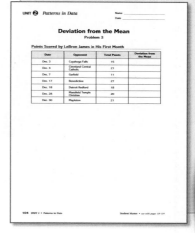

　ii. The games of December 7 and December 17 have the largest deviations from the mean in absolute value, both 8.

　iii. The games of December 18 and December 28 are closest to the mean.

b. James's most typical deviation, −4, was the December 3 game against Cuyahoga Falls. It is not especially large, like 8, or especially small, like 1 or 2.

c. 　**i.** 20.9 + 20.1 = 41 points

　ii. The deviation was 25 − 20.9 = 4.1.

　iii. 20.9 − 12.9 = 8 points

4 **a.** For the data in Problem 3, the sum of the deviations from the mean is 0.

b. Students will create two different sets of values. For each set, the sum of the deviations from the mean will be 0. (You may wish to have groups compare their work.)

c. The sum of the deviations from the mean is always equal to 0. This is equivalent to the mean being the balance point of the distribution.

d. $\Sigma(x - \bar{x}) = 0$

e. No, the sum of the deviations from the median can be any number.

Unit 2

While the standard deviation is most useful when describing distributions that are approximately normal, it also is used for distributions of other shapes. In these cases, the standard deviation is given by a formula. The formula is based on the deviations of the values from their mean.

5 Working in groups of four to six, measure your handspans. Spread your right hand as wide as possible, place it on a ruler, and measure the distance from the end of your thumb across to the end of your little finger. Measure to the nearest tenth of a centimeter.

a. Find the mean of the handspans of the students in your group. Find the deviation from the mean of each student's handspan. Check that the sum of the deviations is 0.

b. Roughly, what is a typical distance from the mean for your group?

c. Compute the standard deviation of your group's handspans by using the steps below. Fill in a copy of the chart as you work, rounding all computations to the nearest tenth of a centimeter.

• In the first column, fill in your group's handspans.

• Write the mean of your group's handspans on each line in the second column.

• Write the deviations from the mean in the third column.

• Write the squares of these deviations in the last column.

• Find the sum of the squared deviations.

• Divide by the number n in your group minus one.

• Take the square root. This final number is the standard deviation.

Span	Mean	Deviation (Span − Mean)	Squared Deviation (Span − Mean)^2
		Add the squared deviations:	
		Divide the sum by $n − 1$:	
		Take the square root:	

d. Have each group write its mean and standard deviation on a piece of paper. Give them to one person who will mix up the papers and write the paired means and standard deviations where everyone in your class can see them. Try to match each pair of statistics with the correct group.

e. Kelsi wrote this sentence: The handspans of our group average 21.2 cm with a handspan typically being about 2.6 cm from average. Write a similar sentence describing your group's handspans.

(5) **NOTE** This problem works best if there are four to six students in each group.

a. Means will vary. The sum of the deviations should be 0 for each group, except for rounding error.

b. Answers will vary. The "typical distance" should be close to the standard deviation computed in Part c.

c. A sample table appears below.

Span	Mean	(Span − Mean)	(Span − Mean)^2
20.1	17.5	2.6	6.76
18.3	17.5	0.8	0.64
15.4	17.5	−2.1	4.41
16.2	17.5	−1.3	1.69
	Add the squared deviations:		13.50
	Divide the sum by $n − 1$:		4.50
	Take the square root:		2.1213

d. NOTE After the means and their standard deviations are written where everyone can see them, have students raise their spread-out hands so students can see the relative sizes. Try to get students to concentrate on both the center and the spread of the handspans for each group.

e. For the group above, the handspans average 17.5 cm, with a handspan typically being about 2.1 cm from average.

NOTE Students may ask why they divide by $n − 1$ rather than n. The calculator and statistical software also divide by $n − 1$ rather than by n for the sample standard deviation. Think of your set of values as a sample from a larger population, as is typically the case. If you want to estimate the mean μ of the entire population, you use the sample mean $\bar{x}$ dividing by n. Sometimes your sample gives an $\bar{x}$ that is larger than μ and sometimes your sample gives an $\bar{x}$ that is smaller than μ. But, on average, $\bar{x}$ is exactly equal to μ. So far, so good.

However, the standard deviation doesn't work so nicely. Suppose you want to use the average squared deviation from your sample of values s^2 to estimate the average squared deviation in the entire population,

$$\sigma^2 = \frac{\sum_{i=1}^{n}(x_i - \mu)^2}{n}.$$ If you divide by n, s^2 tends to be smaller than σ^2,

on average. That is, $\dfrac{\sum_{i=1}^{n}(x_i - \bar{x})^2}{n}$ is a *biased* estimate of σ^2. Dividing

by $n − 1$ makes s^2 a bit larger than if you divide by n and, in fact, makes s^2 exactly equal to σ^2, on average.

A simple experiment that illustrates this fact may be found at mathcentral. uregina.ca/QQ/database/QQ.09.99/freeman2.html.

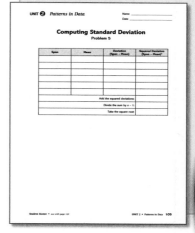
TECHNOLOGY NOTE The sample standard deviation can be found in the LIST MATH calculations of TI graphing calculators:

If students use **1-Var Stats** instead, **Sx** corresponds to the standard deviation formula in this unit.

6 Now consider how standard deviation can be used in the comparison of performance data. Here are Susan's and Jack's homework grades.

Susan's Homework Grades
8, 8, 7, 9, 7, 8, 8, 6, 8, 7,
8, 8, 8, 7, 8, 8, 10, 9, 9, 9

Jack's Homework Grades
10, 7, 7, 9, 5, 8, 7, 4, 7,
5, 8, 8, 8, 4, 5, 6, 5, 8, 7

a. Find the set of deviations from the mean for Susan and the set of deviations for Jack. Who tends to deviate the most from his or her mean?

b. Roughly, what is a typical distance from the mean for Susan? For Jack?

c. Compute the standard deviation of each set of grades. Were these close to your estimates of a typical distance from the mean in Part b?

d. Which student had the larger standard deviation? Explain why that makes sense.

e. Write a sentence about Susan's homework grades that is similar to Kelsi's statement in Problem 5 Part e. Write a similar sentence about Jack's homework grades.

7 Think about the process of computing the standard deviation.

a. What is accomplished by squaring the deviations before adding them?

b. What is accomplished by dividing by the number of deviations (minus 1)?

c. What is accomplished by taking the square root?

d. What unit of measurement should be attached to the standard deviation of a distribution?

8 Look back at your calculations of the standard deviation in Problem 5. Which of the following is the formula for the standard deviation, s?

$$s = \sqrt{\frac{\Sigma(x - \bar{x}^2)}{n - 1}} \qquad s = \sqrt{\frac{\Sigma(x - \bar{x})^2}{n - 1}} \qquad s = \sqrt{\frac{(\Sigma x - \bar{x})^2}{n - 1}} \qquad s = \sqrt{\Sigma\left(\frac{x - \bar{x}}{n - 1}\right)^2}$$

9 Without calculating, match the sets of values below, one from column A and one from column B, that have the same standard deviations.

	Column A			Column B
a.	1, 2, 3, 4, 5		f.	10, 10, 10, 10, 10
b.	2, 4, 6, 8, 10		g.	4, 6, 8, 10, 12
c.	2, 2, 2, 2, 2		h.	4, 5, 6, 7, 8
d.	2, 6, 6, 6, 10		i.	16, 16, 20, 24, 24
e.	2, 2, 6, 10, 10		j.	4, 8, 8, 8, 12

10 Consider the heights of the people in the following two groups.

- the members of the Chicago Bulls basketball team, and

- the adults living in Chicago.

a. Which group would you expect to have the larger mean height? Explain your reasoning.

6 **a.** Susan's mean is 8 and Jack's is 6.737. The deviations are given in the tables at the right. Jack's grades deviate more from their mean than do Susan's.

b. A typical distance from the mean for Susan is about 1, and for Jack is between 1 and 2.

c. Susan's standard deviation is about 0.918, and Jack's is about 1.695.

d. Jack has the larger standard deviation. This makes sense because in Part a, Jack's grades deviated more from the mean than Susan's grades did.

e. Susan's grades have a mean of 8, with a grade typically being about 0.918 from average. Jack's grades have a mean of 6.737, with a grade typically being about 1.695 from average.

Grades for Susan	Susan's Deviations	Grades for Jack	Jack's Deviations
8	0	10	3.263
8	0	7	0.263
7	−1	7	0.263
9	1	9	2.263
7	−1	5	−1.737
8	0	8	1.263
8	0	7	0.263
6	−2	4	−2.737
8	0	7	0.263
7	−1	5	−1.737
8	0	8	1.263
8	0	8	1.263
8	0	8	1.263
7	−1	4	−2.737
8	0	5	−1.737
8	0	6	−0.737
10	2	5	−1.737
9	1	8	1.263
9	1	7	0.263
9	1		

7 **a.** If the differences aren't squared, the sum of the deviations will be zero. (Students may suggest that squaring will make the outliers significant because the square from an outlier will be large compared to the others.)

b. If you divide by n, you would be finding (the square root of) the average squared deviation from the mean. Dividing by $n - 1$ gives almost the same result, especially when n is large. You find a number that is about equal to (the square root of) the average squared deviation.

c. The square root restores the original unit of measurement. If you do not take the square root in the handspan example, the units are centimeters-squared, which are difficult to interpret in terms of the data.

d. The unit of measure for the standard deviation is the same as for the original data.

> **INSTRUCTIONAL NOTE** You may wish to have pairs of students do either Jack's or Susan's standard deviation and compare answers.

8 $s = \sqrt{\dfrac{\Sigma(x - \bar{x})^2}{n - 1}}$

9 a–h   b–g   c–f   d–j   e–i

10 **a.** The Chicago Bulls have the larger mean height. The players are all tall.

b. Which group would you expect to have the larger standard deviation? Explain.

11 Graphing calculators and statistical software will automatically calculate the standard deviation.

a. Enter the handspans for your entire class into a list and use your calculator or software to find the mean $\bar{x}$ and the standard deviation s. Write a sentence using the mean and standard deviation to describe the distribution of handspans.

b. Which handspan is closest to one standard deviation from the mean?

c. If the distribution is approximately normal, determine how many handspans of your class should be in the interval $\bar{x} - s$ to $\bar{x} + s$. How many handspans actually are in this interval?

d. Is the standard deviation of the class larger or smaller than the standard deviation of your group? What characteristic of the class handspans compared to the group handspans could explain the difference?

12 Find the standard deviation of the following set of values.

$$1, 2, 3, 4, 5, 6, 70$$

a. Remove the outlier of 70. Then find the standard deviation of the new set of values. Does the standard deviation appear to be resistant to outliers?

b. Test your conjecture in Part a by working with others to create three different sets of values with one or more outliers. In each case, find the standard deviation. Then remove the outlier(s) and find the standard deviation of the new set of values. Summarize your findings, telling exactly what it is about the formula for the standard deviation that causes the results.

Summarize the Mathematics

In this investigation, you learned how to find and interpret the standard deviation.

a What does the standard deviation tell you about a distribution that is approximately normal? Compare this to what the interquartile range tells you.

b Describe in words how to find the standard deviation.

c Which measures of variation (range, interquartile range, standard deviation) are resistant to outliers? Explain.

d If a deviation from the mean is positive, what do you know about the value? If the deviation is negative? If the deviation is zero? What do you know about the sum of all of the deviations from the mean?

Be prepared to share your thinking and description with the class.

b. The people living in Chicago would have the larger standard deviation, because many short people and many tall people live in Chicago. On the other hand, the Chicago Bulls are all tall.

11 **a.** Means and standard deviations will vary. The sentence should be similar to the one in Problem 5 Part e.

b. Answers will vary.

c. Two-thirds of the handspans would be in this interval, so students should multiply the number of handspans by $\frac{2}{3}$.

d. Results will vary. If, for example, your students are seated by gender and the boys tend to have bigger hands than the girls, the standard deviation for the class will be larger than the standard deviation for the individual groups. There is no general rule indicating whether the standard deviation of a sample is larger or smaller than the standard deviation of the population.

12 **a.** The mean of the original set of values is 13 and the standard deviation is approximately 25.193. When the 70 is removed, the mean drops to 3.5 and the standard deviation to approximately 1.871. The standard deviation seems to not be resistant to outliers.

b. Students should find that the standard deviation is not resistant to outliers. Because the deviations from the mean are squared, any value that is especially far from the mean will have a very large squared deviation, making the standard deviation large.

Summarize
the Mathematics

a For an approximately *normal* distribution, the standard deviation s is the deviation from the mean $\bar{x}$ so that about two-thirds of the values are within the interval between $\bar{x} - s$ and $\bar{x} + s$. For *any* distribution, the IQR tells you the range of the middle half of the values; that is, it is the distance between the lower and upper quartiles. (You might ask students to also express the number of values captured by one standard deviation either side of the mean and by the IQR as percents; 68% and 50%, respectively.)

b First, compute the mean. Then, find the deviation of each value from the mean. Square each of these deviations and add them up. Divide by the number of values minus one. Then take the square root to get back to the original units.

c The interquartile range is the only one of the three that is resistant to outliers. The IQR depends only on the spread of the middle half of the values. Whether there is an outlier or not doesn't matter. The other two measures of spread get larger as an outlier moves farther out.

d If the deviation from the mean is positive, the value is larger than the mean. If the deviation from the mean is negative, the value is smaller than the mean. If the deviation from the mean is 0, the value is equal to the mean. The sum of the deviations from the mean is always 0.

PROMOTING MATHEMATICAL DISCOURSE

Teaching Resources

Transparency Master 106.

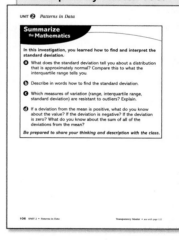

MATH TOOLKIT Once a class discussion for the STM is conducted, students should include this information in their toolkit.

Promoting Mathematical Discourse

Summarize the Mathematics, *page 122*

Teacher: In this investigation we studied how to find and interpret the standard deviation. I would like you to think for just a half a minute about what the standard deviation tells us about a distribution that is approximately normal. *(The teacher gives students time to think individually.)* What do you think? What does the standard deviation tell us about a distribution that is approximately normal?

Raegan: It tells us how the data is spread out.

Kalman: It's spread around the mean.

Teacher: Can you be a bit more specific about what the standard deviation tells us about the spread of the data around the mean?

Kalman: If you go one standard deviation to the right and left of the mean then you should have about two thirds of the data.

Madeline: Actually, a bit more than two thirds. We learned that 68% of the data fall within one standard deviation of the mean.

Teacher: How does this compare with what the interquartile range tells us?

Morris: Well, first of all, the interquartile range can be used with any data. It doesn't have to be approximately normal.

Teacher: What about the standard deviation? Can it be used with any set of data?

Mariah: We read in the investigation that the standard deviation is most helpful when using data that is approximately normal but that it can be used for other shapes, too.

(The teacher notes that some students may still think that about 68% of the data are within one standard deviation of the mean for any distribution. She decides to assign Connections Task 13 and come back to this misconception tomorrow.)

Mackenzie: The IQR tells us about the middle 50% of the data instead of 68% like the standard deviation.

Dakota: It tells us the range of the middle half of the data.

Teacher: How do we find the standard deviation?

Laina: You can use the formula.

Teacher: Laina, can you describe the process in words?

Laina: I can if I look at the formula. Will you write the formula on the board?

Teacher: Sure. We had to decide which formula best represented the process of finding the standard deviation when we did Problem 8. *(The teacher writes the formula for the standard deviation on the board.)* Let's each take time to write a description of the standard deviation in our own words. *(The teacher allows time for students to think about putting the formula into their own words and to record their description. She circulates around the room to make sure each student is making an attempt at the description.)*

Teacher: Laina, would you like to read what you wrote?

Laina: Okay. I just used the formula, that's how I think of it. So, first you find the mean of the data. Then you have to find all the differences of each data value from the mean. Then you have to square each difference. Next you add up all the squared differences and divide by one less than the number of data values in your set. *(The teacher waits for students to process Laina's description.)*

Sonia: You need to take the square root too.

Teacher: What do others think? *(Students indicate that the description now matches the formula.)* All right then let's consider Part c. Which measures of variation, the range, the interquartile range, or the standard deviation, are resistant to outliers?

James: It seems like only the interquartile range would be resistant to outliers.

Teacher: Why do you say that, James?

James: Well, think about how you find the mean. You have to use all the values in the data set, even those that are very far away from the other values. But in the interquartile range you only use the middle half of the data, so the values at the high or low end of the data set will not affect the interquartile range.

Teacher: What do you think about James's idea?

Corey: I agree. I also agree with him that the interquartile range is the only measure that is resistant to outliers.

Teacher: Tell us more about your thinking.

Corey: Well, the standard deviation will have to be affected by outliers because you have to use all the values to calculate the standard deviation. So, if you have a really big or really small data value then the standard deviation will be affected. Any measure that uses all the data values has to be affected by outliers.

Amanda: But to calculate the range you don't use all the values. Isn't it still affected by outliers?

Corey: You're right. To calculate the range we don't use all the values but we do the largest and smallest values. So, maybe it's the idea that when you calculate the range or the standard deviation you use the largest and smallest values from the data so they are not resistant to outliers.

Teacher: Okay. Let's move to considering the deviation from the mean. What do we know about a value if its deviation from the mean is positive? What if its deviation is negative or zero?

Mahmoud: If the deviation is positive then the value is bigger than the mean, and if it is negative then is it smaller than the mean.

Teacher: Will someone either confirm mathematically that Mahmoud is accurate or provide an alternative explanation with supporting mathematical reasoning?

Susan: I agree with Mahmoud. You compute the deviation from the mean by subtracting the mean from the data value. So, if the mean is, say 5, and the value is 7, the deviation from the mean is 7 minus 5, positive 2. If the value is below the mean, like 3, then the deviation is 3 minus 5, negative 2.

Carlos: And the only value that would have a deviation of zero from the mean would be the mean itself.

Teacher: Class, do you think Susan's and Carlos's mathematical explanations are convincing? *(Students agreed.)* What do we know about the sum of all of the deviations from the mean?

Yuri: The sum is zero. We found that out when we were calculating the standard deviation. We forgot to square the sum of the deviations, so we kept getting zero as our standard deviation.

Teacher: I would like you to do the Check Your Understanding and Connections Task 13 for homework tonight so we can make certain that we each have an understanding of some of the ideas we just discussed.

Unit 2

✓ Check Your Understanding

Use the following data on U.S. weather to check your understanding of the standard deviation.

a. The histogram below shows the percentage of time that sunshine reaches the surface of the Earth in January at 174 different major weather-observing stations in all 50 states, Puerto Rico, and the Pacific Islands. The two stations with the highest percentages are Tucson and Yuma, Arizona. The station with the lowest percentage is Quillayute, Washington.

 i. Estimate the mean and standard deviation of these percentages, including the units of measurement.

 ii. About how many standard deviations from the mean are Tucson and Yuma?

 iii. Use the "Estimate Center and Spread" custom tool to check your estimates of the mean and standard deviation.

January Sunshine

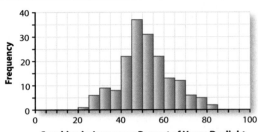

Sunshine in January as Percent of Hours Daylight

Source: www.ncdc.noaa.gov/oa/climate/online/ccd/avgsun.html

b. The normal monthly precipitation (rain and snow) in inches for Concord, New Hampshire, and for Portland, Oregon, is given in the table below.

 i. Using the same scale, make histograms of the precipitation for each of the cities. By examining the plots, how do you think the mean monthly amount of precipitation for the cities will compare? The standard deviation?

 ii. Calculate the mean and standard deviation of the normal monthly precipitation for each city. Write a comparison of the rainfall in the two cities, using the mean and the standard deviation.

	Jan	Feb	Mar	Apr	May	June	July	Aug	Sept	Oct	Nov	Dec
Concord	2.97	2.36	3.04	3.07	3.33	3.10	3.37	3.21	3.16	3.46	3.57	2.96
Portland	5.07	4.18	3.71	2.64	2.38	1.59	0.72	0.93	1.65	2.88	5.61	5.71

Source: National Climate Data Center, 2005

Check Your Understanding

a. **NOTE** Each number is a percentage that is computed by dividing the number of hours of sunshine by the number of hours of daylight. The denominator varies depending on how close the station is to the equator.

i. The mean of the percentages of sunshine during daylight hours is 51%. The standard deviation of the percentages is 12%. Good estimates of the mean are between 47% and 53%, and good estimates of the standard deviation are between 10% and 15%.

ii. Using a mean of 50, and 80 as the percentage of time that is daylight for Tucson and Yuma, the cities are $\frac{30}{12} \approx 2.5$ standard deviations from the mean.

iii. The "Estimate Center and Spread" Custom Tool option in *StatTools* can be used to visually support and check student understanding of the property of the mean as a balance point and of their ability to estimate the standard deviation from a histogram.

b. **NOTE** This task gives students a chance to see how two sets of data can have the same center but distinctly different distributions and standard deviations.

i. The histograms appear below. The mean amounts of rain look about the same. However, the standard deviation for Portland will be larger because Concord has fairly constant rain throughout the year, about 3 inches per month, while Portland has most of its rain in the winter and little in the summer.

Concord

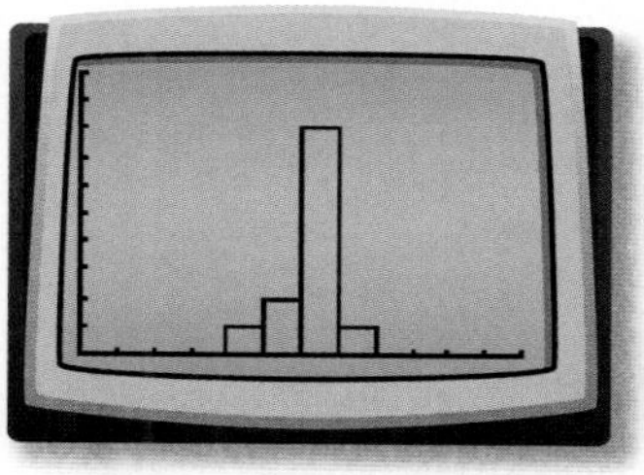

Portland

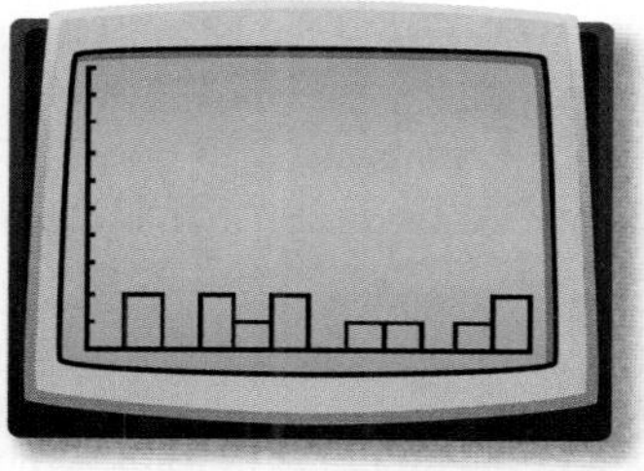

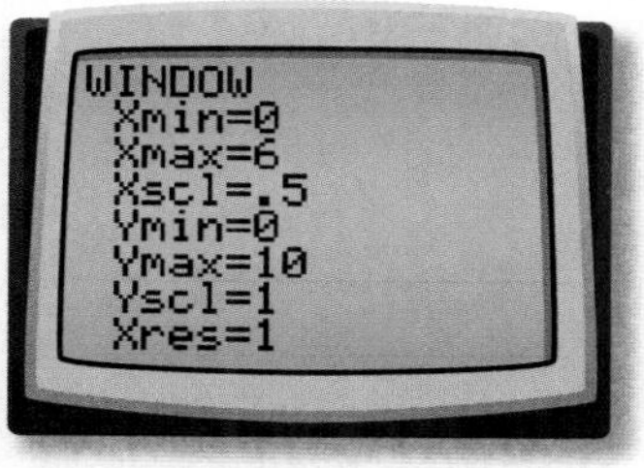
WINDOW
Xmin=0
Xmax=6
Xscl=.5
Ymin=0
Ymax=10
Yscl=1
Xres=1

ii. Concord: mean = 3.13 inches, standard deviation = 0.31 inches
Portland: mean = 3.09 inches, standard deviation = 1.76 inches
The mean monthly amount of precipitation is 3.13 inches in Concord, with a typical month being only about 0.31 inches from that average. In Portland, the mean monthly amount of precipitation is about the same, 3.09 inches, but a typical month is about 1.76 inches from that average. Thus, while there is about the same amount of rainfall in each city per year, there is much more month-to-month variability in Portland than in Concord. In Concord, it rains pretty evenly throughout the year, but Portland gets most of its rain in the winter.

TECHNOLOGY NOTE
The data sets for Concord and Portland precipitation and January sunshine are in *CPMP-Tools*. An additional data set called Sunshine for all Months is included to allow students to ask and answer their own questions.

Investigation 5 — Transforming Measurements

Like all events in life, data do not always come in the most convenient form. For example, sometimes you may want to report measurements in feet rather than meters or percentage correct rather than points scored on a test. Transforming data in this way has predictable effects on the shape, center, and spread of the distribution. As you work on the following problems, look for answers to this question:

What is the effect on a distribution of adding or subtracting a constant to each value and of multiplying or dividing each value by a positive constant?

1 Select 10 members of your class to measure the length of the same desk or table to the nearest tenth of a centimeter. Each student should do the measurement independently and not look at the measurements recorded by other students.

   a. As a class, make a dot plot of the measurements.

   b. Calculate the mean $\bar{x}$ and standard deviation s of the measurements. Mark the mean on the dot plot. Then mark $\bar{x} + s$ and $\bar{x} - s$.

   c. What does the standard deviation tell you about the precision of the students' measurements?

2 Suppose that a group of 10 students would have gotten exactly the same measurements as your class did in Problem 1, except the end of their ruler was damaged. Consequently, their measurements are exactly 0.2 cm longer than yours.

   a. What do you think they got for their mean and standard deviation?

   b. Using lists on your calculator, transform your list of measurements into theirs. If M stands for the original measurement and D stands for the corresponding measurement made with the damaged ruler, write a rule that describes how you made this transformation.

   c. Make a dot plot of the transformed measurements and compare its shape to the plot made in Problem 1.

   d. Compute the mean and standard deviation of the transformed measurements.

   e. How is the mean of the transformed measurements related to the original mean?

   f. How is the standard deviation of the transformed measurements related to the original standard deviation?

3 Now examine the effect of transforming the measurements in Problem 1 from centimeters to inches.

   a. Let C stand for a measurement in centimeters and I stand for a measurement in inches. Write a rule that you can use to transform the measurements in Problem 1 from centimeters to inches. (*Note:* There are approximately 2.54 centimeters in an inch.)

Investigation 5 — Transforming Measurements

In this investigation, students will explore the effect on a distribution of adding, subtracting, multiplying, or dividing each value by a positive constant.

Students should not round until they give the summary statistic. The context may determine how summary statistics are rounded. If not, measures of center and spread are often rounded to one more decimal place than the original data.

COMMUNICATION SKILL Keep the group conversation focused on the mathematics in the lesson.

1 The following sample of measurements in centimeters, made by ten students on a desk about 30 inches wide, will be used as a sample in these solutions:

76.1 76.1 76.2 76.2 76.3 76.3 76.4 76.4 76.4 76.5

TECHNOLOGY NOTE
Students should use the sample standard deviation.

NOTE Retain your class measurements for Connections Task 15.

a. Have students mark the scale of the dot plot to the nearest tenth of a centimeter. The measurements should show some variability as students won't all get the same measurement to the nearest tenth of a centimeter.

b. For the sample above, the mean is 76.29 cm and the standard deviation is about 0.14 cm (0.137). The dot plot is shown at the right.

Ten Desk Measurements

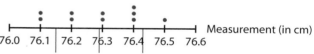

c. For the sample, a typical measurement is 76.29 cm, give or take 0.14 cm. The standard deviation tells how far a typical measurement lies from the mean. A smaller standard deviation means that the measurements were more precise (tended to be closer to the mean) than measurements with a larger standard deviation. If the distribution is approximately normal (which is not possible with only 10 values), then about two-thirds of the measurements will lie within one standard deviation of the mean.

2 **a.** The mean should be 0.2 cm larger. The standard deviation would be unchanged. For the sample, the new mean would be 76.49 cm, but the standard deviation would remain 0.14 cm.

b. The transformed measurements for the sample data above are:

76.3 76.3 76.4 76.4 76.5 76.5 76.6 76.6 76.6 76.7

The formula is $D = M + 0.2$.

c. The dot plot below for the transformed sample measurements has exactly the same shape and spread but has a new center.

Ten Desk Measurements

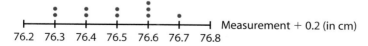

d. The mean is 76.49 cm, and the standard deviation is 0.14.

e. It is 0.2 cm larger.

f. It is the same.

3 **a.** $I = \dfrac{C}{2.54}$ or $I = C\left(\dfrac{1}{2.54}\right)$

Teaching Resources

Student Master 107.

b. Make a dot plot of the transformed data and compare its shape to the plot made in Problem 1.

c. Compute the mean and the standard deviation of the transformed measurements.

d. Write a rule that relates the mean of the transformed measurements $\bar{x}_T$ to the original mean $\bar{x}$.

e. Write a rule that relates the standard deviation of the transformed measurements s_T to the original standard deviation s.

f. Suppose that one student mistakenly multiplied by 2.54 when transforming the measurements. What do you think this student got for the mean and standard deviation of the transformed measurements? Check your prediction.

4 Ms. Brenner polled her mathematics classes to find out the hourly wage of students who had baby-sitting jobs. The results are shown in the following table and histogram.

Student	Hourly Wage (in dollars)
Neil	4.00
Bill	4.25
Dimitri	4.30
José	4.50
Keri	4.75
Emerson	4.75
Rashawnda	4.75
Katie	4.85
Clive	5.00
Jan	5.10
Kyle	5.25
Mike	5.25
Toby	5.25
Nafikah	5.30
Robert	5.30

Student	Hourly Wage (in dollars)
Mia	5.50
Tasha	5.50
Sarah	5.50
Vanita	5.60
Silvia	5.60
Olivia	5.75
Katrina	5.80
Deeonna	5.80
Jacob	6.00
Rusty	6.00
Jennifer	6.25
Phuong	6.25
Corinna	6.30
John	6.50

a. Use the histogram to estimate the average hourly wage of these students. Estimate the standard deviation. Using the values in the table, compute the mean and standard deviation. How close were your estimates?

b. Write a sentence or two describing the distribution. Use the mean and standard deviation in your description.

b. The dot plot for the transformed sample measurements has exactly the same shape as that of the original plot even though it has a new center and has shrunk in spread.

Ten Desk Measurements

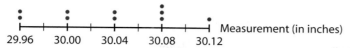

c. $\bar{x} \approx 30.035$ inches

$s \approx 0.054$ inches

d. $\bar{x}_T = \dfrac{\bar{x}}{2.54}$ or $\bar{x}_T \approx 0.4\,\bar{x}$

e. $s_T = \dfrac{s}{2.54}$ or $s_T \approx 0.4s$

f. The mean would be 2.54 times as big as the mean of the original measurements, and the standard deviation would be 2.54 times as big. For the sample data, the mean would be $2.54(76.29) \approx 193.78$ cm, and the standard deviation would be $2.54(0.14) \approx 0.36$ cm.

NOTE If students use the rounded value of the standard deviation in Problem 1 Part b to compute the standard deviation of the transformed data in Problem 3 Part f, they may not get exactly the same value when they check their prediction by computing directly from the transformed measurements.

4   **a.** The mean wage is about $5.34. Any estimate between about $5.25 and $5.60 is reasonable, and an estimate between $5.25 and $5.50 is very good. The standard deviation is $0.65. Any estimate between about $0.50 and $0.75 is good.

b. The distribution of babysitting wages is approximately normal, with a mean of $5.34 and a typical student earning within $0.65 of that.

Unit 2

c. Keri decided that it was too much work to enter the decimal point in the wages each time in her calculator list, so she entered each wage without it.

    i. Will the shape of her histogram be different from the given histogram? Explain.

    ii. Predict the mean and standard deviation for Keri's wage data. Check your predictions.

d. Suppose each student gets a 4% raise. How will the shape of the histogram of the new hourly wages be different from the original one? Predict the mean and standard deviation for the new wages of the students. Check your predictions.

e. Suppose that instead of a 4% raise, each student gets a raise of 25¢ per hour. Will the shape of the histogram of the new hourly wages be different from the original one? How will the mean and standard deviation change?

f. Let W_O represent the original hourly wage and W_N represent the new hourly wage. Write a rule that can be used to compute the new wage from the original wage

    i. for the case of a 4% raise, and

    ii. for the case of a 25¢ per hour raise.

⑤ Now try to generalize your discoveries in Problems 2–4. Consider a set of data that has mean $\bar{x}$ and standard deviation s.

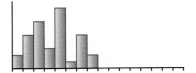

a. Suppose you add the same positive number d to each value. Use the histogram below to explain why the shape of the distribution does not change, the mean of the transformed data will be $\bar{x} + d$, and the standard deviation will remain s.

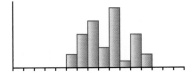

c. **i.** Keri's method is equivalent to multiplying each wage by 100 (i.e., converting dollars to cents) and so doesn't change the shape.

 ii. The mean will be $100(5.34) = 534$¢ and the standard deviation will be $100(0.65) = 65$¢.

d. The new wage is equal to 1.04 times the original wage. The shape won't change. The mean will increase to $1.04(5.34) \approx \$5.55$ and the spread will be larger—the standard deviation will be $1.04(0.65) \approx \$0.68$. To check their predictions, students should multiply each original wage by 1.04 and then compute the mean and standard deviation of these transformed wages.

e. The shape and the standard deviation won't change as the entire distribution is shifted upwards by 0.25. The mean will increase to $5.34 + 0.25 = \$5.59$.

f. **i.** $W_N = 1.04W_O$

 ii. $W_N = W_O + 0.25$

5 **NOTE** Transforming distributions using histograms is a little more complicated than the examples in the text. To retain shape, the horizontal scale should change corresponding to the transformation. For example, suppose $c = 2$ in Part d below. If the scale on the original histogram was 1, then the width of the bars of the transformed histogram is $\frac{1}{2}$. Students need not deal with this idea in this unit.

a. Adding a positive constant is equivalent to sliding the entire distribution to the right along the x-axis by the distance d. Such a slide won't change the shape or spread, but increases the mean by d.

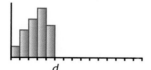 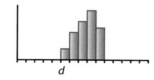

b. Write a summary statement about shape, center, and spread similar to that in Part a for the case of subtracting the same positive number from each value. Illustrate this by showing the effect of such a transformation on a histogram.

c. Write a summary statement similar to that in Part a for the case of multiplying each value by a positive number. Explain how the effect of such a transformation is illustrated by the histogram below.

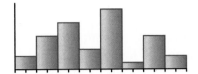

d. Write a similar statement for the case of dividing each value by a positive number. Illustrate this by showing the effect of such a transformation by drawing on a histogram.

e. Does the name "slide" or "stretch" best describe the transformation in Part a? In Part b? In Part c? In Part d?

6 One of the most common transformations is changing points scored to percentages such as on tests. The following display gives the points scored by a class of 32 students on a test with 75 possible points.

Test Scores

[Histogram: x-axis "Number of Points" from 30 to 80, y-axis "Frequency" from 0 to 4]

Summary Statistics	
Mean	59.34
Median	62
Stand Dev	11.29
IQR	16

a. Kim earned a score of 54 and Jim earned a score of 65. Change their scores to percentages (to the nearest tenth of a percent) of the possible points.

b. Describe the transformation you used by writing a formula. Be sure to define your variables.

c. Make a new table of summary statistics, using the percentages rather than the number of points scored.

b. Subtracting a positive constant d slides the distribution left. Such a slide won't change the shape or spread, but decreases the mean by d.

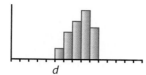   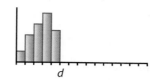

c. Suppose a set of data has mean $\bar{x}$ and standard deviation s. If you multiply each value by the same positive number c, the shape of the distribution does not change, the mean of the transformed data will be $c \cdot \bar{x}$ and the standard deviation will be $c \cdot s$. On a histogram, the distribution shifts so it is centered at c times the original center and stretches by a factor of c (or shrinks by a factor of c if $0 < c < 1$).

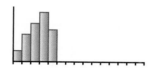   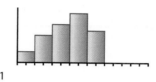

$c > 1$

d. The mean of the data transformed by dividing by a positive number c will be $\frac{\bar{x}}{c}$, and the standard deviation will be $\frac{s}{c}$. On a histogram, the distribution will shrink by a factor of c (or stretch by a factor of c if $0 < c < 1$).

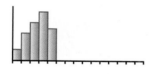   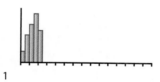

$c > 1$

e. Parts a and b represent slides. Parts c and d represent stretches.

6 **a.** Kim: $\frac{54}{75} = 72.0\%$; Jim: $\frac{65}{75} \approx 86.7\%$

b. If S was the original score and P is the percentage of possible points, then the transformation was $P = \frac{S}{75} \times 100$.

c. **New Summary Statistics**

Mean	$\frac{59.34}{75} \times 100 = 79.12\%$
Median	$\frac{62}{75} \times 100 \approx 82.7\%$
Stand Dev	$\frac{11.29}{75} \times 100 \approx 15.05$
IQR	$\frac{16}{75} \times 100 \approx 21.3$

Summarize the Mathematics

In this investigation, you discovered that transforming each value of a set of data affects the shape of the distribution, its center, and its spread in predictable ways.

a What is the effect on the mean of transforming a set of data by adding or subtracting the same number to each value? What is the effect on the standard deviation? On the shape of the distribution? Explain why this is the case.

b What is the effect on the mean of transforming a set of data by multiplying or dividing each value by the same positive number? What is the effect on the standard deviation? On the shape of the distribution? Explain why this is the case.

Be prepared to share your ideas and reasoning with the class.

✓ Check Your Understanding

In the Carlyle family, the mean age is 26 with a standard deviation of 22.3 years.

a. What will be their mean age in 5 years? Their standard deviation in 5 years?

b. What is their mean age now in months? Their standard deviation in months?

c. The ages of the people in the Carlyle family are 1, 5, 9, 28, 31, 50, and 58.

 i. Compute the mean and standard deviation of their ages in 5 years. Was your prediction in Part a correct?

 ii. Compute the mean and standard deviation of their current ages in months. Was your prediction in Part b correct?

Summarize
the Mathematics

(a) The mean will be increased or decreased by that number. (Students will see an algebraic proof of this fact in Connections Task 15.) The shape and the spread will not change, so the standard deviation will be the same. Think of the histogram being shifted to the right or the left by that number.

(b) The mean is multiplied by that number, as is the standard deviation. The shape of the distribution does not change. Think of the histogram as being stretched (or shrunk) along the x-axis.

UNIT 2 *Patterns in Data*

Summarize the Mathematics

In this investigation, you discovered that transforming each value of a set of data affects the shape of the distribution, its center, and its spread in predictable ways.

a What is the effect on the mean of transforming a set of data by adding or subtracting the same number to each value? What is the effect on the standard deviation? On the shape of the distribution? Explain why this is the case.

b What is the effect on the mean of transforming a set of data by multiplying or dividing each value by the same positive number? What is the effect on the standard deviation? On the shape of the distribution? Explain why this is the case.

Be prepared to share your ideas and reasoning with the class.

108 UNIT 2 • Patterns in Data

Unit 2

PROCESSING PROMPT We helped our group stay focused on the mathematics by _____ .

✓ Check Your Understanding

MATH TOOLKIT Students should record the effect of transformations on the mean and standard deviation in their toolkit.

a. The mean age will be $5 + 26 = 31$ years; the standard deviation will remain 22.3 years.

b. The mean age is $12(26) = 312$ months; the standard deviation is $(12)(22.3) \approx 268$ months.

c. **i.** Yes, the mean and standard deviation will be 31 years and 22.3 years. (Subject to round-off error.)

 ii. Yes, the mean and standard deviation are 312 months and 268 months. (Subject to round-off error.)

Applications

1 The table below gives the percentiles of recent SAT mathematics scores for national college-bound seniors. The highest possible score is 800 and the lowest possible score is 200. Only scores that are multiples of 50 are shown in the table, but all multiples of 10 from 200 to 800 are possible.

College-Bound Seniors

SAT Math Score	Percentile	SAT Math Score	Percentile
750	98	450	28
700	93	400	15
650	85	350	7
600	74	300	3
550	60	250	1
500	43	200	0

Source: *2005 College-Bound Seniors Total Group Profile Report*, The College Board

a. What percentage of seniors get a score of 650 or lower on the mathematics section of the SAT?

b. What is the lowest score a senior could get on the mathematics section of the SAT and still be in the top 40% of those who take the test?

c. Estimate the score a senior would have to get to be in the top half of the students who take this test.

d. Estimate the 25th and 75th percentiles. Use these quartiles in a sentence that describes the distribution.

2 In a physical fitness test, the median time it took a large group of students to run a mile was 10.2 minutes. The distribution had first and third quartiles of 7.1 minutes and 13.7 minutes. Faster runners (shorter times) were assigned higher percentiles.

a. Sheila's time was at the 25th percentile. How long did it take Sheila to run the mile?

b. Mark was told that his time was at the 16th percentile. Write a sentence that tells Mark what this means.

On Your Own

Applications

1 **a.** 85%

   b. 550

   c. Above around 520

   d. About 440 and 600
   The middle half of the scores lie between about 440 and 600.

2 **a.** 7.1 minutes

   b. Mark, about 16% of the people who participated in the race took longer to run the race than you did, and about 84% ran it faster than you did.

3 The histogram below gives the marriage rate per 1,000 people for 49 U.S. states in 2004. (Nevada, with a rate of 62 marriages per 1,000 people, was left off so the plot would fit on the page.)

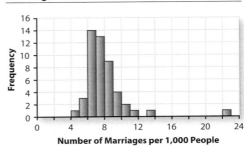

Marriage Rate

Frequency vs. Number of Marriages per 1,000 People

a. Hawaii had about 1,262,840 residents and 28,793 marriages. What is the marriage rate per 1,000 residents for Hawaii? Where is Hawaii located on the histogram?

b. New York had about 130,744 marriages and 19,227,088 residents. What is the marriage rate per 1,000 residents for New York? Where is it located on the histogram?

c. Why do you think that Nevada's rate of 62 marriages per 1,000 people can't be interpreted as "62 out of every 1,000 residents of Nevada were married in 2004"?

d. The quartiles, including the median, divide a distribution, as closely as possible, into four equal parts. Estimate the median and lower and upper quartiles of the distribution and make a box plot of the distribution. Include Nevada in the distribution.

e. Now estimate the percentile for the following states.

   i. Tennessee, with a marriage rate of 11.4

   ii. Minnesota, with a marriage rate of 6.0

4 Suppose that you want to estimate the thickness of a piece of paper in your textbook. Compress more than a hundred pages from the middle of the book and measure the thickness to the nearest half of a millimeter. Divide by the number of sheets of paper. Round the result to four decimal places.

a. How can you determine the number of sheets of paper by using the page numbers?

b. Make ten more estimates, taking a different number of pages each time. Record your measurements on a dot plot.

c. What is the median of your measurements? What is the interquartile range?

d. Write a sentence or two reporting what you would give as an estimate of the thickness of the piece of paper.

TECHNOLOGY NOTE The data for this task are in *CPMP-Tools* under Statistics.

a. Hawaii's marriage rate per 1,000 people is about 22.8. This state is the only one in the bar from 22 up to 23.

b. New York's marriage rate per 1,000 people is 6.8. This state is one of the eight states in the bar from 6 up to 7.

c. This rate would be much too high (almost one marriage per resident every 13 or so years). There are a lot of people who get married in Nevada, especially in Las Vegas, who are not residents of Nevada.

d. From the histogram, the lower quartile is between 6 and 7; the median is between 7 and 8, and the upper quartile is between 8 and 9. Students' box plots will vary slightly depending on their choice of values in the intervals and whether they show the known outliers.

Marriage Rate

e. i. All but 3 of the 50 states (6%) have a marriage rate less than or equal to 11.4, so Tennessee is in about the 94th percentile.

ii. Only 4 states have a lower marriage rate than Minnesota, so it is at about the 8th percentile.

4 a. Subtract the number of the last page you are holding (an even page number) and the number of the last page you are *not* holding, then divide by 2. For example, if the pages you are holding have numbers from 101 to 154, then you have $\frac{154 - 100}{2} = 27$ sheets of paper.

b–d. Estimates will vary. You may need to remind students that they should include units with their estimates.

TECHNOLOGY NOTE Part d offers an opportunity to address the limits of technology. If students use ZoomStat to scale this box plot, the median does not appear to be in the center of the box. Switching the Xmin and Xmax to 0 and 70, respectively, displays the median in the center because there is only 1 pixel that can be used. Using 0 to 65 displays the median next to Q_3.

Unit 2

5 The table below gives the price and size of 20 different boxed assortments of chocolate as reported in *Consumer Reports*.

Boxed Assortments of Chocolate

Brand	Price (in $)	Size (in oz)	Cost per oz
John & Kira's Jubilee Wood Gift Box	65	18	3.69
Martine's Gift Box Assorted with Creams	63	16	3.93
Norman Love Confections	37	8	4.62
Candinas	40	16	2.50
La Maison du Chocolat Coffret Maison with assorted chocolates	76	21	3.59
Moonstruck Classic Truffle Collections	70	20	3.50
Jacques Torres Jacques' Assortment	43	16	2.69
Fran's Assorted Truffles Gift Box	58	16	3.63
Godiva Gold Ballotin	35	16	
Leonidas Pralines General Assortment		16	1.75
See's Famous Old Time Assorted	13	16	
Ethel M Rich Deluxe Assortment	26	16	1.62
Lake Champlain Selection Fine Assorted	40	18	2.22
Rocky Mountain Chocolate Factory Gift Assortment Regular	19	14.5	1.31
Hershey's Pot of Gold Premium Assortment	8	14.1	0.57
Russell Stover Assorted	8	16	0.50
Whitman's Sampler Assorted	10	16	0.62
Rocky Mountain Chocolate Factory Sugar-Free Regular Gift Assortment	19	14.5	1.31
Russell Stover Net Carb Assorted	8	8.25	0.97
Ethel M Sugar-Free Truffle Collection	32	15	2.13

Source: *Consumer Reports*, February 2005

a. The cost per ounce is missing for Godiva and for See's. The price is missing for Leonidas Pralines. Compute those values.

b. The histogram to the right shows the cost-per-ounce data. Examine the histogram and make a sketch of what you think the box plot of the same data will look like. Then, make the box plot and check the accuracy of your sketch.

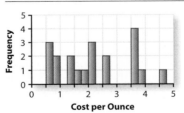

Boxed Assortments of Chocolate

c. Identify any outliers in the cost-per-ounce data.

d. What information about boxed assortments of chocolate can you learn from the histogram that you cannot from the box plot? What information about boxed assortments of chocolate can you learn from the box plot that you cannot from the histogram?

e. Why is it more useful to plot the cost-per-ounce data than the price data?

5

a. Godiva: $2.19 per ounce; See's: $0.81 per ounce; Leonidas: $28

b. The following box plot shows the actual distribution of the cost-per-ounce data. Student box plots will not be this accurate.

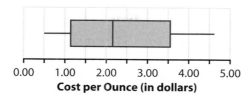

Cost per Ounce (in dollars)

The five-number summary appears below.

$$\text{minimum} = 0.5,\ Q_1 = 1.14,\ \text{median} = 2.16,$$
$$Q_3 = 3.55,\ \text{maximum} = 4.62$$

c. Using Jolaina's idea on page 114, you can tell that there are no outliers by observing that the whiskers are less than 1.5 times as long as the box. So, there are no outliers. Some students may choose to compute using the outlier identification rule. (Any outlier falls below $1.14 - 1.5(3.55 - 1.14) = -2.475$ or above $3.55 + 1.5(3.55 - 1.14) = 7.165$. There are no outliers according to this rule.)

d. The histogram allows you to estimate individual costs with fairly good accuracy and to count the number of chocolates plotted. The histogram shows that there are no values between $2.75 and $3.50. Further, the histogram shows that at $4.62 per ounce, Norman Love Confections is separated from the rest of the cost-per-ounce amounts by a small gap. The box plot shows none of these things.

The box plot shows that this gap isn't large enough to make this amount an outlier. Also, you can see the five-number summary from the box plot and know that, for example, half of the costs per ounce are less than the median ($2.25 or $2.16, if you use the Trace function) and half are more. (Some students may answer this question without constructing the boxplot.)

e. Boxes of chocolate come in different sizes, so to compare price you should take size into account. The best way to do that is cost per ounce.

INSTRUCTIONAL NOTE You may wish to have students explain their thinking for Part c in class. This allows students to be exposed to visual and numerical reasoning.

Unit 2

6 The table below shows the total points scored during the first eight years of the NBA careers of Kareem Abdul-Jabbar and Michael Jordan.

Two Shooting Stars

Kareem Abdul-Jabbar		Michael Jordan	
Year	Points Scored	Year	Points Scored
1970	2,361	1985	2,313
1971	2,596	1986	408
1972	2,822	1987	3,041
1973	2,292	1988	2,868
1974	2,191	1989	2,633
1975	1,949	1990	2,753
1976	2,275	1991	2,580
1977	2,152	1992	2,404

a. Which player had the higher mean number of points per year?

b. What summary statistics could you use to measure consistency in a player? Which player was more consistent according to each of your statistics?

c. Use the rule to determine if there are any outliers for either player.

d. Jordan had an injury in 1986. If you ignore his performance for that year, how would you change your answers to Parts a and b?

7 The histogram below gives the scores of the ninth-graders at Lakeside High School on their high school's exit exam.

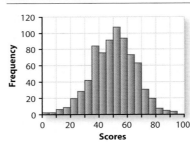

Exit Exam Scores

a. Estimate the mean and the standard deviation of the scores.

b. Estimate the percentile of a student whose score is one standard deviation below the mean. Then estimate the percentile corresponding to a score one standard deviation above the mean.

6 **a.** Michael Jordan has a mean of 2,375 points per year and narrowly beats out Kareem Abdul-Jabbar who, has a mean of 2,330.

b. The standard deviation or the interquartile range could be used to measure consistency. Which one to select depends on how you want to handle Jordan's outlier in 1986. The interquartile range will be resistant to this outlier. Jordan has a standard deviation of 829 points per year, and Abdul-Jabbar has a standard deviation of 271. Jordan was *much* less consistent using this measure. And this is not entirely because of his atypical performance in 1986. His interquartile range of 452 is quite a bit larger than Abdul-Jabbar's of 307.

c. Jordan's number of points in 1986 is an outlier. The five-number summaries for the two players appear below.

Abdul-Jabbar: minimum = 1,949.0, Q_1 = 2,171.5, median = 2,283.5, Q_3 = 2,478.5, maximum = 2,822.0

Jordan: minimum = 408, Q_1 = 2,358.5, median = 2,606.5, Q_3 = 2,810.5, maximum = 3,041

For Jordan, outliers appear below $2,358.5 - 1.5(452) = 1,680.5$, or above $2,810.5 + 1.5(452) = 3,488.5$, so only the minimum of 408 is an outlier.

d. If the 1986 results are omitted, Jordan's mean increases to 2,656 points per year, and his standard deviation decreases to 255 points per year. He now is clearly the better player as he has a higher mean and is more consistent.

7 **a.** The mean is 50.4 and the standard deviation is about 10.2, so estimates of 50 and 10 are very good.

b. Since about $\frac{1}{3}$, or 33%, of the scores lie between the mean and the point one standard deviation below the mean, the percentile one standard deviation below the mean is about $50 - 33 = 17$. The percentile one standard deviation above the mean is about $50 + 33 = 83$.

8 The numbers below are the play times (using the battery) in hours of 19 models of MP3 players. (Source: *Consumer Reports*, December 2005)

63, 45, 32, 30, 26, 18, 17, 17, 16,
16, 14, 14, 13, 10, 10, 10, 10, 9, 7

a. Compute the median and interquartile range and the mean and standard deviation of the play times.

b. One MP3 player has a play time of 10 hours. What is the deviation from the mean for that MP3 player?

c. Remove the 63 from the list and recompute the summary statistics in Part a.

d. How do you think the play times should be summarized? Explain.

9 In an experiment to compare 2 fertilizers, 12 trees were treated with Fertilizer A, and a different 12 trees were treated with Fertilizer B. The table below gives the number of kilograms of oranges produced per tree.

Kilograms of Oranges per Tree

Fertilizer A	Fertilizer B
3	14
14	116
19	33
0	40
96	10
92	72
11	8
24	10
5	2
31	13
84	15
15	44

a. Make a back-to-back stemplot of the number of kilograms of oranges produced by trees with Fertilizer A and with Fertilizer B. (See pages 97 and 98 for examples of stemplots.)

b. Use the stemplot to estimate the mean of each group.

c. Which group appears to have the larger standard deviation? How can you tell?

d. Compute the mean and standard deviation of each group. How close were your estimates in Part b?

8 **a.** The median is 16 and interquartile range is 26 − 10 = 16. The mean is 19.8 and the standard deviation is 14.2.

  b. The MP3 Player has a deviation of 10 − 19.8 = −9.8.

  c. After removing the hours for the outlier, the median is 15, the interquartile range is 18 − 10 = 8, the mean is 17.4, and the standard deviation is 9.9.

  d. The mean and standard deviation are sensitive to the outlier of 63. Thus, they change quite a bit when this MP3 player is removed. The median changes hardly at all. However, this is an interesting case where the IQR also changes quite a bit, which can happen in small sets of data that have internal gaps. Consequently, it looks like both measures of spread are too sensitive to small changes in the data. So, there are three reasonable choices:

   • Give just the median (half of the players last longer than 17 hours and half last less).

   • Give the entire five-number summary: 7, 10, 16, 26, 63.

   • Don't summarize at all. There are only 19 numbers, which aren't a lot to take in at once if they are listed in order or put on a dot plot.

9 **a.** **Mass of Oranges (in Kilograms)**

Fertilizer A		Fertilizer B
5 3 0	0	2 8
9 5 4 1	1	0 0 3 4 5
4	2	
1	3	3
	4	0 4
	5	
	6	
	7	2
4	8	
6 2	9	
	10	
	11	6 1|4 represents 14 kg

> **ASSIGNMENT NOTE** If students have not done Extensions Task 20 of Lesson 1, they may need a review of back-to-back stemplots before doing this task.

  b. Estimates of the means should be between 25 and 35 for each fertilizer.

  c. Fertilizer A has the larger standard deviation. The slightly larger standard deviation for Fertilizer A is due to the three values in the 80s and 90s. (Students may incorrectly choose Fertilizer B since the range of Fertilizer B is larger than that of Fertilizer A. They will compute these statistics in Part d.)

> **INSTRUCTIONAL NOTE** Be sure that students recognize that the data set with the larger range is not the one with the larger standard deviation.

  d.

	Fertilizer A	Fertilizer B
Mean	32.8 kg	31.4 kg
Standard Deviation	36.0 kg	33.4 kg

e. What are the shape, mean, and standard deviation of the distribution of the number of *pounds* of oranges for Fertilizer A? For Fertilizer B? (There are about 2.2 pounds in a kilogram.)

f. Is a scatterplot an appropriate plot for these data? Why or why not?

(10) All 36 members of the Caledonia High School softball team reported the number of hours they study in a typical week. The numbers are given below.

5	5	5	6	10	11
12	12	12	13	14	15
15	16	16	16	17	17
17	17	18	19	19	20
20	20	20	20	20	23
25	25	25	27	28	40

Study Time of Softball Team Members

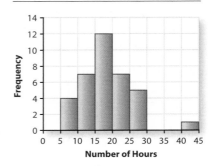

a. Estimate the mean and standard deviation of the distribution from the histogram.

b. Compute the mean and standard deviation of the distribution. How close were your estimates in Part a?

c. Akemi is the student who studies 40 hours a week. She is thinking of quitting the softball team. How will the mean and standard deviation change if Akemi quits and her number of hours is removed from the set of data?

d. Describe two ways to find the mean and standard deviation of the number of hours studied *per semester* (20 weeks) by these students. Find the mean and standard deviation using your choice of method.

e. The softball coach expects team members to practice a total of 10 hours. If practice hours are added to the weekly study hours for each student, how will the mean and standard deviation change?

e. The shapes of the distributions are unchanged. To find these summary statistics in number of pounds, multiply each of the numbers in Part c by 2.2. Alternatively, you could convert each of the 24 measurements to pounds and then re-compute the means and standard deviations.

	Fertilizer A	Fertilizer B
Mean	72.2 lbs	69.1 lbs
Standard Deviation	79.2 lbs	73.5 lbs

f. No, these are not paired data. For example, there is no connection between the 3 and 14 in the first row of the table in the student text.

10 a. A good estimate is about 17 hours for the mean and 7 hours for the standard deviation.

b. The mean is 17.2 hours and the standard deviation is about 7.1 hours (7.1479 hours).

c. Both the mean and the standard deviation will be smaller.

d. You could multiply each of the hours worked by 20 to get the number of hours each student works per semester and then compute the mean and standard deviation of the semester hours. Alternatively, you could simply multiply the mean and the standard deviation from Part b by 20. The mean is 344 hours per semester, with a standard deviation of about 142 or 143 hours.

e. The mean will increase by 10 hours, to 27.2 hours per week, and the standard deviation will remain unchanged at about 7.1 hours.

TECHNOLOGY NOTE The data for this task are in *CPMP-Tools* under Statistics.

Unit 2

Connections

11 Consider the box plot below.

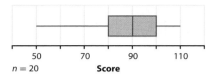

$n = 20$ **Score**

a. What does the "$n = 20$" below the plot mean?

b. About how many scores are between 50 and 80? Between 80 and 100? Greater than 80?

c. Is it possible for the box plot to be displaying the scores below? Explain your reasoning.

> 50, 60, 60, 75, 80, 80, 82, 83, 85, 90, 90,
> 91, 91, 94, 95, 95, 98, 100, 106, 110

d. Create a set of scores that could be the ones displayed by this box plot.

12 The box plots below represent the amounts of money (in dollars) carried by the people surveyed in four different places at a mall.

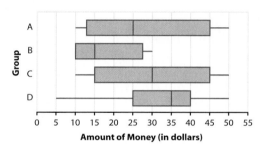

Amounts of Money Carried By Mall Shoppers

a. Which group of people has the smallest range? The largest?

b. Which group of people has the smallest interquartile range? The largest?

c. Which group of people has the largest median amount of money?

d. Which distribution is most symmetric?

e. Which group of people do you think might be high school students standing in line for tickets at a movie theater on Saturday night? Explain your reasoning.

Connections

11 **a.** The 20 means that there are 20 values represented in the box plot.

b. The interval between 50 and 80 is represented by the lower whisker and therefore contains 25% of the data, or 5 values.

The interval between 80 and 100 is represented by the box and therefore contains 50% of the data, or 10 values.

The interval greater than 80 is represented by the box and upper whisker and therefore contains 75% of the data, or 15 values.

c. No, because there aren't five values greater than 100 as shown on the plot.

d. One idea is to use the numbers in Part c but change 95, 95, and 98 to 100, 100, and 105. Another option would be to use the numbers in Part c but change one 95 to 105, 98 to 106, and 100 to 106.

12 **a.** Group B has the smallest range.
Group D has the largest range.

b. Group D has the smallest interquartile range.
Group A has the largest interquartile range.

c. Group D has the largest median.

d. Group C might have a symmetric distribution.

e. Responses will vary depending on how much pocket money students in your area typically carry around with them. Typically students will select Group B because each student needs to have at least $10 to go to the movies, and no student carries around very much money.

Teaching Resources

Student Master 109.

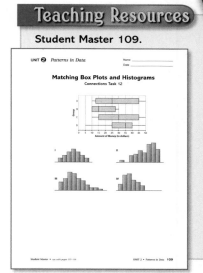

f. Match each of the groups A, B, C, and D with its histogram below.

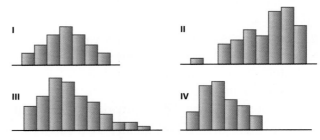

13 The histogram below (reprinted from page 92) displays the number of video games that are available for 43 different platforms. The mean number of video games per platform is about 426, with a standard deviation of about 751.

Number of Video Games

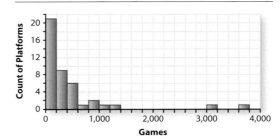

a. Do about 68% of the platforms fall within one standard deviation of the mean?

b. Why aren't the mean and standard deviation very informative summary statistics for these data?

14 Give counterexamples that show the statements below are not true in general.

a. If two sets of numbers have the same range, you should consider them to have the same variability.

b. If two sets of numbers have the same mean and the same standard deviation, they have the same distribution.

15 Refer to Problem 1 of Investigation 5 (page 124) for the 10 measurements of a desk or table.

a. Find the median and interquartile range of the original measurements.

b. Find the median and interquartile range after each measurement is transformed to inches.

　i. How do the median and interquartile range of the transformed data compare to those of the original data?

　ii. In general, what is the effect on the median and interquartile range if you divide each value in a data set by the same number?

f.

Histogram	Group
I	C
II	D
III	A
IV	B

13 **a.** Only 4 of the 43 games fall more than one standard deviation from the mean. This is less than 10% of the games, so about 90% of the games are within one standard deviation of the mean.

b. The mean is sensitive to the skew and to the outliers and so is larger than at least 30 of the 43 platforms. Thus, it is not a very useful measure of center. Similarly, the standard deviation is sensitive to the skew and the outliers and also is quite large. This shows why the mean and standard deviation are considered appropriate as summary statistics only for approximately normal distributions.

14 **a.** These two sets of values have the same range of 9, but the second one varies more from its mean:

1, 5, 5, 5, 5, 5, 5, 5, 5, 5, 10   and   1, 1, 1, 1, 1, 10, 10, 10, 10, 10.

b. Finding two different sets of values with the same mean and standard deviation is quite challenging. So, in most cases, students will have two sets of numbers with approximately the same standard deviation.

If you have the same number of values, all you need is to be sure that Σx and Σx^2 are equal for both sets. An example is

1, 1, 2, 2, 4, 5, 6   and   0, 2, 2, 3, 3, 5, 6.

Both sets have a mean of 3 and a standard deviation of 2.

15 The answers below are for the sample measurements in centimeters used in the solution to Problem 1 in Investigation 5 (76.1, 76.1, 76.2, 76.2, 76.3, 76.3, 76.4, 76.4, 76.4, 76.5). The results from your class will be different.

a. The median is 76.3 cm. The quartiles are 76.2 and 76.4, so the interquartile range is 0.2 cm.

b. The median is about 30.04 inches. The quartiles are 30.00 and about 30.08, so the interquartile range is about 0.08 inches.

  i. The median of the transformed data, 30.04, is equal to $\frac{76.3}{2.54} \approx 30.04$. The interquartile range of the transformed data, 0.08, is equal to $\frac{0.2}{2.54} \approx 0.08$.

  ii. The median and interquartile range of the transformed data are equal to the original median and interquartile range divided by the number.

c. Find the median and interquartile range after adding 0.2 cm to each original measurement.

   i. How do the median and interquartile range of the transformed data compare to those of the original data?

   ii. In general, what is the effect on the median and interquartile range of adding the same number to each value of a data set? Explain your reasoning.

Reflections

16 On page 112, you read about a study of lead in the blood of children. Each child who had been exposed to lead on the clothing of a parent was paired with a child who had not been exposed. A complete analysis should take this pairing into account. One way of doing that is to subtract the lead level of the control child from the lead level of the exposed child.

a. Find these differences and make a box plot of the differences.

b. If the exposure to lead makes no difference in the level of lead in the blood, where would the box plot be centered?

c. What conclusion can you draw from examining the box plot of the differences?

d. What additional information does this analysis take into account that the analysis in the Check Your Understanding did not?

e. Another way to look at these data is to make a scatterplot. What can you learn from the scatterplot below that you could not see from the other plots?

Blood Lead Level
(in micrograms per deciliter)

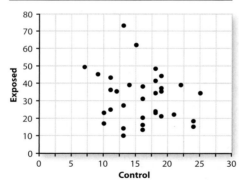

c. The median is 76.5 cm. The quartiles are 76.4 and 76.6, so the interquartile range is 0.2 cm.

    i. The median of the transformed data, 76.5, is equal to 76.3 + 0.2. The interquartile range of the transformed data, 0.2, is equal to the original IQR.

    ii. The median of the transformed data is equal to the original median plus the number as the entire distribution is slid by that amount. The IQR does not change, because, like the median, each quartile increases by the same number. Therefore, the difference between quartiles remains the same. Some students may explain using sketches of distributions; others may explain symbolically, $(Q_3 + d) - (Q_1 + d) = Q_3 - Q_1$.

Reflections

16   **a.** The differences and box plot appear below.

    Differences: −3, −3, 1, −9, 0, 7, −6, 4, 2, 1, 13, 5, 6, 14, 14, 15, 16, 9, 23, 16, 25, 18, 22, 25, 17, 23, 32, 25, 36, 30, 42, 47, 60

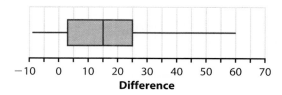

b. If the exposure made no difference, the box plot would be centered at 0.

c. Almost all of the values are positive, meaning that a child who had a parent exposed to lead at work tended to have a higher lead level in his or her blood than did a child matched by age and neighborhood.

d. This analysis takes into account the fact that the children were in "matched pairs." By subtracting the lead levels within each pair, you get a good indication of how much the lead level is affected in *similar* children by a parent who is exposed to lead at work.

e. Because there is no pattern on this scatterplot, you can say that there doesn't appear to be any relationship between the level of lead in the control child and the paired exposed child. Specifically, control children with higher lead levels didn't tend to be paired with exposed children with higher lead levels. (So, perhaps the pairing wasn't necessary.)

17 These box plots represent the scores of 80 seniors and 80 juniors on a fitness test. List the characteristics you know will be true about a box plot for the combined scores of the seniors and the juniors. For example, what will the minimum be?

Fitness Test Scores

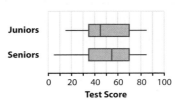

18 John Tukey, the same statistician who invented stemplots and box plots, established the standard rule for identifying possible outliers. When asked why he used 1.5 rather than some other number, he replied that 1 was too small and 2 was too big. Explain what he meant.

19 There are 15 outliers on the low end plus 2 outliers on the high end in the box plot below that shows the maximum temperatures ever recorded at the 289 U.S. weather stations in the 50 states, Puerto Rico, and the Pacific Islands.

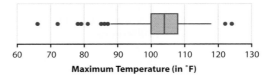

Maximum Recorded Temperature at U.S. Weather Stations

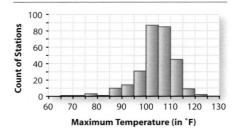

a. Study the histogram of the maximum temperatures. How can you tell from this histogram that there are outliers?

b. What are some geographical explanations for why there are so many outliers?

20 Is a minimum or a maximum value always an outlier? Is an outlier always a maximum or minimum value? Explain your answers.

17 Possible responses:

    The total number of scores will be 160.

    The minimum will be 5, the lower extreme for the seniors' data.

    The maximum will be 85, the upper extreme for both data sets.

    The lower quartile will remain at 35.

    The upper quartile will remain at 70.

    Half, or 80, of the scores will be between 35 and 70.

    The median will be between the current medians of 42 and 55.

18 John Tukey (1915–2000) developed many of the tools of modern data analysis. It was his vast experience with data that gave him a very good sense of which values should rightfully be identified as outliers. He found that if he used 1 as the multiplier, he got more values identified as outliers than he wanted. If he used 2, he got too few.

    For more about Tukey's extraordinary contributions, see www-groups.mcs.st-and.ac.uk/~history/Mathematicians/Tukey.html.

19 **a.** The middle half of the temperatures lie roughly in the interval between 100 and 110, so these would be the edges of the box on a box plot. The temperatures of 85 and below are more than one-and-a-half box lengths below 100. It isn't so easy to estimate whether or not there are outliers on the high end. (The five-number summary for these temperatures is 66, 100, 104, 108, 124.)

    b. Most of the outliers on the low end are stations in Alaska. Most of Alaska is much farther north (where it never gets very warm), than the rest of the country. The other low outliers are Eureka, on the coast of Northern California, and Mt. Washington in New Hampshire. The two outliers on the high side are Phoenix and Yuma, Arizona, which are in the desert.

20 No. A maximum that is not an outlier would occur in a data set where all values, or the top 25% of the values, are clustered closely together. For example, a maximum that is not an outlier occurs in the box plot of fitness test scores in Reflections Task 20. An outlier that is not a maximum would occur if there is more than one outlier, with one higher than the other. For example, an outlier that is not a maximum or minimum occurs in the box plot for the maximum temperatures in Reflections Task 21.

21 List the summary statistics that do not change when the same number is added to, or subtracted from, each value in a set of data. What do these statistics have in common?

22 When Nikki looked at the summary statistics for the 32 student tests in Problem 6 of Investigation 5 on page 127, she said, "These statistics can't be right. One standard deviation either side of the mean captures $\frac{2}{3}$ of the data and the IQR captures 50% of the data. So, the standard deviation should be larger than the IQR." Do you agree or disagree? Explain your reasoning.

Extensions

23 If your family has records of your growth, plot your own height over the years on a copy of the appropriate National Center for Health Statistics growth chart. How much has the percentile for your age varied over your lifetime?

24 Consider the position of the lower quartile for data sets with n values.

  a. When n is odd and the values are placed in order from smallest to largest, explain why the position of the lower quartile is

$$\frac{n+1}{4}.$$

  b. What is the position of the lower quartile when n is even?

25 Examine the 1999 U.S. Population by Race data set in your data analysis software. That data set includes the percentage of the population in each state and the District of Columbia who are Hispanic, Black, American Indian, Native Alaskan, Asian, or Pacific Islander. It also indicates which presidential candidate got the majority of votes cast in the 2000 presidential election in each state.

United States of America

21 The interquartile range, range, and standard deviation do not change. These are all measures of spread.

22 One standard deviation above *and* one below the mean will capture about $\frac{2}{3}$ of the data when the distribution is approximately normal. Thus, twice the standard deviation will usually be larger than the IQR. The standard deviation in Problem 6 is 11.29, and the IQR is 16. Twice the standard deviation, or about 22.6 in this case, is in fact greater than the IQR of 16.

Extensions

23 **NOTE** Students' records should be treated confidentially.

24 **NOTE** Students probably will use examples to find the formulas below rather than working through the algebra. That's fine at this stage.

a. When n is odd, the median is positioned at $\frac{n+1}{2}$, which is a whole number. Leaving that number out, the positions below the median are $1, 2, 3, \ldots, \frac{n+1}{2} - 1 = \frac{n}{2} - \frac{1}{2}$. The median of the lower half is positioned at $\dfrac{\frac{n}{2} - \frac{1}{2} + 1}{2} = \dfrac{\frac{n}{2} + \frac{1}{2}}{2} = \frac{n+1}{4}$, or $\frac{n}{4} + \frac{1}{4}$.

b. When n is even, the median is positioned at $\frac{n+1}{2} = \frac{n}{2} + \frac{1}{2}$, which is not a whole number. So, the positions below the median are $1, 2, \ldots, \frac{n}{2}$. The median of these $\frac{n}{2}$ numbers is positioned at $\dfrac{\frac{n}{2} + 1}{2} = \frac{n+2}{4}$, or $\frac{n}{4} + \frac{1}{2}$. In words, this formula is: "To get the position of the first quartile, divide the number of values by 4 and add $\frac{1}{2}$."

a. Which state has the largest percentage of people who are Hispanic, Black, American Indian, Native Alaskan, Asian, or Pacific Islander? The largest number?

b. If you find the mean of these 51 percentages, will that necessarily give you the percentage for the United States as a whole? Give a small example to illustrate your answer.

c. Make box plots of the percentages for states that favored Bush in the 2000 election and for the states (and Washington, D.C.) that favored Gore.

d. Describe the differences between the box plots. Why do you think there are these differences?

e. What other plot could be used to compare the two distributions? Make this plot that shows the two distributions. Can you see anything interesting that you could not see from the box plots?

f. Write a brief report that compares the two distributions. Explain your choice of summary statistics.

 Madeline thought that a good measure of spread would be simply to
- find the deviations from the mean,
- take the absolute value of each one, and
- average them.

Madeline calls her method the MAD: **Mean Absolute Deviation**.

a. Use Madeline's method and the table below to find the MAD for these numbers:

1, 4, 6, 8, 9, 14

Number	Mean	(Number − Mean)	|Number − Mean|

Add the absolute differences:

Divide the sum by n:

b. Why does Madeline have to take the absolute value before averaging the numbers?

c. Write a formula using Σ that summarizes Madeline's method.

25

a. Hawaii, with 71.4%, has the largest percentage. California has the largest number. Although Washington, D.C., Hawaii, and New Mexico have larger percentages, they have much smaller populations than California. (Students may need to be reminded that a large percentage does not necessarily mean the largest number.)

b. No. For example, suppose there are only two states, *A* with a population of 1,000,000 and a percentage of 50%, and *B* with a population of 200,000 and a percentage of 20%. The mean of these percentages is 35%. However, the national percentage is
$$\frac{0.50(1,000,000) + 0.20(200,000)}{1,000,000 + 200,000} = 45\%.$$

c. The five-number summary for the thirty states that favored Bush is: 3.8, 10.5, 19.1, 29.7, 44.7. The five-number summary for the twenty states and D.C. that favored Gore is: 2.3, 11.5, 19.1, 35.3, 71.4.

"Bush" States and "Gore" States

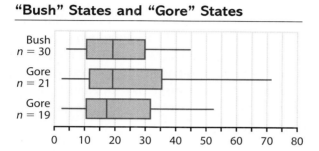

d. The Bush states tend to have a smaller percentage of people who are from these ethnic groups. The minimum, lower quartile, and median values are about the same for the two groups of states. However, the upper quartile and maximum percentages are larger for the Gore states. Overall, there is more variation in the Gore states percentages. If Hawaii and Washington, D.C., are deleted from the Gore distribution because they are outliers or thought to be different in terms of minority population than other states, the Gore distribution still has more variation than the Bush distribution.

   Minority populations have historically tended to vote Democratic, so that may explain why the states with higher percentages of people from these groups voted in favor of Gore. The state with the highest percentage that favored Bush (44.7%) was Texas. This is Bush's home state. The next highest percentage for Bush is 38.3, which is only slightly higher than the upper quartile of the states who favored Gore.

Teaching Resources

Student Master 110.

UNIT ② *Patterns in Data*   Name _____
                                            Date _____

Mean Absolute Deviation
Extensions Task 25

Number	Mean	(Number – Mean)	(Number – Mean)
		Add the absolute differences	
		Divide the sum by *n*	

110 UNIT 2 • Patterns in Data   Student Master • use with pages 139-140

TECHNOLOGY NOTE
Students can find these data in *CPMP-Tools*.

e. Either a back-to-back stem-and-leaf plot or two histograms are acceptable plots. Here are the histograms for the two groups of states.

"Bush" States

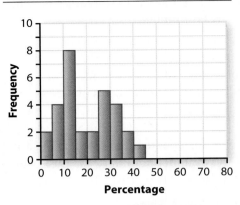

"Gore" States

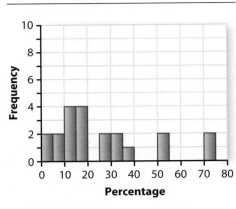

These histograms don't show much more than the box plots. However, the histograms do indicate that there are gaps in the data for the Gore states, and there are no gaps in the data for the Bush states.

Below is the back-to-back stem-and-leaf plot. The numbers have been rounded to the nearest whole percent. This plot shows us the actual percentages. It also shows us that there are more Bush states than Gore states.

Bush States		Gore States
9 9 7 4 4	0	2 2 6 9
9 9 4 4 4 2 1 1 1 0 0	1	1 3 3 4 6 7 9
8 8 8 7 2 0	2	0 5 9
8 6 4 2 2 2 0	3	2 5 6
5	4	
	5	0 3
	6	
	7	1 1 2|5 represents 25.

f. Students' reports should include displays and summary statistics. These data provide an opportunity for students to think from a data analyst's perspective. With outliers in one set, should the outliers be retained and data presented both ways, or should the outliers be removed? Justification for their choices should be included in the report.

26 **a.**

Number	Mean	(Number − Mean)	|Number − Mean|
1	7	−6	6
4	7	−3	3
6	7	−1	1
8	7	1	1
9	7	2	2
14	7	7	7

Add the absolute differences: 20

Divide the sum by *n*: $\frac{20}{6} = 3\frac{2}{3}$

For more information, see http://exploringdata.cqu.edu.au/why_var.htm.

b. Otherwise, the sum of the differences would be 0.

c. $MAD = \dfrac{\Sigma|x - \bar{x}|}{n}$

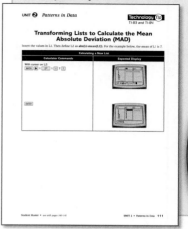
Unit 2

NOTE The MAD doesn't have useful properties like the standard deviation does. Students will see in Courses 2 and 3 how helpful statistics can be when they involve a sum of squared deviations.

d. Compute the standard deviation of the number above. How does the standard deviation compare to the MAD?

e. Madeline has indeed invented an appealing measure for describing spread. However, the MAD does not turn out to be as useful a summary statistic as the standard deviation, so it does not have a central place in the theory or practice of statistics. Does your calculator or statistical software have a function for the MAD?

27 Suppose each of the 32 students at Price Lab School tried to cut a square out of cardboard that was 24.6 mm on each side. A histogram of the actual perimeters of their squares is displayed below. The mean perimeter was 98.42 mm.

Square Perimeters

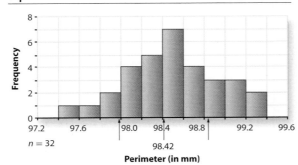

a. What might explain the variability in perimeters?

b. An interval one standard deviation above and below the mean is marked by arrows on the histogram. Use it to estimate the standard deviation.

c. Estimate the percentage of the perimeters that are within one standard deviation of the mean.

d. Estimate the percentage of the perimeters that are within two standard deviations of the mean. (For a normal distribution, this is about 95%.)

d. The standard deviation is approximately 4.47, which is a bit larger than the MAD.

e. Calculators and statistical software do not have functions for the MAD because it doesn't have a place in statistical inference and so is not a very useful summary statistic.

NOTE The standard deviation s is always greater than or equal to the MAD. Equality occurs only when all of the values are equal, and so both the MAD and s are 0. The population standard deviation σ, computed by dividing by n instead of $n-1$, is also greater than or equal to the MAD. Equality occurs only when all of the values are equal (and so both σ and the MAD are 0) or when there are only two different values, each occurring the same number of times. (For the definition of σ, see the teacher notes for Problem 5 Part e of Investigation 4.)

 a. Variability will result from whether the cardboard bends while it is being measured, the accuracy of the measuring instrument, how careful the measurer and cutter are, and whether the cut is made exactly at the spot measured.

b. The standard deviation is about $98.42 - 98 = 0.42$ mm.

c. There are 20 out of 32, or 62.5%, of the measurements within one standard deviation of the mean. (This is pretty close to the expected two-thirds for a normal distribution.)

d. There are about 29 out of 32, or 90.6%, of the measurements within two standard deviations of the mean, pretty close to the 95% expected with a normal distribution.

Unit 2

28 The following are the resting pulse rates of a group of parents of ninth-graders at Beaverton High School.

Parent Pulse Rates

60	62	67	68	70	72	74	75
76	76	77	78	80	81	81	82
83	84	84	84	86	88	88	88
89	90	91	94	107			

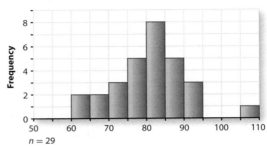

$n = 29$

Pulse Rate (in beats per minute)

a. Describe the distribution of the parents' pulse rates.

b. Dion's mother thinks she may have lost count since her pulse rate was the lowest, 60. Does her reported pulse rate look unusually low to you? Explain.

c. The teacher said that anyone with a resting rate of more than two standard deviations from the mean should repeat the test to check the results. How many students had their parents repeat the test? Did Dion's mother need to repeat the test?

d. The parents did two minutes of mild exercise, then counted their rates again. This time the mean was 90, and the standard deviation was 12.4. Cleone's mother had a pulse rate of 95 after exercising.

   i. Is her rate unusually high? How can the standard deviation help explain your answer?

   ii. What would your conclusion be about Cleone's mother's pulse rate if the standard deviation was 1.24?

Review

29 The number 20,000 can be written as $2(10,000) = 2 \cdot 10^4$ and 2,000,000 can be written as $2(1,000,000) = 2 \cdot 10^6$.

a. On your calculator when you multiply 20,000 by 2,000,000 you get "4E10." What does this mean?

b. Predict what you will get when you use your calculator to multiply 2,000,000 by 4,000,000.

c. Predict what you will get when you use your calculator to multiply 2,400,000 by 20,000. What rule does the calculator appear to be using to format the answer?

28 a. The distribution looks approximately normal except for a gap between 94 and 107. The pulse rates of the parents ranged from a low of 60 beats per minute to a high near 110 beats per minute. All but five parents had pulse rates between 70 and 95. The average was around 80.5 beats per minute with a standard deviation of 10 beats per minute.

b. No, although it was the lowest, it was only about two standard deviations below average and not out of the general pattern.

c. A parent would have to repeat the test if his or her rate was below $80.5 - 2(10) = 60.5$ or above $80.5 + 2(10) = 100.5$. So, Dion's mother was asked to repeat the test, as was the parent with the pulse rate of 107.

d. i. No, Cleone's mother's rate is less than one standard deviation above average.

ii. If the standard deviation were 1.24, then her rate would be unusually high as it would be more than three standard deviations above the mean of 90.

Review

 29 a. "4E10" means $4(10^{10}) = 40{,}000{,}000{,}000$.

b. "8E12" or 8,000,000,000,000

c. The answer is 48,000,000,000. The calculator will say "4.8E10." The calculator reports the answer as a number between 1 and 10 and the number of factors of 10 needed to make the answer correct. This is similar to scientific notation; for this number, 4.8×10^{10}.

30 If 10% of a number is 20, use mental computation to find the following.

   a. 30% of the number   **b.** 150% of the number

   c. One half of the number   **d.** 35% of the number

31 Using a protractor, draw and label each angle. If you do not have a protractor, place a sheet of paper over the protractor to the right.

   a. m∠$BAC = 90°$ **b.** m∠$FDE = 30°$ **c.** m∠$PQR = 120°$

   d. m∠$XZY = 65°$ **e.** m∠$STV = 180°$

32 Find results for each of these calculations.

   a. $12 - (-8)$ **b.** $-3 - 7$ **c.** $-3 - (-7)$

   d. $8 - 12$ **e.** $-8 + (-12)$ **f.** $2.5 - (-1.3)$

33 An amusement park reports an increase of 21 bungee customers from Saturday to Sunday. If this represents an increase of 7% in the number of customers:

   a. What would a 1% increase be?

   b. What would a 10% increase be?

   c. What would a 5.1% increase be?

   d. What was the original number of customers?

   e. What is 5.1% of your answer for Part d?

   f. What is 7% of your answer for Part d?

34 Use a protractor (or place a sheet of paper over the protractor in Task 31) to help you draw two lines $\overrightarrow{AB}$ and $\overleftrightarrow{CD}$ that intersect at point O so that m∠$AOC = 52°$. Label your diagram. What are the measures of ∠COB, ∠BOD, and ∠DOA?

35 Express each of these fractions in equivalent simplest form.

   a. $\dfrac{-12}{-30}$ **b.** $\dfrac{20}{-12}$ **c.** $\dfrac{5-8}{9-5}$

   d. $\dfrac{-5-8}{-5-(-8)}$ **e.** $\dfrac{78-6}{9-(-18)}$ **f.** $\dfrac{5-7}{10+14}$

36 Mike has the following coins in his pocket: a penny, a nickel, a dime, and a quarter. Two of these coins fall out of his pocket. What is the probability that their total value is less than fifteen cents?

37 Suppose that you have twelve 1-inch square tiles.

   a. Sketch diagrams of all possible ways that you can arrange the tiles so that they form a rectangle. Each rectangle must be completely filled in with tiles.

   b. Find the perimeter of each rectangle in Part a.

38 Without computing, determine if each expression is greater than 0, equal to 0, or less than 0.

   a. $-5.75(-0.35)$ **b.** $(-1.56)^4 - 123$

   c. $-5,768 + 10,235$ **d.** $\dfrac{783(-52.6)}{-12.85}$

30 **a.** $3(20) = 60$ **b.** $15(20) = 300$
 c. $5(20) = 100$ **d.** $3.5(20) = 7(10) = 70$

31 To be able to check student's drawings quickly, you may wish to make a transparency that shows the correct angles. You or the students can place the transparency over their drawings to check their accuracy.

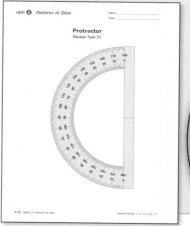

 Just in Time

32 **a.** 20 **b.** -10 **c.** 4 **d.** -4 **e.** -20 **f.** 3.8

33 **a.** A 1% increase would be $\frac{1}{7}$ of 21 customers, or 3 customers.

 b. A 10% increase would be 10 times a 1% increase, or $10 \cdot 3 = 30$ customers.

 c. A 5.1% increase would be 5.1 times a 1% increase, or $5.1 \cdot 3 = 15.3$ customers. This should be rounded to 15 or 16 customers depending on the intended use of the information by the park. (Sometimes businesses would rather overestimate than underestimate values.)

 d. 7% of the original number of customers is 21. So, the original number of customers is $\frac{21}{7\%} = 300$ customers.

 e. 5.1% of 300 customers is 15.3 customers.

 f. 7% of 300 customers is 21 customers.

34

 Just in Time

35 **a.** $\frac{2}{5}$ **b.** $-\frac{5}{3}$ **c.** $-\frac{3}{4}$ **d.** $-\frac{13}{3}$ **e.** $\frac{8}{3}$ **f.** $-\frac{1}{12}$

36 The coins that fell out of his pocket could be in any of the following combinations: PN, ND, PD, NQ, PQ, DQ

Two of the six possibilities total less than 15¢. So, the probability is $\frac{1}{3}$.

37 **a–b.**

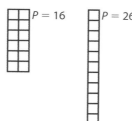

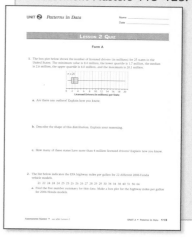
38 **a.** Greater than 0 **b.** Less than 0
 c. Greater than 0 **d.** Greater than 0

LESSON 3

Looking Back

In this unit, you learned how to display data using dot plots, histograms, and box plots. Examination of these plots gave you information about the shape, the center, and the variability (spread) of the distributions.

You also learned how to compute and interpret common measures of center (mean and median) and common measures of variability (interquartile range and standard deviation).

Finally, you explored the effects on a distribution of transforming by adding a constant and by multiplying by a positive constant. While exploring the following data set you will review these key ideas.

A California psychologist, Robert V. Levine, noticed that the *pace of life* varies from one U.S. city to another and decided to quantify that impression.

For each city, he measured

- how long on average it took bank clerks to make change,
- the average walking speed of pedestrians on an uncrowded downtown street during the summer, and
- the speaking rate of postal clerks asked to explain the difference between regular mail, certified mail, and insured mail.

These three measurements were combined into one total score for each city, given in the table at the top of the next page. A higher total score means a faster pace of life.

Looking Back

In this unit, students learned how to analyze single-variable data. For each set of data, the fundamental technique is the same:

- select a plot that shows the shape of the distribution,
- compute and interpret an appropriate measure of center, and
- compute and interpret an appropriate measure of spread.

Each problem in the Looking Back section is based on the same small data set, which includes measures of the pace of life in various U.S. cities. By examining this same data set in different ways, students have the opportunity to look back at what they have learned. They may feel overwhelmed by the number of new statistical ideas. Try to help students see that these are not just miscellaneous topics, but are organized by the fundamental statistical idea of a distribution, which has a shape, center, and spread.

Pace of Life in U.S. Cities

Total Score	City	Region	Total Score	City	Region
83	Boston	NE	75	Houston	SO
76	Buffalo	NE	79	Atlanta	SO
71	New York	NE	67	Louisville	SO
75	Worcester	NE	58	Knoxville	SO
80	Providence	NE	70	Chattanooga	SO
79	Springfield, MA	NE	54	Shreveport	SO
78	Paterson, NJ	NE	67	Dallas	SO
62	Philadelphia	NE	70	Nashville	SO
73	Rochester	NE	66	Memphis	SO
79	Columbus	MW	60	San Jose	WE
66	Canton	MW	79	Salt Lake City	WE
60	Detroit	MW	72	Bakersfield	WE
74	Youngstown	MW	61	San Diego	WE
72	Indianapolis	MW	59	San Francisco	WE
72	Chicago	MW	61	Oxnard	WE
77	Kansas City	MW	61	Fresno	WE
68	East Lansing	MW	50	Sacramento	WE
68	St. Louis	MW	45	Los Angeles	WE

Source: The Pace of Life, *American Scientist, 78.* September–October 1990.

1 The histogram below shows the distribution of the total scores for the pace of life in the 36 cities.

Pace of Life in U.S. Cities

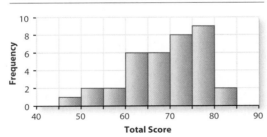

a. Describe the shape of the distribution.

b. Estimate the five-number summary from the histogram.

1 **a.** The distribution is skewed left. It has no outliers or gaps.

b. The minimum is between 45 and 50; the first quartile is between 60 and 65; the median is between 70 and 75; the third quartile is between 75 and 80; the maximum is between 80 and 85.

c. The mean of the distribution is 68.5.

    i. What is the deviation from the mean for Philadelphia? For New York?

    ii. Which of the 36 cities has a total score that is the largest deviation from the mean?

d. Without computing, is the standard deviation closer to 5, or 10, or 20? Explain.

2 The box plots below show the nine cities in each of three regions: the Midwest, the South, and the West.

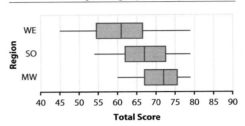

Pace of Life by Geographic Region

a. The box plot for the Northeast is missing. Find the five-number summary for the Northeast and determine if there are any outliers. Then make the box plot, showing any outliers.

b. If the cities selected are typical, in which region of the country is the pace of life fastest? Explain your reasoning.

c. Without computing, how can you tell which region has the largest standard deviation? Compute and interpret the standard deviation for that region.

3 Suppose that each city's *total score* was transformed to its *mean score* by dividing by 3.

a. The average of the distribution of total scores is 68.5 and the median is 70. Find the mean and median of the distribution of mean scores.

b. How would each measure of spread change, if at all?

146 UNIT 2 • Patterns in Data

c. **i.** The deviation from the mean for Philadelphia is $62 - 68.5 = -6.5$. The deviation for New York is $71 - 68.5 = 2.5$.

  ii. Los Angeles has the total that is farthest from the mean: $45 - 68.5 = -23.5$.

d. The standard deviation is closest to 10. (It is actually about 9.04.) Looking 5, 10, and 20 points on both sides of the mean, it seems that about $\frac{2}{3}$ of the data is within 10 points of the mean.

② **a.** The five-number summary for the Northeast is 62, 72, 76, 79.5, 83. The interquartile range is $79.5 - 72 = 7.5$ and $1.5 \cdot \text{IQR} = 11.25$. Then $Q_1 - 1.5 \cdot \text{IQR} = 60.75$ and $Q_3 + 1.5 \cdot \text{IQR} = 90.75$. There are no total scores outside these values, so there are no outliers.

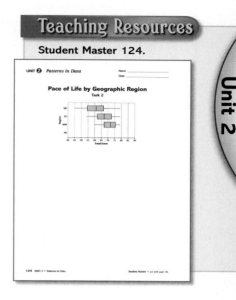
Pace of Life by Geographic Region

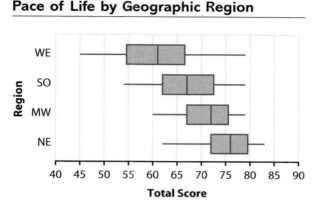

Region / Total Score

b. The Northeast has the fastest pace since each number in its five-number summary is larger than the corresponding values for the other three regions. The box plot for the Northeast is farther to the right.

c. The West has the largest IQR, so probably will have the largest standard deviation. A typical city in the West has a mean total pace of life of about 60.9, give or take about 10.2.

③ **a.** $\frac{68.5}{3} = 22.8\overline{3}$; $\frac{70}{3} = 23.\overline{3}$

b. They would all be divided by a factor of 3. So, for example, the standard deviation would change from about 27 to about 9.

Summarize
the Mathematics

Patterns in data can be seen in graphical displays of the distribution and can be summarized using measures of center and spread.

a Describe the kinds of information you can get by examining:

   i. a dot plot,

   ii. a histogram and a relative frequency histogram, and

   iii. a box plot.

b Describe the most common measures of center, how to find them, and what each one tells you.

c Describe the most common measures of variability, how to find them, and what each one tells you.

d What measures can you use to tell someone the position of a value in a distribution?

e How do you identify outliers and what should you do once you identify them? Which summary statistics are resistant to outliers?

f What is the effect on measures of center of transforming a set of data by adding a constant to each value or multiplying each value by a positive constant? On measures of variation?

Be prepared to share your ideas and reasoning with the class.

✓ Check Your Understanding

Write, in outline form, a summary of the important mathematical concepts and methods developed in this unit. Organize your summary so that it can be used as a quick reference in future units and courses.

Summarize
the Mathematics

Teaching Resources

Transparency Master 125.

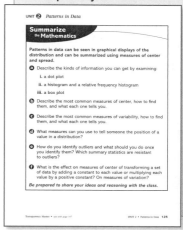

a From all of these plots, you can get some idea of the shape, center, and spread of a distribution.

   i. From a dot plot you can count how many values there are, and you can easily see gaps, clusters, and outliers. You can estimate individual values pretty accurately.

   ii. You can use a histogram or a relative frequency histogram when you have too many values for a dot plot, but you cannot see individual values and lose some of the detail. Also, gaps can be obscured if the bars are too wide.

   iii. From a box plot you can read off the five-number summary and know which values are classified as outliers. You lose most of the detail and cannot see gaps or clusters in the data.

b The three most common measures of center are the mean, median, and mode, described below. Which of the three is the most appropriate to use in a given situation ultimately depends on the reason for wanting a measure of center.

   Mean—The mean, or average, is the measure of center most commonly used and is the sum of the values divided by the number of values. It tells you the "balance" point of the distribution. The mean is sensitive to outliers and so may not be of much use as a measure of "center" if there are outliers in the data.

   Median—The median is the middle value when the values are lined up in order (or the midpoint between the two middle values if there are an even number of values). Half of the values are above the median and half are below. Because the median is resistant to outliers, it is preferred to the mean with a distribution that is strongly skewed or has outliers.

   Mode—The mode, or most frequent value, is usually easy to find. It is occasionally helpful to know the most common value, but usually it doesn't mean much.

c As with a measure of center, when choosing a measure of variability you need to consider the type of data and how the summary statistic will be used. The most common measures of spread are the range, the interquartile range, and the standard deviation.

   Range—The range is the difference between the maximum value and the minimum value. You can say that all of the values fall within the range. That is easy to understand, but isn't a useful measure of spread because it is so sensitive to outliers and tends to be larger with a larger sample size than with a smaller sample size.

   Interquartile range—The IQR is the difference between the first and third quartiles. You can say that the middle half of the values fall within the interquartile range. The IQR tends to be used as the measure of spread when the median is used as the measure of center.

Standard deviation—The standard deviation is essentially the square root of the average of the squared differences from the mean. It gives you a "typical" distance from the mean. The standard deviation is used as the measure of spread when the mean is used as the measure of center, most commonly with symmetric, mound-shaped distributions.

d You can give the percentile of the value in the distribution (the percentage of values less than or equal to that value) or the deviation from the mean (*value – mean*).

e Outliers are values that lie far away from the bulk of the values in their distribution. One rule for finding them is to identify an outlier as any value that is more than $1.5 \cdot$ IQR above Q_3 or below Q_1. The median and interquartile range are resistant to outliers.

f When a positive constant is added to (subtracted from) each value in a distribution, the mean, median, and mode will all be increased (decreased) by the same amount. When each value is multiplied (divided) by a positive constant, the measures of center will be multiplied (divided) by that factor.

Transforming each value by addition slides the distribution but does not change its spread. So, it does not change the value of the range, interquartile range, or standard deviation. Transforming each value by multiplication stretches or shrinks the distribution and multiplies each measure of spread by that factor.

Teaching Resources

Student Masters 126–128.

Student Masters 153–154.

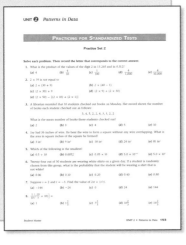

✔ Check Your Understanding

You may wish to have students use the Teaching Master, *Patterns in Data* Unit Summary, to help them organize the information. Above all, this should be something that is useful to the individual student.

Practicing for Standardized Tests

Each Practicing for Standardized Tests teaching master presents ten questions that draw on all content strands. The questions are presented in the form of test items similar to how they often appear in standardized tests such as state assessment tests, the Preliminary Scholastic Aptitude Test (PSAT), or the ACT PLAN. We suggest using these practice sets following the unit assessment so students can become familiar with the formats of standardized tests and develop effective test-taking strategies for performing well on such tests. Answers are provided below.

Answers to Practice Set 2

1. (e)   **2.** (c)   **3.** (b)   **4.** (e)   **5.** (d)
6. (c)   **7.** (b)   **8.** (b)   **9.** (b)   **10.** (b)

One of the assessment projects with this unit is Using Statistical Analysis Software. These data are included in *CPMP-Tools* as the last data set for Unit 2.

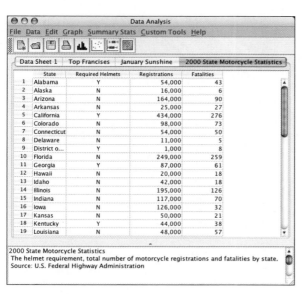

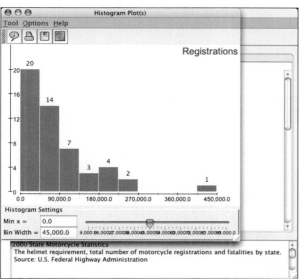

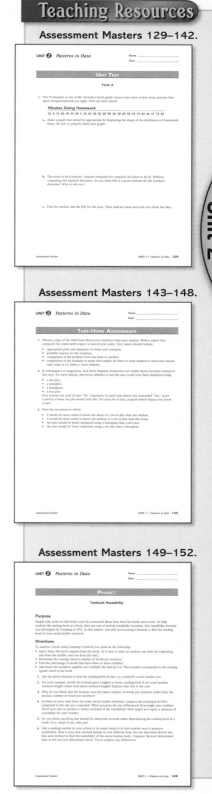

UNIT 3

LINEAR FUNCTIONS

In the *Patterns of Change* unit, you explored a variety of situations in which variables change over time or in response to changes in other variables. Recognizing patterns of change enabled you to make predictions and to understand situations better.

In this unit of *Core-Plus Mathematics*, you will focus on patterns in tables, graphs, and rules of the simplest and one of the most important relationships among variables, linear functions. The understanding and skill needed to analyze and use linear functions will develop from your work on problems in three lessons.

Lessons

1 Modeling Linear Relationships

Identify problem conditions, numeric patterns, and symbolic rules of functions with graphs that are straight lines. Write rules for linear functions given a problem situation or data in a table or a graph. Fit lines and function rules to data patterns that are approximately linear.

2 Linear Equations and Inequalities

Express questions about linear functions as equations or inequalities. Use function tables, graphs, and symbolic reasoning to answer those questions.

3 Equivalent Expressions

Use context clues and algebraic properties of numbers and operations to recognize and write equivalent forms of symbolic representations of linear functions.

LINEAR FUNCTIONS

Unit Overview

The simplest but most important patterns relating variables are those with graphs that are straight lines. This is a unit about linear functions.

To be proficient in the use of linear functions for problem solving, students must have a clear and connected understanding of the numeric, graphic, verbal, and symbolic representations of linear functions and the ways that those representations can be applied to patterns in real data. The lessons of this unit are planned to develop each student's intuitive understanding of linearity and technical skills for reasoning with the various representations of linearity. The understanding and skill in working with linear functions is developed in four lessons.

The first lesson develops students' understanding of the characteristics of linear functions and the connections among the various representations. The lesson then applies the understanding and skills developed in the first two investigations to model patterns in data that are approximately linear. In Lesson 2, students use the various representations of linear functions to solve linear equations and inequalities. Lesson 3 explores ways of rewriting linear expressions in equivalent forms. The final lesson takes a look back and reviews the key concepts and skills of the unit.

The unit was written assuming that most students entering this curriculum will have had fairly extensive experience with linear equations of the form $a + bx = c$ and will have learned some systematic methods for solving them. However, most of that experience may have focused on "finding the unknown x," not on how a function of the form $y = a + bx$ relates all values of x to values of y. The emphasis in this unit is on linear functions, and linear equations arise as a way of expressing questions about linear functions. The approach in the unit assumes that the development of an understanding of linear functions in realistic situations will make manipulating symbols much more meaningful.

Further work toward developing proficiency with manipulating symbols occurs in subsequent units and courses. Practice for the skills developed in this unit is incorporated in the On Your Own Review tasks and the Practicing for Standardized Test masters at the end of this and subsequent units.

Unit Objectives

- Recognize patterns in tables of sample values, in problem conditions, and in data plots that can be described by linear functions
- Write linear function rules to describe linear, or approximately linear, patterns in graphs or numerical data

- Use table, graph, or symbolic representations of linear functions to answer questions about the situations they represent: (1) Calculate y for a given x (i.e., evaluate functions); (2) Find x for a given y (i.e., solve equations and inequalities); and (3) Describe the rate at which y changes as x changes (i.e., determine slope)
- Rewrite linear expressions in equivalent forms

CPMP-Tools

In this unit, students are offered opportunities to use the custom tool "Modeling Line" and CAS technologies. *CPMP-Tools* includes a computer algebra system that will be useful in this unit. Alternatively, calculators or computer software with CAS capabilities could be used. The custom tool "Modeling Line" under *Statistics* allows students to manipulate a moveable line on a scatterplot of data. They can then select the regression line and compare their line placement and equation to the linear regression model.

Data sets included in *CPMP-Tools* for this unit are:

Page 163 Chicago Flight Data
Page 165 Los Angeles Flight At. and Temp.
Page 171 Riverdale Adventure Club
Page 172 Cricket Chirps
Page 173 Selected Fast Food
Page 174 Median Income
Page 176 Taking Chances
Page 181 Winning Times for Men: Olympic 100 Meters
Page 182 Winning Times for Women: Olympic 100 Meters
Page 207 Olympic 100-meter Freestyle Swim Times
Page 233 Health and Nutrition

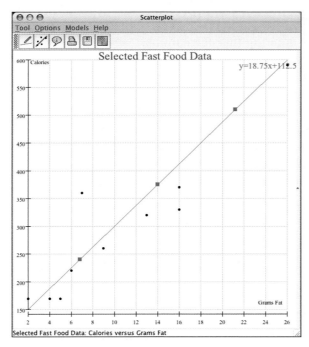

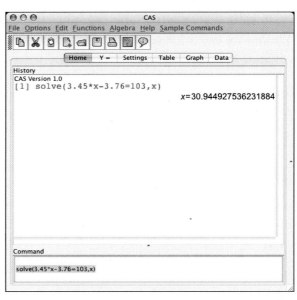

Suggestions to integrate these technologies are included in the student text and teacher notes at point of use.

Unit 3

Lesson Objectives	On Your Own Assignments*	Suggested Pacing	Materials
Lesson 1 *Modeling Linear Relationships* • Calculate the rate of change in one variable as another variable increases • Describe the relationships among the graph, symbolic rule, table of values, and related situation for a linear function • Interpret the meaning of the slope and *y*-intercept of the graph of a linear function in a context • Write a rule for a linear function given its graph, two points, or a table of sample values • Use linear functions to answer questions about the situations that they describe • Estimate the graph and function rule for a line that fits a given set of data • Use a linear model to predict the value of one variable given the value of the other and describe the rate of change in one variable as the other increases in a meaningful way • Use a calculator or computer software to find the linear regression model for a set of data	**After Investigation 1:** Choose two of A1–A4, C14, C15, C20, R23, Rv36–Rv39 **After Investigation 2:** A5, A6 or A7, A8, A9, C16 or C17, C21, C22, R24, R25, choice of E29–E31, Rv40 **After Investigation 3:** A10 or A11, A12 or A13, C19, R26, R27, R28, choice of E32–E35, Rv41–Rv43	9 days	• *Optional: CPMP-Tools* custom tool "Modeling Line" • *Optional:* Spreadsheet software • Teaching Resources • Assessment Resources
Lesson 2 *Linear Equations and Inequalities* • Write linear equations and inequalities to express questions about linear functions • Estimate solutions to linear equations and inequalities by inspecting appropriate graphs and tables of values and interpret the meaning of the solution in the real-world context • Use "undoing" and "balancing" methods to solve simple linear equations and inequalities • Use tables of values, graphs, and symbolic reasoning to solve systems of linear equations of the form $y = a + bx$ and $y = c + dx$	**After Investigation 1:** Choose two of A1–A3, C14, R19, E25, Rv32, Rv33 **After Investigation 2:** Choose two of A4–A6, C15, C16, Rv34–Rv36 **After Investigation 3:** A7; A8; C17; C18; R20–R22; E26, E27, or E29; Rv37, Rv38 **After Investigation 4:** Choose two of A9–A11, A12, A13, R23, R24, choose two of E28 and E30–E32, Rv39–Rv41	11 days	• *Optional:* CAS technology • *Optional: CPMP-Tools* custom tool "Modeling Line" • Teaching Resources • Assessment Resources
Lesson 3 *Equivalent Expressions* • Write multiple expressions to represent a variable quantity from a real-world situation • Use tables, graphs, and properties of numbers and operations to reason about the equivalence of expressions • Rewrite linear expressions in equivalent forms by expanding, combining like terms, and factoring	**After Investigation 1:** Choose two of A1–A3, C8, R14, R15, Rv24–Rv27 **After Investigation 2:** A4–A7, choose two of C9–C12, R16 or R17, R18, E19, choice of E20–E24, Rv28–Rv30	6 days	• *Optional:* CAS technology • Teaching Resources • Assessment Resources
Lesson 4 *Looking Back* • Review the major objectives of the unit		3 days (including testing)	• *CPMP-Tools* custom tool "Modeling Line" • Teaching Resources • Assessment Resources

* *When choice is indicated, it is important to leave the choice to the student.*

Note: *It is best if Connections tasks are discussed as a whole class after they have been assigned as homework.*

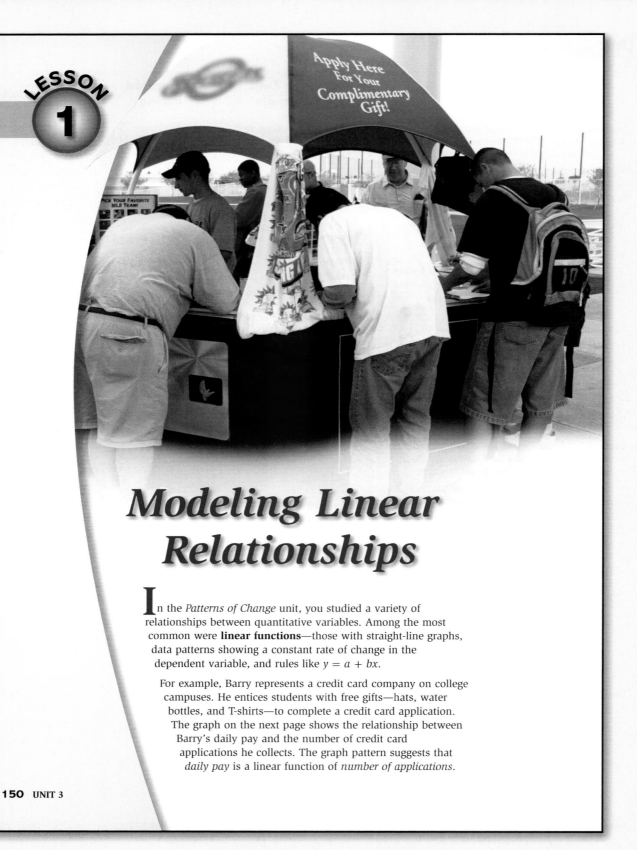

LESSON
1

Modeling Linear Relationships

In the *Patterns of Change* unit, you studied a variety of relationships between quantitative variables. Among the most common were **linear functions**—those with straight-line graphs, data patterns showing a constant rate of change in the dependent variable, and rules like $y = a + bx$.

For example, Barry represents a credit card company on college campuses. He entices students with free gifts—hats, water bottles, and T-shirts—to complete a credit card application. The graph on the next page shows the relationship between Barry's daily pay and the number of credit card applications he collects. The graph pattern suggests that *daily pay* is a linear function of *number of applications*.

150 UNIT 3

Modeling Linear Relationships

Among the most common and important relationships between quantitative variables are those in which the dependent variable is a *linear* function of the independent variable. In all such situations, the rate of change in the dependent variable is constant, the graph is a straight line, and the relationship can be expressed in the form $y = mx + b$.

This lesson of *Linear Functions* builds on students' prior experiences with linear relationships to strengthen their ability to recognize data patterns, graphs, and problem situations that indicate such linearity conditions. It then focuses on further development of the skills needed to represent linear functions with symbolic function rules—both formal techniques for representing exact linear relationships and data-modeling techniques for representing approximately linear patterns.

The first investigation engages students in work on a series of problems designed to highlight the ways that parameters in linear function rules relate to patterns in numeric and graph patterns formed by samples of (x, y) values.

The second investigation emphasizes strategies for using graphic, numeric, and verbal information about linear relationships to find symbolic function rules connecting values of the dependent variable to values of the independent variable.

The third investigation focuses on the problem of modeling relationships in which linearity is suggested by approximately linear numeric and graphic data patterns.

Lesson Objectives

- Calculate the rate of change in one variable as another variable increases
- Describe the relationships among the graph, symbolic rule, table of values, and related situation for a linear function
- Interpret the meaning of the slope and y-intercept of the graph of a linear function in a context
- Write a rule for a linear function given its graph, two points, or a table of sample values
- Use linear functions to answer questions about the situations that they describe
- Estimate the graph and function rule for a line that fits a given set of data
- Use a linear model to predict the value of one variable given the value of the other and describe the rate of change in one variable as the other increases in a meaningful way
- Use a calculator or computer software to find the linear regression model for a set of data

Pay for Soliciting Credit Card Customers

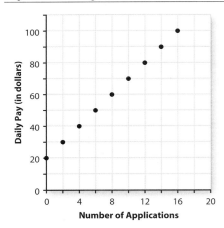

Think About This Situation

Think about the connections among graphs, data patterns, function rules, and problem conditions for linear relationships.

a How does Barry's daily pay change as the number of applications he collects increases? How is that pattern of change shown in the graph?

b If the linear pattern shown by the graph holds for other (*number of applications, daily pay*) pairs, how much would you expect Barry to earn for a day during which he collects just 1 application? For a day he collects 13 applications? For a day he collects 25 applications?

c What information from the graph might you use to write a rule showing how to calculate daily pay for any number of applications?

Working on the problems of this lesson will develop your ability to recognize linear relationships between variables and to represent those relationships with graphs, tables of values, and function rules.

Investigation 1 — Getting Credit

Information about a linear function may be given in the form of a table or graph, a symbolic rule, or a verbal description that explains how the dependent and independent variables are related. To be proficient in answering questions about linear functions, it helps to be skillful in translating given information from one form into another.

Students might not have personal experience with credit cards, but they will probably have seen people soliciting credit card customers in situations like those described in the story about Barry's work. As a preview lesson on intelligent financial behavior, it might be useful to have a short discussion about why credit card companies are eager to sign up college students and the risks that can ensue from careless use of those cards. Research suggests that this practice of helping students understand the context promotes equity. See the Teacher's Guide pages xvi–xvii for reference.

Think About This Situation

ⓐ Barry's pay increases steadily from a base of $20 that is paid even if he is unsuccessful in getting anyone to sign up for a credit card. This is shown in the graph by the y-intercept of (0, 20) and the linear upward trend of the data points. The pattern indicates that for every two card applications he collects, his pay increases by $10, or a rate of $5 per card applicant. (It is not essential for students to be able to make all of these observations in fluent mathematical language—use this question to get a reading of the prior knowledge that your students have about linearity. Subsequent investigations will review and extend student understanding and skill in this area.)

ⓑ Linearity implies proportional interpolation and extrapolation of the pattern. So, one would expect Barry's pay to be $25 if he collects only 1 credit card application, $85 for 13 applications, and $145 for 25 applications.

ⓒ Two standard ways of representing the pattern in the graph are $y = 5x + 20$, or $y = 20 + 5x$. (Students may or may not recall enough about linear functions to be able to write a rule for the pay function. Again, use this item as an opportunity to discover students' prior knowledge. Don't stop at this problem to "teach" students how to find the equation for a line if they seem shaky on that skill or don't recall how. Subsequent problems will give students opportunities to review and enhance their skills in writing rules for linear functions.)

Investigation 1 Getting Credit

The problems of this investigation are designed to sharpen student skills in seeing the connections between symbolic rules for linear functions and the patterns in tables and graphs of sample (x, y) values. Problems 1–3 focus on increasing functions of various slopes and y-intercepts in the context of different pay schemes for the work of collecting credit card applications. Problems 4 and 5 focus on decreasing linear functions in the context of buying over time.

As you work on problems of this investigation, look for clues to help you answer this question:

How are patterns in tables of values, graphs, symbolic rules, and problem conditions for linear functions related to each other?

Selling Credit Cards Companies that offer credit cards pay the people who collect applications for those cards and the people who contact current cardholders to sell them additional financial services.

1. For collecting credit card applications, Barry's daily pay B is related to the number of applications he collects n by the rule $B = 20 + 5n$.

   a. Use the function rule to complete this table of sample (n, B) values:

Number of Applications	0	1	2	3	4	5	10	20	50
Daily Pay (in dollars)									

   b. Compare the pattern of change shown in your table with that shown in the graph on the preceding page.

   c. How much will Barry earn on a day when he does not collect any credit card applications? How can this information be seen in the rule $B = 20 + 5n$? In the table of sample (n, B) values? In the graph on the preceding page?

   d. How much additional money does Barry earn for each application he collects? How can this information be seen in the rule $B = 20 + 5n$? In the table? In the graph?

   e. Use the words *NOW* and *NEXT* to write a rule showing how Barry's daily pay changes with each new credit card application he collects.

2. Cheri also works for the credit card company. She calls existing customers to sell them additional services for their account. The next table shows how much Cheri earns for selling selected numbers of additional services.

Number of Services Sold	10	20	30	40	50
Daily Pay (in dollars)	60	80	100	120	140

   a. Does Cheri's daily pay appear to be a linear function of the number of services sold? Explain.

   b. Assume that Cheri's daily pay is a linear function of the number of services she sells, and calculate the missing entries in the next table.

Number of Services Sold	0	10	15	20	25	30	40	50	100	101
Daily Earnings (in dollars)		60		80		100	120	140		

The final segment of the investigation (including the Summarize the Mathematics) asks students to think about the relationships between linear function rules, tables, and graphs without reference to any specific context.

COMMON ERROR Students sometimes do not pay attention to the scale of a graph and may misinterpret a graph because of this. Watch for an opportunity to address scales on graphs as students work on this unit. Problem 6 in this investigation, when students select their own scales, may be one such opportunity. Alternatively, you might help them be attentive to scales by giving transparency grids with different scales to various groups. Then compare the graphs and ask why they look different.

(1) **a.** Sample (n, B) values:

Number of Applications	0	1	2	3	4	5	10	20	50
Daily Pay (in dollars)	20	25	30	35	40	45	70	120	270

b. The y values in the table increase by 5 for each increase by 1 of the n values. The graph shows a vertical increase of 10 for every horizontal increase of 2 which is equivalent to the change in the table.

c. For 0 credit card applications collected, Barry will still be paid $20. This is shown in the rule by the number 20, the constant term; in the table by the entry (0, 20); and in the graph by the y-intercept (0, 20).

d. Barry earns an additional $5 for each credit card application he collects. This is shown by the coefficient of n in the rule, in the table by the increase of 5 in pay for each increase of 1 in the number of applications, and by the slope of the graph points (up 10 for every 2 units over from one point to the next on the graph).

e. $NEXT = NOW + 5$, starting at 20

(2) **a.** Cheri's pay plan seems to be linear because for every additional 10 services sold, her pay goes up $20. (Encourage students to plot the points to determine linearity if they are not sure.)

b. **DIFFERENTIATION** Some students may find it helpful to fill in the "missing" entries so that the number of services sold always increases by 5. If some students are not able to fill in the last entry in the table, refer them to the paragraph on the top of p. 153 and then return to complete Part b.

Number of Services Sold	0	10	15	20	25	30	40	50	100	101
Daily Earnings (in dollars)	40	60	70	80	90	100	120	140	240	242

INSTRUCTIONAL NOTE You might assign student groups to work Problems 1–5. Ask each group to write the answers to one of the problems (assigned by you) on a half sheet of chart paper and post them around the room. As groups complete the other problems, they can take a "gallery walk" and check their answers.

COLLABORATION SKILL Help each other to make sure answers make sense.

Unit 3

Teaching Resources

Transparency Master 156.

UNIT 3 Linear Functions

Selling Credit Card Applications
Problem 2

A key feature of any function is the way the value of the dependent variable changes as the value of the independent variable changes. Notice that as the number of services Cheri sells increases from 30 to 40, her pay increases from $100 to $120. This is an increase of $20 in pay for an increase of 10 in the number of services sold, or an average of $2 per sale. Her pay increases at a *rate* of $2 per service sold.

c. Using your table from Part b, study the *rate of change* in Cheri's daily pay as the number of services she sells increases by completing entries in a table like the one below.

Change in Sales	Change in Pay (in $)	Rate of Change (in $ per sale)
10 to 20		
20 to 25		
25 to 40		
50 to 100		

What do you notice about the rate of change in Cheri's daily pay as the number of services she sells increases?

d. Use the words *NOW* and *NEXT* to write a rule showing how Cheri's pay changes with each new additional service she sells.

e. Consider the following function rules.

$$C = 2 + 40n \qquad C = n + 2 \qquad C = 40 + 2n$$
$$C = 50 + \frac{n}{2} \qquad C = 2n + 50$$

i. Which of the rules show how to calculate Cheri's daily pay C for any number of services n she sells? How do you know?

ii. What do the numbers in the rule(s) you selected in part i tell you about Cheri's daily pay?

3. The diagram below shows graphs of pay plans offered by three different banks to employees who collect credit card applications.

Atlantic Bank: $A = 20 + 2n$
Boston Bank: $B = 20 + 5n$
Consumers Bank: $C = 40 + 2n$

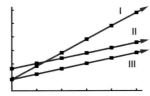

a. Match each function rule with its graph. Explain how you can make the matches without calculations or graphing tool help.

b. What do the numbers in the rule for the pay plan at Atlantic Bank tell you about the relationship between daily pay and number of credit card applications collected?

c.

Change in Sales	Change in Pay (in $)	Rate of Change (in $ per sale)
10 to 20	20	$\frac{20}{10} = 2$ per sale
20 to 25	10	$\frac{10}{5} = 2$ per sale
25 to 40	30	$\frac{30}{15} = 2$ per sale
50 to 100	100	$\frac{100}{50} = 2$ per sale

INSTRUCTIONAL NOTE It is often helpful for students to write the units in tables (such as $). This helps interpret the meaning of the rate of change and determine its units of measure for the situation.

Notice that the rate of change in pay is always $2 per sale.

d. $NEXT = NOW + 2$, starting at 40

e. **i.** The only rule that is correct is $C = 40 + 2n$. Reasoning might simply point out that the other rules don't give (n, C) pairs like those in the table of Part a.

  ii. The 40 is the pay with no sales, and the 2 is the amount of additional pay for each sale.

3 **a.** Graph I matches Boston Bank because it rises the fastest.
Graph II matches Consumers Bank because it rises at the same rate as Atlantic Bank, but greater y-intercept.
Graph III matches Atlantic Bank because it rises at the same rate as Consumers, but lower y-intercept.

  b. The Atlantic Bank pay rule $A = 20 + 2n$ shows that workers there will get a base pay of $20 whether or not they collect any credit card applications and an additional $2 for each card application they collect.

ELL TIP Establish consistent daily routines (Consistent routines are relatively non-verbal.)
- Have an established location where students automatically pick up tools and materials for the day's lesson.
- Have an established location where the agenda for the day and the assignment are posted.
- Be consistent in cues to signal when to speak, when to work in groups, and when to work independently.
- Have established expectations for working with a partner or in groups. These expectations should be continually reinforced.

Buying on Credit Electric Avenue sells audio/video, computer, and entertainment products. The store offers 0% interest for 12 months on purchases made using an Electric Avenue store credit card.

4 Emily purchased a television for $480 using an Electric Avenue store credit card. Suppose she pays the minimum monthly payment of $20 each month for the first 12 months.

a. Complete a table of (*number of monthly payments, account balance*) values for the first 6 months after the purchase, then plot those values on a graph.

Number of Monthly Payments	0	1	2	3	4	5	6
Account Balance (in dollars)							

b. Will Emily pay off the balance within 12 months? How do you know?

c. If you know Emily's account balance *NOW*, how can you calculate the *NEXT* account balance, after a monthly payment?

d. Which of the following function rules gives Emily's account balance *E* after *m* monthly payments have been made?

$$E = 20m - 480 \qquad E = m - 20 \qquad E = -20m + 480$$
$$E = 480 + 20m \qquad E = 480 - 20m$$

e. Determine the rate of change, including units, in the account balance as the number of monthly payments increases from:

0 to 2;

2 to 3;

3 to 6.

   i. How does the rate of change reflect the fact that the account balance *decreases* as the number of monthly payments increases?

   ii. How can the rate of change be seen in the graph from Part a? In the function rule(s) you selected in Part c?

f. How can the starting account balance be seen in the table in Part a? In the graph? In the function rule(s) you selected in Part d?

4 **a.**

Number of Monthly Payments	0	1	2	3	4	5	6
Account Balance (in $)	480	460	440	420	400	380	360

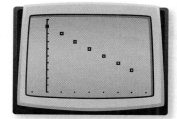 

b. At this rate she won't pay off the balance in 12 months. She will have $240 left to pay because $480 - 20(12) = 240$. (Some students might find each account balance up to 12 to find their answer.)

c. $NEXT = NOW - 20$, starting at 480

d. $E = -20m + 480$ and $E = 480 - 20m$

e.

Change in Number of Payments	Rate of Change in Account Balance
0 to 2	$-\dfrac{\$40}{2 \text{ mo}} = -\$20/\text{mo}$
2 to 3	$-\dfrac{\$20}{1 \text{ mo}} = -\$20/\text{mo}$
3 to 6	$-\dfrac{\$60}{3 \text{ mo}} = -\$20/\text{mo}$

   i. Rates of change are negative.

   ii. The graph has a downward slope of down 20 for each 1 unit to the right. The rate of change is the -20 in the function rule.

f. The starting account balance appears in the table as the balance at 0 monthly payments. The starting account balance appears in the graph as the y-intercept. The starting account balance appears in the rule as the constant term.

INSTRUCTIONAL NOTE Part e does not include a table for organizing results in the student text. This is an opportunity for students to plan the organization. You may wish to have some students share their methods.

Unit 3

5 The diagram below shows graphs of account balance functions for three Electric Avenue customers.

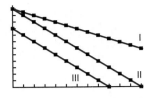

Emily: $E = 480 - 20m$
Darryl: $D = 480 - 40m$
Felicia: $F = 360 - 40m$

a. Match each function rule with its graph. Explain how you could make the matches without calculations or graphing tool help.

b. What do the numbers in the rules for Darryl's and Felicia's account balances tell you about the values of their purchases and their monthly payments?

Linear Functions Without Contexts When studying linear functions, it helps to think about real contexts. However, the connections among graphs, tables, and symbolic rules are the same for linear functions relating *any* two variables.

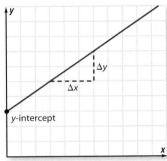

You've probably noticed by now that the rate of change of a linear function is constant and that the rate of change corresponds to the direction and steepness of the graph, or the *slope* of the graph.

You can determine the **rate of change** of y as x increases, or the **slope** of the graph between two points, using the ratio:

$$\frac{\text{change in } y}{\text{change in } x} \text{ or } \frac{\Delta y}{\Delta x}.$$

(Δ is the Greek letter "delta," which is used to represent "difference" or "change.")

Another key feature of a linear function is the **y-intercept** of its graph, the point where the graph intersects the y-axis.

6 Draw a graph for each function on a separate set of coordinate axes.

a. $y = 1 + \frac{2}{3}x$ **b.** $y = 2x$

c. $y = 2x - 3$ **d.** $y = 2 - \frac{1}{2}x$

Then analyze each function rule and its graph as described below.

i. Label the coordinates of three points A, B, and C on each graph. Calculate the slopes of the segments between points A and B, between points B and C, and between points A and C.

ii. Label the coordinates of the y-intercept on each graph.

iii. Explain how the numbers in the symbolic rule relate to the graph.

⑤ **a.** Graph I matches $E = 480 - 20m$ because it decreases more slowly than Graphs II and III. Graph II matches $D = 480 - 40m$ because it decreases at the same rate as Graph III but starts higher. Graph III matches $F = 360 - 40m$ because it starts lower than Graphs I and II.

b. In Darryl's rule, the 480 tells initial balance of $480 and the -40 tells a monthly payment of $40. In Felicia's rule, the 360 tells initial balance of $360 and the -40 tells a monthly payment of $40.

⑥ **a.**

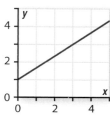

i. The slope calculations will yield fractions equivalent to $\frac{2}{3}$, regardless of the points chosen.

ii. The y-intercept will have coordinates $(0, 1)$.

iii. The $\frac{2}{3}$ in the rule means that the graph goes up 2 units for every 3 units of increase along the x-axis. The 1 is the y-coordinate of the y-intercept.

b.

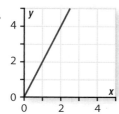

i. The slope calculations will yield fractions equivalent to 2, regardless of the points chosen.

ii. The y-intercept will have coordinates $(0, 0)$.

iii. The 2 in the rule means that the graph goes up 2 units for every 1-unit increase along the x-axis. The absence of a constant means that the y-intercept is the origin.

c.

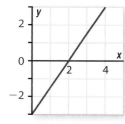

i. The slope calculations will yield fractions equivalent to 2, regardless of the points chosen.

ii. The y-intercept will have coordinates $(0, -3)$.

iii. The 2 in the rule means that the graph goes up 2 units for every 1-unit increase along the x-axis. The subtraction of 3 means that the y-coordinate of the y-intercept is -3.

d.

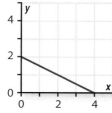

i. For any two points, the slope calculations will be equivalent to $-\frac{1}{2}$.

ii. The y-intercept will have coordinates $(0, 2)$.

iii. The $-\frac{1}{2}$ in the rule means that the graph will go down 0.5 unit for every 1-unit increase along the x-axis (or down 1 unit for every increase of 2 units along the x-axis). The 2 is the y-coordinate of the y-intercept.

POSSIBLE COMMON ERROR Sometimes students think about slope by going over and then up (or down). This order of identifying change might lead to the common error of stating slope as $\frac{\Delta x}{\Delta y}$. It may be helpful to ask students what the slope of a line means (rate it rises or falls). Then connect the meaning to the slope ratio. How does the meaning of slope help you understand that the change in y values should be in the numerator of the slope ratio?

Unit 3

Summarize
the Mathematics

Linear functions relating two variables x and y can be represented using tables, graphs, symbolic rules, or verbal descriptions. Key features of a linear function can be seen in each representation.

a How can you determine whether a function is linear by inspecting a:

   i. table of (x, y) values?   **ii.** graph of the function?

   iii. symbolic rule relating y to x?   **iv.** *NOW-NEXT* rule?

b How can the rate of change and the slope of the graph for a linear function be found from a:

   i. table of (x, y) values?   **ii.** graph of the function?

   iii. symbolic rule relating y to x?   **iv.** *NOW-NEXT* rule?

c How can the y-intercept of the graph of a function be seen in a:

   i. table of (x, y) values?   **ii.** graph of the function?

   iii. symbolic rule relating y to x?

Be prepared to share your ideas and reasoning with the class.

✓ Check Your Understanding

Linear functions can be used to describe the action of springs that stretch, like those in telephone cords, and springs that compress, like those in a mattress or a bathroom scale. Hooke's Law in science says that, for an ideal coil spring, the relationship between weight and length is perfectly linear, within the elastic range of the spring.

The table below shows data from an experiment to test Hooke's Law on different coil springs.

Spring 1		Spring 2		Spring 3		Spring 4	
Weight (ounces)	Length (inches)	Weight (ounces)	Length (inches)	Weight (ounces)	Length (inches)	Weight (ounces)	Length (inches)
0	12	0	5	0	18	0	12
4	14	2	7	3	15	4	10
8	16	4	9	6	12	8	8
12	18	6	11	9	9	12	6
16	20	8	13	12	6	16	4

For each spring:

a. Identify the length of the spring with no weight applied.

b. Describe the rate of change of the length of the spring as weight is increased. Indicate units.

Summarize
the Mathematics

Linear functions have tables, graphs, and rules that are related in ways that make reasoning about them easy.

a
  i. In tables with uniform change in the independent variable, the change in the dependent variable is constant. In any case, look for a constant ratio of change in *y* to change in *x*.

  ii. The graph will be a straight line or the data points will lie on a straight line.

  iii. When the symbolic rule is written in the "*y* = ..." form, the function relating *y* to *x* is linear if *x* is multiplied by a number (including zero). There may also be a constant added to or subtracted from the *x* term.

  iv. The *NOW-NEXT* rule will be of the form *NEXT* = *NOW* + *b*, where *b* is a constant.

b
  i. Select two pairs of (*x*, *y*) values in the table and calculate the ratio "change in *y* to change in *x*." Be careful to make sure that each change is calculated "in the same direction" or there will be a sign error in the rate of change or slope calculation. (One way to check the sign would be to make sure that when table *y*-values increase the slope is positive and when the *y*-values decrease the slope is negative. This assumes increasing *x*-table values.)

  ii. Select two points on the graph and use their coordinates as explained in part i.

  iii. The slope or rate of change is the coefficient of *x* in the rule (when written in "*y* = ..." form).

  iv. The slope is the constant term *b* in any equation of the form *NEXT* = *NOW* + *b*.

c The *y*-intercept of the graph is shown by:

  i. The table entry (0, *y*).

  ii. Coordinates of the point where the graph crosses the *y*-axis.

  iii. The constant term in the function rule.

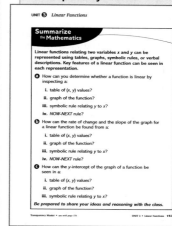
Unit 3

MATH TOOLKIT Provide students a specific linear function in table, graph, and rule form to answer the following tasks.

  a. For the function shown above, explain how you know that it is linear from the graph. From the rule. From the table.

  b. How do you find the slope from the graph? From the rule? From the table?

  c. How do you find the *y*-intercept from the graph? From the rule? From the table?

✓ Check Your Understanding

	Spring 1	Spring 2	Spring 3	Spring 4
a.	12 inches	5 inches	18 inches	12 inches
b.	0.5 in./oz	1 in./oz	−1 in./oz	−0.5 in./oz
c.	Stretched	Stretched	Compressed	Compressed
d.	*NEXT* = *NOW* + $\frac{1}{2}$ starting at 12	= *NOW* + 1 starting at 5	= *NOW* − 1 starting at 18	= *NOW* − $\frac{1}{2}$ starting at 12
e.	$\ell = 12 + \frac{1}{2}w$	$\ell = 5 + w$	$\ell = 18 - w$	$\ell = 12 - \frac{1}{2}w$
f.	Graph II	Graph I	Graph IV	Graph III

c. Decide whether the experiment was designed to measure spring stretch or spring compression.

d. Write a rule using *NOW* and *NEXT* to show how the spring length changes with each addition of one ounce of weight.

e. Match the spring to the rule that gives its length ℓ in inches when a weight of w ounces is applied.

$$\ell = 12 - \tfrac{1}{2}w \qquad \ell = 12 + \tfrac{1}{2}w \qquad \ell = 5 + w \qquad \ell = 18 - w$$

f. Match the spring to the graph in the diagram below that shows ℓ as a function of w.

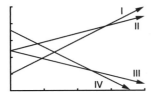

Investigation 2 — Symbolize It

A symbolic rule showing how values of one variable can be calculated from values of another is a concise and simple way to represent a function. Mathematicians typically write the rules for linear functions in the form $y = mx + b$. Statisticians prefer the general form $y = a + bx$. In a linear function rule like $y = 3x + 7$, or equivalently $y = 7 + 3x$, the number 3 is called the **coefficient of x** and the number 7 is called the **constant term**.

You probably have several strategies for finding values of the constant term and the coefficient of x in rules for particular linear functions. As you complete the problems in this investigation, look for clues that will help you answer this basic question:

How do you use information in a table, a graph, or the conditions of a problem to write a symbolic rule for a linear function?

1. **Dunking Booth Profits** The student council at Eastern High School decided to rent a dunking booth for a fund-raiser. They were quite sure that students would pay for chances to hit a target with a ball to dunk a teacher or administrator in a tub of cold water.

The dunking booth costs $150 to rent for the event, and the student council decided to charge students $0.50 per throw.

The purpose of this investigation is to sharpen students' skills in finding rules for linear functions when given information in the form of a verbal description, a data table, a graph, or specific pairs of values related by the function.

Problems 1–4 situate the work in different problem contexts, with different kinds of information provided. Problems 5–6 challenge students to generalize their understanding for work without context cues.

The text preceding the problems introduces some notational and vocabulary conventions related to linear functions—*coefficient of* x, *constant term*, and two symbolic rule patterns used by mathematicians and statisticians to represent linear relationships.

In mathematics, function rules are often expressed in symbolic forms that look like equations that are to be solved. Thus, mathematicians and scientists often talk about "finding the equation for a line" or "writing a *NOW-NEXT* equation" when they want a symbolic rule for a linear function. In general, CPMP developers have been urged by our mathematical consultants to reserve use of the word "equation" for situations in which the implied task is to find values of the variable(s) that make left and right side expressions equal in value; that is, for situations involving "solving" for unknowns. This material will most often use phrasing like "find the rule" or "find the function" when the task is to express the relationship between dependent and independent variables.

a. How do you know from the problem description that *profit* is a linear function of the *number of throws*?

b. Use the words *NOW* and *NEXT* to write a rule showing how fund-raiser profit changes with each additional customer.

c. Write a rule that shows how to calculate the profit *P* in dollars if *t* throws are purchased. Explain the thinking you used to write the rule.

d. What do the coefficient of *t* and the constant term in your rule from Part c tell about:

  i. the graph of profit as a function of number of throws?

  ii. a table of sample (*number of throws, profit*) values?

The description of the dunking booth problem included enough information about the relationship between number of customers and profit to write the profit function. However, in many problems, you will have to reason from patterns in a data table or graph to write a function rule.

② **Arcade Prices** Every business has to deal with two important patterns of change, called *depreciation* and *inflation*. When new equipment is purchased, the resale value of that equipment declines or depreciates as time passes. The cost of buying new replacement equipment usually increases due to inflation as time passes.

   The owners of Game Time, Inc. operate a chain of video game arcades. They keep a close eye on prices for new arcade games and the resale value of their existing games. One set of predictions is shown in the graph below.

a. Which of the two linear functions predicts the future price of new arcade games? Which predicts the future resale value of arcade games that are purchased now?

Arcade Prices

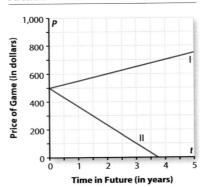

a. The condition $0.50 per throw implies a constant rate of change and thus linearity.

b. $NEXT = NOW + 0.50$

c. $P = -150 + 0.50t$ or $P = 0.50t - 150$

Student explanations should include starting with a $150 cost ($-$150) or subtracting the $150 cost and an income of $0.50 per throw.

d. i. The coefficient tells that the slope of the graph is 0.5 and the constant tells that the y-intercept is $(0, -150)$.

    ii. The table values of P will increase at a rate of 0.5 (the coefficient of t) for each increase of 1 in t, and the pair $(0, -150)$ will appear in the table.

 a. Graph I predicts future price of new arcade games and Graph II predicts the depreciating resale value of games purchased now.

b. For each graph:

    i. Find the slope and *y*-intercept. Explain what these values tell about arcade game prices.

    ii. Write a rule for calculating game price *P* in dollars at any future time *t* in years.

3 **Turtles** The Terrapin Candy Company sells its specialty—turtles made from pecans, caramel, and chocolate—through orders placed online. The company web page shows a table of prices for sample orders. Each price includes a fixed shipping-and-handling cost plus a cost per box of candy.

Number of Boxes	1	2	3	4	5	10
Price (in dollars)	20	35	50	65	80	155

a. Explain why that price seems to be a linear function of the number of boxes ordered.

b. What is the rate of change in order price as the number of boxes increases?

c. Write a rule for calculating the price *P* in dollars for *n* boxes of turtle candies.

d. Use your rule to find the price for 6 boxes and the price for 9 boxes of turtle candies.

4 **Drink Sales** The Washington High School store sells bottled drinks before and after school and during lunch.

During the first few weeks of school, the store manager set a price of $1.25 per bottle, and daily sales averaged 85 bottles per day. She then increased the price to $1.75 per bottle, and sales decreased to an average of 65 bottles per day.

a. What is the rate of change in average daily sales as the price per bottle increases from $1.25 to $1.75? What units would you use to describe this rate of change?

b. Assume that sales are a linear function of price. Use the rate of change you found in Part a to reason about expected daily "sales" for a price of $0. Then explain why you would or would not have much confidence in that prediction.

c. Use your answers to Parts a and b to write a rule for calculating expected sales *y* for any price *x* in dollars. Check that your rule matches the given information.

d. Use your rule to estimate the expected daily sales if the price is set at $0.90 per bottle.

b. **i.** Graph I: Slope of approximately 50 and y-intercept of $(0, 500)$ tell us that the current price of a new game is $500, and that the price of new games will increase at a rate of approximately $50 per year.

Graph II: Slope of approximately -133 and y-intercept of $(0, 500)$ tell us that the current price of a new game is $500 and the resale price of a game purchased now is expected to decline at a rate of about $133 per year.

ii. Graph I: $P = 500 + 50t$
Graph II: $P = 500 - 133t$

3 **a.** Price is a linear function of the number of boxes ordered because the cost increases at a constant rate of $15 per box of turtles.

b. $15 increase in price for every additional box ordered.

c. $P = 5 + 15n$

d. $P = 5 + 15(6) = \$95$ for 6 boxes.
$P = 5 + 15(9) = \$140$ for 9 boxes.

4 **a.** The rate of change in average daily sales is -20 bottles per $0.50 price increase or -40 bottles per dollar price increase. (Students should check that their rules are correct.)

b. Expected daily sales for a price of $0 per bottle would be 135 bottles. (Students may express concerns about this estimate, claiming that if the drinks were given away, students would be more inclined to have one.)

c. $y = -40x + 135$ or $y = 135 - 40x$

d. At $0.90 per bottle, the store can expect sales of 99 bottles.

5 **Alternate Forms** It is natural to write rules for many linear functions in **slope-intercept form** like $y = a + bx$ or $y = mx + b$. In some problems, the natural way to write the rule for a linear function leads to somewhat different symbolic forms. It helps to be able to recognize those alternate forms of linear functions. Several rules are given in Parts a–e. For each rule:

    i. Decide if it represents a linear function. Explain your reasoning.

    ii. If the rule defines a linear function, identify the slope and the y-intercept of the function's graph. Write the rule in slope-intercept form.

    a. $y = 10 + 2(x - 4)$ **b.** $m = n(n - 5)$

    c. $y = 2x^2 - 3$ **d.** $p = (2s + 4) + (3s - 1)$

    e. $y = \dfrac{2}{x + 1}$

6 **Given Two Points** Each pair of points listed below determines the graph of a linear function. For each pair, give the following.

    i. the slope of the graph

    ii. the y-intercept of the graph

    iii. a rule for the function

    a. (0, 5) and (2, 13)   **b.** (−3, 12) and (0, 10)

    c. (−1, 6) and (1, 7)   **d.** (3, 9) and (5, 5)

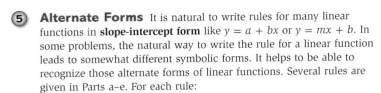

Summarize
the Mathematics

There are several different methods of writing rules for linear functions.

a To write a rule in the form $y = a + bx$ or $y = mx + b$, how can you use information about:

    i. slope and y-intercept of the graph of that function?

    ii. rate of change and other information in a table of (x, y) values?

b How can you determine the rate of change or slope if it's not given directly?

c How can you determine the y-intercept if it's not given directly?

d What is the *NOW-NEXT* rule for a linear function with rule $y = mx + b$? For a function with rule $y = a + bx$?

Be prepared to share your ideas and reasoning with the class.

5 **INSTRUCTIONAL NOTE** Lesson 3 of this unit will deal explicitly with equivalent linear expressions and provide algebraic language for operations that check equivalence and produce equivalent expressions. This problem previews that issue, so it will give you some diagnostic sense of what students already know about symbol manipulation rules. However, the problem can also be done without formal reasoning, by checking some sample (x, y) pairs or looking at a graph of the given function. At this point, it will be best to let students explain their thinking, not to teach the formal rules like expanding and combining like terms.

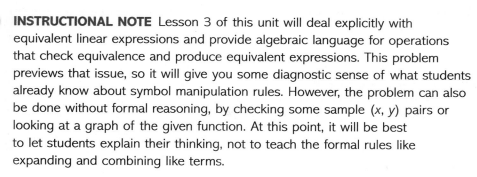
a. **i.** Students can verify that $y = 10 + 2(x - 4)$ is linear by graphing.

    ii. $y = 10 + 2(x - 4)$ is equivalent to $y = 2x + 2$. The slope is 2 and the y-intercept is $(0, 2)$.

b. **i.** $m = n(n - 5)$ is not linear because the graph is not a straight line and the rate of change in y is not constant, a fact that can be seen by checking some sample (n, m) value pairs such as $(0, 0)$, $(5, 0)$, and $(10, 50)$.

c. **i.** $y = 2x^2 - 3$ is not linear because the graph is not a straight line and the rate of change in y is not constant, as can be seen in (x, y) pairs like $(0, -3)$, $(1, -1)$, and $(2, 5)$.

d. **i.** $p = (2s + 4) + (3s - 1)$ is linear.

    ii. The slope is 5 and the p-intercept is $(0, 3)$. The slope-intercept form is $p = 5s + 3$. (Note that the variable assigned to the vertical axis is p, not y.)

e. **i.** $y = \dfrac{2}{x + 1}$ is not linear, as can be seen in a graph or by noticing that the rate of change in y is not constant. For example, $(0, 2)$, $(1, 1)$, and $\left(2, \dfrac{2}{3}\right)$ are points with equally-spaced x-coordinates but not equally-spaced y-coordinates. Students may also recall that when the x variable is in the denominator, the graph produced will never be a straight line.

6 **INSTRUCTIONAL NOTE** Students might use a variety of strategies for finding the equations of the lines determined by these pairs of points. The standard algorithm for finding slope and intercept by using the slope formula and then substituting one of the given (x, y) value pairs is developed in Applications Task 21. Students will use mostly numerical reasoning at this point, but you might want to introduce a more systematic method after they've applied their informal skills.

a. **i.** Slope is 4.

    ii. y-intercept is $(0, 5)$.

    iii. Rule is $y = 4x + 5$ or $y = 5 + 4x$.

b. **i.** Slope is $-\dfrac{2}{3}$.

    ii. y-intercept is $(0, 10)$.

    iii. Rule is $y = -\dfrac{2}{3}x + 10$ or $y = 10 - \dfrac{2}{3}x$.

c. **i.** Slope is $\dfrac{1}{2}$.

    ii. y-intercept is $(0, 6.5)$.

    iii. Rule is $y = 0.5x + 6.5$ or $y = 6.5 + 0.5x$

d. **i.** Slope is -2.

    ii. y-intercept is $(0, 15)$.

    iii. Rule is $y = -2x + 15$ or $y = 15 - 2x$.

NOTE The STM answers are on page T161.

✔Check Your Understanding

Write rules in the *NOW-NEXT* and $y = mx + b$ forms for the linear functions that give the following tables and graphs. For the graphs, assume a scale of 1 on each axis.

a.

x	y
5	20
15	40
25	60
35	80

b.

x	y
−1	8
0	5
1	2
2	−1

c.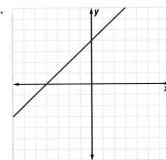

d.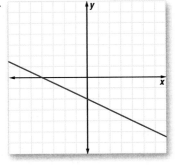

Investigation 3   Fitting Lines

Linear functions provide useful representations for relationships between variables in many situations, including cases in which data patterns are only approximately linear. As you work on this investigation, look for clues that will help you answer this question:

> *How can you produce and use function rules to represent data patterns that are not perfectly linear?*

Shadows On sunny days, every vertical object casts a shadow that is related to its height. The following graph shows data from measurements of flag height and shadow location, taken as a flag was raised up its pole. As the flag was raised higher, the location of its shadow moved farther from the base of the pole.

Although the points do not all lie on a straight line, the data pattern can be closely approximated by a line.

Summarize
the Mathematics

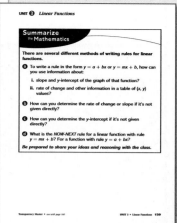
a i. The slope of the graph is the coefficient of x and the y-coordinate of the y-intercept is the constant term for the rule.

   ii. To use a table of values, you would determine the coefficient of x by finding the change in y for unit changes in x. The constant term would be the y value paired with $x = 0$.

b You can also find the rate of change or slope from any two given (x, y) pairs by comparing the change in y to the change in x as a ratio (as long as the function is known or assumed to be linear). Sometimes these pairs are embedded in the problem situation (Problem 4), sometimes they can be found on the graph (Problem 2), and sometimes they can be read from the table (Problem 3).

c On a graph, the y-intercept can be determined by locating coordinates of the point where the graph crosses the y-axis or by extrapolating or interpolating from points with known coordinates using the slope determined by those points. The y-intercept can be found in a similar way by extrapolating or interpolating from situation conditions or table entries.

d $NEXT = NOW + m$, starting at b when $y = mx + b$. $NEXT = NOW + b$, starting at a when $y = a + bx$.

MATH TOOLKIT In general, how can you determine the slope and y-intercept of a line given a table of values? Given the graph of the line? How can the slope and y-intercept of a line be used to write a rule for the line?

✔ Check Your Understanding

a. $y = 2x + 10$; $NEXT = NOW + 2$, starting at 10

b. $y = -3x + 5$; $NEXT = NOW - 3$, starting at 5

c. $y = x + 4$; $NEXT = NOW + 1$, starting at 4

d. $y = -\frac{1}{2}x - 2$; $NEXT = NOW - \frac{1}{2}$, starting at -2

Unit 3

Flag Height and Shadow Location

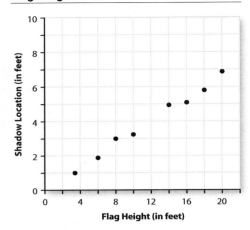

1 Consider the (*flag height, shadow location*) data plotted above.

   a. On a copy of the plot, use a straight edge to find a line that fits the data pattern closely. Compare your line with those of your classmates. Discuss reasons for any differences.

   b. Write the rule for a function that has your line as its graph.

The line and the rule that match the (*flag height, shadow location*) data pattern are **mathematical models** of the relationship between the two variables. Both the graph and the rule can be used to explore the data pattern and to answer questions about the relationship between flag height and shadow location.

2 Use your mathematical models of the relationship between shadow location and flag height to answer the following questions. Be prepared to explain your strategies for answering the questions.

   a. What shadow location would you predict when the flag height is 12 feet?

   b. What shadow location would you predict when the flag height is 25 feet?

   c. What flag height would locate the flag shadow 6.5 feet from the base of the pole?

   d. What flag height would locate the flag shadow 10 feet from the base of the pole?

Investigation 3 Fitting Lines

The central goal of this investigation is to introduce the notion of linear functions serving as models or idealizations of approximately linear patterns in (x, y) data tables or plots. The sequence of problems encourages students to begin by making "eyeball" fits of lines to data plots and finding the related rules. Then students are asked to use their calculators to make data plots and to experiment with function graphs to find a linear model that fits well, and finally to use the *linear regression* tool that is available in most graphing calculators and computer software packages. Full development of the least squares criterion for fitting lines to data patterns will be done in the Course 2 unit *Regression and Correlation*.

 a. Students might reasonably place their modeling line in a variety of positions.

> **INSTRUCTIONAL NOTE** It will probably be useful to spend some time asking students to articulate their ideas about the line that would be a good match for the data pattern. Some might suggest joining the first and last points; in this case, that doesn't give a bad fit. Other students might suggest having equal numbers of points above and below the line. Still other students might suggest trying to draw a line that passes through as many points as possible. Students should think about whether these strategies have any flaws.

b. Linear function rules may vary. A line with function rule $y = \frac{1}{3}x$ is quite a good fit.

2 This problem is answered using $y = \frac{1}{3}x$.

a. 4 feet from the base of the flag pole

b. About 8 or 9 feet from the base of the pole when the flag is 25 feet up the pole

c. A flag height of about 19 or 20 feet should produce a shadow about 6.5 feet from the base of the pole.

d. A flag height of about 30 feet should produce a shadow about 10 feet from the base of the pole.

> **INSTRUCTIONAL NOTE**
> When the student text indicates, "Be prepared to explain ... ," students need not write these explanations. As you circulate among groups, you should ask them to verbalize their strategies. Strategies will likely be in the form of moving from an *x* value, to the line, and then over to the *y*-axis to read the corresponding *y* value.

Time Flies Airline passengers are always interested in the time a trip will take. Airline companies need to know how flight time is related to flight distance. The following table shows published distance and time data for a sample of United Airlines nonstop flights to and from Chicago, Illinois.

Nonstop Flights to and from Chicago

Travel Between Chicago and:	Distance (in miles)	Flight Time (in minutes)	
		Westbound	Eastbound
Boise, ID	1,435	220	190
Boston, MA	865	160	140
Cedar Rapids, IA	195	55	55
Frankfurt, Germany	4,335	550	490
Hong Kong, China	7,790	950	850
Las Vegas, NV	1,510	230	210
Paris, France	4,145	570	500
Pittsburgh, PA	410	95	85
San Francisco, CA	1,845	275	245
Tokyo, Japan	6,265	790	685

Source: www.uatimetable.com

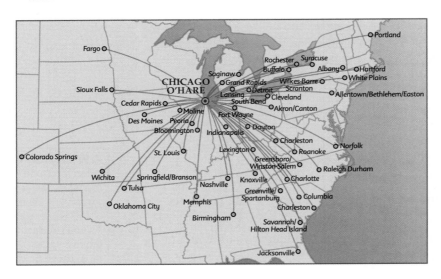

Scheduled flight time for a given distance depends on many factors, but the factor that has the greatest effect is the speed of prevailing winds. As you can see in the table, westbound flights generally take longer, since the prevailing wind patterns blow from west to east. Therefore, it makes sense to consider westbound flights and eastbound flights separately.

EXTENSIONS You might wish to have students collect their own data on heights of objects and lengths of shadows, create a model, and compare their model to that in the launch of the investigation. They could be asked to explain why there might be differences (time of year or day). Another extension idea is to select a nearby airline hub and search its schedule for nonstop flights of varying distances east and west. Alternatively, students might look up the distance between their hometown and Chicago and estimate the flight time in each direction.

TECHNOLOGY NOTE In this investigation students will have the opportunity to place lines on scatterplots using technology. Fitting lines to data plots by adjusting the parameters for slope and *y*-intercept of the function rule help students see the effect of these parameters.

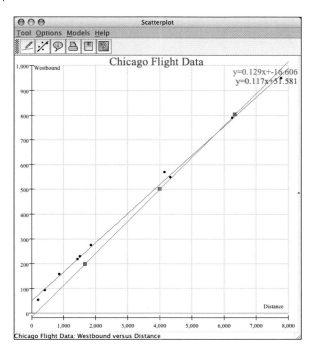

Unit 3

3 To analyze the relationship between westbound flight time and flight distance, study the following scatterplot of the data on westbound flight distance and flight time.

Westbound Flight Distance and Time

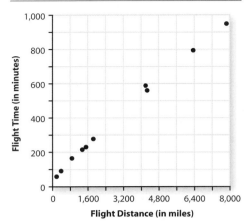

a. On a copy of the plot, locate a line that you believe is a good model for the trend in the data. You might find a good modeling line by experimenting with a transparent ruler and pencil. Alternatively, if you have access to data analysis software like the "Modeling Line" custom tool, you can manipulate a moveable line on a scatterplot of the data.

When you've located a good modeling line, write a rule for the function that has that line as its graph, using d for distance and t for time.

b. Explain what the coefficient of d and the constant term in the rule tell about the relationship between flight time and flight distance for westbound United Airlines flights.

4 Linear models are often used to summarize patterns in data. They are also useful in making predictions. In the analysis of connections between flight time and distance, this means predicting t from d when no (d, t) pair in the data set gives the answer.

a. United Airlines has several daily nonstop flights between Chicago and Salt Lake City, Utah—a distance of 1,247 miles. Use your linear model from Problem 2 to predict the flight time for such westbound flights.

b. The scheduled flight times for Chicago to Salt Lake City flights range from 3 hours and 17 minutes to 3 hours and 33 minutes. Compare these times to the prediction of your linear model. Explain why there might be differences between the predicted and scheduled times.

(3) **TECHNOLOGY NOTE** The (*flight distance, flight time*) data are in the *CPMP-Tools* under Statistics. Since these data are very linear, student-located lines and the regression line given in Problem 8 are close together. You may wish to have pairs of students complete this problem using the custom tool "Modeling Line". Entering data and creating scatterplots in calculators or statistical software is introduced in Problem 5. See also the summary teacher notes on page T167. An additional data set including information for twenty cities is available so that students can ask and answer their own questions.

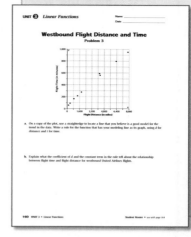
a. The function rule about $t = 0.12d + 52$ turns out to be the linear regression equation for the given data.

   (Student answers based on "eyeball" modeling should be somewhere in that ballpark. But the important issue is to have them explain their reasoning and calculations that led to the rule they came up with.)

b. The coefficient of d tells the rate at which flight time increases as flight distance increases. For example, the coefficient 0.12 tells us that the flight time increases at a rate of 0.12 minutes per mile. The constant term of 52 tells us that 52 minutes of trip time will be consumed when the plane is not flying. The constant term might include time spent in taxiing to the runway, time waiting after leaving the gate, and time from landing to gate arrival.

(4) **a.** A flight time of 202 minutes (3 hours and 22 minutes) for a trip of 1,247 miles is predicted by $t = 0.12d + 52$.

b. The predicted time is about 3 hours and 22 minutes and is somewhat to the low end of the scheduled flight times. The modeling line will give only one time for a distance of 1,247 miles, not two times or a range of times. Also, the predicting line is a summary of the relationship; you would not expect the predicted and scheduled times to be exactly the same. Reasons for these differences could include the actual wind speed or the time of day at which the plane leaves (high volume of traffic on runway vs. low volume of traffic).

How's the Weather Up There? Linear functions are also useful for modeling patterns in climate data. You may have noticed that mountain tops can remain snow-covered long after the snow has melted in the areas below. This is because, in general, the higher you go above sea level, the colder it gets.

Extreme adventurers, such as those who attempt to climb Mt. Everest or those who jump from planes at high altitudes, must protect themselves from harsh temperatures as well as from the lack of oxygen at high altitudes. As skydiver Michael Wright explains about skydiving from 30,000 feet, "Cool? Yes it is. Cold? You bet. Typically 25 below zero (don't be concerned if that is °F or °C, it's still cold)."

An airplane descending to Los Angeles International Airport might record data showing a pattern like that in the next table.

Airplane Altitude and Temperature Data Above Los Angeles

Altitude (in 1,000s of feet)	Temperature (in °F)	Altitude (in 1,000s of feet)	Temperature (in °F)
34.6	−58	6.6	39
27.3	−35	4.2	49
20.5	−14	2.1	57
13.0	13	0.6	63
9.5	27	0.1	65

5 When working with paired data, it is helpful to use the list operations provided by calculators and statistical software. To get started, you need to enter the altitude data in one list and the temperature data in another list. Select an appropriate viewing window and produce a plot of the (*altitude, temperature*) data.

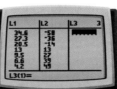

a. Describe the overall pattern of change in temperature as altitude increases.

b. Use two data points to estimate the rate of change in temperature as altitude (in thousands of feet) increases.

c. Use the data to make a reasonable estimate of the temperature at an altitude of 0 feet. Then use this value, together with the estimated rate of change from Part b, to write a rule for calculating temperature T as a function of altitude x (in thousands of feet).

d. Graph the function from Part c on a scatterplot of the data. Adjust the constant term and the coefficient of x in your rule until you believe the graph of your function closely matches the pattern in the data. Explain how you decided when the line was a good fit.

e. The highest elevation in Los Angeles is 5,080 feet at Elsie Peak. Use your linear model from Part d to predict the temperature at Elsie Peak on the day that the other data were collected.

LESSON 1 • Modeling Linear Relationships **165**

5 INSTRUCTIONAL NOTE To launch this temperature/altitude context, you might ask, "Does it ever make sense for the altitude to be a negative value? If so, where?" followed by, "Will the same pattern continue?"

a. Overall, the temperature declines as altitude increases. (See plots below.)

b. Student answers will vary, depending on the particular pair of points used to estimate the overall rate of change. However, the data pattern is quite linear, so the various slope estimates should be between -3 and -4 degrees per thousand feet.

c. A reasonable estimate of the temperature at altitude of 0 feet above sea level might be something like $66°F$. Using this y-intercept coordinate and the slope estimate from Part b leads to an equation of $T = 66 - 3.5x$. (Note that in this situation, it seems natural to use the $y = a + bx$ form of the rule.)

d. Adjustments will vary. We show here graphs on data plots for two linear models. The second uses the equation produced by the calculator linear regression routine discussed in Problem 6.

$$T = 66 - 3.5x \qquad\qquad T = 63.4 - 3.6x$$

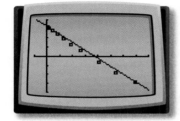
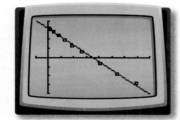

e. INSTRUCTIONAL NOTE In Part e, students might, in error, enter 5080 into the function as the altitude. Since original data are in thousands of feet, what should be entered is 5.08. It would be best if students make and correct their own error, but you may wish to watch for this. By acknowledging in a class discussion the value of identifying and correcting one's own errors, you will help students develop that habit of mind.

The temperature atop Elsie Peak on that day was probably about $45°F$, according to the regression equation. Using the model $T = 66 - 3.5x$, the temperature estimate is $48°F$.

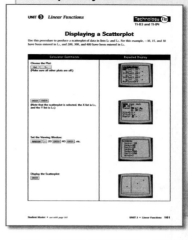
TECHNOLOGY NOTE The data from Problems 5–8 can be found in *CPMP-Tools*, under Data Analysis, Data, Unit 3.

Unit 3

Linear regression is a branch of statistics that helps in studying relationships between variables. It uses a mathematical algorithm to fit linear models to scatterplot patterns. You will learn more about the algorithm in the Course 2 unit on *Regression and Correlation*. But the algorithm is programmed in most graphing calculators and statistical software for computers, so you can put it to use in mathematical modeling right now.

6 Use the linear regression algorithm available on your calculator or computer to find a linear function that models the pattern in the (*altitude, temperature*) data, rounding the coefficient of x and the constant term to the nearest tenth.

   a. Display the graph of this function on your data plot and compare its fit to that of the function you obtained in Problem 5, Part d.

   b. What do the coefficient of x and the constant term in the linear regression rule tell you about the relationship between altitude and temperature?

7 Skydivers typically jump from altitudes of 10,000 to 15,000 feet. However, high altitude jumping, from 24,000 to 30,000 feet, is becoming popular. Use your linear regression model from Problem 6 to study the temperatures experienced by skydivers at different altitudes on the day the data were collected.

   a. Estimate the temperature at altitudes of 10,000, 15,000, 24,000, and 30,000 feet.

   b. What change in temperature can be expected as altitude decreases from 30,000 to 24,000 feet? From 24,000 to 15,000 feet? From 15,000 to 10,000 feet? What is the rate of change in temperature as altitude changes in each situation?

   c. Frostbite does not occur at temperatures above 28° Fahrenheit. Estimate the altitudes at which temperature is predicted to be at least 28°F.

   d. The current world record for skydiving altitude is 102,800 feet, set by Joe Kittinger Jr. in 1960. What temperature does your model predict for an altitude of 102,800 feet? What does this prediction suggest about limits on the linear model for predicting temperature from altitude?

8 Look back at the scatterplot of United Airlines westbound flight distances and times on page 164. The linear regression model for westbound flight time as a function of flight distance to and from Chicago is approximately $t = 0.12d + 52$.

   a. What do the coefficient of d and the constant term in this rule tell you about the relationship between westbound flight time and flight distance?

6 a. $y = 63.4 - 3.6x$

(The plot of that function is shown in the answer to Problem 5, Part d on the previous page.)

b. The coefficient of x tells us that temperature declines at a rate of about 3.6°F per thousand feet of elevation increase; the constant term tells us that the sea level temperature would be about 63.4°F.

7 Skydiving predictions, using $y = 63.4 - 3.6x$:

a.

Altitude (in feet)	Temperature (in °F)
10,000	27.4
15,000	9.4
24,000	−23
30,000	−44.6

b.

Altitude Change (in 1,000s feet)	Temperature Change (in °F)	Rate of Change (in °F/1,000 ft)
30 to 24	21.6	$\frac{21.6}{-6} \approx -3.6$
24 to 15	32.4	$\frac{32.4}{-9} \approx -3.6$
15 to 10	18	$\frac{18}{-5} \approx -3.6$

c. Temperature will be above 28°F for altitudes below about 9,833 feet.

d. Temperature at 102,800 feet is predicted to be −306°F. (In fact, the composition of the atmosphere and its relationship to solar radiation changes at quite high altitudes, so it is reasonable to expect that temperature will change in a different pattern at very high altitudes and the rate of cooling might not be as great. A temperature of −306°F is very low to imagine!)

8 a. The coefficient of d tells us that flight time increases by about 0.12 minutes for each mile of distance. The constant term tells us that about 52 minutes will be used in nonflying time.

b. Since these data are very linear, there may not be much difference between their line and the line of best fit on student hand-made graphs. (See the Summary below and the screen at the right.)

c. **i.** The rate $\frac{12}{100}$ tells us twelve one-hundredths of a minute per mile.

ii. A more natural way to explain what the fraction tells is to say 12 minutes per 100 miles.

iii. The fraction is equivalent to $\frac{60}{500}$, which tells us 60 minutes per 500 miles, or, in more customary language, 500 miles per hour.

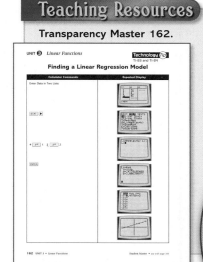

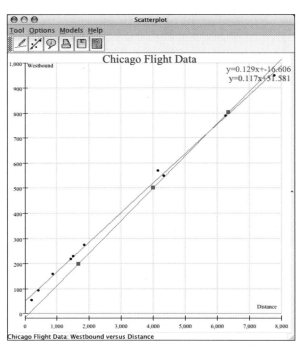

Unit 3

b. Display the graph of the linear regression model on the scatterplot of (*flight distance, flight time*) data. Compare its fit to that of the modeling function you developed in Problem 3 Part a.

c. Describing the rate of change in flight time as flight distance increases in terms of hundredths of a minute per mile is not very informative.

    i. Rewrite the rate of change 0.12 as a fraction and explain what the numerator and the denominator of this fraction tell about the relationship between flight time and flight distance.

    ii. Express the rate of change in flight time as flight distance increases in terms of minutes per 100 miles.

    iii. Write the fraction from part i in an equivalent form that shows the rate of change in minutes per 500 miles. Explain what this fraction suggests about the average speed of westbound planes.

Summarize
the Mathematics

In this investigation, you analyzed tables and plots of sample (x, y) data to find linear functions that model relationships between variables.

a   How do you decide if a line is a good fit for the pattern in a data set?

b   How do you find rules for linear functions that model data patterns that are approximately linear?

c   How do you use a linear model to estimate y values related to given x values? To estimate the x values that will predict any given y values?

Be prepared to share your thinking and methods with the entire class.

✓ Check Your Understanding

Look back at the United Airlines eastbound flight data on page 15. Since these flights have a tailwind as opposed to a headwind, they take less time.

a. On a plot of the eastbound (*flight distance, flight time*) data, locate a line that you believe is a good fit for the pattern in the data.

b. What linear function has the line you located in Part a as its graph? What do the coefficient of the independent variable and the constant term in the rule for that function tell about flight distance and flight time for eastbound flights?

c. United Airlines has nonstop flights between Chicago and Portland, Maine—a distance of 898 miles. Use your linear model to predict the time for an eastbound flight of 898 miles.

d. The scheduled flight times for the Chicago to Portland flights range from 2 hours and 10 minutes to 2 hours and 31 minutes. If your prediction was not in that range, what factors might explain the error of prediction?

You may use the custom tool "Modeling Line" to draw a line and compare the placement to the linear regression line for the STM discussion of Part a. The data for nonstop flights to and from Chicago are in the software.

Summarize the Mathematics

a There are several criteria one might consider for making a good linear model for a data pattern, but the basic idea is that the line drawn seems, on balance, to represent the data pattern well. What is perhaps most important is *avoiding* the temptation to use "rules" like "join the first and last points" or "go through the maximum number of points" or "have equal numbers of points above and below the line." Each of those strategies can lead to quite poor linear models.

b Once a modeling line is located on a plot, select points on that line for which coordinates can be fairly accurately read and use those coordinates to find the equation in the ways practiced in Investigation 2. Alternatively, you could use linear regression tools.

c When given a rule $y = mx + b$, finding y corresponding to given x is simply a matter of plugging the value of x into the rule. Finding x corresponding to given y requires solving the equation for x.

When using a graph of a linear function to estimate y values for related x values, you identify the point on the line that has the x-coordinate and identify the y-coordinate by reading it off the y-axis. A similar approach can be used for estimating an x value that will predict a given y value.

(You may wish to refer students to Problem 2, Parts a and b and Problem 7, Part c if they are unsure of the second question here.)

Teaching Resources

Transparency Master 163.

UNIT ❸ *Linear Functions*

Summarize the Mathematics

In this investigation, you analyzed tables and plots of sample (x, y) data to find linear functions that model relationships between variables.

a How do you decide if a line is a good fit for the pattern in a data set?

b How do you find rules for linear functions that model data patterns that are approximately linear?

c How do you use a linear model to estimate y values related to given x values? To estimate the x values that will predict any given y values?

Be prepared to share your thinking and methods with the entire class.

Transparency Master • see unit page 167   UNIT 3 • Linear Functions   163

Unit 3

MATH TOOLKIT Describe two ways to find a rule for data patterns that are approximately linear.

✓ Check Your Understanding

TECHNOLOGY NOTE These data are in the *CPMP-Tools*.

a. The data and the linear regression model $y = 0.1x + 47$ are shown here.

b. The linear regression model is $y = 0.1x + 47$. The 0.1 tells us that flights take about one-tenth of a minute to cover one mile; the 47 tells us that about 47 minutes are used by nonflying time. (It's a bit curious that the constant term for eastbound flights is somewhat less than that for westbound flights. It might be a result of the small data set.)

c. The linear regression model predicts a time of 137 minutes (2 hours and 17 minutes) for the flight from Chicago to Portland, Maine.

d. The prediction is about midway in the schedule range.

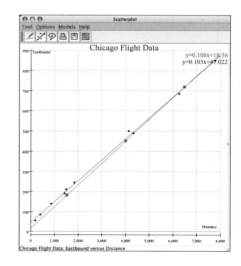

On Your Own

1 Lake Aid is an annual benefit talent show produced by the students of Wilde Lake High School to raise money for the local food bank. Several functions that relate to Lake Aid finances are described in Parts a–c. For each function:

  i. Explain what the numbers in the function rule tell about the situation.

  ii. Explain what the function rule tells you to expect in tables of values for the function.

  iii. Explain what the function rule tells you to expect in a graph of the function.

  iv. Write a *NOW-NEXT* rule to describe the pattern of change in the dependent variable.

a. Several of the show organizers researched the possibility of selling DVDs of the show to increase donations to the food bank. They would have to pay for recording of the show and for production of the DVDs. The cost C (in dollars) would depend on the number of DVDs ordered n according to the rule $C = 150 + 2n$.

b. Proceeds from ticket sales, after security and equipment rental fees are paid, are donated to the local food bank. Once the ticket price was set, organizers determined that the proceeds P (in dollars) would depend on the number of tickets sold t according to the rule $P = 6t - 400$.

c. The organizers of the event surveyed students to see how ticket price would affect the number of tickets sold. The results of the survey showed that the number of tickets sold T could be predicted from the ticket price p (in dollars) using the rule $T = 950 - 75p$.

2 Given below are five functions and at the right five graphs. Without doing any calculating or graphing yourself, match each function with the graph that most likely represents it. In each case, explain the clues that helped you make the match.

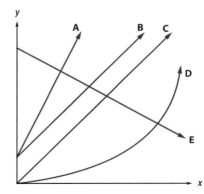

a. $y = x$

b. $y = 2x + 2$

c. $y = 0.1x^2$

d. $y = x + 2$

e. $y = 9 - 0.5x$

Applications

1 **a.** **i.** In the rule $C = 150 + 2n$, the 150 tells us that the fixed cost of recording the show is $150, and the 2 tells us that reproduction of individual copies of the DVD will cost $2 apiece.

ii. The rule says that the ordered pair $(0, 150)$ will appear in the table and that as n increases in steps of 1, the values of C will increase in steps of 2.

iii. The graph will be a line with y-intercept $(0, 150)$ and slope 2.

iv. The *NOW-NEXT* rule describing the pattern of change in total cost will be $NEXT = NOW + 2$, starting at 150.

b. **i.** In the rule $P = 6t - 400$, the 400 tells us that the fixed cost of security and equipment rental fees for operating the show is $400. The 6 tells us that sales of individual tickets will bring in $6 each.

ii. The rule says that the ordered pair $(0, -400)$ will appear in the table and that as t increases in steps of 1, the values of P will increase in steps of 6.

iii. The graph will be a line with y-intercept $(0, -400)$ and slope 6.

iv. The *NOW-NEXT* rule describing the pattern of change in total cost will be $NEXT = NOW + 6$, starting at -400.

c. **i.** In the rule $T = 950 - 75p$, the 950 tells us the number of tickets that could be given away for free, and the -75 tells us that each increase of $1 in ticket price will result in 75 fewer tickets sold.

ii. The rule says that the ordered pair $(0, 950)$ will appear in the table and that as t increases in steps of 1, the values of T will decrease in steps of 75.

iii. The graph will be a line with y-intercept $(0, 950)$ and slope -75.

iv. The *NOW-NEXT* rule describing the pattern of change in total cost will be $NEXT = NOW - 75$, starting at 950.

2 **a.** Graph C: $y = x$ is the only linear function with y-intercept $(0, 0)$.

b. Graph A: $y = 2x + 2$ is a linear function with intercept on the positive y-axis and it has steeper slope than Graph C.

c. Graph D: $y = 0.1x^2$ is the only nonlinear function.

d. Graph B: $y = x + 2$ has the same slope as $y = x$ but does not pass through $(0, 0)$. Another way to identify $y = x + 2$ as Graph B is to notice that it has the same y-intercept as Graph A but is less steep due to a slope of 1 rather than 2.

e. Graph E: $y = 9 - 0.5x$ is the only linear function with negative slope.

3 The graph below shows the relationship between weekly profit and the number of customers per week for Skate World Roller Rink.

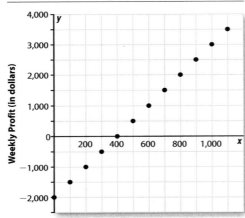

Skate World Weekly Profit

Number of Customers per Week

a. Determine the slope and *y*-intercept of the line that fits this data pattern.

b. Explain what the slope and *y*-intercept of the line tell you about the relationship between Skate World profit and number of customers per week.

c. If Skate World reached maximum capacity during each skating session for a week, admissions for that week would total 2,400 customers. Estimate the rink's profit in this situation. Explain your reasoning.

4 The table below gives the amount of money spent on national health care for every ten years from 1960 to 2000.

U.S. Health-Care Expenditures, 1960–2000
(in billions of dollars)

1960	1970	1980	1990	2000
26.7	73.1	245.8	696.0	1,299.5

Source: *The World Almanac and Book of Facts 2003.* New York, NY: World Almanac Education Group, Inc. 2003.

a. Was the amount of money spent on national health care a linear function over time from 1960 to 2000? Explain how you could tell without plotting the data.

b. What is the rate of change in health-care expenditures from 1960 to 1970? From 1970 to 1980? From 1980 to 1990? From 1990 to 2000? From 1960 to 2000? What does this suggest about the probable shape of a plot of the data?

LESSON 1 • Modeling Linear Relationships **169**

3 **a.** Slope is 5; *y*-intercept is at −2,000

b. The *y*-intercept tells us that without income from customers, the business has $2,000 in weekly operating expenses; slope tells us that each customer brings in $5 in revenue.

c. With 2,400 customers in a week, the rink will earn $5(2,400) − 2,000 = \$10,000$ profit. Income will be $5 per customer and expenses are $2,000. Another way to reason would be that profit appears to be going up by $500 for every increase of 100 customers. Counting on from the data point (1,100, 3,500) one would arrive at (2,400, 10,000).

4 **a.** The table does not show a constant additive change over every time interval, so the change in expenditures is not a linear function of time.

b. 1960 to 1970: $\dfrac{73.1 - 26.7}{10} = \$4.64$ billion per year

1970 to 1980: $\dfrac{245.8 - 73.1}{10} = \$17.27$ billion per year

1980 to 1990: $\dfrac{696.0 - 245.8}{10} = \$45.02$ billion per year

1990 to 2000: $\dfrac{1,299.5 - 696.0}{10} = \$60.35$ billion per year

1960 to 2000: $\dfrac{1,299.5 - 26.7}{40} = \$31.82$ billion per year

The shape of the graph should be increasing at an increasing rate, so curved upward.

(5) Victoria got a job at her school as scorekeeper for a summer basketball league. The job pays $450 for the summer and the league plays on 25 nights. Some nights Victoria will have to get a substitute for her job and give her pay for that night to the substitute.

   a. What should Victoria pay a substitute for one night?

   b. Use the letters n for nights a substitute works, S for pay to the substitute, and E for Victoria's total summer earnings.

      i. Write a rule for calculating S as a function of n.

      ii. Write a rule for calculating E as a function of n.

   c. Sketch graphs of the functions that relate total substitute pay and Victoria's total summer earnings to the number of nights a substitute works. Compare the patterns in the two graphs.

(6) Some of the best vacuum cleaners are only sold door-to-door. The salespeople demonstrate the cleaning ability of the appliance in people's homes to encourage them to make the purchase. Michael sells vacuum cleaners door-to-door. He earns a base salary plus a commission on each sale. His weekly earnings depend on the number of vacuum cleaners he sells as shown in the table below.

Michael's Earnings

Number of Vacuum Cleaners Sold in a Week	2	4	6	8
Weekly Earnings (in dollars)	600	960	1,320	1,680

   a. Verify that weekly earnings are a linear function of the number of vacuum cleaners sold.

   b. Determine the rate of change in earnings as sales increase. What part of Michael's pay does this figure represent?

   c. What would Michael's earnings be for a week in which he sold 0 vacuum cleaners?

   d. Use your answers to Parts b and c to write a rule that shows how Michael's weekly earnings E can be calculated from the number of vacuum cleaners sold in a week S.

   e. Company recruiters claim that salespeople sell as many as 15 vacuum cleaners in a week. What are the weekly earnings for selling 15 vacuum cleaners?

(7) The table below shows the pattern of growth for one bean plant grown under special lighting.

Day	Height (in cm)
3	4.2
4	4.7
5	5.1
7	6.0

5 **a.** $450 \div 25 = 18$; so, she should pay $18 per night if she wants to pay the same rate she earns.

b. **i.** $S = 18n$

ii. $E = 450 - 18n$

c. $S = 18n$

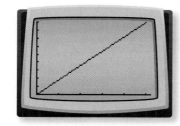 

$E = 450 - 18n$

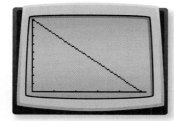 

Both patterns are linear. The graph representing total substitute pay has a *y*-intercept of (0, 0) and a constant positive rate of change. The graph representing total summer earnings has a *y*-intercept of 450 and a negative slope, so it decreases at a constant rate of change.

6 **a.** Weekly earnings increase at a constant rate of $180 per unit sold, so the function is linear.

b. The rate of change is $180, which represents the additional pay for each vacuum cleaner sold.

c. Even if Michael sells no vacuum cleaners, he will earn $240 per week.

d. $E = 240 + 180S$ or $E = 180S + 240$

e. For selling 15 vacuum cleaners, a salesperson will earn $2,940 in a week. (Since this comes out to over $150,000 per year, it sounds almost too good to be true! So, one should be suspicious of the recruiter's claim.)

a. Plot the (*day, height*) data and draw a line that is a good fit for the trend in the data.

b. Write a function rule for your linear model. What do the numbers in the rule tell about days of growth and height of the bean plant?

c. Predict the height of the plant on day 6 and check to see if that prediction seems to fit the pattern in the data table.

8 For each of these function rules, explain what the constant term and the coefficient of the independent variable tell about the tables and graphs of the function.

a. $y = -4 + 2x$

b. $p = 7.3n + 12.5$

c. $y = 200 - 25x$

d. $d = -9.8t + 32$

9 Write rules for linear functions with graphs containing the following pairs of points.

a. $(0, 3)$ and $(6, 6)$

b. $(0, -4)$ and $(5, 6)$

c. $(-4, -3)$ and $(2, 3)$

d. $(-6, 4)$ and $(3, -8)$

10 The Riverdale Adventure Club is planning a spring skydiving lesson and first jump. Through the club newsletter, club members were asked to take a poll as to whether or not they would purchase a video of their jump for various prices.

The results of the poll are shown in the table below.

Cost (in dollars)	25	30	35	40	50	60	75
Number of Buyers	93	89	77	71	64	55	38

a. Create a linear model for the (*cost, number of buyers*) data. Represent your linear model as a graph and as a function rule.

b. Use your linear model from Part a to predict the number of members who would purchase a video of their jump for $45. For $70. For $90. For $10. Which estimates would you most trust? Why?

c. Should you use your model to predict the number of buyers if videos cost $125? Why or why not?

d. For what cost of a video would you predict 50 buyers? 75 buyers? 100 buyers?

7 **a.** The next plot shows the data and the linear regression model $y = 0.45x + 2.9$. Student eyeball fits should be reasonably close to this drawing.

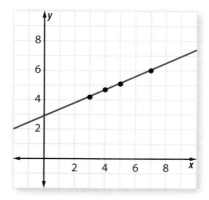

b. The rules that students come up with might be about $y = 0.4x + 3$. In that case, the 0.4 tells that the plant grows a bit less than half an inch per day over the period in which it was observed. The 3 tells its height at the start of the observation period. (This initial height might not be so unreasonable, because those who have seen beans grow will have noticed that they seem to pop out of the ground quickly, and the stem sort of unfolds to an initial height of several inches.)

c. Using $y = 0.4x + 3$, the predicted height on day 6 is 5.4 inches, which is between the data values for days 5 and 7. One might choose 5.55 as a better estimate of the height on day 6, using linear interpolation between the two nearest data points. However, the linear model is not far off, and it accounts for more data about the overall growth relationship.

8 **a.** The constant term tells that $(0, -4)$ appears in the table and that the y-intercept is $(0, -4)$. The coefficient of x tells that the table y values increase by 2 for each increase of 1 in x and that the slope of the graph is 2.

b. The constant term tells that $(0, 12.5)$ appears in the table and that the p-intercept is $(0, 12.5)$. The coefficient of n tells that the table p values increase by 7.3 for each increase of 1 in n and that the slope of the graph is 7.3.

c. The constant term tells that $(0, 200)$ appears in the table and that the y-intercept is $(0, 200)$. The coefficient of x tells that the table y values decrease by 25 for each increase of 1 in x and that the slope of the graph is -25.

d. The constant term tells that $(0, 32)$ appears in the table and that the d-intercept is $(0, 32)$. The coefficient of t tells that the table d values decrease by 9.8 for each increase of 1 in t and that the slope of the graph is -9.8.

9 **a.** $y = 3 + 0.5x$ or $y = 0.5x + 3$

b. $y = -4 + 2x$ or $y = 2x - 4$

c. $y = x + 1$

d. $y = -\frac{4}{3}x - 4$

10 **a.** The graph at the right shows a data plot and the linear regression model $y = 118 - 1.07x$. Student equations might be more like $y = 120 - x$. Answers to this and the subsequent parts will vary a bit, depending on the model used.

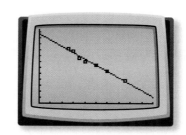

> **INSTRUCTIONAL NOTE**
> Students should probably be asked whether they think this linear model is likely to be useful for the full life of the plant. They should realize that plants (like people) tend to reach a maximum height at maturity, so the model is probably only useful for modest extrapolation beyond the available data.

> **TECHNOLOGY NOTE**
> The data for Task 10 are in *CPMP-Tools*.

> **NOTE** Answers to Task 10 Parts b–d are on page T172.

Unit 3

11 The snowy tree cricket is known as the "thermometer cricket" because it is possible to count its chirping rate and then estimate the temperature.

The table below shows the rate of cricket chirps at various temperatures.

Temperature (in °F)	50	54	58	61	66	70	75	78	83	86
Chirps per Minute	41	57	78	90	104	120	144	160	178	192

a. Use a calculator or computer software to determine the linear regression model for chirp rate *C* as a function of temperature *T*.

b. At what rate do you predict crickets will chirp if the temperature is 70°F? 90°F?

c. Now find the linear regression model for temperature *T* as a function of chirp rate *C*.

d. Use the linear regression model from Part c to predict the temperature when crickets are chirping at a rate of 150 chirps per minute. At a rate of 10 chirps per minute. Which prediction would you expect to be more accurate? Why?

e. Caution must be exercised in using linear regression models to make predictions that go well beyond the data on which the models are based.

   i. For what range of temperatures would you expect your linear model in Part a to give accurate chirping rate predictions?

   ii. For what range of chirping rates would you expect your linear model in Part c to give accurate temperature predictions?

b. Using $y = 120 - x$, the predicted numbers of customers would be:

Cost (in dollars)	10	45	70	90
Number of Buyers	110	75	50	30

The predictions that one should trust most are those that are interpolations of values between available data points. It is always risky to extrapolate far beyond available data in any situation.

c. The model $y = 120 - x$ predicts -5 customers if the price is \$125, underscoring the point in Part b.

d.

Cost (in dollars)	70	45	20
Number of Buyers	50	75	100

Students might get these answers by studying a graph or table of $y = 120 - x$ to see what values of x give the prescribed values of y, or they might solve equations like $120 - x = 50$.

11 **a.** $C = 4.15T - 166.10$

b. A rate of 124 chirps per minute if the temperature is 70°F
A rate of 207 chirps per minute if the temperature is 90°F

c. $T = 0.24C + 40$

d. At a rate of 150 chirps per minute, the temperature would be 76°F. At a rate of 10 chirps per minute, the temperature would be 43°F.

   The prediction of temperature for 150 chirps per minute is more likely to be accurate, because the model is based on data that surround 150 chirps per minute, while we have no data for anything near 10 chirps per minute.

   (Notice that if you use the regression equation showing chirps as a function of temperature and ask for the temperature that would predict 150 chirps per minute, solving $4.15T - 166 = 150$ gives $T = 76$°F. This agreement of predictions is not always the case. But when the relationship is quite close to perfectly linear, the equations will be compatible.)

e. **i.** The prediction should be accurate for temperatures between approximately 50°F and 90°F.

   ii. The prediction should be accurate for chirping rates between approximately 40 and 200 chirps per minute.

TECHNOLOGY NOTE
The data for Task 11 are in *CPMP-Tools*.

INSTRUCTIONAL NOTE Be sure that students understand that, in general, it is risky to make predictions from a model when the value of the independent variable is far outside the range of the data on which the model is based.

12 Many Americans love to eat fast food, but also worry about weight. Many fast-food restaurants offer "lite" items in addition to their regular menu items. Examine these data about the fat and calorie content of some fast foods.

Item	Grams of Fat	Calories
McDonald's		
Grilled Chicken Bacon Ranch Salad	9	260
Grilled Chicken Caesar Salad	6	220
McChicken	16	370
Hardee's		
Charbroiled Chicken Sandwich	26	590
Regular Roast Beef	16	330
Wendy's		
Mandarin Chicken Salad	2	170
Jr. Cheeseburger	13	320
Ultimate Chicken Grill Sandwich	7	360
Taco Bell		
Ranchero Chicken Soft Taco, "Fresco Style"	4	170
Grilled Steak Taco, "Fresco Style"	5	170

Source: www.mcdonalds.com; www.hardees.com; www.wendys.com; www.tacobell.com

a. Make a scatterplot of the data relating calories to grams of fat in the menu items shown.

b. Draw a modeling line using the points (6, 220) and (16, 370). Write a rule for the corresponding linear function. Explain what the constant term and the coefficient of x in that rule tell about the graph and about the relation between calories and grams of fat.

c. Use your calculator or computer software to find the linear regression model for the (*grams of fat, calories*) data in the table. Compare this result to what you found in Part b.

13 Over the past 40 years, more and more women have taken full-time jobs outside the home. There has been controversy about whether they are being paid fairly. The table below shows the median incomes for men and women employed full-time outside the home from 1970 to 2003. These data do not show pay for comparable jobs, but median pay for all jobs.

12 **a.** The next graph shows a plot of the (*grams of fat, calories*) data.

TECHNOLOGY NOTE
The data for Task 12 are in *CPMP-Tools* under Data Analysis, Data, Unit 3.

b. The rule of the line containing (6, 220) and (16, 370) is $y = 15x + 130$. The coefficient of x says that each gram of fat contributes about 15 calories. The 130 says that with no fat content, the food would have 130 calories.

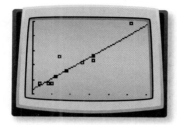

c. The linear regression model for the given (*grams of fat, calories*) data is $y = 16.4x + 126$; quite close to the fit obtained by eyeball fit.

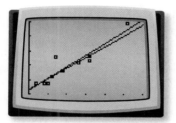

Median Income (in dollars)

Year	Men	Women	Year	Men	Women
1970	6,670	2,237	1990	20,293	10,070
1975	8,853	3,385	1995	22,562	12,130
1980	12,530	4,920	2000	28,343	16,063
1985	16,311	7,217	2003	29,931	17,259

Source: www.census.gov/hhes/income/histinc/p02.html

a. What do you believe are the most interesting and important patterns in these data?

b. Did women's incomes improve in relation to men's incomes between 1970 and 2003?

c. The diagram below shows a plot of the (*years since 1970, median income*) data for women, using 0 for the year 1970. A linear model for the pattern in those data is drawn on the coordinate grid. Write a function rule for this linear model.

Women's Median Income

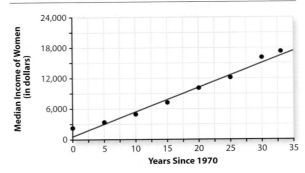

d. Using the linear model, estimate the median income of women in 1983 and 2007.

e. Is it reasonable to use the model to estimate the median income of women in 1963? Explain.

f. Now find the linear regression model for the (*years since 1970, median income*) data. (The data set is in *CPMP-Tools*.) Compare the predictions of that model with your results from Part d.

g. What do the coefficient and the constant term in the linear model of Part f tell about the pattern of change in median income as time passed between 1970 and 2000?

13

a. Student observations about the patterns in the given data will vary. They should at least note that the absolute gap between median men's and women's income grew between 1970 and 2003. In 2003, the greatest gap exists at about $12,672 per year. Calculating median women's income as a fraction of men's income shows that it grew to a somewhat larger fraction (about 34% in 1970 and about 58% in 2003).

b. In absolute terms, women's median income fell farther behind men's income; in relative terms, women seemed to gain (see discussion in Part a).

c. Using coordinates for points (5, 3,000) and (30, 15,000), the function rule is $y = 480x + 600$. (The linear regression model is approximately $y = 474x + 980$.)

d. Using the linear model from Part c, one gets women's income estimates of $6,840 for 1983 (year 13) and $18,360 for 2007 (year 37).

e. The model predicts median women's salary of −$2,700 for 1963 (*year* − 7), raising questions about the value of extrapolating that far backward. Because there is a floor on possible median salaries, it is unlikely that the linear pattern of change would have held in effect for the early years, when salaries in general were low. In fact, an exponential model may be more appropriate for these data as evidenced by the pattern of points above-below-above the modeling line. In addition, since inflation and salary increases are quite often calculated on a percentage basis, one would expect exponential growth. (Unit 5 focuses on exponential growth.)

f. $y = 474x + 980$
This model yields a salary of $7,142 in 1983 and $18,518 in 2007, both fairly close to the estimates in Part d.

g. The coefficient of x tells us that the median income for women is increasing at a rate of $474 per year. The constant term tells us that in 1970 (year zero), the median salary for women should have been approximately $980.

TECHNOLOGY NOTE These data are in the *CPMP-Tools*. Students can access this Web-based tool to find the linear regression model to compare to their model.

DIFFERENTIATION Data being available in *CPMP-Tools* for use with the custom tool "Modeling Line" provides an opportunity for accommodation for students who have difficulty entering data.

Unit 3

Connections

14 Recall the formulas for the circumference of a circle and for the area of a circle.

$$\text{Circumference: } C = 2\pi r \qquad \text{Area: } A = \pi r^2$$

  a. Is circumference a linear function of the radius of a circle? Explain how you know.

  b. What does the formula for circumference tell about how circumference of a circle changes as the radius increases?

  c. Is area a linear function of the radius of a circle? Explain how you know.

  d. What does the formula for area tell about how area of a circle changes as the radius of a circle increases?

15 On hilly roads, you sometimes see signs warning of steep grades ahead. What do you think a sign like the one at the right tells you about the slope of the road ahead?

16 The diagram at the right shows four linear graphs. For each graph I–IV, do the following.

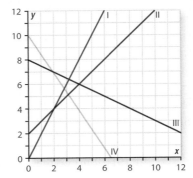

  a. Find the rate at which y changes as x increases.

  b. Write a *NOW-NEXT* rule that describes the pattern of change shown by the graph.

  c. Write a rule for calculating y as a function of x.

  d. Explain how your answers relate to each other.

17 For each table of values (in Parts a and b) use a spreadsheet to reproduce the table.

  • Enter the first value for x from the table in cell **A1** and the corresponding value for y in cell **B1**.

  • Plan the spreadsheet so that: (1) the values of x appear in column **A**; (2) the corresponding values of y are calculated using *NOW-NEXT* reasoning in column **B**; and (3) the corresponding values of y are calculated with an appropriate "$y = ...$" formula in column **C**.

  • Enter formulas in cells **A2**, **B2**, and **C1** from which the rest of the cell formulas can be generated by application of "fill down" commands.

Connections

14 **a.** Circumference is a linear function of radius because the formula is in the general pattern $y = mx + b$ with $m = 2\pi$ and $b = 0$.

b. Circumference increases at a rate of 2π units (about 6.28 units) for each increase of 1 unit in radius.

c. Area is not a linear function of radius, because the variable r is squared. This nonlinearity can also be seen in tables or graphs of (r, A) values. They will not show constant rate of increase in area as radius increases.

d. Area increases at an increasing rate as the radius increases.

15 The overall slope of the road is -0.08, or a drop of 8 feet vertically for every 100 feet ahead horizontally. This small number might suggest a gentle slope, but in fact an 8% grade might feel quite steep in a car or on a bicycle. The meaning of slopes is always relative to the situation.

16 **a.** The rate of change of Graph I is 2, Graph II is 1, Graph III is -0.5, and Graph IV is -1.5.

b. Graph I: $NEXT = NOW + 2$, starting at 0
Graph II: $NEXT = NOW + 1$, starting at 2
Graph III: $NEXT = NOW - 0.5$, starting at 8
Graph IV: $NEXT = NOW - 1.5$, starting at 10

c. Graph I: $y = 2x$ Graph II: $y = x + 2$
Graph III: $y = 8 - 0.5x$ Graph IV: $y = 10 - 1.5x$

d. The rate of increase is the number added or subtracted from *NOW* in the *NOW-NEXT* rule and is the coefficient of the x term in the "$y = ...$" rule. The start value in the *NOW-NEXT* rule is the constant term in the "$y = ...$" rule.

> **INSTRUCTIONAL NOTE**
> Students have difficulty viewing π as a number. If unconvinced, students might create a table of sample (r, c) values and verify that the rate of change in circumference as the radius increases is constant, at about 3.

Unit 3

a.

x	0	1	2	3
y	7	10	13	16

b.

x	5	10	15	20
y	30	20	10	0

18 The relationship between the temperature measured in degrees Celsius and the temperature measured in degrees Fahrenheit is linear. Water boils at 100°C, or 212°F. Water freezes at 0°C, or 32°F.

a. Use this information to write a rule for calculating the temperature in degrees Fahrenheit as a function of the temperature in degrees Celsius.

b. Write a rule for calculating the temperature in degrees Celsius as a function of the temperature in degrees Fahrenheit.

c. Recall the quote from skydiver Michael Wright on page 16 about skydiving from 30,000 feet, "Cool? Yes it is. Cold? You bet. Typically 25 below zero (don't be concerned if that is °F or °C, it's still cold)."

   i. Use your rule from Part a to calculate the equivalent of −25°C in degrees Fahrenheit.

   ii. Use your rule from Part b to calculate the equivalent of −25°F in degrees Celsius.

   iii. Use a table or graph to determine when it really doesn't matter whether one is talking about °F or °C—when the temperature is the same in both scales.

19 The table below shows data from the "Taking Chances" investigation (page 9) in Unit 1.

Number of Trials	20	40	60	80	100	120
Cumulative Profit (in $)	3	7	11	13	15	19

a. Explain why a linear model is reasonable for these data.

b. Is cumulative profit an exact linear function of the number of trials? Explain why or why not.

c. Use a graphing calculator or computer software to find a linear model for the (*number of trials, cumulative profit*) data.

d. What is the coefficient of the independent variable in your model of Part c? What does it tell you about the relationship between cumulative profit and number of trials?

20 Which of these situations involve linear functions and which do not? Explain your reasoning in each case.

a. If a race car averages 150 miles per hour, the distance d covered is a function of driving time t.

b. If the length of a race is 150 miles, time t to complete the race is a function of average speed s.

c. If the length of a race is 150 miles, average speed s for the race is a function of race time t.

17 a.
Spreadsheet sample1.xls

◇	A	B	C
1	0	7	=$A1*3+7
2	=A1+1	=B1+3	
3			
4			
5			

b.
Spreadsheet sample2.xls

◇	A	B	C
1	5	30	=40−2*$A1
2	=A1+5	=B1−10	
3			
4			
5			

18 a. $F = 1.8C + 32$ b. $C = \frac{5}{9}F - \frac{160}{9}$ c. i. $-13°F$

ii. $-32°C$ (Approximate)

iii. $-40°F = -40°C$

19 a. A linear model is reasonable for the given data, since when one makes a plot of the (*trials, profit*) data, the pattern is quite linear overall.

TECHNOLOGY NOTE
The data for Task 19 are in *CPMP-Tools*.

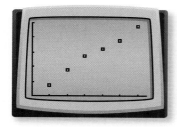 

b. Cumulative profit is not an exact linear function of number of plays since it does not increase at a constant rate as number of plays increases.

c. The linear regression model for the given data is $y = 0.15x + 0.73$.

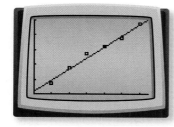 

d. The slope of the regression line is 0.15, predicting profit for the fund-raiser of about 15 cents per play. (When one calculates the theoretical expected value of the game, the result is $\$\frac{1}{6}$. As a decimal this is 0.167, not far from what the data model predicts.)

20 a. $d = 150t$ is a linear function.   b. $t = \frac{150}{s}$ is not linear.

c. $s = \frac{150}{t}$ is not linear.

21 When Robin and Mike had to find a linear function with graph passing through the two points $A(-3, 12)$ and $Q(4, -2)$, they produced the following work.

> The rule will be in the form $y = mx + b$.
> The slope of the line is -2.   (1)
> So, $y = -2x + b$.   (2)
> Since $A(-3, 12)$ is on the line, $12 = -2(-3) + b$ (3)
> So, $6 = b$ (4)
> So, the rule is $y = -2x + 6$ (5)

a. Did Robin and Mike find the correct function rule? If so, what do you think their reasoning was at each step? If not, where did they make an error?

b. Use reasoning similar to that of Robin and Mike to find a function rule for the line through the points $(-2, 2)$ and $(6, 10)$.

c. Use similar reasoning to find a function rule for the line through the points $(3, 5)$ and $(8, -15)$.

22 The diagram at the right shows four *parallel lines*.

a. For each line I–IV, find its slope and a rule for the function with that graph.

b. Write rules for two different linear functions with graphs parallel to the given graphs. Explain how you know that your lines are parallel to the given lines.

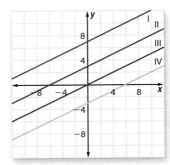

Reflections

23 To use linear functions wisely it helps to be in the habit of asking, "What sorts of numbers would make sense in this situation?" For example, in the function relating profit P to the number of customers n at the Starlight Cinema, it would not make much sense to substitute negative values for n in the formula $P = 6.5n - 2{,}500$. In each of the following situations, decide what range of values for the variables would make sense. It may be helpful to examine tables of values or graphs for some of the functions.

a. Suppose a ball is tossed into the air with an upward velocity of 40 feet per second. Its upward velocity is a function of time in flight, according to the formula $V = 40 - 32T$. Velocity V is in feet per second and time T is in seconds. What range of values for T and V make sense in this context?

b. The resale value R in dollars of an arcade game is given by $R = 500 - 133T$, where T is time in years after the purchase of the new equipment. What range of values for R and T make sense?

LESSON 1 • Modeling Linear Relationships **177**

21 **a.** Yes. Their reasoning was probably as follows:

(1) Slope: $\dfrac{12 - (-2)}{-3 - 4} = \dfrac{14}{-7} = -2$

(2) Since they know the slope, they replace m in $y = mx + b$ with -2 to get $y = -2x + b$.

(3) They replaced x with -3 and y with 12.

(4) They solved $12 = -2(-3) + b$ for b.

(5) They wrote their final rule as $y = -2x + 6$ using the slope and b value they found.

b. The slope is $\dfrac{2 - 10}{-2 - 6} = \dfrac{-8}{-8} = 1$, so $y = 1x + b$. $2 = 1(-2) + b$, so $b = 4$. The rule is $y = x + 4$.

c. The slope is $\dfrac{5 - (-15)}{3 - 8} = \dfrac{20}{-5} = -4$, so $y = -4x + b$. $5 = -4(3) + b$, so $b = 17$. The rule is $y = -4x + 17$.

22 **a.** Graph I: slope is $\dfrac{1}{2}$; $y = \dfrac{1}{2}x + 7$

Graph II: slope is $\dfrac{1}{2}$; $y = \dfrac{1}{2}x + 3$

Graph III: slope is $\dfrac{1}{2}$; $y = \dfrac{1}{2}x$

Graph IV: slope is $\dfrac{1}{2}$; $y = \dfrac{1}{2}x - 3$

b. Answers will vary, but all answers should have $\dfrac{1}{2}$ as the slope. Since the students' two new rules have the same slopes as the given lines, they must be parallel to those lines.

Reflections

23 **a.** In this case, values of T from 0 to about 2.5 seconds make sense. This includes both upward velocity to the apex and downward velocity to the height at which the ball was released. The precise number of seconds to reach the ground depends on how far above the ground the ball is thrown upward. The corresponding range for V is -40 feet per second (downward velocity) to 40 feet per second (upward velocity).

b. Values of T from 0 to about 3.75 years make sense since the resale value R will never be less than \$0. R will range from \$0 to \$500.

c. In one apartment building, new renters are offered $150 off their first month's rent, then they pay a normal rate of $450 per month. The total rent R paid for an apartment in that building is given by $R = 450m - 150$, where m is the number of months. What range of values for R and m make sense?

24 Think about how the values of the constant term and the coefficient are related to the graphs of linear functions. Suppose you enter the rule $y = 2 + 1.5x$ in your graphing calculator and produce a graph in the standard viewing window.

a. How will the graph that you see be different from that of $y = 2 + 1.5x$ if you:

 i. increase or decrease the coefficient of x?

 ii. increase or decrease the constant term?

b. Draw sketches that show possible graphs of functions $y = a + bx$ for each of these cases.

 i. $a < 0$ and $b > 0$ **ii.** $a > 0$ and $b < 0$

 iii. $a < 0$ and $b < 0$ **iv.** $a > 0$ and $b > 0$

25 Answer each of the following questions. In each case, explain how the answers can be determined without actually graphing any functions.

a. Is the point $(-3, -4)$ on the graph of the line $y = \frac{4}{3}x$?

b. Will the graphs of $y = 3x + 7$ and $y = 2 + 3x$ intersect?

c. Will the graphs of $y = 3x + 7$ and $y = 2 - 3x$ intersect?

26 In finding a linear function that models a data pattern, sometimes students simply draw a line connecting two points that are at the left and right ends of the scatterplot. Sketch a scatterplot showing how this simple strategy can produce quite poor models of data patterns.

27 Investigate the linear regression procedure for finding a linear model to fit data patterns.

a. For each of the following data sets, use your calculator or computer software to make a data plot. Then use linear regression to find a linear model and compare the graph produced by the linear regression model to the actual data pattern.

 i.

x	0	1	2	3	4	5	6	7	8
y	3	5	7	9	11	13	15	17	19

 ii.

x	0	1	2	3	4	5	6	7	8
y	1	5	7	9	11	13	15	17	29

 iii.

x	0	1	2	3	4	5	6	7	8
y	4	6	8	10	12	14	16	18	20

 iv.

x	0	1	2	3	4	5	6	7	8
y	1	2	5	10	17	26	37	50	65

c. In this case, values of m from 1 to perhaps 24 or 36 (2 or 3 years) might make sense. The corresponding range for R is from $300 to $10,650 (for 2 years) or $16,050 (for 3 years).

24   **a.** **i.** Increasing the coefficient of x increases the steepness of the slope; decreasing the coefficient of x decreases the slope until it eventually becomes negative (sloping downward left to right) and gets more steeply negative.

   ii. Increasing the constant term slides the graph upward; decreasing the constant term slides the graph downward.

b. **i.** $a < 0$ and $b > 0$ **ii.** $a > 0$ and $b < 0$

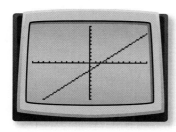   

   iii. $a < 0$ and $b < 0$ **iv.** $a > 0$ and $b > 0$

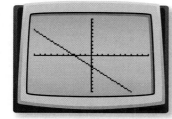   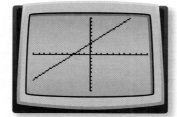

25   **a.** Yes, because $\frac{4}{3}(-3) = -4$.

   b. No, the lines are parallel with the same slope and different y-intercepts.

   c. Yes. The lines have different slopes and thus intersect.

26 At the right is an example of a very poor model, despite the fact that the overall data pattern is quite linear.

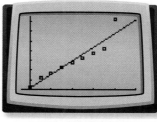

27 **a.** **i.** $y = 2x + 3$ is a perfect fit.

   ii. $y = 2.8x + 0.69$ is a reasonable fit considering the outlier pulling the line up.

   iii. $y = 2x + 4$ is a perfect fit for the given data.

   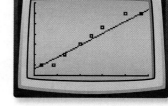

   iv. The linear regression model is $y = 8x - 8.33$.

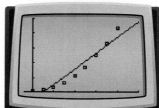   

Unit 3

v.	x	0	1	2	3	4	5	6	7	8
	y	3	8	11	12	12	11	8	3	−4

b. What limitations of the linear regression procedure are suggested by the results of your work in Part a?

28 Consider the information needed to draw a line or find the equation for a line. How many different lines are determined by each of these conditions?

a. pass through the points (−4, 1) and (2, 4)

b. pass through the point (2, 1) and have slope −2

c. pass through the point (2, 4)

d. have slope −2

e. pass through the points (0, 0), (1, 1), and (2, 3)

f. pass through the points (0, 1), (1, 2), (2, 3), and (3, 4)

Extensions

29 In Connections Task 17, you wrote spreadsheet programs to produce tables of x and y values for two linear functions. You can extend those ideas to produce tables of values for any linear function when given only the starting x and y values and the pattern of change in the x and y values, Δx and Δy.

Complete the spreadsheet program begun below in a way that will allow you to enter specific start and change values and see the corresponding table of x and y values automatically.

- Assume that the starting x value will be entered in cell **E1**, the starting y value in cell **E2**, Δx in cell **E3**, and $\Delta y/\Delta x$ in cell **E4**.

- Plan the spreadsheet so that: (1) the values of x appear in column **A**; (2) the corresponding values of y are calculated using *NOW-NEXT* reasoning in column **B**; and (3) the corresponding values of y are calculated with an appropriate "$y = \ldots$" formula in column **C**.

- Enter formulas in cells **A1**, **A2**, **B1**, **B2**, and **C1** from which the rest of the cell formulas can be generated by application of "fill down" commands.

Table of *x* and *y* Values.xls

◇	A	B	C	D	E
1				Start $x =$	
2				Start $y =$	
3				$\Delta x =$	
4				$\Delta y/\Delta x =$	
5					

v. The linear regression model is $y = -.833x + 10.44$.

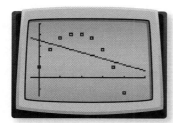 

b. The linear regression procedure works best for data closely resembling a linear pattern, such as in parts i, ii, and iii, but not for data that is curved, such as in parts iv and v.

28
a. Only one since two points determine a unique line

b. Only one since one point and slope determine a unique line

c. An infinite number since one point lies on an infinite number of distinct lines

d. An infinite number of lines have slope -2.

e. No lines since these three points do not lie on a common line

f. Exactly one line passes through these four points.

Extensions

29 **INSTRUCTIONAL NOTE** This task is a particularly tricky one. The formulas in cells **B2** and **C1** are not immediately evident from the information entered in column **E**. It should also be noted that the spreadsheet language complicates the formula which should be entered in **C1**. In mathematics notation, it reads: $C1 = (x - x_0){*}m + y_0$, where m is the slope (value in **E4**). This is a use of the point-slope form for a line which has not yet been introduced to students.

	A	B	C	D	E	
1	=$E$1	=$E$2	=($A1−$E$1)*$E$4+$E$2	Start x =		
2	=$A1+$E$3	=$B1+$E$4*$E$3		Start y =		
3				Δx =		
4				Δy =		
5						
6						

Table of *x* and *y* values.xls

Carefully graph the function $y = \frac{2}{3}x + 1$ on grid paper.

  a. What is the slope of this line?

  b. Using a protractor or mira, carefully draw a line perpendicular to the graph of $y = \frac{2}{3}x + 1$ through the point $(0, 1)$.

  c. What is the slope of the perpendicular line? How does the slope of this line compare to the slope you determined in Part a?

  d. Write an equation for the perpendicular line.

  e. Will all lines having the slope you determined in Part c be perpendicular to all lines having the slope you determined in Part a? Explain why or why not.

  f. Carefully draw another pair of perpendicular lines on grid paper and compare their slopes. Explain your conclusions.

 The graph below illustrates the relationship between time in flight and height of a soccer ball kicked straight up in the air. The relation is given by $H = -4.9t^2 + 20t$, where t is in seconds and H is in meters.

  a. What could it mean to talk about the slope of this curved graph? How could you estimate the slope of the graph at any particular point?

  b. How would you measure the rate of change in the height of the ball at any point in its flight?

  c. What would rate of change in height or slope of the graph tell about the motion of the ball at any point in its flight?

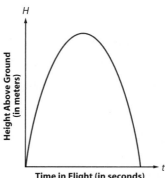

 The following scatterplot shows grade point averages of some Wisconsin students in their eighth- and ninth-grade school years. The graph of $y = x$ is drawn on the plot.

  a. What is true about the students represented by points that lie on the line $y = x$? That lie above the line $y = x$? That lie below the line $y = x$?

  b. The linear regression model for these data is approximately $y = 0.6x + 1.24$. What do the numbers 0.6 and 1.24 tell you about the relationship between eighth- and ninth-grade averages for the sample of students in this study?

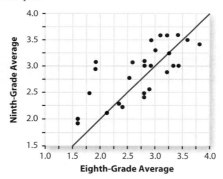

30 **a.** The slope is $\frac{2}{3}$.

b.

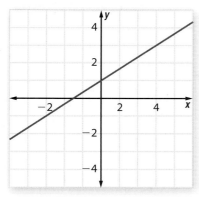

c. The slope is $-\frac{3}{2}$, which is the opposite reciprocal of the original slope.

d. $y = -\frac{3}{2}x + 1$

e. Yes, all lines with slope $-\frac{3}{2}$ are perpendicular to all lines with slope $\frac{2}{3}$. This occurs because all lines with the same slope are parallel to each other. If one line is perpendicular to one of two parallel lines, it must be perpendicular to the other.

f. Students should find similar results to Part e.

31 **a.** Since this graph is not a straight line with a single identifiable slope, it does not make any particular sense to speak of the slope of the whole curve. However, if one focuses on a relatively short segment of the graph, such a segment will look approximately like a line segment. One could estimate the slope of that segment by finding coordinates of the endpoints and using the standard slope calculation procedure.

b. To find the average rate of change between any two points, find the coordinates of those points and find the ratio $\frac{y_2 - y_1}{x_2 - x_1}$.

c. Rate of change or slope will tell vertical velocity of the moving ball because the units are difference in height divided by difference in time. In this case, the units for the rate of change are meters per second.

32 **a.** Points on the graph of $y = x$ represent students with identical grade point averages in the two grades; points above the line represent students who did better in ninth grade; points below the line represent students who did better in eighth grade.

b. The linear regression model would suggest a way of predicting ninth-grade GPA from eighth-grade GPA. The 0.6 as a coefficient of x says that if two students have eighth-grade GPAs that differ by 1, their ninth-grade GPAs will differ by only 0.6. The 1.24 is trickier to interpret. It seems to suggest that a student with GPA of 0 in eighth grade is predicted to have a GPA of 1.24 in ninth grade.

33 In this lesson, you fitted linear function models to data patterns. You can also use lines to analyze data that do not have a functional relationship. For example, consider the next scatterplot that shows average maximum temperatures in January and July for selected cities around the world.

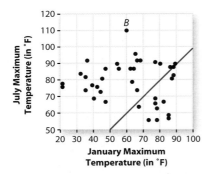

a. What rule describes the line drawn on the scatterplot? If a city is represented by a point on the line, what is true about that city?

b. What is true about the cities represented by points located below the line? Where do you think these cities are located geographically?

c. What is the difference in average temperature in July versus January for the city that is represented by point *B*?

d. Would it be useful to use linear regression on this data set? Explain your reasoning.

34 The 100-meter run for men has been run in the Olympics since 1896. The winning times for each of the years through 2004 are given in the following table.

Winning Times for Men: Olympic 100 Meters

Year	Time (sec)	Year	Time (sec)	Year	Time (sec)
1896	12.0	1936	10.3	1980	10.25
1900	10.8	1948	10.3	1984	9.99
1904	11.0	1952	10.4	1988	9.92
1908	10.8	1956	10.5	1992	9.96
1912	10.8	1960	10.2	1996	9.84
1920	10.8	1964	10.0	2000	9.87
1924	10.6	1968	9.95	2004	9.85
1928	10.8	1972	10.14		
1932	10.3	1976	10.06		

Source: *The World Almanac and Book of Facts 2001*. Mahwah, NJ: World Almanac Education Group, Inc. 2001; www.olympics.com

LESSON 1 • Modeling Linear Relationships **181**

33   **a.** The line drawn on the graph is $y = x$. Points on that line indicate maximum January and June temperatures in cities where those two figures are the same—probably cities on or near the equator.

    b. Cities represented by points below the line have greater maximum January temperature than maximum June temperature. Those cities are probably in the southern hemisphere where summer temperatures occur in November through February.

    c. The difference between maximum June and maximum January temperatures in the city represented by point B is $110 - 60$, or $50°F$.

    d. The data in this plot do not seem to have a linear pattern, so linear regression does not seem a sensible analysis procedure.

a. There are no 100-meter race times for 1916, 1940, and 1944. Why are these data missing?

b. Make a plot of the (*year, time*) data using 1890 as year 0. Then decide whether you think a linear model is reasonable for the pattern in your plot. Explain your reasoning.

c. Find a linear model for the data pattern.

d. Use your model from Part c to answer the following questions.

  i. What winning times would you predict for the 1940 and for the 2008 Olympics?

  ii. In what year is the winning time predicted to be 9.80 seconds or less?

  iii. In what Olympic year does the model predict a winning time of 10.4 seconds? Compare your prediction to the actual data.

e. According to your linear model, by about how much does the men's winning time change from one Olympic year to the next?

f. What reasons can you imagine for having doubts about the accuracy of predictions from the linear model for change in winning time as years pass?

35 Women began running 100-meter Olympic races in 1928. The winning times for women are shown in the table below.

Winning Times for Women: Olympic 100 Meters

Year	Time (sec)	Year	Time (sec)
1928	12.2	1972	11.07
1932	11.9	1976	11.08
1936	11.5	1980	11.60
1948	11.9	1984	10.97
1952	11.5	1988	10.54
1956	11.5	1992	10.82
1960	11.0	1996	10.94
1964	11.4	2000	10.75
1968	11.0	2004	10.93

Source: *The World Almanac and Book of Facts 2001*. Mahwah, NJ: World Almanac Education Group, Inc. 2001; www.olympics.com

34 a. World War I accounts for the 1916 gap, while World War II accounts for the 1940 and 1944 gaps.

b. The data are approximately linear, particularly if you ignore the first data point.

TECHNOLOGY NOTE These data are available in *CPMP-Tools* to use with the custom tool "Modeling Line."

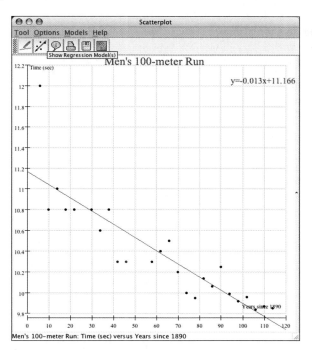

Men's 100-meter Run: Time (sec) versus Years since 1890

c. $y = 11.166 - 0.013x$, where x is the number of years after 1890. This model is used for the remainder of the task.

d. i. 1940: predicted time of around 10.52 seconds; 2008: predicted time of around 9.63 seconds. Compared with the actual data, the 1940 time seems reasonable, while the 2008 prediction seems too low. (Since 1988, the times were all above the regression model, so this may indicate a leveling off of times.)

ii. A winning time of 9.8 seconds is predicted to have occurred around 1996. This fits fairly well with the actual 1996 time of 9.84 seconds, which is just slightly slower.

iii. A winning time of 10.4 seconds is predicted to have occurred around 1949. However, the Olympics only take place every 4 years; the next games were in 1952. This fits fairly well with 10.4 seconds being the winning time in 1952. (Students should be aware that the continuous line models a discrete situation.)

e. The linear regression model predicts a decrease of about $(0.013)(4) = 0.052$ seconds from one Olympic year to the next.

f. It seems reasonable to expect a limit to human ability. Also, the linear model will predict a time of zero eventually.

a. Study the data and describe patterns you see in change of winning race time as years pass.

b. Make a plot and then find a linear model for the data pattern. Use 1900 as year 0.

c. Use your linear model to answer each of the following questions. For questions ii–iv, compare your predictions to the actual data.

  i. What winning time would you predict for 1944?

  ii. What winning time does the model predict for 1996?

  iii. In what Olympic year does the model suggest there will be a winning time of 10.7 seconds?

  iv. According to the model, when should a winning time of 11.2 seconds have occurred?

d. According to the model, by about how much does the women's winning time change from one Olympic year to the next? Compare this to your answer for Part e of Extensions Task 34.

Review

36 Identify all pairs of similar triangles. Then for each pair of similar triangles identify the scale factor.

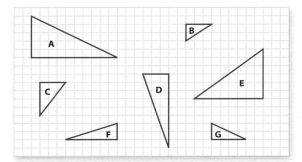

37 Solve each of the following equations for x.

a. $3x = 1$ **b.** $\frac{4}{3}x = 1$ **c.** $4 \div \frac{4}{3} = x$

d. $\frac{4}{5} \div \frac{1}{3} = x$ **e.** $x \div \frac{3}{13} = 1$ **f.** $\frac{1}{5} \div \frac{3}{13} = x$

38 Translating problem conditions into mathematical statements is an important skill.

a. Which of these mathematical statements uses the letters S for number of students and T for number of teachers to express correctly the condition, "At Hickman High School there are 4 student parking places for every teacher parking place"?

$$4S = T \qquad S = 4T \qquad S = T + 4 \qquad T = S + 4$$

35 **a.** Winning times for the Women's Olympic 100-meter race have been declining. No races were run in 1940 or 1944 due to World War II. Some students may note that in 1972, they began recording times to the hundredth of a second.

b.

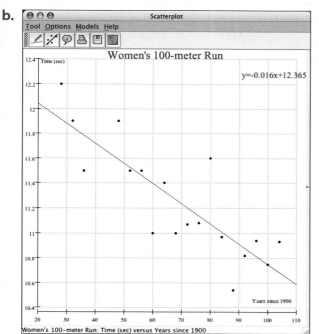

The linear regression model is

$y = 12.365 - 0.016x$,

where x is the number of years after 1900. This model is used for the remainder of the task.

> **TECHNOLOGY NOTE** These data are available in *CPMP-Tools* to use with the custom tool "Modeling Line."

c. **i.** A time of about 11.7 seconds. Compared with the actual data, this seems reasonable when the 1936 time is taken into account.

ii. A time of about 10.83 seconds. This is a bit faster than the actual 1996 time (10.94 seconds), but it does seem a reasonable fit.

iii. The model predicts a winning time of 10.7 seconds around 2004, which is a bit faster than the actual 2004 winning time of 10.93 seconds. The expected time from the linear regression model more accurately reflects what we might expect to happen: the winning time in the next Olympic games would be slightly lower, indicating a faster runner than the previous games.

iv. The model predicts a winning time of 11.2 seconds around 1972. This prediction is a little off considering a time of 11.0 seconds won in both 1960 and 1968. Though some students may point out that an 11.60-second run won in 1980, and the actual winning time in 1972 was 11.07 seconds.

d. The model predicts a decrease of about $(0.016)(4) = 0.064$ seconds from one Olympic year to the next. Based on these models, the winning times for the women are decreasing at a faster rate than are the winning times for the men 0.052 seconds per Olympic year).

> **NOTE** The answers to Problems 36–38 can be found on page T184.

b. Which of these mathematical statements correctly uses T for tax and P for price to express the fact that, "In California stores, an 8% sales tax is charged on the price of every purchase"?

$$0.8T = P \qquad T = 0.8P \qquad P + 0.08 = T \qquad T = 0.08P$$

39 Consider the pentagon shown below.

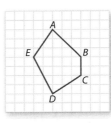

a. How many diagonals does this shape have? Name them.

b. Do any of the diagonals seem to bisect each other? Explain your reasoning.

c. Is $\overline{AD} \perp \overline{BE}$? Explain your reasoning.

40 Smart supermarket shoppers use unit prices to compare values for products.

a. For each of the following comparisons, decide which item is the better buy by finding the unit prices of each.

   i. an 18-ounce box of cereal for $3.50, or a 24-ounce box for $4.50?

   ii. a 32-ounce jar of spaghetti sauce for $4.25, or a 20-ounce jar for $2.50?

   iii. a 6-pack of 20-ounce soft drink bottles for $3.25, or a 12-pack of 12-ounce cans for $4?

b. What is the connection between unit prices and slopes or rates of change for linear functions?

41 Carlos surveyed 120 ninth graders at his school and asked what is their least favorite chore. The results of his survey are provided in the table below.

Chore	Number of People
Cleaning bathroom	45
Mowing lawn	30
Walking the dog	15
Raking leaves	10
Doing the dishes	20

Review

36 △D and △F; scale factor 1.5
△C and △E; scale factor 2
△A and △G; scale factor 2.5

Just in Time

37 **a.** $x = \frac{1}{3}$ **b.** $x = \frac{3}{4}$ **c.** $x = 3$

d. $x = \frac{12}{5}$ **e.** $x = \frac{3}{13}$ **f.** $x = \frac{13}{15}$

Just in Time

38 **a.** $S = 4T$. A common mistake is $4S = T$, in which students are simply translating in the order of the problem's words or using the S as a unit label (as in 4 students equal 1 teacher).

b. $T = 0.08P$

39 **a.** 5; $\overline{AC}$, $\overline{AD}$, $\overline{BE}$, $\overline{BD}$, $\overline{CE}$

b. No, none of the intersections seem to be at the midpoint of diagonals.

c. $\overline{AD} \perp \overline{BE}$ because one segment is vertical and the other is horizontal.

40 **a.** **i.** $\frac{3.50}{18} \approx 0.194$; $\frac{4.50}{24} \approx 0.188$
Best buy is 24-ounce box for $4.50.

ii. $\frac{4.25}{32} \approx 0.133$; $\frac{2.50}{20} = 0.125$
Best buy is 20-ounce jar for $2.50.

iii. $\frac{3.25}{120} \approx 0.0271$; $\frac{4.00}{144} \approx 0.0277$

Best buy is 6-pack of 20-ounce bottles for $3.25.

b. The connection among all of these is the relationship:
total price = unit price × quantity. The unit price is the slope of the total-price graph or the rate at which total price increases as the quantity increases.

a. What percentage of the people surveyed said that cleaning the bathroom is their least favorite chore?

b. Make a bar graph of the survey results.

c. Make a circle graph that displays the results of Carlos's survey.

42 In the figures below, tell whether the gold shape appears to be the reflected image of the green shape across the given line. If it is not, explain how you know.

a.

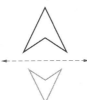

b.

c.

d.

e.

43 On the first three tests in a marking period, D'Qwell has scores of 85, 90, and 75. To earn a B in the course, he needs a mean test score of at least 85, while an A requires a minimum mean score of 93.

a. What score must D'Qwell get on the final test to earn a B?

b. What score, if any, would earn him an A?

c. If D'Qwell has a quiz average of 7 on the first 9 quizzes of a marking period, how will his quiz average change if he gets a 10 on the next quiz?

41 a. $\frac{45}{120} = 37.5\%$

b. **Least Favorite Chores**

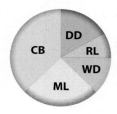

Chore

c. **Least Favorite Chores**

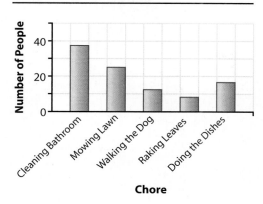

Cleaning bathroom   CB
Mowing lawn   ML
Walking the dog   WD
Raking leaves   RL
Doing the dishes   DD

42 a. No, the gold shape is not congruent to the green shape.

b. Yes

c. No, the gold shape is not the same distance from the line of reflection.

d. Yes

e. No, the gold shape is the same orientation as the green figure.

43 a. 90

b. 122

c. Increase by 0.3 of a point, since $9 \cdot 7 = 63$ and $\frac{73}{10} = 7.3$

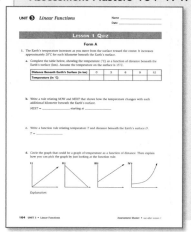

Teaching Resources

Assessment Masters 164–171.

Unit 3

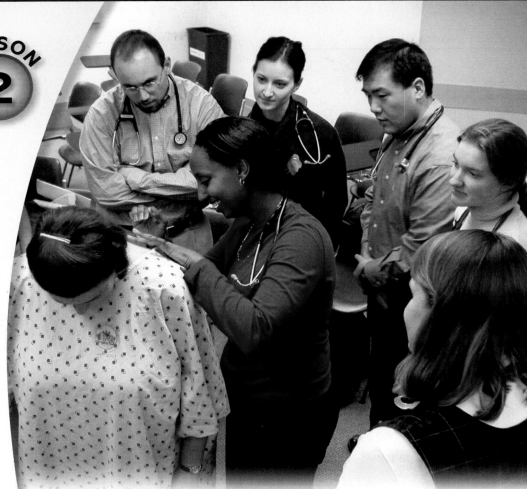

Linear Equations and Inequalities

For most of the twentieth century, the vast majority of American medical doctors were men. However, during the past 40 years there has been a significant increase in the number of women graduating from medical schools. As a result, the percent of doctors who are women has grown steadily to nearly 25% in 2000. The graph on the next page shows this trend.

Linear Equations and Inequalities

This lesson focuses on the formulation and solution of linear equations and inequalities using tables, graphs, and formal reasoning methods.

The lesson is organized into four investigations. The first develops students' ability to represent questions about situations involving linear functions as equations and inequalities and asks them to use tables and graphs to estimate solutions to those equations and inequalities in order to answer the questions. The second investigation develops reasoning methods for solving linear equations by "balancing operations" and "undoing operations." Those methods are extended to linear inequalities in the third investigation. The fourth investigation poses a question of comparing two linear functions representing the costs of two different long-distance companies. Students revisit the idea of representing this question as an equation of the form $a + bx = c + dx$, then an alternative representation as a system of linear equations of the form $y = a + bx$ and $y = c + dx$ is introduced. Students are asked to solve systems of linear equations of this form using tables, graphs, and algebraic reasoning with a single equation in one variable.

It is important to keep in mind that the approach in *Core-Plus Mathematics* emphasizes the functional point of view—for any x there is a corresponding y— and that "find the x that gives the specified y" is only one particular question about a linear function or model with more general information content. This is a significant departure from the traditional view of equations that focuses only on finding the unknown x, but it is a powerful and, with technology, readily accessible extension of the traditional point of view.

Lesson Objectives

- Write linear equations and inequalities to express questions about linear functions
- Estimate solutions to linear equations and inequalities by inspecting appropriate graphs and tables of values and interpret the meaning of the solution in the real-world context
- Use "undoing" and "balancing" methods to solve simple linear equations and inequalities
- Use tables of values, graphs, and symbolic reasoning to solve systems of linear equations of the form $y = a + bx$ and $y = c + dx$

Male and Female Medical Doctors

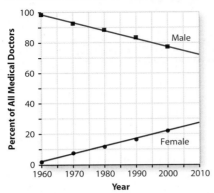

Source: www.ama-assn.org/ama/pub/article/171–195.html

Think About This Situation

Study the trends in the percentage of male and female medical doctors in the United States between 1960 and 2000.

a How would you describe the trends shown in the data plots and the linear models that have been drawn to match patterns in those points?

b Why do you suppose the percentage of women doctors has been increasing over the past 40 years?

c Would you expect the trend in the graph to continue 10 or 20 years beyond 2000?

d How would you go about finding function rules to model the data trends?

e If you were asked to make a report on future prospects for the percentages of male and female doctors, what kinds of questions could you answer using the linear models?

In this lesson, you will explore ways to express questions about linear functions as equations or inequalities. You will use tables, graphs, and symbolic reasoning to solve those equations and inequalities and to interpret your solutions in problem contexts.

Some of the items in the TATS are open to a variety of student responses. Encourage student input by indicating that more than one correct response is possible and that their ideas are valued.

PROMOTING MATHEMATICAL DISCOURSE

Think About This Situation

a The two linear models suggest a steady decline in the percentage of doctors that are male and a steady increase in the percentage of doctors that are female.

b This seems to reflect more general changes in societal norms and expectations. A greater percentage of women have been entering the full-time workforce.

c It seems reasonable to think that the trend might continue for 10 or 20 years beyond 2000, assuming that the factors contributing to this trend continue to be present. One would not expect the trend to continue past the point where the percentage of doctors that are female equals the percentage of doctors that are male, but it does not appear that will happen within the next 20 years.

d To write a function rule for a linear model for either set of data, two methods are available. Data points could be estimated, entered into lists in the calculator or computer, and used to find the linear regression model. Alternatively, the *y*-intercept and a second point on the line could be estimated, the slope between these two points calculated. Then the slope and *y*-intercept could be used to write a function rule.

e Some possible responses: When will the percentage of female doctors be equal to that of male doctors? When will females comprise one-third of all doctors? For how long will the percentage of male doctors remain above 75%? What percentage of U.S. medical doctors will be male in 2025?

Teaching Resources

A possible scenario for Promoting Mathematical Discourse around this TATS is included on the next two pages.

Transparency Master 172.

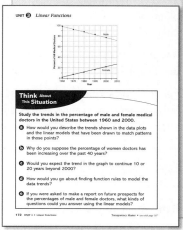

Unit 3

INSTRUCTIONAL NOTE
Part e can be used as a transition to the questions beginning Investigation 1. You may wish to launch the investigation by matching the questions with the equations and inequality.

Promoting Mathematical Discourse

Think About This Situation, *page 187*

Teacher: I am going to read the opening paragraph of the Think About This Situation. I'd like you to follow along with me at the top of page 187. *(Teacher reads aloud.)* Consider the graph of the percentage of male and female medical doctors on this transparency.

Teacher: How would you describe the trends shown in the data plots and the linear models that have been drawn to match those points?

Nadia: I noticed that the percent of female doctors is increasing and that the percent of male doctors is decreasing.

Felix: I noticed the same trend and also noticed that they are both linear patterns of change. It seems obvious because they are straight lines, but it might be important.

Teacher: Why might it be important that the trends are linear?

Calvin: Because that means that the rate of increase and decrease is steady.

Kate: What do you mean by "steady"?

Calvin: Well, since the graphs are lines it means that the increase in the percentage of doctors who are female is the same for each 10-year period between 1960 and 2010. And for the percent of doctors that are male, the percent decrease is the same for each 10-year period. So, it's a steady change.

Teacher: Why do you suppose the percentage of women doctors has been steadily increasing over the past 40 years?

Nate: There are probably more women going to medical school.

Carly: I think that's true. My mom is a doctor and she said when she did her residency, most of the other students were men, but now more of the younger doctors joining the hospital are women.

Forrest: We were just talking about that in our history class the other day. Many fields have more opportunities for women today than they did 40 years ago.

Willow: Yeah. Remember, women couldn't even vote until 1920! Society is a lot different now. I think the graph makes sense, historically.

Teacher: Would you expect the trend in the graph to continue 10 or 20 years beyond 2000?

Nate: I wouldn't. Otherwise, eventually there wouldn't be any male doctors.

Suzuki: Why do you say that?

Nate: I can see it in the graph. If the line representing the percentage of doctors that are male continues, then eventually it will cross the x-axis. That would mean that the percentage of doctors that are male would be 0.

Suzuki: Oh, I see what you are saying.

Brenna: I agree. There is probably a point where the percent of both males and females is closer to 50% and it just stays that way.

Wynn: The trend might be reasonable for the next 10 or 20 years, though.

Teacher: What if we wanted to find function rules to model the data trends. What might we do?

Jean: We know the y-intercept of each line and we could figure out the slope, too.

Teacher: How might someone figure out the slope?

Jean: They could just use the grid of the graph and figure out the change in y and the change in x and compare them.

Teacher: Can someone else tell us what those changes would represent in terms of our problem situation?

Xiang: It would be the change in the percentage of all doctors that are either male or female, depending on what line you are thinking about, compared to the change in the number of years that had occurred.

Teacher: Do we have any other ways to find a function rule for this data?

Marcus: We could just pick any two data points and find the rule. We don't have to choose the y-intercept.

Jean: That's true; but since we need it in our rule anyway, we should probably choose that as one of our points.

Li: We could estimate the data points from our graph and put them in calculator lists, then we could find the linear regression model.

Teacher: Li's suggestion indicated that points would be estimated. Did the other suggestions for finding linear models also use estimates?

Melissa: All of our methods are really using estimates. Even picking points to write a rule meant that we estimated the coordinates from the graph. No points seem to be on grid marks.

Teacher: Let's consider Part e in the Think About This Situation. I will read while you follow along in your book. *(Teacher reads.)* If you were asked to make a report on future prospects for the percentages of male and female doctors, what kinds of questions could you answer using the linear models?

James: I was wondering where the lines might cross.

Teacher: Why did you wonder about that?

James: I was just curious. It seems like a logical question to ask from the graph. I was thinking that it would be when the number of male doctors was exactly the same as the number of female doctors.

Teacher: So, what might be the question we could answer in a report? Someone else try to put James's ideas in the form of a question.

Calvin: When will the percentage of male and female doctors be the same?

Teacher: Any other questions you can think of right now that could be asked and answered in a report?

Marty: What about, "When will the percent of female doctors level off?" Or, even, "Will the percent of female doctors level off?"

Sonya: You could ask similar questions for the percent of male doctors.

Teacher: Any others? *(No new questions surface.)*

Teacher: Let's look at the start of Investigation 1. There are four questions posed here (1)–(4). As you read and talk about the introduction in your groups, be sure that you are able to connect the language in each question to its corresponding equation or inequality (1)–(4).

Investigation 1 · Who Will Be the Doctor?

Several kinds of questions occur naturally in thinking about trends in the percentage of male and female medical doctors. To plan for future educational programs and medical services, medical schools, hospitals, and clinics might wonder:

(1) In 2020, what percent of U.S. medical doctors will be female?
(2) When will the percent of female doctors reach 40%?
(3) When will the percent of male and female doctors be equal?
(4) How long will the percent of male doctors remain above 70%?

The trends in percent of male and female medical doctors can be modeled by these linear functions.

Percentage of Male Doctors: $y_1 = 98 - 0.54t$
Percentage of Female Doctors: $y_2 = 2 + 0.54t$

Here y_1 and y_2 represent the percentage of male and female U.S. medical doctors at a time t years after 1960. An estimate for the answer to question (1) above can be calculated directly from the function giving percentage of female doctors. Since 2020 is 60 years after 1960, to predict the percent of female doctors in that year we evaluate the expression $2 + 0.54t$ for $t = 60$.

$$y_2 = 2 + 0.54(60), \text{ or } y_2 = 34.4$$

The other three questions above can be answered by solving two algebraic equations and an inequality. In each case, the problem is to find values of t (years since 1960) when the various conditions hold.

$$2 + 0.54t = 40 \qquad (2)$$
$$98 - 0.54t = 2 + 0.54t \qquad (3)$$
$$98 - 0.54t > 70 \qquad (4)$$

As you work on the problems of this investigation, keep in mind the following questions:

How do you represent questions about linear functions symbolically?

How can you use tables and graphs to estimate solutions of equations and inequalities?

1 Write equations or inequalities that can be used to estimate answers for each of these questions about the percentage of male and female medical doctors in the United States.

a. In 1985, what percent of U.S. medical doctors were male?
b. When will the percent of male doctors fall to 40%?
c. How long will the percent of female doctors remain below 60%?
d. When will the percent of male doctors decline to only double the percent of female doctors?

Who Will Be the Doctor?

In this investigation, students use tables and graphs to estimate solutions to linear equations and inequalities by inspection, including these cases.

$a + bx = c$
$a + bx \leq c$
$a + bx = c + dx$
$a + bx > c + dx$

Students may have had experience with these tasks and may have a variety of formal routines that they have been trained to use. However, the goal here is for students to realize how those solutions relate to the graph or the table of an entire linear function or pair of functions and to become adept at estimating solutions from graphs and tables.

You may want to use the examples in the introduction to the investigation for a discussion about the connections between the functions that model the trends in the percentages of male and female doctors and the equations and inequalities that represent questions about those trends.

1 **INSTRUCTIONAL NOTE** Students may need reminding that they are not asked to answer these questions, but rather to represent them symbolically as in the examples in the introduction to the investigation. You may need to focus some groups' thinking on what the variables represent as they work on this problem.

a. $y_1 = 98 - 0.54(25)$

b. $98 - 0.54x = 40$

c. $2 + 0.54x < 60$

d. $98 - 0.54x = 2(2 + 0.54x)$

> **TECHNOLOGY NOTE**
> You may wish to have the *CPMP-Tools* CAS available on a class computer for use with Problem 6.

> **COLLABORATION SKILL**
> Seek information and opinions from each other.

Unit 3

2 Write questions about trends in percent of male and female medical doctors that can be answered by solving these equations and inequalities.

a. $98 - 0.54t = 65$

b. $y_2 = 2 + 0.54(50)$

c. $2 + 0.54t < 30$

d. $98 - 0.54t > 2 + 0.54t$

e. $98 - 0.54t = 4(2 + 0.54t)$

Writing equations and inequalities to match important questions is only the first task in solving the problems they represent. The essential next step is to **solve the equations** or to **solve the inequalities**. That is, find values of the variables that satisfy the conditions.

One way to estimate solutions for equations and inequalities that match questions about percentages of male and female medical doctors is to make and study tables and graphs of the linear models.

Trends in Gender

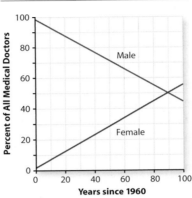

$$y_1 = 98 - 0.54t \quad \text{and} \quad y_2 = 2 + 0.54t$$

t	y₁	y₂
0	98.0	2.0
10	92.6	7.4
20	87.2	12.8
30	81.8	18.2
40	76.4	23.6

t	y₁	y₂
50	71.0	29.0
60	65.6	34.4
70	60.2	39.8
80	54.8	45.2
90	49.4	50.6

3 For the next equations and inequalities:

- Use the tables and graphs above to estimate the value or range of values that satisfy the given condition.

- Explain what each solution tells about the percentages of male and female medical doctors in the United States.

- Be prepared to explain or show how you used a table or graph to estimate the solution.

a. $y_2 = 2 + 0.54(40)$

b. $98 - 0.54t = 90$

c. $98 - 0.54t = 2 + 0.54t$

d. $98 - 0.54t > 80$

e. $y_1 = 98 - 0.54(65)$

f. $2 + 0.54t < 29$

g. $98 - 0.54t = 4(2 + 0.54t)$

h. $70 = 2 + 0.54t$

2
a. When will the percentage of male doctors decline to 65%?

b. What percentage of U.S. medical doctors will be female in 2010?

c. How long will the percentage of female doctors remain below 30%?

d. How long will the percentage of male doctors remain greater than the percentage of female doctors?

e. When was the percentage of male doctors four times the percentage of female doctors?

INSTRUCTIONAL NOTE
Some students find it helpful to have an index card with the expressions in front of them as they do these problems.
98 - 0.54t: % of Male Doctors
2 + 0.54t: % of Female Doctors

3 **INSTRUCTIONAL NOTE** Since students are using the table and graph in the text, their solutions will in many cases be estimates, not the exact solutions that are obtained from algebraic reasoning. You may wish to take time to check students' work after Problem 3. Make sure that students are understanding how to solve these problems before they move on to Problem 4. Some students may find it helpful to write these statements in if-then form. If (what you are given), then (what you are solving for). For example, "If $t = 40$ (or the year is 2000), then y_2 (or the % of female doctors) is about 24%."

Teaching Resources

Transparency Master 173.

UNIT ❸ Linear Functions

Male and Female Doctors
Problem 3

Unit 3

	Solution	Solutions from the Table	Solutions from the Graph	Meaning
a.	$y_2 = 23.6$	Find the value of y_2 on the table when $x = 40$.	Locate 40 on the x-axis, move up to line $y_2 = 2 + 0.54x$, then over to the y-axis.	In 2000, approximately 24% of U.S. medical doctors were female.
b.	$x \approx 15$	Estimate the value of x when $y_1 = 90$, about halfway between $x = 10$ and $x = 20$.	Locate 90% on the y-axis, move across to the line $y_1 = 98 - 0.54x$, then down to the x-axis.	Males represented 90% of the U.S. medical doctors around 1975.
c.	$x \approx 89$	Estimate the x value when $y_1 = y_2$.	Locate the point of intersection of the two lines and move down to the x-axis.	If trends continue, the percentages of male and female doctors will be equal in 2049.
d.	$x < 33\frac{1}{3}$	Find the x values when $y_1 > 80$, prior to about a third of the way between $x = 30$ and $x = 40$.	Locate 80% on the y-axis, move over to the line $y_1 = 98 - 0.54x$. If the line is above 80% to the right or to the left of this point, then read the x value.	Until 1993, the percentage of male doctors was greater than 80%.
e.	$y_1 = 62.9$	Find the y_1 value on the table when $x = 65$, halfway between $y_1 = 65.6$ and $y_1 = 60.2$.	Locate 65 on the x-axis, move up to the line $y_1 = 98 - 0.54x$, then over to the y-axis.	If trends continue, in 2025 about 63% of U.S. medical doctors will be male.
f.	$x < 50$	Find the x values when $y_2 < 29$, prior to $x = 50$.	Locate 29% on the y-axis, move over to the line $y_2 = 2 + 0.54x$, see if it is below 29% to the right or to the left of this point, then move down to the x-axis.	If trends continue, the percentage of female doctors will remain below 29% until 2010.
g.	$x = 33\frac{1}{3}$	Find the x value when $y_1 = 4y_2$. This occurs between $x = 30$ and $x = 40$, closer to $x = 30$.	Find the x value when $y_1 = 4y_2$. This occurs between $x = 30$ and $x = 40$, closer to $x = 30$.	Around 1993, there were four times as many male doctors as female doctors.
h.	$x \approx 126$	Extend the table to find the value of x when $y_2 = 70$. y_2 increases 5.4 for every increase of 10 in x. So when $x = 120$, $y_2 = 66.8$, and when $x = 130$, $y_2 = 72.2$. $y_2 = 70$ at about $x = 126$.	Extend the graph to the right. Locate 70% on the y-axis, move to the line $y_2 = 2 + 0.54x$, then down to the x-axis.	If trends continue, the percentage of female doctors may reach 70% around 2086.

4 Write equations and inequalities to represent the following questions. Then use tables or graphs to estimate the solutions for the equations and inequalities and explain how those solutions answer the original questions. Be prepared to explain or show how you used a table or graph to estimate the solutions.

   a. When will the percent of male doctors decline to 55%?

   b. When will the percent of female doctors reach 35%?

   c. How long will the percent of male doctors be above 40%?

   d. What percent of U.S. medical doctors will be female when you are 20 years old?

   e. Assuming the trends shown in the graph on page 187, when will the percent of male doctors be less than the percent of female doctors?

5 When you solve an equation or inequality, it is always a good idea to check the solution you find.

   a. Suppose one person told you that the solution to $45 = 98 - 0.54t$ is $t = 100$, and another person told you that the solution is $t = 98$. How could you check to see if either one is correct without using a table or a graph?

   b. How do you know whether a solution is *approximate* or *exact*?

   c. If a solution for an equation is exact, does that mean that the answer to the prediction question is certain to be true? Explain.

6 If someone told you that the solution to $2 + 0.54t \le 45$ is $t \le 80$, how could you check the proposed solution:

   a. Using a table?   **b.** From a graph?

   c. Using a computer algebra system?

   d. Without using a table, a graph, or a computer algebra system?

   e. If you wanted to see if a solution is *exact*, which method of checking would you use?

Summarize
the Mathematics

Many questions about linear relationships require solution of linear equations or inequalities, such as $50 = 23 + 5.2x$ or $45 - 3.5x < 25$.

a What does it mean to solve an equation or inequality?

b How could you use tables and graphs of linear functions to solve the following equation and inequality?

    i. $50 = 23 + 5.2x$ **ii.** $45 - 3.5x < 25$

c How can you check a solution to an equation or inequality?

Be prepared to share your ideas with the class.

---

4   **a.** $98 - 0.54x = 55$. In 2040 (that is, when $x = 80$), the percentage of male doctors will have declined to about 55%. In the table and on the graph, $y_1 \approx 55$ when $x = 80$.

INSTRUCTIONAL NOTE In cases where the instructions to students are phrased "be prepared to explain or show," students are not expected to write responses in their notes.

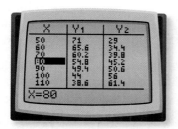
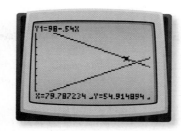

b. $2 + 0.54x = 35$. In 2021 (that is, when $x = 61$), the percentage of female doctors will reach about 35%. In the table and the graph, $y_2 \approx 35$ when $x = 61$.

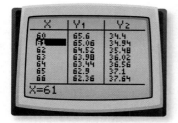
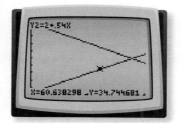

c. $98 - 0.54x > 40$. Until 2067 (that is, when $x < 107$), the percentage of male doctors will remain above 40%. In the table, y_1 is greater than 40 for all entries before $x = 107$. Also, when $x < 107$ on the graph, then $y_1 > 40$.

d. Responses will vary depending on students' ages. For a student born in 1990, $y_2 = 2 + 0.54(50)$. When the student is 20 years old (in 2010, or when $x = 50$), 29% of U.S. medical doctors will be female. In the table and on the graph, $y_2 = 29$ when $x = 50$.

e. $98 - 0.54x < 2 + 0.54x$. After 2049 (that is, when $x > 89$), the percentage of male doctors will be less than the percentage of female doctors. In the table, the y_1 values are less than the y_2 values after $x = 89$. On the graph, the line for y_1 falls below the line for y_2 at $x = 89$.

5   **a.** You should check the suggested solutions by substituting 100, then 98, for x in the expression $98 - 0.54x$ and see whether the computation results in an answer of 45.

b. When you put the solution value into the expression, for an exact solution you get the number on the other side of the equal sign. For example, $98 - 0.54(100) = 44 \neq 45$, therefore 100 is not an exact solution, but could be considered an approximate solution. $98 - 0.54(98) = 45.08$ is very close to 45, but still not an exact solution.

c. An exact result from the use of a linear model is not certain to indicate that a predicted value will actually occur. For example, in the situation examined in this lesson, when $x = 200$ (year 2160), the estimated percentage of male doctors is given as exactly -10. However, negative percentages do not make sense in this situation.

6　**a.** Using the table for $y = 2 + 0.54x$, check that $y = 45$ when $x = 80$, and $y < 45$ when $x < 80$.

b. Check that the point (45, 80) is on the graph of the line $y = 2 + 0.54x$ and that the line is below $y = 45$ to the left of the point (45, 80).

c. You could instruct a computer algebra system (CAS) to **solve(2+0.54*n≤45,n)**. Alternatively, you could use a CAS to evaluate $2 + 0.54n$ at $n = 80$. Then evaluate $2 + 0.54n$ at a number less than 80 to see if the result is less than 45.

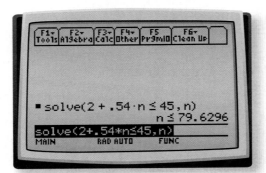
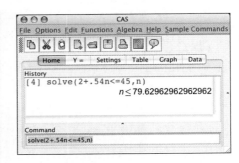

d. You could perform the substitutions suggested above in Part c without the use of a computer algebra system.

e. If you want an *exact* solution, use the computer algebra system or check by substitution. Graphs on a graphing calculator do not allow you to narrow in on exact solutions in all cases.

Summarize
the Mathematics

a To solve an equation or inequality means to find all values of the variables that make the statement true.

b **i.** Use the function $y = 23 + 5.2x$. In the table, find the value of x for which the value of y is 50.
   On the graph of the line, find the value of the x-coordinate of the point on the line that has a y-coordinate of 50.

   ii. Use the function $y = 45 - 3.5x$. In the table, find the values of x for which the values of y are less than 25.
   On the graph of the line, find the values of the x-coordinates that have y-coordinates less than 25 or where the line is below $y = 25$.

c A solution to an equation or inequality can be checked using a table, a graph, or substitution with or without a computer algebra system. (Have students explain how they would check a solution in each of these representations. Discuss the advantages of checking by substitution; you may want to use the examples from Part b for illustration.)

Teaching Resources

A possible scenario for Promoting Mathematical Discourse around this STM is included on the next two pages.

Transparency Master 174.

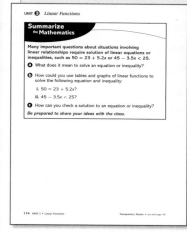

Unit 3

PROCESSING PROMPT We asked for information on _____ and
(*problem #*)

opinions from _____ on our thinking about _____.
(*group member(s)*)

MATH TOOLKIT How is solving an equation different or the same as solving an inequality? How do you check your solutions?

Promoting Mathematical Discourse

Summarize the Mathematics, *page 190*

Teacher: Let's Summarize the Mathematics for this investigation. As you have seen, many questions about problem situations require writing and solving linear equations and inequalities such as these. *(Points to equations on an overhead copy of the STM.)* What does it mean to solve an equation or inequality?

Jeri: It means to find the numbers that work.

Teacher: What does it mean for numbers to "work"?

Cassie: Well, take the equation there: $50 = 23 + 5.2x$. You could look in the table for the number for x that gives a y value of 50.

(The teacher notices that Cassie is picking up Part b to reply more about "how" to solve rather than the meaning of solving, but she chooses to come back to this after they discuss Part b.)

Teacher: How would you get the table if it wasn't given to you in the text?

Ricardo: You would enter $Y = 23 + 5.2X$ in the $Y=$ menu.

Avery: I used a graph of that function.

Teacher: How did you use a graph to find the numbers that worked?

Avery: I found 50 on the y-axis. Then I moved over to the line and read the x-coordinate for that point on the line. It was like this *(motions over and down).*

Teacher: Okay, who can address what it means to solve the inequality $45 - 3.5x < 25$?

Gwen: It's really just the same. When we solved the inequality $45 - 3.5x < 25$ using the table we looked for the x values that made the y values less than 25. On the graph we found 25 on the y-axis, then moved over to the line and read the x-coordinate for that point. Then we had to decide whether our solutions were greater than or less than that x value.

Teacher: Hmm, let's look more specifically at what you are saying. If you were to put the equation $Y = 45 - 3.5X$ in your calculator, how could you use the calculator to help you solve the inequality?

Peyton: I would just trace along the line until I got a y value close to 25. Then check to see which part of the line on each side of that point gives me a y value less than 25.

Teacher: Okay, and in a table, what could you do specifically to solve $45 - 3.5x < 25$?

Cole: We could make a table of x and y values from the $y = 45 - 3.5x$, and look for the table value for x that goes with the table value of 25 for y. Then choose the x values that make the y values less than 25.

Teacher: Let's try that. *(She uses the overhead calculator to display $Y_1 = 45 - 3.5X$ and sets the calculator table to start at 0 and change by 1.)*

Teacher: Cole, could you come up and show us how you would use the table to solve $45 - 3.5x < 25$?

Cole: Sure. Okay, now I just find 25 in the Y_1 column. Hmm, 25 is not a value for Y_1 the way it is set. Let me change the table to go by 0.1. *(Student 5 changes the $\triangle Tbl$ to 0.1.)* Now I just scroll down to find the x value when Y_1 equals 25. We're pretty close here when x is 5.7. I could probably get closer if I change my table to change by 0.01 and start my table at 5.7. There, I am closer to a y value of 25 when x equals 5.71. So, now I can see that my solution is all x values greater than or equal to 5.71.

Amy: We wanted a more accurate answer, so we used a $\triangle Tbl$ of 0.001 and found the solution to be $x > 5.714$.

Teacher: Nice job. Thank you.

Teacher: *(Before moving to Part c the teacher revisits the idea of what it means to solve an equation or inequality from earlier.)* Let's talk for a minute about the difference between what it means to solve an equation or inequality as opposed to *how* to solve one. We have been talking about ways to solve equations and inequalities. The question we started with in the summary was, "What does it *mean* to solve an equation or inequality?" Earlier, Jeri said that it meant to find the numbers that "worked." Jeri, can you talk more about what you meant?

Jeri: Well, when you use one of the methods we just talked about to solve an equation or inequality, we find all the numbers that work.

Teacher: And what does it mean for numbers to work?

Jeri: It means to find all the numbers that make the equation true—well, the equation or inequality.

Teacher: So, solving an equation or an inequality is finding all the numbers that make the equation or inequality a true statement. Does anyone want to add to Jeri's description of what it means to solve?

Teacher: All right, then let's look at the last step in our process. How do you check your solution?

Lilly: You can check the solution for an equality by substituting it back into the expression part of the equation. Like if we thought that $x = 8$ was a solution to $50 = 23 + 5.2x$, we could multiply 8 by 5.2 and add 23 to see if we get 50. If we get 50, then 8 is the solution.

Mason: If you get almost 50, then 8 could be an approximate solution. That is what happened when we did Problem 6.

Gavin: With an inequality like $45 - 3.5x < 25$, you might get a solution like $x > 5.7$. To see if that is correct, you could look at tables to see if all x values greater than 5.7 have y values less than 25. Same thing on the graph, you would look at the x-axis for x values greater than 5.7 and see if the line has y values less than 25 for those x values. If it does, then the solution is right; if no, then the solution is wrong.

Teacher: Let's say that the solution to $45 - 3.5x < 25$ is $x > 5.7$. Without talking to others, take a minute to decide whether that solution is correct. *(Students check solution.)* What did you find?

Maya: Since 5.8 is just larger than 5.7, I calculated $45 - 3.5$ times 5.8 and got 24.7. This is less than 25. Then, I checked $x = 5.6$ and got $y = 2.54$. So the solution $x > 5.7$ makes sense.

Lucas: I think that 5.7 is a good approximation, but when I traced the graph, I found that at about $x = 5.745$, the y value was less than 25 for the first time.

Teacher: Good thinking. In some equations and inequalities, solutions need only be accurate to a whole number, such as chirps per minute for the crickets. In some cases, such as when money is involved, you might wish to have accuracy to hundredths for the cents. In the next investigation, you will be developing ways to solve equations and inequalities by reasoning with the symbols. This will allow you to find exact solutions to inequalities such as the one we were just working with.

✔Check Your Understanding

Bronco Electronics is a regional distributor of electronic products specializing in graphing calculators. When an order is received, the shipping department packs the calculators in a box. The shipping cost C is a function of the number n of calculators in the box. It can be calculated using the function $C = 4.95 + 1.25n$.

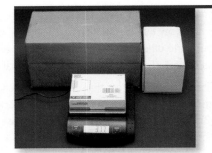

Use your graphing calculator or computer software to make a table and a graph showing the relation between the number of calculators in a box and shipping costs for that box. Include information for 0 to 20 calculators. Use the table, graph, or cost function rule to answer the following questions.

a. How much would it cost to ship an empty box? How is that information shown in the table, the graph, and the cost function rule?

b. How much does the addition of a single calculator add to the cost of shipping a box? How is that information shown in the table, the graph, and the cost function rule?

c. Write and solve equations or inequalities to answer the following questions about Bronco Electronics shipping costs.

   i. What is the cost of shipping 8 calculators?

   ii. If the shipping cost is $17.45, how many calculators are in the box?

   iii. How many calculators can be shipped if the cost is to be held to at most $25?

d. What questions about shipping costs could be answered by solving:

   i. $27.45 = 4.95 + 1.25n$?

   ii. $4.95 + 1.25n \leq 10$?

Investigation 2 — Using Your Head

It is often possible to solve problems that involve linear equations without the use of tables, graphs, or computer algebra systems. Solving equations by symbolic reasoning is called solving *algebraically*. For example, to solve $3x + 12 = 45$ algebraically you might reason like one of these students.

Michael

> The equation tells me to multiply x by 3, then add 12, to get 45. To find out what value of x gives me 45, I have to undo those operations.
>
> That means, starting with 45, I can subtract 12 and then divide by 3 to get
>
> $$x = \frac{(45 - 12)}{3}$$
> $$= \frac{33}{3}$$
> $$= 11$$

> I need a value of x making $3x + 12 = 45$, so the left and right sides are balanced.
>
> If I subtract 12 from both sides, the sides will remain balanced. So, $3x = 33$.
>
> If I divide both sides by 3, the sides will remain balanced. So, $x = 11$.

Natasha

✓ Check Your Understanding

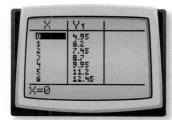 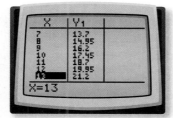 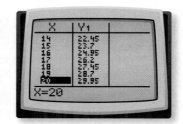

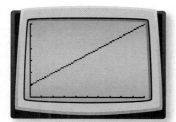 

a. It would cost $4.95 to ship an empty box.

　　Table:　For the entry where $x = 0$, the corresponding y_1 is 4.95.
　　Graph:　If you trace to where $x = 0$, $y_1 = 4.95$.
　　Rule:　　$4.95 + 1.25(0) = 4.95$

b. A single calculator adds $1.25 to the cost of shipping.

　　Table:　The value of y_1 increases by 1.25 for each increase of 1 in x.
　　Graph:　The slope of the graph using any two points on the line is 1.25.
　　Rule:　　The coefficient of n is 1.25.

c. **i.** It costs $14.95 to ship 8 calculators.

　　　$C = 4.95 + 1.25(8); C = 14.95$

　　ii. Ten calculators are in the box if shipping is $17.45.

　　　$4.95 + 1.25n = 17.45; n = 10$

　　iii. Sixteen or fewer calculators can be shipped for $25 or less.

　　　$4.95 + 1.25n \leq 25; n \leq 16.04$

d. **i.** 18; How many calculators could be mailed for a cost of $27.45?

　　ii. 4 or fewer; How many calculators could be mailed for $10 or less?

Investigation 2 　 Using Your Head

This investigation uses a "balancing" strategy and an "undoing" strategy for solving linear equations algebraically. The assumption is that students will come to the course with some strategies for doing this task and thus we do not present detailed step-by-step development of cases. Examples up through equations of the form $a + bx = c + dx$ are considered.

As you work on the problems in this investigation, think about these questions:

Why does solving linear equations by reasoning like that of Natasha and Michael make sense?

How can reasoning like that of Natasha and Michael be used to solve other linear equations algebraically?

1 Analyze the reasoning strategies used by Natasha and Michael by answering the following questions.

  a. Why did Natasha subtract 12 from both sides? Why didn't she add 12 to both sides? What if she subtracted 10 from both sides?

  b. Why did Natasha divide both sides by 3?

  c. What did Michael mean by "undoing" the operations?

  d. Why did Michael subtract 12 and then divide by 3? Why not divide by 3 and then subtract 12?

  e. Both students found that $x = 11$. How can you be sure the answer is correct?

2 Solve the equation $8x + 20 = 116$ algebraically in a way that makes sense to you. Check your answer.

3 A calculator can help with the arithmetic involved in solving equations.

  a. When one student used her calculator to solve an equation by undoing the operations, her screen looked like that at the left. What equation could she have been solving?

  b. What would appear on your screen if you used a calculator to solve the equation $30x + 50 = 120$ by the "undoing" method?

  c. What would appear on your screen if you solved $30x + 50 = 120$ in just one step?

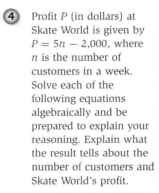

4 Profit P (in dollars) at Skate World is given by $P = 5n - 2{,}000$, where n is the number of customers in a week. Solve each of the following equations algebraically and be prepared to explain your reasoning. Explain what the result tells about the number of customers and Skate World's profit.

  a. $-500 = 5n - 2{,}000$

  b. $0 = 5n - 2{,}000$

  c. $1{,}250 = 5n - 2{,}000$

As examples of linear equations get more complex, involving parentheses and combination of terms, it is customary to derive a collection of formal symbol manipulation rules from the field properties of the real number system. Unfortunately, when those properties are learned in a fairly abstract setting (even with illustrative numerical examples for each), students generally find it very difficult to absorb and recall the rules correctly to know when to use them in other situations. For this reason and the availability of calculator methods, both tabular and graphical, the textbook presents an informal "undoing" or "operation reversibility" approach to solving equations where reasoning in a problem context very strongly suggests the correct operations on symbolic expressions. In Lesson 3, Investigation 2, some of the principles that abstract the operations will be stated explicitly. Other field properties will be introduced in later courses.

  a. Natasha subtracted 12 because this will "undo" the addition of 12 in the equation. If she only subtracted 10, it would not fully "undo" the addition of 12.

   b. Natasha divided by 3 to "undo" the multiplication by 3 in the equation.

   c. "Undoing" the operations means performing some other operation that will "cancel out" the one you are undoing.

   d. He must undo the operations in the reverse order that they are done in the equation. (If you put on socks, then shoes, you must take off your shoes first, then your socks.)

   e. Substitute 11 for x in the equation, then see whether $3(11) + 12 = 45$.

2 $x = 12$; $8(12) + 20 = 116$, so 12 is the correct solution.

3 **a.** $5x + 15 = 35$

   b.
   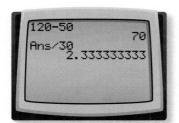

   c.

4 **a.** $n = 300$. Skate World will have a profit of $-\$500$ if it has 300 customers in a week.

   b. $n = 400$. Skate World will break even (have a $0 profit) if it has 400 customers in a week.

   c. $n = 650$. Skate World will have a profit of $1,250 if it has 650 customers in a week.

5. Martin and Anne experimented with the strength of different springs. They found that the length of one spring was a function of the weight upon it according to the function $L = 9.8 - 1.2w$. The length was measured in inches and the weight in pounds. To determine the weight needed to compress the spring to a length of 5 inches, they reasoned as follows.

We need to solve $9.8 - 1.2w = 5$.

Martin:

If $9.8 - 1.2w = 5$, then
$9.8 = 5 + 1.2w$.
Then $4.8 = 1.2w$.
So, $w = \frac{4.8}{1.2}$,
or $w = 4$.

Anne:

If $9.8 - 1.2w = 5$, then
$9.8 - 5 = 1.2w$.
This means that $4.8 = 1.2w$.
So, $w = \frac{4.8}{1.2}$,
or $w = 4$.

a. Is each step of their reasoning correct? If so, how would you justify each step? If not, which step(s) contains errors and what are those errors?

b. What does the answer tell about the spring?

6. Bronco Electronics received bids from two shipping companies. For shipping n calculators, Speedy Package Express would charge $3 + 2.25n$ dollars. The Fly-By-Night Express would charge $4 + 2n$ dollars. Solve the equation $3 + 2.25n = 4 + 2n$. Explain what the solution tells about the shipping bids.

Summarize
the Mathematics

It is often relatively easy to solve problems involving linear equations algebraically.

a Suppose you are going to tell someone how to solve an equation like $43 = 7 - 4x$ algebraically. What steps would you recommend?

b When would you recommend solving an equation algebraically? When would you advise use of a table, graph, or computer algebra system?

Be prepared to explain your procedure and thinking with the class.

⑤ **a. INSTRUCTIONAL NOTE** Students may have other ways of solving and should be encouraged to compare their own solutions with those presented to look for connections.

Each step of the reasoning for both Martin and Ann is correct. Martin uses a balancing approach. First he adds $1.2w$ to both sides, then he subtracts 5 from both sides, and finally he divides both sides by 1.2.

Ann reasons from the arithmetic property that if $a - b = c$, then $a - c = b$, then calculates $9.8 - 5$, then reasons from the arithmetic property that if $ab = c$, then $c \div a = b$, and finally calculates $4.8 \div 1.2$.

b. A weight of 4 lbs will compress the spring to a length of 5 inches.

⑥ **INSTRUCTIONAL NOTE** Students may resort to using a graph or table to solve this, but encourage them to think through the algebraic solution by extending the undoing idea. Students will work more with this type of algebraic solution in Investigation 4.

The solution below involves implicit applications of several properties. For instance, simplifying $2.25n - 2n$ formally relies on a Distributive Property of Multiplication over Subtraction. At this point, students should rely on their natural context-guided intuition to make that simplification. Formal articulation of the Distributive Property and the connection between subtraction and addition occurs in Lesson 3.

This equation might be solved like this, with informal reasoning applied:

$3 + 2.25n = 4 + 2n$	Undo adding 3 by subtracting 3.
$2.25n = 1 + 2n$	Undo adding $2n$ by subtracting $2n$.
$0.25n = 1$	Undo multiplying by 0.25 by dividing by 0.25.
$n = 4$	

Shipping costs for the two companies are equal for 4 calculators in a box.

Summarize
the Mathematics

Seek a variety of responses for this Summarize the Mathematics.

(a) Sample response: Undo the addition of 7 by subtracting 7 from both sides to get $36 = -4x$. Then divide both sides by -4 to get $x = -9$.

(b) Responses may vary. If the equation has multiple-digit numbers, several operations, or complicated expressions, then using a table, graph, or computer algebra system would be advised.

Teaching Resources

Transparency Master 175.

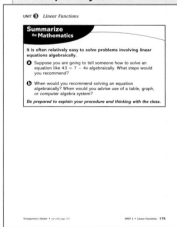

UNIT 3 *Linear Functions*

Summarize
the Mathematics

It is often relatively easy to solve problems involving linear equations algebraically.

ⓐ Suppose you are going to tell someone how to solve an equation like $43 = 7 - 4x$ algebraically. What steps would you recommend?

ⓑ When would you recommend solving an equation algebraically? When would you advise use of a table, graph, or computer algebra system?

Be prepared to explain your procedure and thinking with the class.

Transparency Master • use with page 193   UNIT 3 • Linear Functions **175**

MATH TOOLKIT What is meant by "solve an equation algebraically"? What are some advantages of solving algebraically?

✓ Check Your Understanding

When a soccer ball, volleyball, or tennis ball is hit into the air, its upward velocity changes as time passes. **Velocity** is a measure of both speed and direction. The ball slows down as it reaches its maximum height and then speeds up in its return flight toward the ground. On its way up, the ball has a positive velocity, and on its way down it has a negative velocity. Suppose the upward velocity of a high volleyball serve is given by the function:

$$v = 64 - 32t$$

where t is time in seconds and v is velocity in feet per second.

a. Solve each of the following equations algebraically. Show your reasoning and explain what each solution tells about the flight of the ball.

  i. $16 = 64 - 32t$

  ii. $64 - 32t = -24$

  iii. $64 - 32t = 0$

  iv. $96 = 64 - 32t$

b. If you were to estimate solutions for the equations in Part a using a table of (t, v) values for the function $v = 64 - 32t$, what table entries would provide each solution? Record your answers in a table like this.

Equation	t	v
i		
ii		
iii		
iv		

c. If you were to estimate solutions for the equations in Part a using a graph of $v = 64 - 32t$, what points would provide each solution? Record your answers on a sketch of the graph, labeling each point with its equation number and coordinates.

d. What is the rate of change in velocity as time passes? What units describe this rate of change? (This rate of change represents the *acceleration* due to gravity.)

Investigation 3 · Using Your Head ... More or Less

The reasoning you used in Investigation 2 to solve linear equations can be applied to solve linear inequalities algebraically. However, unlike equations, the direction of an inequality matters. If $x = 2$, then $2 = x$. On the other hand, $3 < 5$ is true but $5 < 3$ is not. As you work through the problems of this investigation, make notes of answers to the following question:

How can you solve a linear inequality algebraically?

✓ Check Your Understanding

a. **INSTRUCTIONAL NOTE** Students may be able to guess solutions to several of these equations. Ask them to show reasoning that would apply as well, when the numbers are not so simple.

   i. $t = 1.5$; the ball is moving upward and its velocity has slowed to 16 feet per second after 1.5 seconds.

   ii. $t = 2.75$; the ball is falling back toward the volleyball court at a speed of 24 feet per second after 2.75 seconds in flight.

   iii. $t = 2$; the velocity is zero after 2 seconds in flight. The ball momentarily stops its upward flight and begins to fall with negative velocity. (This puzzles many people.)

   iv. $t = -1$; the ball will not ever have a velocity of 96 feet per second because the time -1 is not realistic for this situation.

b.

Equation	t	v
i	1.5	16
ii	2.75	−24
iii	2	0
iv	−1	96

c. Each equation can be solved using the graph by tracing to the desired coordinate pair, or by locating the desired y-coordinate on the y-axis, going over to the line, then up or down to the x-axis. The points listed in Part b should be labeled on the graph.

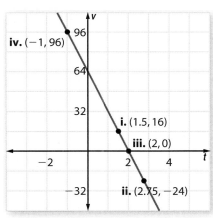

d. The rate of change in velocity as time passes is -32 feet per second per second.

Investigation 3 Using Your Head ... More or Less

In this investigation, students explore the effect of multiplying or dividing an inequality by a negative number. The techniques for solving equations by undoing are then extended to solve simple linear inequalities.

1 Begin by exploring the effect of multiplying both sides of an inequality by a negative number.

   a. Consider the following true statements.

   $$3 < 7 \qquad -2 < 1 \qquad -8 < -4$$

   For each statement, multiply the number on each side by -1. Then indicate the relationship between the resulting numbers using $<$ or $>$.

   b. Based on your observations from Part a, complete the statement below.

   If $a < b$, then $(-1)a$ __?__ $(-1)b$.

   c. Next, consider relations of the form $c > d$ and multiplication by -1. Test several examples and then make a conjecture to complete the statement below.

   If $c > d$, then $(-1)c$ __?__ $(-1)d$.

2 Pairs of numbers are listed below. For each pair, describe how it can be obtained *from the pair above it*. Then indicate whether the direction of the inequality stays the same or reverses. The first two examples have been done for you.

$9 > 4$	Inequality operation	Inequality direction
12 _>_ 7	add 3 to both sides	stays the same
24 _>_ 14	multiply both sides by 2	stays the same
a. 20 _?_ 10		
b. -4 _?_ -2		
c. -2 _?_ -1		
d. 8 _?_ 4		
e. 6 _?_ 2		
f. -18 _?_ -6		
g. 3 _?_ 1		
h. 21 _?_ 7		

3 Look back at your answers to Problem 2 and identify cases where operations reversed the direction of inequality.

   a. What operations seem to cause this reversal of inequality relationships?

   b. See if you can explain why it makes sense for those operations to reverse inequality relationships. Compare your ideas with those of your classmates and resolve any differences.

4 In Investigation 1, you saw that the percentages of male and female doctors can be estimated from the number of years since 1960 using the following functions.

   Percentage of Male Doctors:

   $y_1 = 98 - 0.54t$

   Percentage of Female Doctors:

   $y_2 = 2 + 0.54t$

1 **a.** It may be easier for students to see the connection if they organize their work like this.

$3 < 7$	$-2 < 1$	$-8 < -4$
$-3 > -7$	$2 > -1$	$8 > 4$

b. If $a < b$, then $(-1)a$ _$>$_ $(-1)b$.

c. If $c > d$, then $(-1)c$ _$<$_ $(-1)d$. Responses will vary. Sample responses are:

$7 > 3$	$1 > -2$	$-4 > -8$
$-7 < -3$	$-1 < 2$	$4 < 8$

2

	Inequality Operation:	**Inequality Direction:**
a. 20 _$>$_ 10	subtract 4 from both sides	stays the same
b. -4 _$<$_ -2	divide both sides by -5	reverses
c. -2 _$<$_ -1	divide both sides by 2	stays the same
d. 8 _$>$_ 4	multiply both sides by -4	reverses
e. 6 _$>$_ 2	subtract 2 from both sides	stays the same
f. -18 _$<$_ -6	multiply both sides by -3	reverses
g. 3 _$>$_ 1	divide both sides by -6	reverses
h. 21 _$>$_ 7	multiply both sides by 7	stays the same

3 **a.** Multiplying or dividing both sides of an inequality by a negative number will reverse the direction of the inequality.

b. Students will present various reasons for why the inequality reverses, and should be able to explain their reasoning to others.

Teaching Resources

Student Master 176.

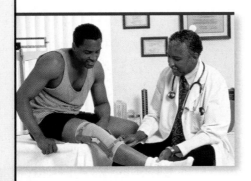

When their class was asked, "For how long will the majority of U.S. medical doctors be male?",

Taylor wrote this inequality: $98 - 0.54t > 50$.

Jamie wrote this inequality: $2 + 0.54t < 50$.

a. Explain the reasoning that Jamie may have used to create her inequality. Do you think that the solution to either inequality will answer the question? Why or why not?

b. Taylor's and Jamie's solutions are given below. Based on what you know about the percentages of male and female doctors in the United States, which answer makes more sense? Why?

Taylor's solution:	**Jamie's solution:**
I need to solve $98 - 0.54t > 50$.	I need to solve $2 + 0.54t < 50$.
Subtract 98 from both sides: $-0.54t > -48$	Subtract 2 from both sides: $0.54t < 48$
Then divide both sides by -0.54: $t > 88.9$	Then divide both sides by 0.54: $t < 88.9$
So the majority of U.S. medical doctors will be males beginning approximately 89 years from 1960, or after 2049.	So the majority of U.S. medical doctors will be males for approximately 89 years from 1960, or until 2049.

c. What is the error in the incorrect solution?

5 Solve the following linear inequalities using reasoning similar to that used in solving simple linear equations algebraically. Pay careful attention to the direction of the inequality. Be sure to check your solutions.

a. $1.5t - 150 > 450$ **b.** $4.95 + 1.25n \le 10$ **c.** $45 - 3.5x < 25$

d. $32 \le 6p - 10$ **e.** $100 > 250 - 7.5d$

Summarize
the Mathematics

Just as with linear equations, it is often relatively easy to solve linear inequalities algebraically.

a Suppose you are going to tell someone how to solve an inequality like $7 - 4x > 43$ algebraically. What steps would you recommend? Why?

b How would you check your solution to an inequality like $7 - 4x > 43$? To an inequality like $7 - 4x \ge 43$?

c How is solving a linear inequality algebraically similar to, and different from, solving a linear equation algebraically?

d When would you recommend solving an inequality like the ones you've seen so far algebraically? When would you advise use of a table, graph, or computer algebra system?

Be prepared to explain your procedures and reasoning.

4 **INSTRUCTIONAL NOTE** This problem is intended to help students make sense of the need to reverse the direction of the inequality when multiplying or dividing both sides by a negative number while solving. Through the use of a familiar context, students can reason what the solution should be.

a. Either inequality will answer the question.

   If the majority of medical doctors are male, then the minority of medical doctors are female. So another way of asking the question is: How long will females remain the minority of U.S. medical doctors? Alternatively, the total percentage of male and female doctors will always be 100, so when the percentage of male doctors is greater than 50%, the percentage of female doctors must be less than 50%.

b. Currently, most doctors are male, so Taylor's answer of the majority of doctors being male after 2049 does not make sense at all. Jamie's solution of mostly male doctors until 2049 seems reasonable.

   (This could be checked using specific values greater than or less than 89 also. The exact solution is $x < 88\frac{8}{9}$ years.)

c. Taylor divided both sides of the inequality by -0.54. Taylor should have reversed the direction of the inequality at this step.

5 **INSTRUCTIONAL NOTE** Encourage students to use their calculators for the arithmetic so they can focus thought and time on choosing appropriate solving operations. For each solution, students should check their result. One efficient method to check is to use a table. Set the table start to the value in the solution and a table increment that allows you to find the values just less than or greater than the solution value.

a. $1.5t - 150 > 450$
   $1.5t > 600$
   $t > 400$

b. $4.95 + 1.25n \le 10$
   $1.25n \le 5.05$
   $n \le 4.04$

c. $45 - 3.5x < 25$
   $-3.5x < -20$
   $x > 5.71$

d. $32 \le 6p - 10$
   $42 \le 6p$
   $7 \le p$ or $p \ge 7$

e. $100 > 250 - 7.5d$
   $-150 > -7.5d$
   $20 < d$ or $d > 20$

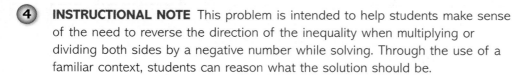

Unit 3

✔Check Your Understanding

In Lesson 1, you examined the effects of inflation and depreciation. You developed the following functions to model the change over time in the price of a new video arcade game and the change over time in the resale value of a game purchased new in 2002. Here, x represents years since 2002.

Price of New Game: $y_1 = 500 + 50x$

Resale Value of Used Game: $y_2 = 500 - 133x$

Solve each of the following inequalities algebraically.

- Show your reasoning in finding the solutions.
- Check your solutions.
- Explain what each solution tells about game prices.
- Make a table and sketch a graph of the price functions for $0 \leq x \leq 5$. Highlight the table entries and graph points that indicate the solutions for each inequality.

a. $500 + 50x > 600$

b. $500 - 133x < 100$

c. $700 \geq 500 + 50x$

d. $300 \leq 500 - 133x$

Investigation 4 ⟩ Making Comparisons

In many problems involving linear functions, the key question asks for comparison of two different functions. For example, in Investigation 1 of this lesson you used linear models to compare the patterns of change in percentage of female and male doctors in the United States. In this investigation, you will examine methods for making sense of situations modeled by other *systems of linear equations*.

Increasing numbers of businesses, including hotels and cafés, are offering access to computers with high-speed Internet. Suppose that while on vacation Jordan would like to read and send e-mail, and two nearby businesses, Surf City Business Center and Byte to Eat Café, advertise their Internet services as shown at the top of the next page.

Summarize
the Mathematics

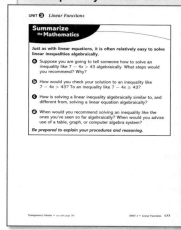

a One sample response: Undo the addition of 7 by subtracting 7 from both sides to get $36 < -4x$. Then divide both sides by -4 and reverse the direction of the inequality to get $-9 > x$, or $x < -9$. (Encourage students to generalize this process.)

b To check either a less-than or less-than-or-equal-to inequality, you need to substitute solution values into the inequality. One efficient way to do this is with tables. (See Problem 4 of this investigation.) The solution boundary value should result in the exact or approximate numerical value (43) when substituted into the variable expression $(7 - 4x)$. Substituting values under and over the solution boundary value into the expression allows you to check the accuracy of the direction of the inequality sign.

c You can apply the same "undoing" strategies to solve a linear inequality as were used to solve linear equations, but when you multiply or divide by a negative number, the direction of the inequality reverses.

d Students should indicate that fairly simple inequalities are typically easier to solve algebraically. If the inequality has multiple digit numbers, several operations, or complicated expressions, using a table, graph, or computer algebra system would be advised. Because of the added complication with an inequality, it may be useful to use a table or graph to check solutions obtained algebraically.

MATH TOOLKIT You may wish to have students summarize methods for solving and checking a linear equality or inequality using examples.

✓ Check Your Understanding

a. $x > 2$; After 2004, the price of a new game will be more than $600. In a table or graph of $y_1 = 500 + 50x$, look for values of x when $y_1 > 600$.

b. $x > 3$; The resale value of a game purchased in 2002 will be less than $100 after 2005. In a table or graph of $y_2 = 500 - 133x$, look for values of x when $y_2 < 100$.

c. $4 \geq x$ or $x \leq 4$; The price of a new game will be $700 or less through 2006. In a table or graph of $y_1 = 500 + 50x$, look for values of x when $y_1 \leq 700$.

d. $1.5 \geq x$ or $x \leq 1.5$; The resale value of a game purchased in 2002 will be at least $300 for a year and a half. In a table or graph of $y_2 = 500 - 133x$, look for values of x when $y_2 \geq 300$.

PROMOTING MATHEMATICAL DISCOURSE

TECHNOLOGY NOTE Remind students to use the table feature of the calculator to help set an appropriate window for these functions. Because $0 \leq x \leq 5$ is given, students should note that the lowest value for either function is -165 and the greatest is 750.

Unit 3

Summarize the Mathematics, *page 196*

Teacher: I notice that some of your groups are not finished with Part e of Problem 5, but I would like all groups to spend a few minutes thinking about the questions in the Summarize the Mathematics so that we can have a class discussion. Those groups that need to finish Problem 5 can do that as part of their homework this evening and check results with each other first thing tomorrow.

In Investigation 3, you learned how to solve linear equations without using tables, graphs, or a computer algebra system. In this investigation, you learned how to solve linear inequalities by reasoning with the symbols themselves. Take a few minutes to discuss the questions in Parts a–d with your group members. These questions will help us think about similarities and differences in solving linear equations and linear inequalities.

(Students work for 5 minutes.)

Teacher: What steps did your group recommend for solving $7 - 4x > 43$ without the use of a table, graph, or computer algebra system?

Olivia: We said that we would first undo adding 7 by subtracting 7 from both sides of the inequality. That would give $-4x > 36$. Then we would undo multiplying by -4 by dividing both sides by -4. That would give the solution $x < -9$. We switched the inequality sign because we divided by a negative number.

Logan: We recommended just calculating $\frac{43 - 7}{-4}$ in one step and writing $x < -9$. It makes more sense to us this way.

Teacher: Did some of you recommend solving the inequality using different steps? *(No response)* Earlier in this lesson, you summarized how you would check the solution to an equation. Let's discuss your checking methods for the inequality $7 - 4x > 43$.

Cooper: We checked by putting -10 in for x because the solutions should be less than -9. We did $7 - 4(-10) = 7 + 40 = 47$. Since $43 < 47$ is a true statement, -10 is a solution. We then checked x values of -9 and -8 to see if we got true statements. We didn't.

Anthony: We used the tables to quickly see what $7 - 4x$ was for lots of values. We put the expression $7 - 4x$ in the Y= menu and set the tables to start at -9 and change one-tenth at a time. It showed that at $x = -9$, y was exactly 43, not greater than 43. It also showed that we had the direction of the inequality correct because the values when x was less than -9 were greater than 43.

Teacher: How would you compare these two methods?

Lauren: They are really about the same, since both look at values on both sides of the solution, $x < -9$. I like to use the tables because you can see lots of y values quickly instead of doing the arithmetic for each calculation with x. It's faster.

Carl: One difference is that the table allows you to easily check values for numbers between -10 and -9. Like you could check really, really close to -9. You might not want to do that by substituting that value into $7 - 4x$.

Teacher: Did anyone check using a graph?

Jasmine: We checked by using a graph of $y = 7 - 4x$ and tracing to where x was -9. We did not end up exactly at -9, but as soon as we traced from to the right of -9 to the left of -9, the y-coordinate went from just under 43 to over 43. So, our solution of $x < -9$ made sense.

Teacher: When you thought about checking the greater than or equal to inequality $7 - 4x \geq 43$, did your thinking change from when you considered only greater than?

Cody: It really wasn't any different for us. When we used the tables, we could see that when x was -9, y was exactly 43. We used the same method, but needed to check the equal part of the inequality, too.

Eric: When we checked the solution for $7 - 4x > 43$, we just checked numbers on both sides of -9, we did not substitute -9 into $7 - 4x$. For the less than or equal to statement, we needed to check -9, too.

Nicole: We used the graph to check both solutions. There was no difference.

Jose: When we traced on the graph, the cursor jumped over $x = -9$. We didn't see exactly $x = -9$. How do we know for sure what the y value is?

Chris: Even when you zoom in on the graph, you may not be able to see exactly $x = -9$. So, substituting -9 with tables or mentally is probably the best way to check the equality part.

Teacher: Let's move to Part c. How is solving a linear inequality by reasoning with the symbols similar to and different from solving a linear equation with symbols?

Travis: Solving inequalities and equations is really the same. You use undoing and balancing methods.

Cody: The one tricky part to watch out for when you are solving an inequality is multiplying or dividing by a negative number. When you do that, you also have to change the direction of the inequality.

Teacher: Now think about the different methods you used to solve equations and inequalities—reasoning directly with symbols, graphs, tables, and computer algebra systems. You discussed when to use each tool in Part d. What did you think?

Mariah: We decided that we would use the symbols when the problem had easy numbers and when the equation was not too complicated.

Rick: We agreed. We thought we would use tables more for checking and when the numbers were large or had many decimals. Graphs are useful when the numbers are messy also, but they do not always give you the exact numbers you want to check. Graphs are useful when you only need approximate solutions.

Carlos: We said we would never use a computer algebra system because we do not really know much about them yet.

Meg: Yeah, we did not learn how to solve inequalities with them. Will we do that later?

Teacher: Well, you might like to just try it on your own during class next week. Or you may check out a TI-89 to use at home if you would like. In the Check Your Understanding, you will be using your methods for solving equations and inequalities to help find answers to questions that involve two different linear models.

Surf City Business Center	Byte to Eat Café
Surf the Internet ~ just $3.95 per day plus $0.05 per minute.	Stop in for a byte— high-speed Internet access for $2 per day plus $0.10 per minute.

As you explore the question of which business offers a more economical deal, keep in mind this question:

How can you represent and solve problems involving comparisons of two linear functions?

1 For both businesses, the daily charge is a function of the number of minutes of Internet use.

a. For each business, write a rule for calculating the daily charge for any number of minutes.

b. What are the daily charges by each business for customers using 30 minutes?

c. How many minutes could Jordan spend on the Internet in a day for $10 using the pricing plans for each of the two businesses?

d. For what number of minutes of Internet use in a day is Surf City Business Center more economical? For what number of minutes of Internet use in a day is Byte to Eat Café more economical?

e. Do you or someone you know use the Internet? For what purposes? Which pricing plan would cost less for this kind of use of the Internet?

2 To compare the price of Internet access from the two businesses, the key problem is to find the number of minutes for which these two plans give the same daily charge. That means finding a value of x (number of minutes) for which each function gives the same value of y (daily cost).

a. Use tables and graphs to find the number of minutes for which the two businesses have the same daily charge. Indicate both the number of minutes and the daily charge.

b. When one class discussed their methods for comparing the price of Internet access from the two businesses, they concluded, "The key step is to solve the equation $3.95 + 0.05x = 2 + 0.10x$." Is this correct? Explain your reasoning.

c. Solve the equation in Part b algebraically. Show your reasoning.

In this investigation, students will revisit the comparison of two linear functions and examine the solution of a system of linear equations of the form $y = a + bx$ and $y = c + dx$. Working from the context of comparing two different Internet cafe pricing plans, students will write function rules to describe the plans, then use a graphing calculator or computer software to graph the lines and determine the point of intersection.

1 a. Let x represent the number of minutes of Internet use in a day. y_1 and y_2 represent the daily charge in dollars for each café.
Surf City: $y_1 = 3.95 + 0.05x$
Byte to Eat: $y_2 = 2 + 0.10x$

b. Surf City: $3.95 + 0.05(30) = \$5.45$
Byte to Eat: $2 + 0.10(30) = \$5.00$

c. Surf City: $10 = 3.95 + 0.05x$, $x = 121$. So she could spend 121 minutes (just over 2 hours) online.
Byte to Eat: $10 = 2 + 0.10x$, $x = 80$. So she could spend 80 minutes (1 hour, 20 minutes) online.

d. For more than 39 minutes of Internet use, Surf City costs less. Byte to Eat costs less for less than 39 minutes of Internet use.

e. Responses will vary. Be sure that students use the functions to justify their choices.

2 a. For 39 minutes, the two plans have the same cost, $5.90 per day.

 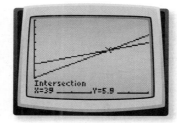 

b. Yes, their reasoning was correct. This is how similar questions about the percentages of male and female doctors were represented in Investigation 1. If you find the x value for which each of these functions has the same y value, one company's price will be less than the other for x values on one side of that x value, and the other company will have a lower price for x values on the other side of that value.

c. This equation might be solved something like this:

$3.95 + 0.05x = 2 + 0.10x$	Subtract $0.05x$ from both sides.
$3.95 = 2 + 0.05x$	Subtract 2 from both sides.
$1.95 = 0.05x$	Divide both sides by 0.05.
$39 = x$	

INSTRUCTIONAL NOTE
You may wish to give your overhead teaching calculator to a student who is solving Problem 1 using the calculator. Have the student explain the answers to the class after they have had time to complete them.

Unit 3

The questions about daily Internet access charges from two different businesses involve comparisons of two linear functions. The functions can be expressed with rules.

Surf City Business Center: $y_1 = 3.95 + 0.05x$

Byte to Eat Café: $y_2 = 2 + 0.10x$

If you think about what values of x and y will make $y = 3.95 + 0.05x$ and $y = 2 + 0.10x$ true, then you are thinking about $y = 3.95 + 0.05x$ and $y = 2 + 0.10x$ as equations. The pair of linear equations is sometimes called a **system of linear equations**.

3 Finding the pairs of numbers x and y that satisfy both equations is called **solving the system**.

  a. Does the pair (1, 7) satisfy either equation in the system above? If so, what does this solution say about Internet access charges? What about the pairs (10, 3) and (20, 8)?

  b. Find a pair of numbers x and y that satisfies both equations. What does this solution say about Internet access charges?

  c. Is there another solution of the system, that is, another pair of numbers (x, y) that satisfies both equations? How do you know?

Thinking about comparing costs is helpful when developing strategies for solving systems of linear equations. You can use the same strategies for solving when you do not know what x and y represent.

4 Use tables, graphs, or algebraic reasoning to solve each system. Use each method of solution at least once. Check each solution by substituting the values of x and y into both original equations. If a system does not have a solution, explain why.

  a. $\begin{cases} y = 2x + 5 \\ y = 3x + 1 \end{cases}$

  b. $\begin{cases} y = 10 - 1.6x \\ y = 2 + 0.4x \end{cases}$

  c. $\begin{cases} y = 1.5x + 2 \\ y = 5 + 1.5x \end{cases}$

  d. $\begin{cases} y = 2(3 + 0.8x) \\ y = 1.6x + 6 \end{cases}$

5 Describe a situation (like the Internet access situation) that involves comparing two linear functions. Set up and solve a system of linear equations that might model the situation and explain what the solution tells you about the situation.

If students are having difficulty reasoning through solving equations with the variable on both sides, you may wish to turn to On Your Own Reflection Task 22 after work on Problem 3 of this investigation but before moving on to Problem 4. This problem presents sample student reasoning while solving a similar system of linear equations.

3 **a.** (1, 7) satisfies neither equation. This means that you cannot be charged $7 for one minute of Internet usage at either café. (10, 3) is a solution to y_2, which says that you will pay $3 for 10 minutes of Internet use at Byte to Eat Café. (20, 8) is a solution to neither equation, so neither café will charge $8 for 20 minutes of use.

b. (39, 5.90) is a solution to both equations. In both cafés, 39 minutes of Internet use costs $5.90.

c. No, there isn't another solution of the system. Two distinct lines can intersect in at most one point. (In Problem 4, students will refine their thinking about the number of solutions.)

4 **a.** (4, 13); Check: $13 = 2(4) + 5$ and $13 = 3(4) + 1$

b. (4, 3.6); Check: $3.6 = 10 - 1.6(4)$ and $3.6 = 2 + 0.4(4)$

c. No solution. The lines are parallel; there is no point of intersection.

d. All points on the line $y = 1.6x + 6$ are solutions because they are the same line.

> **INSTRUCTIONAL NOTE**
> The idea that equivalent expressions represent the same line and that all points on the line are solutions will be revisited in Lesson 3.

5 **INSTRUCTIONAL NOTE** This problem need not be completed by all groups prior to the STM discussion. Groups not completing Problem 5 during class time might complete it as a homework assignment.

Student situations will vary.

Summarize
the Mathematics

In solving a system of linear equations like $y = 5x + 8$ and $y = 14 - 3x$:

a What is the goal? How is it similar to and different from the goal in solving the single equation $5x + 8 = 14 - 3x$?

b How could the solution to the system be found on a graph of the two functions?

c How could the solution be found in a table of (x, y) values for both functions?

d How could the solution be found algebraically?

e What patterns in the tables, graphs, and equations of a system indicate that there is no (x, y) pair that satisfies both equations? What patterns indicate that there are many (x, y) pairs that satisfy both equations?

Be prepared to explain your solution methods and reasoning.

✔ Check Your Understanding

Charter-boat fishing for walleyes is popular on Lake Erie. The charges for an eight-hour charter trip are:

Charter Company	Boat Rental	Charge per Person
Wally's	$200	$29
Pike's	$50	$60

Each boat can carry a maximum of ten people in addition to the crew.

a. Write rules for calculating the cost for charter service by Wally's and by Pike's.

b. Determine which service is more economical for a party of 4 and for a party of 8.

c. Assuming you want to minimize your costs, under what circumstances would you choose Wally's charter service? How would you represent your answer symbolically?

Summarize
the Mathematics

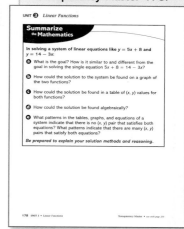
(a) The objective for the system is to find the pair of values (x, y) that satisfies both equations.

It is similar to the objective in solving the single equation $5x + 8 = 14 - 3x$ in that here you are also interested in the x value for which the "y" values (both sides of the equation) are the same. In the single equation, the objective is only to find the value of x.

(b) Find the coordinates of the point of intersection of the graphs of the two lines.

(c) Find the value of x where the y values are the same for both functions.

(d) Set the two expressions in x equal to each other and solve the equation by undoing operations. Then substitute the value of x into either function to determine the corresponding value of y.

(e) A system of linear equations has no solutions (or points of intersection) when the graphs of the two functions are parallel lines. In tables, the rate of change in y values as the x values increase will be the same for both functions. If the two equations are written in "$y = ...$" form, the coefficients of x (i.e., the slopes of the lines) are the same, and the constant terms differ, then the lines will not intersect.

A system of linear equations has all solutions in common when the graphs of the two functions are the same line. In tables, the y values for both functions will be the same for every value of x. If the two equations are written in $y = a + bx$ form, the coefficients of x and the constant terms are the same, then the lines are the same.

MATH TOOLKIT There are three cases for systems of linear equations. Tell how many points the solution set has and how you can tell which case you have by examining the equations.

Case	Number of Points of Intersection

✓Check Your Understanding

a. Let x represent the number of people on a charter trip. y_1 and y_2 represent the charge in dollars for each company.

Wally's: $y_1 = 200 + 29x$ Pike's: $y_2 = 50 + 60x$

b. For a party of 4, Wally's will charge $200 + 29(4)$, or \$316, and Pike's will charge $50 + 60(4)$, or \$290. For a party of 8, Wally's will charge $200 + 29(8)$, or \$432, and Pike's will charge $50 + 60(8)$, or \$530. So for a party of 4, Pike's costs less, but for a party of 8, Wally's costs less.

c. For 5 or more people (or for more than 4 people), Wally's is less expensive; $x \geq 5$ (or $x > 4$).

INSTRUCTIONAL NOTE Students may respond using tables, graphs, or symbolic reasoning. Multiple approaches promote access.

Unit 3

On Your Own

Applications

1. Parents often weigh their child at regular intervals during the first several months after birth. The data usually can be modeled well with a linear function. For example, the rule $y = 96 + 2.1x$ gives Rachel's weight in ounces as a function of her age in days.

   a. How much did Rachel weigh at birth?

   b. Make a table and a graph of this function for $0 \le x \le 90$ with $\Delta x = 15$.

   c. For each equation or inequality below, use the table or graph to estimate the solution of the equation or inequality. Then explain what the solution tells you about Rachel's weight and age.

       i. $y = 96 + 2.1(10)$ ii. $159 = 96 + 2.1x$

      iii. $264 = 96 + 2.1x$ iv. $96 + 2.1x \le 201$

2. Mary and Jeff both have jobs at their local baseball park selling programs. They get paid $10 per game plus $0.25 for each program they sell.

   a. Write a rule for pay earned as a function of number of programs sold.

   b. Write equations, inequalities, or calculations that can be used to answer each of the following questions.

       i. How many programs does Jeff need to sell to earn $25 per game?

      ii. How much will Mary earn if she sells 75 programs at a game?

      iii. How many programs does Jeff need to sell to earn at least $35 per game?

   c. Produce a table and a graph of the relation between program sales and pay from which the questions in Part b can be answered. Use the graph and the table to estimate the answers.

LESSON 2 • Linear Equations and Inequalities **201**

Unit 3

On Your Own

Applications

1 **a.** Rachel weighed 96 ounces at birth.

b.
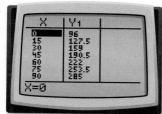

c. Students should use their tables or graphs to find the solutions below.

> **i.** $y = 117$. When Rachel is 10 days old, she will weigh 117 ounces.
>
> **ii.** $x = 30$. If Rachel weighs 159 ounces, then she is 30 days old.
>
> **iii.** $x = 80$. If Rachel weighs 264 ounces, then she is 80 days old.
>
> **iv.** $x \leq 50$. Rachel will weigh 201 ounces or less as long as she is 50 days old or younger.

> **INSTRUCTIONAL NOTE** For some students, writing the statements in Part c in if-then form is helpful. If (what you are given), then (what you are solving for).

2 **a.** $y = 10 + 0.25x$, where x is the number of programs sold and y is the total pay per game.

b. **i.** $10 + 0.25x = 25$

> **ii.** $10 + 0.25(75)$
>
> **iii.** $10 + 0.25x \geq 35$

c.
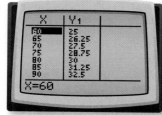 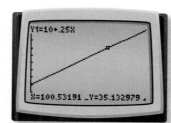 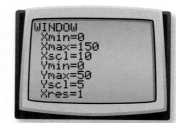

> **i.** $x = 60$. Jeff needs to sell 60 programs per game in order to earn $25 per game.
>
> **ii.** $y = 28.75$. If Mary sells 75 programs, she will earn $28.75.
>
> **iii.** $x \geq 100$. To earn at least $35 per game, Jeff needs to sell at least 100 programs per game.

3 Ella works as a server at Pietro's Restaurant. The restaurant owners have a policy of automatically adding a 15% tip on all customers' bills as a courtesy to their servers. Ella works the 4 P.M. to 10 P.M. shift. She is paid $15 per shift plus tips.

a. Write a rule for Ella's evening wage based on the total of her customers' bills. Use your graphing calculator or computer software to produce a table and a graph of this function.

b. If the customers' bills total $310, how much will Ella earn?

c. Write and solve an equation to answer the question, "If Ella's wage last night was $57, what was the total for her customers' bills?"

4 The Yogurt Shop makes several different flavors of frozen yogurt. Each new batch is 650 ounces, and a typical cone uses 8 ounces. As sales take place, the amount A of each flavor remaining from a fresh batch is a function of the number n of cones of that flavor that have been sold. The function relating amount of yogurt left to number of cones sold is $A = 650 - 8n$.

a. Solve each equation related to sales of chocolate-vanilla swirl yogurt. Show your work. Explain what your solution tells about sales of chocolate-vanilla yogurt and the amount left.

    i. $570 = 650 - 8n$

    ii. $250 = 650 - 8n$

    iii. $A = 650 - 8(42)$

b. Use the function $A = 650 - 8n$ to write and solve equations to answer the following questions.

    i. How many cones have been sold if 390 ounces remain?

    ii. How much yogurt will be left when 75 cones have been sold?

    iii. If the machine shows 370 ounces left, how many cones have been sold?

5 Victoria can earn as much as $450 as a scorekeeper for a summer basketball league. She learned that she must pay $18 per game for substitutes when she misses a game. So, her summer earnings E will depend on the number of games she misses g according to the function $E = 450 - 18g$. Solve each of the following equations and explain what the solutions tell you about Victoria's summer earnings.

a. $306 = 450 - 18g$

b. $360 = 450 - 18g$

c. $0 = 450 - 18g$

d. $E = 450 - 18(2)$

e. $315 = 450 - 18g$

f. $486 = 450 - 18g$

a. $w = 15 + 0.15b$, where b is the total of customers' bills and w is Ella's daily wage in dollars.

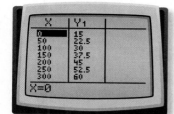 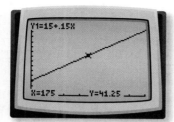 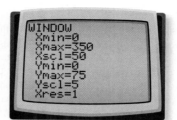

b. $15 + 0.15(310) = \$61.50$ earnings

c. $57 = 15 + 0.15b$
$280 = b$
The total for Ella's customers' bills for the evening was $280.

4 See margin note.

a. **i.** $n = 10$. There will be 570 ounces of yogurt left after 10 cones have been sold.

ii. $n = 50$. There will be 250 ounces of yogurt left after 50 cones have been sold.

iii. $A = 314$. After 42 cones have been sold, there will be 314 ounces of yogurt left.

b. **i.** $650 - 8n = 390$, $n = 32.5$. Approximately 32 or 33 cones have been sold if 390 ounces of yogurt remain.

ii. $A = 650 - 8(75)$, $A = 50$. When 75 cones are sold, 50 ounces of yogurt are left.

iii. $650 - 8n = 370$, $n = 35$. Thirty-five cones have been sold if the machine shows 370 ounces left.

5 See margin note.

a. $g = 8$. Victoria can only miss 8 games if she wants to earn $306.

b. $g = 5$. Victoria can only miss 5 games if she wants to earn $360.

c. $g = 25$. If Victoria misses 25 games, she will not earn any money.

d. $E = 414$. If Victoria misses 2 games, she will earn $414.

e. $g = 7.5$. It is not possible for Victoria to earn exactly $315, but to earn just slightly more than $315, she could only miss 7 games.

f. $g = -2$. It is impossible for Victoria to miss a negative number of games. This answer does not make sense.
   (Students might suggest that perhaps this solution means that Victoria herself was paid $18 per game as a substitute for somebody else. In other words, perhaps Victoria was scorekeeper for two *extra* games during the summer and thus earned more than $450.)

DIFFERENTIATION From Task 3 and on in this homework set, unless specified, some students may solve algebraically, others using technology. Multiple approaches promote access for all students.

Unit 3

6. When people shop for cars or trucks, they usually look closely at data on fuel economy. The data are given as miles per gallon in city and in highway driving. Let *c* stand for miles per gallon in city driving and *h* stand for miles per gallon in highway driving. Data from tests of 20 of the most popular American cars and trucks show that the function $h = 1.4 + 1.25c$ is a good model for the relation between the variables. Solve the following equations algebraically. Explain what the results tell you about the relation between city and highway mileage. Be prepared to explain the reasoning you used to find each solution.

   a. $35 = 1.4 + 1.25c$

   b. $10 = 1.4 + 1.25c$

   c. $h = 1.4 + (1.25)(20)$

7. Describe a problem situation which could be modeled by the function $y = 10 + 4.35x$.

   a. What would solving $109 \geq 10 + 4.35x$ mean in your situation?

   b. Solve $109 \geq 10 + 4.35x$ algebraically. Then show how the solution could be estimated from a table or graph.

8. Solve each of the following equations and inequalities algebraically and check your answers. Show the steps in your solutions and in your checks.

   a. $25 = 13 + 3x$

   b. $74 = 8.5x - 62$

   c. $34 + 12x < 76$

   d. $76 \geq 34 - 12x$

   e. $3,141 = 2,718 + 42x$

9. Refer back to the Internet pricing plans for Surf City Business Center and Byte to Eat Café given on page 198. Suppose Surf City Business Center wants to become more competitive for customers looking for high-speed Internet access. The owner decides to change the daily base charge from $3.95 to $2.95, but maintain the $0.05 per minute charge.

   a. Write a rule for the daily charges under the new program.

   b. How are the graphs of the new and old Internet access charges related?

   c. What would be the daily charge for 30 minutes of Internet use using the new program?

   d. How many minutes would one need to spend on the Internet in order for Surf City Business Center's new program to be more economical than Byte to Eat Café?

   e. If a customer is charged $5.20 for one day's Internet use under the new Surf City Business Center pricing plan, how many minutes did he or she spend online?

   f. What would Byte to Eat Café have charged for the same number of minutes?

(6) **NOTE** See margin note on page T202.

  a. $c = 26.88$. If a car or truck gets 35 miles per gallon in highway driving, then it ought to get about 27 miles per gallon in city driving.

  b. $c = 6.88$. If a car or truck gets 10 miles per gallon in highway driving, then it ought to get about 7 miles per gallon in city driving.

  c. $h = 26.4$. If a car or truck gets 20 miles per gallon in city driving, then it ought to get about 26 miles per gallon in highway driving.

(7) **a.** Student responses will depend on their context.

  b. $109 \geq 10 + 4.35x$
   $99 \geq 4.35x$
   $22.75862 \geq x$

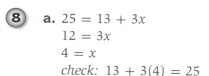
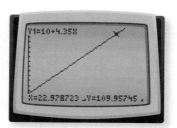

From this table, you can see that the y values are less than or equal to 109 when x is a little less than 23, but greater than 22.

From this graph, you can see that the y values are less than or equal to 109 when x is less than or equal to approximately 22.97.

(8) **a.** $25 = 13 + 3x$
   $12 = 3x$
   $4 = x$
   check: $13 + 3(4) = 25$

  b. $74 = 8.5x - 62$
   $136 = 8.5x$
   $16 = x$
   check: $8.5(16) - 62 = 74$

  c. $34 + 12x < 76$
   $12x < 42$
   $x < 3.5$
   check: $34 + 12(3.5) = 76$
    $34 + 12(0) < 76$

  d. $76 \geq 34 - 12x$
   $42 \geq -12x$
   $-3.5 \leq x$ or $x \geq -3.5$
   check: $34 - 12(-3.5) = 76$
    $76 > 34 - 12(0)$

  e. $3{,}141 = 2{,}718 + 42x$
   $423 = 42x$
   $10.07143 \approx x$
   check: $2{,}718 + 42(10.07143) \approx 3{,}141$

> **TECHNOLOGY NOTE**
> Look for student-generated opportunities to address displays that might be misinterpreted such as the nonlinear look to the graphs in Task 9. The table values show a constant increase, while graphically rounding to pixels gives the appearance of steps.

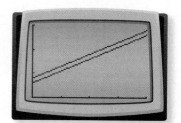

(9) **a.** $y = 2.95 + 0.05x$, where x is the number of minutes used in a day and y is the total daily charge.

  b. The old service charge is always greater than the new. They both increase at the same rate, so they are parallel lines.

  c. $4.45 per day

  d. The new Surf City program costs less when you spend more than 19 minutes online.

  e. The customer spent 45 minutes online.

  f. Byte to Eat would have charged $6.50 for 45 minutes.

Unit 3

10 Surf City Business Center did not notice any large increase in customers when they changed their base daily charge from $3.95 to $2.95. They decided to change it back to $3.95 and reduce the per-minute charge from $0.05 to $0.03.

   a. Write a rule that models their new Internet access charge.

   b. How are the graphs of this new and the original Internet access charges related?

   c. What is the cost of 30 minutes of Internet use under this new plan?

   d. For how many minutes of Internet use is this new Surf City Business Center pricing plan competitive with Byte to Eat Café?

   e. Compare the cost of Internet access under this plan with that proposed in Applications Task 9. Which plan do you think will attract more customers? Explain your reasoning.

11 Recall Bronco Electronics, a regional distributor of graphing calculators, from the Check Your Understanding on page 191. Their shipping cost C can be calculated from the number n of calculators in a box using the rule $C = 4.95 + 1.25n$. Bronco Electronics got an offer from a different shipping company. The new company would charge based on the rule $C = 7.45 + 1.00n$. Write and solve equations or inequalities to answer the following questions:

   a. For what number of calculators in a box will the two shippers have the same charge?

   b. For what number of calculators in a box will the new shipping company's offer be more economical for Bronco Electronics?

12 From the situations described below, choose two situations that most interest you. Identify the variables involved and write rules describing one of those variables as a function of the other. In each case, determine conditions for which each business is more economical than the other. Show how you compared the costs.

   a. A school club decides to have customized T-shirts made. The Clothing Shack will charge $30 for setup costs and $12 for each shirt. The cost of having them made at Clever Creations is a $50 initial fee for the setup and $8 for each T-shirt.

   b. Speedy Messenger Service charges a $30 base fee and $0.75 per ounce for urgent small package deliveries between office buildings. Quick Delivery charges a $25 base and $0.90 per ounce.

   c. Cheezy's Pies charges $5 for a 12-inch sausage pizza and $5 for delivery. The Pizza Palace delivers for free, but they charge $7 for a 12-inch sausage pizza.

   d. The *Evening News* has a minimum charge of $4 for up to 3 lines and $1.75 for each additional line of a listing placed in the classified section. The *Morning Journal* charges $8 for the first 5 lines and $1.25 for each additional line.

10   **a.** $y = 3.95 + 0.03x$, where x is the number of minutes used in a day and y is the total daily charge.

     b. The two service charges begin at the same base price, so both graphs have the same y-intercept. Since the original charge per minute was greater than the new, the graph of the original pricing plan is steeper.

     c. The cost of 30 minutes of Internet use under the new plan is $4.85.

     d. For 27 minutes, Surf City will be more expensive than Byte to Eat. For 28 minutes, Surf City will be cheaper than Byte to Eat.

     e. Customers who anticipate using more than 27 minutes of Internet access per day (could be advertised as a half hour or more) will probably prefer to use Surf City, while customers who anticipate using less than 28 minutes per day will probably prefer to use Byte to Eat.

11   **a.** The two companies will charge the same for shipping 10 calculators in a box. $4.95 + 1.25n = 7.45 + 1.00n$, $n = 10$.

     b. The new shipping company is more economical for shipping more than 10 calculators in a box. $7.45 + 1.00n < 4.95 + 1.25n$, $n > 10$.

12   Students may use tables or graphs to solve algebraically.

     a. Clothing Shack: $y = 30 + 12x$
Clever Creations: $y = 50 + 8x$
x represents the number of T-shirts and y represents the total cost. The Clothing Shack charges less for fewer than 5 T-shirts. Clever Creations charges less for more than 5 T-shirts. Both companies charge the same for 5 T-shirts.

     b. Speedy Messenger: $y_1 = 30 + 0.75x$
Quick Delivery: $y_2 = 25 + 0.90x$
x represents the number of ounces and y represents the total cost of delivery. Quick Delivery is more economical if your package is 33 ounces or less, whereas Speedy is more economical if your package is 34 ounces or more.

     c. Cheezy's Pies: $y = 5 + 5x$
Pizza Palace: $y = 7x$
Pizza Palace costs less if you order 1 or 2 12-inch sausage pizzas for delivery. But if you order 3 or more 12-inch sausage pizzas for delivery, then Cheezy's Pies is the better deal.

     d. *Evening News:* $y = 4 + 1.75(x - 3)$; $x \geq 3$
Morning Journal: $y = 8 + 1.25(x - 5)$; $x \geq 5$
x represents the number of lines in the ad and y is the total cost. The *Evening News* charges less for 1 to 5 lines. The *Morning Journal* charges less for 7 or more lines. They charge the same for 6 lines. The table showing charges allows a systematic analysis of this system.

Lines	*Evening News*	*Morning Journal*
1–3	4.00	8.00
4	5.75	8.00
5	7.50	8.00
6	9.25	9.25
7	11.00	10.50
8	12.75	11.75

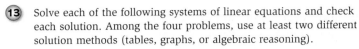

13 Solve each of the following systems of linear equations and check each solution. Among the four problems, use at least two different solution methods (tables, graphs, or algebraic reasoning).

a. $\begin{cases} y = x + 4 \\ y = 2x - 9 \end{cases}$

b. $\begin{cases} y = -2x + 18 \\ y = -x + 10 \end{cases}$

c. $\begin{cases} y = 3x - 12 \\ y = 1.5x + 3 \end{cases}$

d. $\begin{cases} y = x \\ y = -0.4x + 7 \end{cases}$

Connections

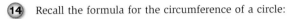

14 Recall the formula for the circumference of a circle:

$$C = \pi d.$$

Write equations or inequalities that can be used to answer the following questions. Then find answers to the questions.

a. A 16-inch pizza has a diameter of 16 inches. What is the circumference of a 16-inch pizza?

b. The average arm span of a group of 10 first graders is 47 inches. If they hold hands and stretch to form a circle, what will be the approximate diameter of the circle?

c. If you have 50 inches of wire, what are the diameters of the circles you could make with all or part of the wire?

15 There are two especially useful properties of arithmetic operations. The first relates addition and subtraction. The second relates multiplication and division.

- *For any numbers a, b, and c, a + b = c is true if and only if a = c − b.*
- *For any numbers a, b, and c, a × b = c is true if and only if a = c ÷ b and b ≠ 0.*

Erik solved the equation $3x + 12 = 45$ given at the beginning of Investigation 2 as follows:

If $3x + 12 = 45$, then $3x = 45 - 12$, or $3x = 33$.

If $3x = 33$, then $x = 33 ÷ 3$, or $x = 11$.

a. Explain how the above properties of operations can be used to support each step in Erik's reasoning.

b. Solve the equation $130 + 30x = 250$ using reasoning like Erik's that relies on the connection between addition and subtraction and the connection between multiplication and division. Check your answer.

13 Both methods result in the same x and y values. Students should check by substituting the solution values back into the original equations.

  a. (13, 17)

  b. (8, 2)

  c. (10, 18)

  d. (5, 5)

Connections

14 **a.** $C = \pi(16)$
  $C = 16\pi$ inches or $C \approx 50$ inches

  b. $(10 \cdot 47) = \pi d$
  $\frac{470}{\pi} = d$
  $d \approx 150$ inches

  c. $50 \geq \pi d$
  $d \leq \frac{50}{\pi}$ inches or $d \leq 15.9$ inches

15 **a.** If $3x + 12 = 45$, then $3x = 45 - 12$, or 33. If we suppose $a = 3x$, and $b = 12$, and $c = 45$, then this matches the addition ... subtraction property.
  If $3x = 33$, then $x = 33 \div 3$, or 11. If we suppose $a = x$ and $b = 3$ and $c = 33$, then this matches the multiplication ... division property.

  b. If $130 + 30x = 250$, then $30x = 250 - 130$, or 120, then this matches the addition ... subtraction property.
  If $30x = 120$, then $x = 120 \div 30$, or 4, then this matches the multiplication ... division property.

  Check:
  $130 + 30(4) = 250$
  $130 + 120 = 250$

Unit 3

16 When you know the algebraic operations that you want to use in solving an equation, you can get help with the details from a computer algebra system (CAS). For example, to solve $3x + 11 = 5x + 7$, you can proceed as in the screen below.

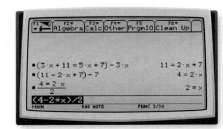

Study this work to figure out what each entered instruction is asking the CAS to do. Then apply your understanding to solve the following equations in a similar way with the CAS available to you. Record the steps you enter at each step in the solution process and the results of those steps.

a. $-3x + 72 = 4x - 5$

b. $\frac{2}{5}x - \frac{9}{5} = \frac{7}{10}$

c. $2.5t - 5.1 = 9.3 - 0.7t$

17 Here are the first three shapes in a geometric pattern of Xs made from identical squares.

| 1st | 2nd | 3rd |

a. Write a rule showing how to calculate the number of squares in the *NEXT* shape from the number of squares *NOW*.

b. Write a rule for the number S of squares in the nth shape.

c. Solve these equations and inequalities, and explain what the solutions tell about the pattern.

   i. $4n + 1 = 49$ **ii.** $4n + 1 = 81$

   iii. $S = 4(8) + 1$ **iv.** $4n + 1 < 100$

18 The table on page 207 shows winning times for women and men in the Olympic 100-meter freestyle swim for games since 1912.

a. Make plots of the (*year, winning time*) data for men and for women. Use 0 for the year 1900.

b. Find the linear regression model for each data pattern.

16 **a.**

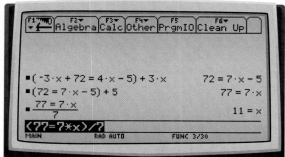

b.

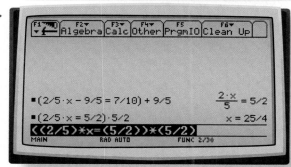

c.

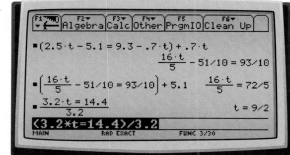

17 **a.** *NEXT = NOW* + 4, starting at 5

b. The number of squares in the *n*th shape of the sequence is $S = 4n + 1$.

c. **i.** $n = 12$. The shape with 49 squares is 12th in the sequence of shapes.

ii. $n = 20$. The shape with 81 squares is 20th in the sequence of shapes.

iii. $S = 33$. The 8th shape in the sequence of shapes has 33 squares.

iv. $n < 24.75$. The shapes with less than 100 squares are 24th and earlier in the sequence of shapes.

> **TECHNOLOGY NOTE**
> The data for Task 18 are in *CPMP-Tools*.

18 **a.**

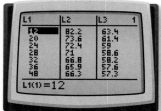 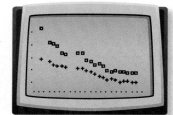

b. Women: $y = -0.269x + 78.666$ Men: $y = -0.165x + 64.139$

c. Which group of athletes has shown a greater improvement in time, men or women? Explain.

d. What are the approximate coordinates of the point where the linear regression lines intersect?

e. What is the significance of the point of intersection of the two lines in Part d? How much confidence do you have that the lines accurately predict the future? Explain.

Olympic 100-meter Freestyle Swim Times

Year	Women's Time (in seconds)	Men's Time (in seconds)	Year	Women's Time (in seconds)	Men's Time (in seconds)
1912	82.2	63.4	1968	60.0	52.2
1920	73.6	61.4	1972	58.59	51.22
1924	72.4	59.0	1976	55.65	49.99
1928	71.0	58.6	1980	54.79	50.40
1932	66.8	58.2	1984	55.92	49.80
1936	65.9	57.6	1988	54.93	48.63
1948	66.3	57.3	1992	54.64	49.02
1952	66.8	57.4	1996	54.50	48.74
1956	62.0	55.4	2000	53.83	48.30
1960	61.2	55.2	2004	53.84	48.17
1964	59.5	53.4			

Source: *The World Almanac and Book of Facts 2003.* Mahwah, NJ: World Almanac Education Group, Inc. 2003; www.olympics.com

Reflections

19 The function $y = 43 + 5x$ and the equation $78 = 43 + 5x$ are closely related to each other.

   a. How can you use $y = 43 + 5x$ to solve $78 = 43 + 5x$?

   b. What does solving $78 = 43 + 5x$ tell you about $y = 43 + 5x$?

20 When solving equations or inequalities that model real situations, why should you check not only the solution, but also whether the solution makes sense? Illustrate your thinking with an example.

c. Women athletes have shown a greater improvement over time. The slope of the linear regression model for the women's times is negative and of larger absolute value than that for men's time. This means that the women's times are decreasing at a greater rate than the rate at which men's times are decreasing.

d. The regression lines intersect at approximately (140, 41).

TECHNOLOGY NOTE These data are available in *CPMP-Tools* to use with the custom tool "Modeling Line."

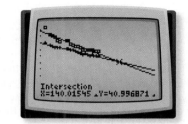

e. The intersection point predicts when the women's winning time in the Olympic 100-meter freestyle swim will be the same as the men's winning time in that same event; it predicts that in around 2035, both the men's and women's winning time in the Olympic 100-meter freestyle swim will be about 41 seconds.

It is reasonable to expect the model to accurately predict the future for a relatively short amount of time into the future (in this case, perhaps for the next two Olympics, or 8 years into the future). In this model, the record time for both men and women keeps decreasing at a constant rate forever, which is not humanly possible. Obviously, at a certain point the model will no longer be accurate, and a better model will have to be found. Some students may suggest that the linear model for the women's times already seems inaccurate since the last four Olympic times are above the modeling line.

Reflections

19 **a.** You could either graph the rule $y = 43 + 5x$, or create a table of values to find the x-coordinate of the point on the line, which has a y-coordinate of 78.

b. The point (7, 78) lies on the graph of $y = 43 + 5x$.

20 Oftentimes in real-world situations, only whole-number values for x are sensible. For example, in Applications Task 5 Part e, in order to earn \$315 during the summer, Victoria can only miss 7.5 games. She may not be able to pay for a substitute scorekeeper for only half a game. In this case, although the solution 7.5 is correct, it does not necessarily make sense in the given situation. In other cases, negative solution values may not make sense in particular situations.

Unit 3

21 Consider Mary and Jeff's pay possibilities for selling programs at the ballpark. The rule $P = 10 + 0.25s$ gives their pay P in dollars for selling s programs in a night.

a. What operations are needed to calculate the pay for selling 36 programs in a single night?

b. What operations are needed to solve the equation $10 + 0.25s = 19$? What will the solution tell you?

c. In what sense do the operations in Part b "undo" the operations in Part a?

d. How does the order in which you do the operations in Part a compare with the order in Part b? Why does this make sense?

e. How, if at all, does the procedure for solving change if you are asked to solve the inequality $10 + 0.25s \geq 19$? How does the meaning of the solution change?

22 How could you use a graph of the function $y = 7 - 4x$ to decide, without calculation or algebraic solution, whether the solutions to $7 - 4x > 43$ will be an inequality like $x < a$ or like $x > a$ and whether a will be positive or negative?

23 Consider the inequality $2x + 8 > 5x - 4$.

a. What are two different, but reasonable, first steps in solving $2x + 8 > 5x - 4$?

b. What does the solution to the inequality tell you about the graphs of $y = 2x + 8$ and $y = 5x - 4$?

c. What does the solution tell you about tables of values for $y = 2x + 8$ and $y = 5x - 4$?

24 When asked to solve the system of linear equations

$$\begin{cases} y = 2x + 9 \\ y = 5x - 18 \end{cases}$$

Sabrina reasoned as follows:

I want x so that $2x + 9 = 5x - 18$.

Adding 18 to each side of that equation gives me $2x + 27 = 5x$, and the sides remain balanced.

Subtracting $2x$ from each side of the new equation gives $27 = 3x$, and the sides remain balanced.

Dividing each side of that equation by 3 gives $x = 9$, and the sides remain balanced.

If $x = 9$, then one equation is $y = 2(9) + 9$ and the other equation is $y = 5(9) - 18$. Both equations give $y = 27$.

The solution of the system must be $x = 9$ and $y = 27$.

a. Do you agree with each step of her reasoning? Why or why not?

b. Use reasoning like Sabrina's to solve the following system of linear equations.

$$\begin{cases} y = 8x + 3 \\ y = 2x - 9 \end{cases}$$

a. First you perform multiplication: $0.25 \cdot 36 = 9$. Then you perform addition: $10 + 9 = 19$.

b. First you perform subtraction: $19 - 10 = 9$. Then you perform division: $9 \div 0.25 = 36$. The solution ($s = 36$) means that 36 programs must be sold to make $19.

c. Addition and subtraction are inverse operations, as are multiplication and division.

d. Since subtraction "undoes" addition, and division "undoes" multiplication, the operations in Part b "undo" the operations from Part a in reverse order. This makes sense because to "undo" a chain of operations, you must start at the end of the chain.

e. In this case, the procedure for solving does not change, because we do not perform any multiplication or division by negative numbers. The meaning of the solution is different. The solution ($s \geq 36$) means that selling at least 36 programs will result in pay of at least $19.

 The graph of $y = 7 - 4x$ is a line with negative slope and y-intercept $(0, 7)$. So points with y-coordinates greater than 43 will be to the left of the y-axis and to the left of the point $(0, 43)$. This implies that the solution will have the form $x < a$ with a negative.

 a. Four possible (and reasonable, or productive) first steps:

(1) subtracting 8 from both sides, $2x > 5x - 12$;

(2) adding 4 to both sides, $2x + 12 > 5x$;

(3) subtracting $2x$ from both sides, $8 > 3x - 4$;

(4) subtracting $5x$ from both sides, $-3x + 8 > -4$.

b. The solution tells the x values where the graph of $y = 2x + 8$ is above the graph of $y = 5x - 4$. (The solution is $x < 4$.)

c. The solution tells the x values that will have y values for $y = 2x + 8$ that are greater than the y values for $y = 5x - 4$. ($x < 4$.)

24 **a.** Yes, because each step is correct in itself, and all of the steps follow each other in a logically correct manner.

b. To solve $y = 8x + 3$ and $y = 2x - 9$:

• I want x so that $8x + 3 = 2x - 9$.

• Subtracting 3 from each side of that equation gives me $8x = 2x - 12$, and the sides remain balanced.

• Subtracting $2x$ from each side of the new equation gives $6x = -12$, and the sides remain balanced.

• Dividing each side of that equation by 6 gives $x = -2$, and the sides remain balanced.

• If $x = -2$, then one equation is $y = 8(-2) + 3$ and the other equation is $y = 2(-2) - 9$. Both equations give $y = -13$.

• The solution of the system must be $x = -2$ and $y = -13$.

Unit 3

Extensions

25 Refer back to Applications Task 3. Suppose a new policy at the restaurant applies an automatic service charge of 15% to each bill. Servers will receive $20 per shift plus 10% of the bills for customers they serve. Busers will receive $25 per shift plus 5% of the bills for customers at tables they serve.

a. Write rules for the functions that show how:

   i. a server's daily earnings depend on the total of bills for customers at tables he or she serves.

   ii. busers' daily earnings depend on the total of bills for customers at tables he or she serves.

   Graph these two functions on the same coordinate axes.

b. Write three questions about the wages for wait staff and busers. Write equations or inequalities corresponding to your questions. Then solve the equations or inequalities and answer the questions. Show how you arrived at your solution for each equation or inequality.

26 The diagram at the right shows graphs of two functions:

$y = x + 3$ and $y = x^2 - 3$.

Reproduce the graphs on your graphing calculator or computer and use the graphs to solve each equation or inequality.

a. $x + 3 = x^2 - 3$

b. $x + 3 \geq x^2 - 3$

c. $x + 3 < x^2 - 3$

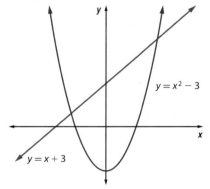

27 One linear function relating grams of fat F and calories C in popular "lite" menu items of fast-food restaurants is given by $C = 300 + 16(F - 10)$. Solve each equation or inequality below, and explain what your solution tells you about grams of fat and calories in fast-food. Use each of the following strategies at least once.

- Use a graph of the function.
- Use a table for the function.
- Use algebraic reasoning, as in the examples of this lesson.

a. $430 = 300 + 16(F - 10)$

b. $685 = 300 + 16(F - 10)$

c. $140 = 300 + 16(F - 10)$

d. $685 \geq 300 + 16(F - 10)$

Extensions

25 **a.** **i.** Wait staff's wages: $y = 20 + 0.10x$

  ii. Busers' wages: $y = 25 + 0.05x$

  x represents the total customers' bills in dollars and y represents the wage in dollars, as seen at the right.

b. One example follows.
  What would the total customers' bills have to come to in order for a buser to make the same as a member of the wait staff?

  $25 + 0.05b = 20 + 0.10b$, $b = 100$. The total customers' bills for the shift would have to come to $100 for a buser to make the same as a member of the wait staff.

26 **a.** The two solutions are $(-2, 1)$ and $(3, 6)$.

b. $-2 \leq x \leq 3$; the graph of the line is above the graph of the parabola between the x values of -2 and 3.

c. $x < -2$ or $x > 3$; the graph of the line is below the graph of the parabola to the left of $(-2, 1)$ and to the right of $(3, 6)$.

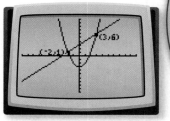

27

Graph	**Table**	**Symbolic**	**Information**
a. 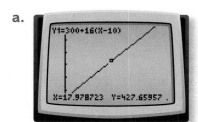	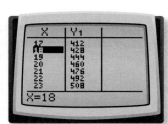	$430 = 300 + 16(F - 10)$ $130 = 16F - 160$ $290 = 16F$ $F \approx 18$	A meal with 430 calories will have around 18 grams of fat.
b. 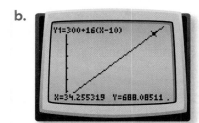	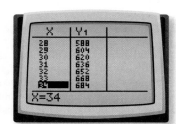	$685 = 300 + 16(F - 10)$ $385 = 16F - 160$ $545 = 16F$ $F \approx 34$	A meal with 685 calories will have around 34 grams of fat.
c. 		$140 = 300 + 16(F - 10)$ $-160 = 16F - 160$ $0 = 16F$ $F = 0$	A meal with 140 calories will have around 0 grams of fat.
d. 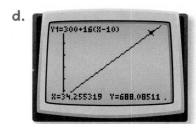		$685 \geq 300 + 16(F - 10)$ $385 \geq 16F - 160$ $545 \geq 16F$ $F \leq 34$	A meal with less than 34 grams of fat should have no more than 685 calories.

28 Any linear function can be described by a rule of the form $y = a + bx$. Explain, with sketches, how to solve each of the following using graphs of linear functions. Describe the possible number of solutions. Assume $b \neq 0$ and $d \neq 0$.

  a. equations of the form $c = a + bx$

  b. inequalities of the form $c \leq a + bx$

  c. equations of the form $a + bx = c + dx$

  d. inequalities of the form $a + bx \leq c + dx$

29 The student government association at the Baltimore Freedom Academy wanted to order Fall Festival T-shirts for all students. Thrifty Designs charges a one-time art fee of $20 and then $6.25 per shirt.

  a. What rule shows how to calculate the cost c_1 of purchasing n shirts from Thrifty Designs?

  b. For each of the following questions:

    • Write an equation or inequality with solutions that will answer the question.

    • Explain how the solution for the equation or inequality is shown in a table or graph of (n, c_1) values.

    • Write an answer to the given question about T-shirt purchase.

    i. How much would it cost to buy T-shirts for 250 people?

    ii. How many T-shirts could be purchased for $1,000?

  c. Suppose that Tees and More quotes a cost of $1,540 for 250 T-shirts and $1,000 for 160 T-shirts.

    i. If the cost of T-shirts from Tees and More is a linear function of the number of shirts purchased, what rule shows the relationship between number of shirts n and cost c_2?

    ii. What one-time art fee and cost per shirt are implied by the Tees and More price quotation?

    iii. Write and solve an inequality that answers the question, "For what numbers of T-shirts will Tees and More be less expensive than Thrifty Designs?" Be sure to explain how the solution is shown in a table or graph of (n, c_1) and (n, c_2) values.

30 Refer back to the Internet access pricing plans for Surf City Business Center and Byte to Eat Café given on page 198. Suppose Surf City Business Center decides to lower its base daily charge to $2.95 but is unsure what to charge per call. They want to advertise daily charges that are lower than Byte to Eat Café if one spends more than 20 minutes online per day.

  a. To meet their goal, at what point will the Surf City Business Center graph need to cross the Byte to Eat Café graph?

  b. What charge per minute by Surf City Business Center will meet that condition?

28 **a.** Graph $y = a + bx$, and use the trace function to find where $y = c$ (or $a + bx = c$) on the line. The solution is the corresponding value of x.

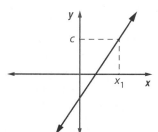

b. Graph $y = a + bx$, and use the trace function to find where $y \geq c$ (or $a + bx \geq c$) on the line. The solution is the set of corresponding values of x.

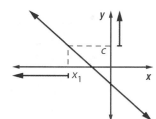

c. Graph $y = a + bx$ and $y = c + dx$. Use the trace function to find where the lines intersect. The solution is the corresponding value of x. If the lines do not intersect ($b = d$), then there is no solution for x. If the lines are the same, then all values of x will satisfy $a + bx = c + dx$.

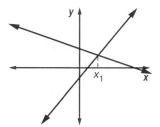

d. Graph $y = a + bx$ and $y = c + dx$ and find where the lines intersect. There are five possibilities. The solution is the set of x values where the line $y = a + bx$ is below $y = c + dx$ (see Diagrams 1 and 2). If the lines are parallel, then either $y = a + bx$ is above $y = c + dx$ (see Diagram 3) and there are no solutions, or $y = a + bx$ is below $y = c + dx$ (see Diagram 4) and any value of x is a solution. If the lines are the same (see Diagram 5), then any value of x is a solution.

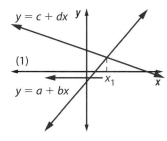

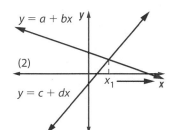

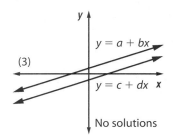

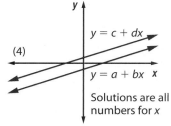

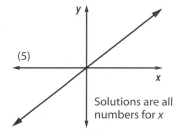

Unit 3

29 **a.** $c_1 = 20 + 6.25n$

b. **i.** Equation: $c_1 = 20 + 6.25(250)$; $c_1 = 1,582.50$; The c_1 value can be found on a table or graph as the value that corresponds to the n value of 250. It will cost $1,582.50 to get 250 T-shirts from Thrifty Designs.

ii. Equation: $1,000 = 20 + 6.25n$; $n = 156.8$; The solution can be found in a table of values for $y = 20 + 6.25x$ between the value pairs (156, 995) and (257, 1,001.25). On the graph, they identify the point with c_1 value 1,000 and read the n value from the horizontal axis. It means that 156 T-shirts could be purchased for $1,000.

c. **i.** $c_2 = 40 + 6n$

ii. This means a $40 one-time art fee and $6 per T-shirt.

iii. $40 + 6n < 20 + 6.25n$ has solution $80 < n$ meaning that Tees and More will charge less for any number of T-shirts at or beyond 80. This solution will appear in tables of values for the two cost functions beyond $n = 80$. On a graph showing the two cost functions, the graph of $c_1 = 40 + 6n$ will lie below that for $c_2 = 20 + 6.25n$ when $n > 80$.

 30 **a.** They will cross at or before (20, 4), since Byte to Eat charges $4 for 20 minutes of Internet use in a day.

b. $2.95 + p(20) = 4$; $p = 0.0525$. Around $0.05 per minute will meet the condition.

The following template might be used to help students organize their work and thinking related to systems of equations.

ALGEBRA/DATA ANALYSIS   NAME: _____
MAKING COMPARISONS

Problem Description:

Define Variables:

Let _____ = _____

Let _____ = _____

System of Equations:

Single Equation:

Finding the Solution in a Table:

X	Y_1	Y_2

Finding the Solution on a Graph:

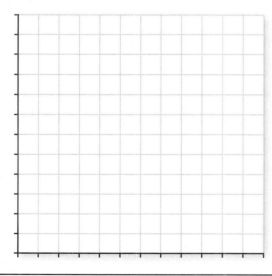

Checking the Solution:

Describing the Solution:

Which should I choose?

c. Suppose a customer spends 60 minutes online per day. By how much is the new Surf City Business Center plan lower than the Byte to Eat Café plan for this many minutes?

d. If a person spends only 10 minutes online per day, how much less will he or she spend by using Byte to Eat Café rather than the new Surf City Business Center plan?

31 Refer back to the Check Your Understanding on page 200. Suppose it was noticed that most fishing parties coming to the dock were 4 or fewer persons.

a. How should Wally revise his boat rental fee so that his rates are lower than the competition's (Pike's) for parties of 3 or more? Write a rule for the new rate system.

b. How much less would a party of four pay by hiring Wally's charter service instead of Pike's?

c. Which service should you hire for a party of 2? How much will you save?

d. Suppose Pike's charter service lowers the per-person rate from $60 to $40. For what size parties would Pike's be less expensive?

e. If Wally wants to change his per-person rate so that both services charge the same for parties of 4, what per-person rate should Wally charge? Write a rule that models the new rate structure.

32 Create a linear system relating cost to number of uses of a service for which Company A's rate per service is 1.5 times that of Company B's, but Company B's service is not more economical until 15 services have been performed.

Review

33 Match each triangle description with the sketch(es) to which it applies.

a. An acute triangle

b. A scalene triangle

c. An obtuse triangle

d. An isosceles triangle

e. An equilateral triangle

f. A right scalene triangle

g. An obtuse isosceles triangle

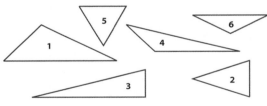

34 Use the fact that 5% of $50,000 = $2,500 to calculate the following percentages.

a. 0.5% of $50,000

b. 5.5% of $50,000

c. 105% of $50,000

d. 95% of $50,000

c. Surf City is about $2.05 cheaper for 60 minutes ($5.95 versus $8.00).

d. Byte to Eat is about $0.45 cheaper for 10 minutes ($3.00 versus $3.45).

31
a. Pike's charges $230 for a party of 3. $R + 29(3) < 230$; $R < 143$. Wally should now charge $142 for boat rental. The new rule would be: $y = 142 + 29x$.

b. Wally's would be $32 cheaper ($258 versus $290).

c. Pike's would be $30 cheaper ($170 versus $230).

d. Pike's would be cheaper for parties of 8 or smaller.

e. $50 + 60(4) = 142 + p(4)$; $37 = p$. Wally's new rate should be $37. The new rule would be $y = 142 + 37x$.

32 One possibility: Company A: $y = 4.5x$
   Company B: $y = 3x + 22$.

Review

33
a. 2, 5   **b.** 1, 3, 4   **c.** 1, 4, 6   **d.** 2, 5, 6

e. 5   **f.** 3   **g.** 6

34
a. 0.5% of $50,000 will be a tenth of $2,500, or $250.

b. 5.5% of $50,000 will be the sum of 5% of $50,000 and 0.5% of $50,000, which is $2,750.

c. 105% of $50,000 will be the sum of 5% of $50,000 and 100% of $50,000, which is $52,500.

d. 95% of $50,000 = 100% of $50,000 − 5% of $50,000 = 50,000 − 2,500 = $47,500.

35 Use the fact that $13 \times 14 = 182$ to mentally calculate the value for each of the following expressions.

a. $(-13)(-14)$　　　　　　**b.** $(14)(-13)$

c. $(13)(14) + (-13)(14)$　　**d.** $\dfrac{(13)(-14)}{(-14)(-13)}$

36 Write an equation for the line passing through the points with coordinates $(-1, -2)$ and $(2, 0)$.

37 Find the area and perimeter of each figure. Assume that all angles that look like right angles are right angles and all segments that look parallel are parallel.

a.

12 cm

8 cm

b.

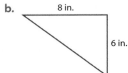

8 in.

6 in.

c.

15 m

10 m

6 m

d.

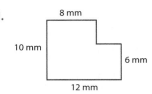

8 mm

10 mm

6 mm

12 mm

38 List all of the 2-digit numbers that can be made from the digits 3, 4, and 5. Digits may be repeated.

a. Suppose that you randomly choose one of the numbers you listed. What is the probability that it is divisible by 5?

b. Suppose that you randomly choose one of the numbers you listed. What is the probability that it is divisible by 3?

c. Suppose that you randomly choose one of the numbers you listed. What is the probability that it is divisible by 5 or 3?

d. Suppose that you randomly choose one of the numbers you listed. What is the probability that it is divisible by 5 and 3?

39 The following four expressions look very similar.

$$2 - x - 5 \qquad 2 - (x - 5) \qquad 2 - (x + 5) \qquad 2 - 5 - x$$

a. Substitute $x = 0$ into each expression to find the value for each expression.

b. Substitute $x = -1$ into each expression to find the value for each expression.

c. Substitute $x = 1$ into each expression to find the value for each expression.

d. Substitute $x = 2$ into each expression to find the value for each expression.

e. Which of the above expressions will always have equal value when you substitute the same number for x in the expressions? Explain.

Just in Time

35 **a.** $(-13)(-14) = 182$

b. $(14)(-13) = -182$

c. $(13)(14) + (-13)(14) = 182 + (-182) = 0$

d. $\frac{(13)(-14)}{(-14)(-13)} = \frac{-182}{182} = -1$

36 $y = \frac{2}{3}x - \frac{4}{3}$

37 **a.** $P = 40$ cm
$A = 96$ cm^2

b. $P = 10 + 8 + 6 = 24$ in.
$A = 24$ in.^{2}

c. $P = 10 + 15 + 6 + 15 + 8 = 54$ m
$A = \frac{1}{2}(6)(15 + 23) = 114$ m^2

d. $P = 2(10 + 12) = 44$ mm
$A = 10 \cdot 12 - 4 \cdot 4 = 104$ mm^2

38 List of two-digit numbers: 33, 34, 35, 43, 44, 45, 53, 54, 55

a. $\frac{3}{9} = \frac{1}{3}$ **b.** $\frac{3}{9} = \frac{1}{3}$

c. $\frac{5}{9}$ **d.** $\frac{1}{9}$

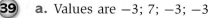

Just in Time

39 **a.** Values are -3; 7; -3; -3

b. Values are -2; 8; -2; -2

c. Values are -4; 6; -4; -4

d. Values are -5; 5; -5; -5

e. They are all equivalent except $2 - (x - 5)$. Student explanations might involve comparing tables, graphs, or symbolic reasoning.

40 Pentagon *ABCDE* is congruent to pentagon *PQRST*. Find each indicated angle measure or side length.

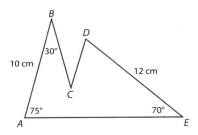 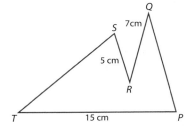

a. *BC*

b. m∠*T*

c. *AE*

d. m∠*P*

e. *ST*

f. *QP*

41 Tom and Jenny each drew a line to fit the same linear pattern of data. They wrote rules to make predictions for the value of *y* for different values of *x*. Complete the table below to compare their predictions.

x	0	1	2	3
(Tom's Rule) $y = 0.5x + 7$	7	7.5		
(Jenny's Rule) $y = 0.6x + 7$	7	7.6		
Difference in Predictions	0	0.1		

Why does the difference in predictions change? When is the difference greater than 0.5?

40   **a.** 7 cm

     b. 70°

     c. 15 cm

     d. 75°

     e. 12 cm

     f. 10 cm

41

x	0	1	2	3
(Tom's Rule) $y = 0.5x + 7$	7	7.5	8	8.5
(Jenny's Rule) $y = 0.6x + 7$	7	7.6	8.2	8.8
Difference in Predictions	0	0.1	0.2	0.3

The lines have the same y-intercept, but the slopes are different. This means that the gap between the lines increases as x increases. When $x > 5$, the difference is more than 0.5.

Teaching Resources

Assessment Masters 179–187.

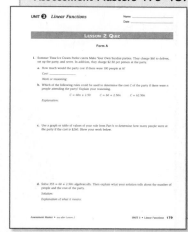

Unit 3

Equivalent Expressions

Entertainment is a big business in the United States—from network television, movies, and concert tours to local school plays and musical shows. Each live or recorded performance is prepared with weeks, months, or even years of creative work and business planning.

For example, a recording label might have the following costs to produce a CD by a popular music artist.

- $100,000 to record the tracks;
- $1.50 per copy for materials and reproduction;
- $2.25 per copy for royalties to the writers, producers, and performers.

The record label might receive income of about $5 per copy from the stores that sell the CD.

Equivalent Expressions

With the launch of this lesson, students look at different expressions for the same quantity. Equivalence of expressions is the focus of this investigation. Students will use context clues and compare tables and graphs of linear functions described by different expressions to reason about equivalence. Students will then abstract basic principles for determining algebraically when two expressions for *y* are equivalent.

The lesson is organized into two investigations. In the first investigation, context clues guide the development of equivalent expressions. In the second, students apply key properties of numbers and operations to evaluate the equivalence of expressions and to rewrite algebraic expressions in equivalent forms without the aid of contexts.

Lesson Objectives

- Write multiple expressions to represent a variable quantity from a real-world situation
- Use tables, graphs, and properties of numbers and operations to reason about the equivalence of expressions
- Rewrite linear expressions in equivalent forms by expanding, combining like terms, and factoring

Think About This Situation

The record label's profit on a CD is a function of the number of copies that are made and sold. A function rule for profit gives an *expression* for calculating profit. This lesson will focus on expressions for calculating various quantities.

a Using the given numbers, how would you calculate the label's net profit for 100,000 copies made and sold? For 1 million copies made and sold? For n copies made and sold?

b One group of students wrote the expression $5n - (3.75n + 100{,}000)$ to calculate the label's net profit on sales of n copies. Is this correct? How do you know? Why might they have expressed profit this way?

c Another group of students wrote the expression $-100{,}000 + 1.25n$ to calculate the label's net profit on sales of n copies. Is this correct? How do you know? Why might they have expressed profit this way?

d Could you represent the profit for n copies in other different ways?

e How could you convince another student that two different expressions represent the same quantity? Consider the expressions for profit you produced or those given in Parts b and c.

Two expressions are **equivalent** if they produce identical outputs when given identical inputs. In this lesson, you will develop your ability to recognize, write, and reason with equivalent linear expressions.

Investigation 1 — Different, Yet the Same

Your thinking about possible profit rules for a new CD release showed an important fact about linear expressions: Several different expressions can each represent the same quantity.

Tables and graphs are one way to explore whether two expressions are equivalent, but it is helpful to be able to tell by looking when two expressions are equivalent. As you work on the problems of this investigation, keep in mind the following question:

> *What operations on linear expressions lead to different, but equivalent, expressions?*

Think About This Situation

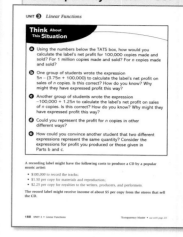

a The record label's profit is $25,000 when 100,000 copies are sold and $1,150,000 when 1 million copies are sold. Focus class discussion on *how* different students calculated these figures. (Expressions for profit when *n* copies are sold are given in Parts b–d.)

b $5n - (3.75n + 100,000)$ correctly shows income ($5n$) minus expenses, where the expenses for making the CDs and for royalties have been combined ($3.75n + 100,000$).

c $-100,000 + 1.25n$ correctly shows the fixed expense ($-100,000$) and combines all of the variable factors affecting profit (income, materials and reproduction, and royalties) into one term ($1.25n$).

d Encourage the class to generate as many different expressions as they can and to describe their reasoning for each. These might include: $5n - (1.50n + 2.25n + 100,000)$, $1.25n - 100,000$, $5n - 3.75n - 100,000$, $5.00n - 1.50n - 2.25n - 100,000$.

e Students may appeal to the identical tables and graphs. Some may not be completely convinced by the tables and graphs, which cannot show all possible values, and may suggest previously learned techniques for combining like terms and distributing or factoring.

Investigation 1 — Different, Yet the Same

> **COLLABORATION SKILL**
> Make group discussion fruitful.

The problems in this investigation are designed to make the principles for rewriting algebraic expressions into equivalent forms more explicit without prematurely attaching the formal abstract algebra terminology. The use of context is intended to help students make sense of why particular rearrangements of algebraic expressions are equivalent.

In this first investigation, students should be writing different expressions based on thinking about the context, not by manipulating expressions. After students have written several different expressions to represent the same quantity, then you might encourage them to step back and look at how those different expressions relate to each other.

Before students progress to the context-free symbol manipulation in Investigation 2, you should be sure that they have developed an understanding of rewriting symbolic expressions attached to a real-world context. A context gives a point of reference that will aid the abstraction in Investigation 2.

Movie Production Studios that make motion pictures deal with many of the same cost and income questions as music producers. Contracts sometimes designate parts of the income from a movie to the writers, directors, and actors. Suppose that for one film those payments are:

4% to the writer of the screenplay;
6% to the director;
15% to the leading actors.

1 What payments will go to the writer, the director, the leading actors, and to all these people combined in the following situations?

  a. The studio receives income of $25 million from the film.

  b. The studio receives income of $50 million from the film.

2 Suppose the studio receives income of I million dollars from the film.

  a. Write an expression for the total payment to the writer, the director, and the leading actors in a form that shows the breakdown to each person or group.

  b. Write another expression for the total payment that shows the combined percent of the film income that is paid out to the writer, the director, and the leading actors.

3 A movie studio will have other costs too. For example, there will be costs for shooting and editing the film. Suppose those costs are $20 million.

  a. Assume that the $20 million for shooting and editing the film and the payments to the writer, the director, and the leading actors are the only costs for the film. What will the studio's profit be if the income from the film is $50 million?

  b. Consider the studio's profit (in millions of dollars) when the income from the film is I million dollars.

   i. Write an expression for calculating the studio's profit that shows the separate payments to the writer, the director, and the leading actors.

   ii. Write another expression for calculating the studio's profit that combines the payments to the writer, the director, and the leading actors.

   iii. Is the following expression for calculating the studio's profit correct? How do you know?

$$I - (20 + 0.25I)$$

   iv. Write another expression for calculating the studio's profit and explain what that form shows.

1   **a.** Writer: 0.04(25 million) = \$1 million
Director: 0.06(25 million) = \$1.5 million
Leading Actors: 0.15(25 million) = \$3.75 million
All Combined: (1 + 1.5 + 3.75) million = \$6.25 million

b. Writer: 0.04(50 million) = \$2 million
Director: 0.06(50 million) = \$3 million
Leading Actors: 0.15(50 million) = \$7.5 million
All Combined: (2 + 3 + 7.5) million = \$12.5 million

2   In millions of dollars, the total payments are as follows.

a. $0.04I + 0.06I + 0.15I$

b. $0.25I$

3   **a.** In millions of dollars, the profit will equal $50 - 0.25(50) - 20$ or \$17.5 million.

b. **i.** In millions of dollars, the profit will equal
$I - 0.04I - 0.06I - 0.15I - 20$.

ii. $I - 0.25I - 20$

iii. The expression is correct.
$20 + 0.25I$ represents the total expenses for the movie: the fixed expenses and the 25% of the movie's income paid to the writer, director, and leading actors. Profit is equal to income minus expenses.

iv. $0.75I - 20$
This form shows that the studio's income is effectively 75% of the total income.

INSTRUCTIONAL NOTE
In your launch of this investigation, you may wish to discuss the relationship between "profit," "income," and "costs."

DIFFERENTIATION If you have students who need help with reading and/or organization, you may want to do Problems 1 and 2 together with the entire class. This suggestion is made because in order to complete these problems, students need to keep going back to information that is given earlier.

Unit 3

Movie Theaters For theaters, there are two main sources of income. Money is collected from ticket sales and from concession stand sales.

Suppose that a theater charges $8 for each admission ticket, and concession stand income averages $3 per person.

④ Income Consider the theater income during a month when they have *n* customers.

   a. Write an expression for calculating the theater's income that shows separately the income from ticket sales and the income from concession stand sales.

   b. Write another expression for calculating income that shows the total income received per person.

⑤ Expenses Suppose that the theater has to send 35% of its income from ticket sales to the movie studio releasing the film. The theater's costs for maintaining the concession stand stock average about 15% of concession stand sales. Suppose also that the theater has to pay rent, electricity, and staff salaries of about $15,000 per month.

   a. Consider the theater's expenses when the theater has *n* customers during a month.

     i. How much will the theater have to send to movie studios?

     ii. How much will the theater have to spend to restock the concession stand?

     iii. How much will the theater have to spend for rent, electricity, and staff salaries?

   b. Write two expressions for calculating the theater's total expenses, one that shows the breakdown of expenses and another that is as short as possible.

⑥ Profit Consider next the theater's profit for a month in which the theater has *n* customers.

   a. Write an expression for calculating the theater's profit that shows each component of the income and each component of the expenses.

   b. Write another expression for calculating the theater's profit that shows the total income minus the total expenses.

   c. Write another expression for calculating the theater's profit that is as short as possible.

⑦ Taxes The movie theater charges $8 per admission ticket sold and receives an average of $3 per person from the concession stand. The theater has to pay taxes on its receipts. Suppose the theater has to pay taxes equal to 6% of its receipts.

   a. Consider the tax due if the theater has 1,000 customers.

     i. Calculate the tax due for ticket sales and the tax due for concession stand sales, then calculate the total tax due.

     ii. Calculate the total receipts from ticket sales and concession stand sales combined, then calculate the tax due.

LESSON 3 • Equivalent Expressions **217**

4   **a.** $8n + 3n$

     b. $11n$

5   **a.**   **i.** $0.35(8n)$ or $2.80n$

        ii. $0.15(3n)$ or $0.45n$

       iii. $15,000

     b. $0.35(8n) + 0.15(3n) + 15,000$ or $2.80n + 0.45n + 15,000$, and $3.25n + 15,000$

6   **a.** $8n + 3n - 0.35(8n) - 0.15(3n) - 15,000$

     b. $11n - (3.25n + 15,000)$

     c. $7.75n - 15,000$

7   **a.**   **i.**   The tax due for ticket sales is $0.06(8)(1,000)$, or $480. The tax due for concession stand sales is $0.06(3)(1,000)$, or $180. The total tax due is $660.

       ii. The total receipts from ticket sales and concession stand sales combined is $8(1,000) + 3(1,000) = \$11,000$. The tax due is $0.06(11,000) = \$660$.

Unit 3

b. Write two expressions for calculating the tax due if the theater has *n* customers, one for each way of calculating the tax due described in Part a.

8 In Problem 6, you wrote expressions for the monthly theater profit after all operating expenses. A new proposal will tax profits only, but at 8%. Here is one expression for the tax due under this new proposal.

$$0.08(7.75n - 15,000)$$

a. Is the expression correct? How can you be sure?

b. Write an expression for calculating the tax due under the new proposal that is as short as possible. Show how you obtained your expression. Explain how you could check that your expression is equivalent to the one given above.

Summarize
the Mathematics

In many situations, two people can suggest expressions for linear functions that look quite different but are equivalent. For example, these two symbolic expressions for linear functions are equivalent.

$$15x - (12 + 7x) \quad \text{and} \quad 8x - 12$$

a What does it mean for these two expressions to be equivalent?

b How could you test the equivalence of these two expressions using tables and graphs?

c Explain how you might reason from the first expression to produce the second expression.

Be prepared to explain your responses to the entire class.

✔ Check Your Understanding

Many college basketball teams play in winter tournaments sponsored by businesses that want the advertising opportunity. For one such tournament, the projected income and expenses are as follows.

- Income is $60 per ticket sold, $75,000 from television and radio broadcast rights, and $5 per person from concession stand sales.
- Expenses are $200,000 for the colleges, $50,000 for rent of the arena and its staff, and a tax of $2.50 per ticket sold.

a. Find the projected income, expenses, and profit if 15,000 tickets are sold for the tournament.

b. Write two equivalent expressions for tournament income if *n* tickets are sold. In one expression, show each source of income. In the other, rearrange and combine the income components to give the shortest possible expression.

b. $0.06(8n) + 0.06(3n)$
$0.06(8n + 3n)$, or $0.06(11n)$

8 **a.** The expression is correct. From Problem 6 Part c, profit is given by $7.75n - 15,000$. Tax is 8% of this amount, or $0.08(7.75n - 15,000)$.

b. $0.62n - 1,200$
$0.08(7.75n) + 0.08(-15,000)$
Equivalence could be checked by tables and graphs of
$y_1 = 0.08(7.75n - 15,000)$ and $y_2 = 0.62n - 1,200$.

Summarize
the Mathematics

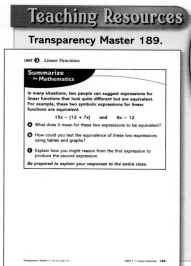

Teaching Resources

Transparency Master 189.

(a) For any value of x, the result when substituting that value of x into each of the two expressions will be the same.

(b) Enter $y_1 = 15x - (12 + 7x)$ and $y_2 = 8x - 12$. Look to see whether the tables and graphs are identical for both functions.

(c) A possible response follows:

To subtract the total of 12 and $7x$, I can subtract them together or one at a time. When I subtract $7x$ from $15x$, I'm left with $8x$. I still have to subtract the 12 to get $8x - 12$.

PROCESSING PROMPT Think back to your work. On which problem was your discussion particularly fruitful? Identify reasons for this.

✔ Check Your Understanding

a. Income: $60(15,000) + 75,000 + 5(15,000) = \$1,050,000$
Expenses: $200,000 + 50,000 + 2.50(15,000) = \$287,500$
Profit: $1,050,000 - 287,500 = \$762,500$

b. Income in dollars: $60n + 75,000 + 5n$
Income in dollars: $65n + 75,000$

MATH TOOLKIT Give at least one reason why different forms of an expression may be needed in certain situations. How can you determine if two expressions are algebraically equivalent?

DIFFERENTIATION
Suggested question for a class that likes challenges: Are these two expressions equivalent? Justify your answer.

$3x$ and $\dfrac{6x(x - 2)}{2(x - 2)}$

c. Write two equivalent expressions for tournament expenses if n tickets are sold. In one expression, show each source of expense. In the other, rearrange and combine the expense components to give the shortest possible expression.

d. Write two equivalent expressions for tournament profit if n tickets are sold. In one expression, show income separate from expenses. In the other, rearrange and combine components to give the shortest possible expression.

Investigation 2   The Same, Yet Different

In Investigation 1, you translated information about variables into expressions and then into different, but equivalent, expressions. You used facts about the numbers and variables involved to guide and check the writing of new equivalent symbolic expressions.

The examples in Investigation 1 suggest some ways to rewrite symbolic expressions that will produce equivalent forms, regardless of the situation being modeled. Think about how you can rewrite expressions involving variables in equivalent forms even if you do not know what the variables represent. As you work on the problems of this investigation, look for answers to this question:

> *How can algebraic properties of numbers and operations*
> *be used to verify the equivalence of expressions*
> *and to write equivalent expressions?*

1 These expressions might represent the profit for a given number of sales. Using your thinking from Investigation 1 as a guide, write at least two different but equivalent expressions for each.

a. $8x - 3x - 2x - 50$ **b.** $6a - (20 + 4a)$

c. $0.8(10n - 30)$ **d.** $t - 20 - 0.3t$

2 Think about how you might convince someone else that the expressions you wrote in Problem 1 are, in fact, equivalent.

a. How might you use tables and graphs to support your claim?

b. How might you argue that two expressions are equivalent without the use of tables or graphs? What kind of evidence do you find more convincing? Why?

3 Determine which of the following pairs of expressions are equivalent. If a pair of expressions is equivalent, explain how you might justify the equivalence. If a pair is not equivalent, show that the pair is not equivalent.

a. $3.2x + 5.4x$ and $8.6x$ **b.** $3(x - 2)$ and $6 - 3x$

c. $4y + 7y - 12$ and $-12 + 11y$ **d.** $7x + 14$ and $7(x + 2)$

e. $8x - 2(x - 3)$ and $6x - 6$ **f.** $3x + 7y - 21$ and $10xy + (-21)$

g. $\dfrac{8y + 12}{4}$ and $2y + 3$ **h.** $x + 4$ and $3(2x + 1) - 5x + 1$

c. Expenses in dollars: $200{,}000 + 50{,}000 + 2.50n$
Expenses in dollars: $250{,}000 + 2.50n$

d. Profit in dollars: $(65n + 75{,}000) - (250{,}000 + 2.50n)$
Profit in dollars: $62.50n - 175{,}000$

Investigation 2 — The Same, Yet Different

This investigation is intended to help students abstract what they have been doing in regard to writing equivalent expressions in order to apply algebraic properties of numbers and operations, to evaluate the equivalence of expressions, and to generate equivalent expressions without a context to guide their thinking.

Students may use tables and graphs to help them decide whether the pairs of expressions given in Problem 3 are equivalent. Encourage them to also think about how they might reason about the equivalence of those pairs without using tables or graphs. Following Problem 3, four useful properties for rewriting expressions are given. It is not intended for students to memorize these properties or to identify how each is applied in simplifying expressions in a formal proof fashion. Rather, these properties serve to formalize the kind of thinking students have already been using.

As students work on the remaining problems of the investigation, encourage them to check their work by comparing tables and graphs produced by the resulting expressions, to see whether they have reasoned correctly.

1 Responses will vary. Encourage students to talk about how these expressions might relate to ideas about income, expenses, and profit. They may want to refer back to examples from Investigation 1 to defend various operations.

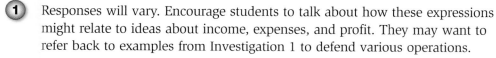

a. $8x - (3x + 2x + 50)$
  $3x - 50$

b. $6a - 20 - 4a$
  $2a - 20$

c. $0.8(10n) - 0.8(30)$
  $8n - 24$

d. $t - (20 + 0.3t)$
  $0.7t - 20$

2 **a.** You can use each expression to define a function and compare the tables and graphs generated by each. If the tables and graphs are identical, then this suggests that the expressions are equivalent.

  b. Students might make "common sense" arguments, with supporting examples in context, to defend various operations. Others might refer to commutative, associative, or distributive properties of operations.

> **COMMON ERROR** Students often have trouble distributing when negative signs are involved. If you notice incorrect answers to Parts b and d, ask students to check by graphing $y_1 = 6a - (20 + 4a)$ and $y_2 = $ *their expression* and determine their error.

> **NOTE** The answers to Problem 3 can be found on page T220.

There are five properties of numbers and operations that are especially helpful in transforming algebraic expressions to useful equivalent forms.

- **Distributive Property of Multiplication over Addition**—For any numbers a, b, and c:

$$a(b + c) = ab + ac \text{ and } ac + bc = (a + b)c.$$

This property can be applied to write expressions with or without the use of parentheses. For example,

$$5(2x + 3) = 10x + 15.$$

The distributive property can also be applied to the sums of products with common factors. For example,

$$3x + 7x = (3 + 7)x \qquad \text{and} \qquad 6\pi + 8\pi = (6 + 8)\pi$$
$$= 10x \qquad\qquad\qquad\qquad\qquad = 14\pi.$$

- **Commutative Property of Addition**—For any numbers a and b:

$$a + b = b + a.$$

- **Associative Property of Addition**—For any numbers a, b, and c:

$$a + (b + c) = (a + b) + c.$$

The commutative and associative properties are often used together to rearrange the addends in an expression. For example,

$$3x + 5 + 4x + 7 = (3x + 4x) + (5 + 7)$$
$$= 7x + 12.$$

- **Connecting Addition and Subtraction**—For any numbers a and b:

$$a - b = a + (-b).$$

This property can be applied to rewrite an expression that involves subtraction so that the terms involved can be rearranged using the commutative and associative properties of addition. For example,

$$4x - 3 - 5x + 7 = 4x + (-3) + (-5x) + 7$$
$$= 4x + (-5x) + (-3) + 7$$
$$= -x + 4.$$

The property can also be used with the distributive property to expand a product that involves subtraction. For example,

$$5(2x - 3) = 5(2x + (-3))$$
$$= 10x + (-15)$$
$$= 10x - 15.$$

- **Connecting Multiplication and Division**—For any numbers a and b with $b \neq 0$:

$$\frac{a}{b} = a \cdot \frac{1}{b}.$$

This property can be combined with the distributive property to rewrite an expression that involves division. For example,

$$\frac{20 - 15x}{5} = (20 - 15x)\frac{1}{5}$$
$$= 4 - 3x.$$

Students might use tables, graphs, or algebraic reasoning to show equivalence.

a. Equivalent—It may be helpful for students to make up contexts for thinking about equivalence. For example, if a movie theater's income from ticket sales is $5.40 per person and its income from concession stand sales is about $3.20 per person, then their total income is about $8.60 per person.

b. Not equivalent—If $x = 0$, then $3(x - 2) = -6$ and $6 - 3x = 6$. For any value of $x \neq 2$, these two expressions will have different values.

c. Equivalent—Similar reasoning to that in Part a can be applied to combine $4y + 7y$. The 12 is similar to fixed expenses in the profit expressions. You can think of subtracting the fixed expenses, or you can think about starting "in the hole."

d. Equivalent—This is similar to computing the tax on a sum; you can compute the tax on each component of the sum and then add, or you can compute the sum and then calculate tax on the total.

e. Not equivalent—These two expressions will have different values for any value of x.

f. Not equivalent—Possible counterexample: If $x = 2$ and $y = 0$, then $3x + 7y - 21 = -15$ and $10xy + (-21) = -21$.

g. Equivalent—If two amounts are to be divided evenly among 4 people, then you can combine the amounts and divide them, or you can divide up each amount individually.

h. Equivalent—Students may use algebraic thinking here to reason that $3(2x + 1)$ is the same as $6x + 3$, and then subtract $5x$ from $6x$ and add 1 to 3 to get $x + 4$.

④ When you are given an expression and asked to write an equivalent expression that does not contain parentheses, this is called **expanding** the expression. Use the distributive property to rewrite the following expressions in *expanded* form.

a. $4(y + 2)$ **b.** $(5 - x)(3y)$ **c.** $-2(y - 3)$

d. $-7(4 + x)$ **e.** $\frac{(16x - 8)}{4}$ **f.** $\frac{1}{3}(2x + 3)$

⑤ When you are given an expression and asked to write an equivalent expression that gives a product, this is called **factoring** the expression. For example, in Problem 4 Part a you wrote $4(y + 2) = 4y + 8$. Writing $4y + 8$ as $4(y + 2)$ is said to be writing $4y + 8$ in *factored* form. Use the distributive property to rewrite the following expressions in factored form.

a. $2x + 6$ **b.** $20 - 5y$ **c.** $6y - 9$

d. $8 + 12x$ **e.** $3x + 15y$ **f.** $xy - 7x$

⑥ Using the distributive property to add or subtract products with common factors is called **combining like terms**. Use the distributive property to rewrite the following expressions in equivalent shorter form by combining like terms.

a. $7x + 11x$ **b.** $7x - 11x$

c. $5 + 3y + 12 + 7y$ **d.** $2 + 3x - 5 - 7x$

e. $\frac{3x}{4} - 2x + \frac{x}{4}$ **f.** $10x - 5y + 3y - 2 - 4x + 6$

⑦ Write each of the following expressions in its *simplest* equivalent form by expanding and then combining like terms.

a. $7(3y - 2) + 6y$ **b.** $5 + 3(x + 4) + 7x$

c. $2 + 3x - 5(1 - 7x)$ **d.** $10 - (5y + 3)$

e. $10 - \frac{15x - 9}{3}$ **f.** $5(x + 3) - \frac{4x + 2}{2}$

g. $7y + 4(3y - 11)$ **h.** $8(x + 5) - 3(x - 2)$

⑧ Write each of the following expressions in equivalent form by combining like terms and then factoring.

a. $7 + 15x + 5 - 6x$ **b.** $x - 10 + x + 2$

c. $20x + 10 - 5x$ **d.** $24 - 5x - 4 + 6x - 8 + 2x$

⑨ When *simplifying* an expression, it is easy to make mistakes. Some of the pairs of expressions below are equivalent and some are not. If a pair of expressions is equivalent, describe the properties of numbers and operations that justify the equivalence. If a pair is not equivalent, correct the mistake.

a. $2(x - 1)$ and $2x - 1$ **b.** $4(3 + 2x)$ and $12 + 8x$

c. $9 - (x + 7)$ and $16 - x$ **d.** $\frac{6x + 12}{6}$ and $x + 12$

e. $5x - 2 + 3x$ and $8x - 2$ **f.** $4x - x + 2$ and 6

4 **a.** $4y + 8$ **b.** $15y - 3xy$ **c.** $-2y + 6$
     d. $-28 - 7x$ **e.** $4x - 2$ **f.** $\frac{2}{3}x + 1$

5 **a.** $2(x + 3)$ **b.** $5(4 - y)$ **c.** $3(2y - 3)$
     d. $4(2 + 3x)$ **e.** $3(x + 5y)$ **f.** $x(y - 7)$

6 **a.** $18x$ **b.** $-4x$ **c.** $17 + 10y$
     d. $-3 - 4x$ **e.** $-x$ **f.** $6x - 2y + 4$

7 **a.** $27y - 14$ **b.** $17 + 10x$ **c.** $38x - 3$
     d. $7 - 5y$ **e.** $13 - 5x$ **f.** $3x + 14$
     g. $19y - 44$ **h.** $5x + 46$

8 **a.** $3(4 + 3x)$ **b.** $2(x - 4)$
     c. $5(3x + 2)$ **d.** $3(4 + x)$

9 **a.** not equivalent; did not multiply both x *and* -1 by 2

     b. equivalent; Distributive Property of Multiplication over Addition

     c. not equivalent; did not subtract both x *and* 7

     d. not equivalent; did not divide both $6x$ *and* 12 by 6

     e. equivalent; Commutative and Associative Properties of Addition

     f. not equivalent; $4x$ is not $4 + x$, but 4 times x, so $4x - x$ is not 4, but $3x$

INSTRUCTIONAL NOTE If expanding, factoring, and combining like terms were not familiar tasks for your students, you may want to look at On Your Own Tasks 5 and 18 before moving on.

Unit 3

Computer algebra systems (CAS) have been programmed to use properties of numbers and operations like those described early in this investigation to expand, factor, and simplify algebraic expressions. To use a CAS for this purpose you need only enter the expression accurately and then apply the "expand" or "factor" commands from the CAS algebra menu.

You can also check equivalence of two given expressions by entering each as part of an equation and pressing the [ENTER] key. If the expressions are equivalent, the CAS will respond with "true."

10 Compare the CAS output shown below with your answers to the following problems. Discuss and reconcile any differences.

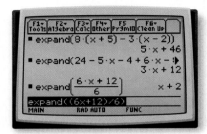

a. Problem 7 Part h

b. Problem 8 Part d

c. Problem 9 Part d

11 Use the CAS that is available to you to perform the following algebraic procedures. Compare the CAS output with what you expect from your knowledge of algebraic manipulations and reconcile any differences.

a. What is the shortest expression equivalent to $25x - 4(3x + 7) + 106$?

b. What expression equivalent to that in Part a is in simplest factored form?

c. What expression is equivalent in expanded form to $5(7 - 3x) - (8x + 12)23$?

d. What results from asking your CAS to factor $a \cdot x + a \cdot c$?

e. What results from asking your CAS to factor $a \cdot (x + b) - c \cdot (x + b)$?

f. What results from asking your CAS to expand $a \cdot (x + b) - c \cdot (x + b)$?

11 **a.**

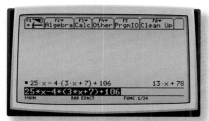

TECHNOLOGY NOTE The screens for parts e and f are from *CPMP-Tools* with the Auto Numeric option unchecked.

b.

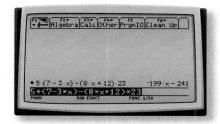

c.

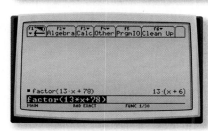

d.

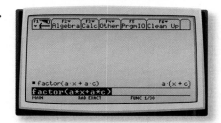

e.

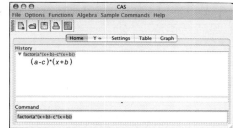

Answers will vary, depending on how the *factor* command is structured in any particular CAS. One fairly standard CAS produces $(a - c)(x = b)$.

f.

Answers will vary, depending on how the *expand* command is structured in any particular CAS. One common display is $a * x - c * x + a * b - b * c$.

Summarize the Mathematics

In this investigation, you applied key properties of numbers and operations to evaluate the equivalence of expressions and to create equivalent expressions.

a Summarize these algebraic properties in your own words and give one example of how each property is used in writing equivalent expressions.

b How can you tell if expressions such as those in this investigation are in simplest form?

c What are some easy errors to make that may require careful attention when writing expressions in equivalent forms? How can you avoid making those errors?

Be prepared to explain your thinking and examples to the class.

✔ Check Your Understanding

For each of the following expressions:

- Write two expressions equivalent to the original—one that is as short as possible.
- Describe the algebraic reasoning used to obtain each expression.
- Test the equivalence of each expression to the original by comparing tables and graphs.

a. $9x + 2 - x$

b. $3(x + 7) - 6$

c. $\dfrac{20 - 4(x - 1)}{2}$

d. $2(1 + 3x) - (5 - 6x)$

A variety of responses are possible for each of these questions. Encourage students to share their thinking. A blackline master is available for student examples different from those in the text.

Summarize
the Mathematics

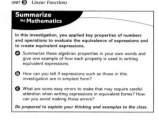
a The distributive property says that when you want to multiply a sum, you can compute the sum first and then multiply, or you can multiply each component of the sum and then add. The commutative and associative properties say that you can add terms in any order. The Addition ... Subtraction Property says that subtraction can be rewritten as the addition of the opposite. The Multiplication ... Division Property says that division can be rewritten as multiplication by the reciprocal.

b The expression should be in the form $a + bx$ or $cx + d$.

c Some common errors, highlighted in Problems 3 and 9, include removing parentheses without distributing, failing to "distribute" when subtracting or dividing, combining *unlike* terms, and commuting subtraction.

MATH TOOLKIT Students may use the blackline master provided to summarize the properties of numbers and operations in the Teaching Resources on page 190.

✓ Check Your Understanding

a. (1) $9x + 2 - x = 8x + 2$: rearrange and combine like terms (addition ... subtraction, commutative, and distributive properties).
   (2) $8x + 2 = 2(4x + 1)$: use the distributive property to factor.

b. (1) $3(x + 7) - 6 = 3x + 15$: expand $3(x + 7)$ to $3x + 21$, then combine $21 - 6$.
   (2) $3x + 15 = 3(x + 5)$: use the distributive property to factor.

c. (1) $\dfrac{20 - 4(x - 1)}{2} = 12 - 2x$; Option 1: distribute -4 first (-4 is $+(-4)$) and combine like terms to get $\dfrac{24 - 4x}{2}$, then distribute division by 2; Option 2: distribute division by 2 to get $10 - 2(x - 1)$, then distribute -2 and combine like terms.
   (2) $12 - 2x = 2(6 - x)$: use the distributive property to factor.

d. (1) $2(1 + 3x) - (5 - 6x) = 12x - 3$: distribute and combine like terms.
   (2) $12x - 3 = 3(4x - 1)$: use the distributive property to factor.

On Your Own

Applications

1 To advertise a concert tour, the concert promoter paid an artist $2,500 to design a special collector's poster. The posters cost $2.50 apiece to print and package in a cardboard cylinder. They are to be sold for $7.95 apiece.

a. Write expressions that show how to calculate cost, income, and profit if n posters are printed and sold.

b. Write two expressions that are different from, but equivalent to, the profit expression you wrote in Part a. Explain why you are sure they are equivalent.

2 The video game industry is a big business around the world. Development of a new game might cost millions of dollars. Then to make and package each game disc will cost several more dollars per copy. Suppose the development cost for one game is $5,000,000; each disc costs $4.75 to make and package; and the wholesale price is set at $35.50 per disc.

a. Write expressions that show how to calculate the cost of designing and making n discs and the income earned from selling those n discs.

b. Write two different but equivalent expressions for profit from selling n discs.

c. Use evidence in tables, graphs, or properties of numbers and operations to justify equivalence of the two expressions from Part b.

3 The historic Palace Theater offers students and seniors a $2 discount off the regular movie ticket price of $7.50. The theater has 900 seats and regularly sells out on the weekends. Marcia and Sam wrote the following expressions for income from ticket sales based on the number x of discounted tickets sold for a sold-out show.

Marcia's expression: $5.5x + 7.5(900 - x)$
Sam's expression: $900(7.5) - 2x$

a. Explain how Marcia and Sam may have reasoned in writing their expressions.

Applications

1 **a.** $C = 2.5n + 2,500$, where n represents the number of posters printed and C represents the cost.
$I = 7.95n$, where n represents the number of posters printed and I represents the income.
$P = 5.45n - 2,500$, where n represents the number of posters printed and P represents the profit.

b. $7.95n - (2.5n + 2,500)$ and $7.95n - 2.5n - 2,500$
To justify equivalence, students should note that table entries or graphs for their two expressions entered as functions are the same. Students might also verify equivalence using algebraic reasoning.

2 **a.** The total cost in dollars is $5,000,000 + 4.75n$.
The income in dollars is $35.5n$.

b. $35.5n - 5,000,000 - 4.75n$ and $30.75n - 5,000,000$

c. To justify equivalence, students should note that table entries or graphs for their two expressions entered as functions are the same. Students might also verify equivalence using properties.

3 **a.** Marcia expressed the number of discount tickets as x, and calculated that the number of regular tickets would be expressed as $900 - x$. Sam calculated a base full-price income of $900(7.5)$, and expressed the number of discount tickets sold as x. He then subtracted two dollars per discount ticket sold by writing "$-2x$".

b. Use tables and graphs to check whether Marcia's and Sam's expressions are equivalent.

c. Write a simpler expression for income based on the number x of discounted tickets sold for a sold-out show. Show how you could reason from Marcia's and Sam's expressions to this simpler expression.

4. In art class, students are framing square mirrors with hand-painted ceramic tiles as shown at the right. Each tile is one inch by one inch.

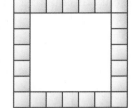

a. How many tiles are needed to frame a square mirror with side length 5 inches? 3 inches? 10 inches?

b. Write an expression for the number of tiles needed to frame a square mirror with side length x inches.

c. One group of students came up with the following expressions for the number of tiles needed to frame a square mirror with side length x inches. Explain the thinking that might have led to each of these expressions. Use tables, graphs, or algebraic reasoning to demonstrate the equivalence of the expressions.

  i. $(x + 1) + (x + 1) + (x + 1) + (x + 1)$

  ii. $(x + 2) + x + (x + 2) + x$

  iii. $4x + 4$

  iv. $4(x + 1)$

  v. $2(x + 2) + 2x$

5. Are the following pairs of expressions equivalent? Explain your reasoning in each case.

a. $7 - 5(x + 4 - 3x)$ and $7 - 5x + 20 - 15x$

b. $7x - 12 + 3x - 8 + 9x - 5$ and $7x - 4 + 2x + 8 + 10x - 13$

6. For each of the following expressions, write an equivalent expression that is as short as possible.

a. $3x + 5 + 8x$ **b.** $7 + 3x + 12 + 9x$

c. $8(5 + 2x) - 36$ **d.** $2(5x + 6) + 3 + 4x$

e. $\dfrac{10x - 40}{5}$ **f.** $5x + 7 - 3x + 12$

g. $3x + 7 - 4(3x - 6)$ **h.** $-7x + 13 + \dfrac{12x - 4}{4}$

7. For each of the following expressions, combine like terms and then write in factored form.

a. $6x + 5 + 9x$ **b.** $20 + 6x + 4 + 10x$

c. $32 + 20x$ **d.** $13x + 6 - (2 - 3x)$

b. Tables and graphs are identical.

c. $6{,}750 - 2x$, where x is the number of discounted tickets sold

Marcia's expression:

$5.5x + 7.5(900 - x) = 5.5x + 6{,}750 - 7.5x$ because 7.5 is
multiplied times both
900 and x

$\qquad\qquad\qquad\qquad = 6{,}750 - 2x$ by combining like terms

Sam's expression:

$900(7.5) - 2x = 6{,}750 - 2x$ by arithmetic

4   **a.** 5 in. $-$ 24 tiles
3 in. $-$ 16 tiles
10 in. $-$ 44 tiles

     b. Expressions should be equivalent to $4x + 4$.

     c.   **i.** Imagine that for each side, measured in x inches, you need x tiles, plus one "extra" to "round the corner."

        ii. Imagine that two sides are "full sides," and two fit within.

        iii. $4x + 4$: Four sides of x inches long, plus four corner pieces.

        iv. $4(x + 1)$: A condensed way of writing the thinking behind part i: Four sides, each measures x inches plus one "extra" to "round the corner."

        v. A condensed way of writing the thinking behind part ii: Two sides are "full sides," of length $x + 2$, and two sides "fit within" and are of length x.

     Students should justify the equivalence of these expressions using tables, graphs, or algebraic properties.

5   Students may answer this task using the number and operation properties or as below.

     a. No, because $7 - 5x - 20 - 15x \neq 7 - 5x + 20 - 15x$. That is, $-5(4) = -20$, not $+20$. For any value of x, these expressions will have different values.

     b. No. The constant terms combine to -25 in the first expression and to -9 in the second expression. For any value of x, these expressions will have different values.

6   **a.** $11x + 5$ **b.** $12x + 19$ **c.** $4 + 16x$

     d. $14x + 15$ **e.** $2x - 8$ **f.** $2x + 19$

     g. $-9x + 31$ **h.** $-4x + 12$

7   **a.** $15x + 5 = 5(3x + 1)$ **b.** $24 + 16x = 8(3 + 2x)$

     c. $4(8 + 5x)$ **d.** $16x + 4 = 4(4x + 1)$

Connections

8 One expression for predicting the median salary in dollars for working women since 1970 is $4{,}000 + 750(y - 1970)$, where y is the year.

a. Write an equivalent expression in the form $a + by$. Explain how you know the new expression is equivalent to the original.

b. What do the numbers 4,000, 750, and the expression $(y - 1970)$ tell about the salary pattern?

c. What do the numbers a and b that you found in Part a tell about the salary pattern?

9 Consider the following formula for transforming temperature in degrees Fahrenheit F to temperature in degrees Celsius C.

$$C = \frac{5}{9}(F - 32)$$

a. Use the distributive property to rewrite the expression for temperature in degrees Celsius in the form $aF + b$.

b. Write a question that is more easily answered using the original expression for calculating the temperature in degrees Celsius. Write another question that is more easily answered using the expression from Part a. Explain why you think one expression is better for each question.

10 Consider the following set of instructions.
Pick any number.
Multiply it by 2.
Subtract 10 from the result.
Multiply the result by 3.
Add 30 to the result.
Finally, divide by your original number.

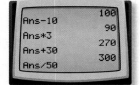

a. Repeat the process several times with different starting numbers. What are your answers in each case?

b. Let x represent the starting number. Write an expression showing the calculations for any value of x.

c. Write the expression from Part b in simplest equivalent form. Explain how it makes the results in Part a reasonable.

11 The length of a rectangle is ℓ and the width is w.

a. Write at least three different expressions that show how to calculate the perimeter of the rectangle. Explain how you might reason from a drawing of a rectangle to help you write each expression.

b. Use the properties of numbers and operations, discussed in this lesson, to reason about the equivalence of the expressions you wrote in Part a.

Connections

8 **a.** $4,000 + 750(y - 1970) = 4,000 + 750y - 1,477,500$
$$= -1,473,500 + 750y$$

Students might explain equivalence by comparing graphs, tables, or algebraic thinking.

b. $4,000 is the median salary in year 1970. $750 is the annual increase in median salary. $y - 1970$ is the number of years since 1970.

c. $a = -1,473,500$ would be the predicted median salary in the year 0. $b = 750$ is the annual increase in the median salary.

9 **a.** $\frac{5}{9}F - \frac{160}{9}$

b. One example for the original form:

If the temperature is 32°F, what is the temperature in °C? The original form is better for this question because, using the original form, one can answer the question with a minimum of calculations. One can immediately see that $(F - 32)$ for $F = 32$ gives us zero, and that therefore $C = \frac{5}{9}(0)$, or simply 0°C. Using the new form we must first perform the calculation $\frac{5}{9}(32)$, which gives us $\frac{160}{9}$ before it becomes clear that $C = 0$°C.

One example for the new form:

If the temperature is 0°F, what is the temperature in °C? The new form is better for this question because, using the new form, one can answer the question with a minimum of calculations. One can immediately see that $\frac{5}{9}F$ for $F = 0$ gives us zero, and that therefore $C = -\frac{160}{9}$, or approximately -18°C. The original form would have involved calculations that are not as quickly done in your head: $C = \frac{5}{9}(0 - 32) = \frac{5}{9}(-32) = -\frac{160}{9} \approx -18$°C.

10 **a.** 6, for any starting number except 0

b. $\dfrac{3(2x - 10) + 30}{x}$

c. $\dfrac{3(2x - 10) + 30}{x} = \dfrac{6x}{x} = 6$. This makes the results in Part a reasonable because for any x (except 0) the expression is equivalent to 6.

11 **a.** $P = \ell + \ell + w + w$ $\qquad$ $P = 2\ell + 2w$ $\qquad$ $P = 2(\ell + w)$
The drawing of the rectangle suggests seeing the perimeter as the sum of the widths and lengths.

b. Combining like terms allows us to simplify from the first to the second expression. Factoring allows us to simplify from the second to the third expression. The first and the third expressions are equivalent because they both are equivalent to the second.

12 Recall the formula $A = \frac{1}{2}bh$ for the area of a triangle where b is the length of the base and h is the height of the triangle. A trapezoid with bases of lengths b_1 and b_2 and height h is shown below.

a. Make a copy of the diagram.

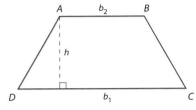

b. Draw $\triangle ACD$ and write an expression showing how to calculate its area.

c. Write an expression showing how to calculate the area of $\triangle ABC$.

d. Write an expression showing how to calculate the area of trapezoid $ABCD$.

e. Write a different but equivalent expression for the area of the trapezoid.

13 Refer back to the Check Your Understanding problem of Investigation 1 (page 218). To study the profit prospects of different options in organizing a college basketball tournament, it might be helpful to construct a spreadsheet to calculate income, expenses, and profit that will result from various decisions.

a. Copy the expressions you developed for income, expenses, and profit in terms of the number of tickets sold n based on the following information.

- Income is $60 per ticket sold, $75,000 from television and radio broadcast rights, and $5 per person from concession stand sales.

- Expenses are $200,000 for the colleges, $50,000 for rent of the arena and its staff, and a tax of $2.50 per ticket sold.

b. Use those expressions to complete the following spreadsheet so that you could explore effects of different ticket sale numbers. Enter the required numbers and formulas in column **B** of the spreadsheet.

Profit Prospects.xls		
◇	**A**	**B**
1	Tickets Sold =	
2	Income =	
3	Expenses =	
4	Profit =	

c. Expand and modify the spreadsheet so that you could also adjust ticket price, average concession stand income, ticket tax, and television/radio broadcast rights to see immediately how profit changes. (*Hint:* Put the labels for those factors in cells of column **C** and then the values in adjacent cells of column **D**.)

LESSON 3 • Equivalent Expressions **227**

12 a–b. $\dfrac{b_1 h}{2}$

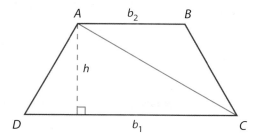

c. $\dfrac{b_2 h}{2}$ d. $\dfrac{b_1 h}{2} + \dfrac{b_2 h}{2}$ e. $\dfrac{h(b_1 + b_2)}{2}$

13 a–b.

Profit Prospects.xls

◇	A	B	
1	Tickets Sold =		
2	Income =	=65*B1+75000	
3	Expenses =	=2.5*B1+250000	
4	Profit =	=B2−B3	
5			

c.

Profit Prospects.xls

◇	A	B	C	D	
1	Tickets Sold =		Ticket Price =		
2	Income =	=(D1+D2)*B1+D4	Concessions =		
3	Expenses =	=D3*B1+250000	Ticket Tax =		
4	Profit =	=B2−B3	Broadcast Rights =		
5					

Reflections

14 In Applications Task 2 about video game discs, any one of the following expressions could be used to calculate profit when n discs are sold.

$$35.50n - 4.75n - 5,000,000$$
$$30.75n - 5,000,000$$
$$35.50n - (5,000,000 + 4.75n)$$

  a. Explain how you can be sure that all three expressions are equivalent.

  b. Which expression do you believe shows the business conditions in the best way? Explain the reasons for your choice.

15 Think about a real situation involving a changing quantity. Write at least two different but equivalent expressions that show how to calculate the quantity.

16 How do you prefer to check whether two expressions are equivalent: using tables of values, graphs, or algebraic reasoning? Why? Which gives the strongest evidence of equivalence?

17 Each of the expressions in Applications Tasks 5–7 defines a linear function. However, none of those expressions looks exactly like $a + bx$, the familiar form of an expression for a linear function.

  a. What features of expressions like those in the Applications tasks suggest that the graph of the function defined by that expression will be a line?

  b. What might appear in an expression that would suggest that the graph of the corresponding function would not be a line? Give some examples and sketch the graphs of those examples.

18 In transforming algebraic expressions to equivalent forms, it's easy to make some mistakes and use "illegal" moves. Given below are six pairs of algebraic expressions. Some are equivalent and some are not.

  • Use tables, graphs, and/or algebraic reasoning to decide which pairs are actually equivalent and which involve errors in reasoning.

  • In each case of equivalent expressions, describe algebraic reasoning that could be used to show the equivalence.

  • In each case of an algebra mistake, spot the error in reasoning. Write an explanation that would help clear up the problem for a student who made the error.

  a. Is $3(2x + 8)$ equivalent to $6x + 8$?

  b. Is $4x - 6x$ equivalent to $2x$?

  c. Is $8(2 - 6x)$ equivalent to $16 - 48x$?

  d. Is $10 + 3x - 12$ equivalent to $3x + 2$?

  e. Is $\dfrac{5x + 10}{5}$ equivalent to $x + 10$?

  f. Is $-4(x - 3)$ equivalent to $-4x - 12$?

Reflections

14 **a.** Students might explain equivalence by comparing graphs, tables, or algebraic thinking.

b. One possible response: The best expression showing all the conditions is the first one, $35.50N - 4.75N - 5,000,000$, because it shows each condition separately—sale price, production cost, and fixed development cost.

15 One example: Suppose a school booster club can purchase custom printed sweatshirts for $12 each, plus an initial set-up fee of $35. The club plans to sell the sweatshirts for $15 each. In dollars, the profit for selling n sweatshirts is $15n - (12n + 35)$, or $3n - 35$.

16 Algebraic reasoning gives the strongest evidence of equivalence, because it is possible to be misled by graphs and tables, especially if they are produced by calculator or computer software.

For example, consider Applications Task 2 Part c, where you are asked to justify the equivalence of two expressions using a table. Here is a slightly different view of the table we generated.

It is possible to modify the example just slightly, and change it so that the two expressions are *not* equivalent (change the 5,000,000 in the second expression to 5,000,001).

And yet, if you leave all the table settings the same, you see the exact same table as before. This may lead to the conclusion that the two expressions are equivalent, when in fact they are not. This slight modification in one expression may not be visible from the graphical display of the two expressions.

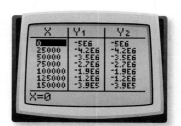

17 **a.** The expressions involve only addition and subtraction of linear expressions in the form $a + bx$ and similar expressions multiplied by a constant. These expressions are such that, through distribution and combining like terms, they can *always* be reduced to the form $a + bx$.

b. Besides expressions that involve powers of x, exponents in x, or division by expressions in x, other examples might include products of linear expressions such as $x(2x + 3)$.

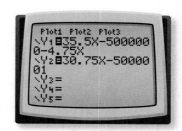

18 Students will be able to identify equivalent expressions using tables, graphs, or algebraic reasoning.

a. $3(2x + 8) \neq 6x + 8$. The student forgot to distribute multiplication by 3 to the 8.

b. $4x - 6x \neq 2x$. The student forgot the negative sign in the result, or the student used $6x - 4x$ instead of $4x - 6x$.

c. $8(2 - 6x) = 16 - 48x$. The student applied the distributive property correctly.

d. $10 + 3x - 12 \neq 3x + 2$. When subtracting $10 - 12$, the student may have incorrectly commuted subtraction to $12 - 10$ or not recognized that the result should be negative.

e. $\dfrac{5x + 10}{5} \neq x + 10$. The student did not distribute division by 5 to the 10.

f. $-4(x - 3) \neq -4x - 12$. The student evaluated $-4(-3)$ as -12 rather than 12; he or she did not distribute the negative sign to the -3.

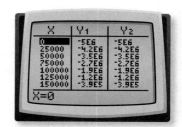

Extensions

19 Solve these equations. Show your work and check your solutions.

a. $3(x - 4) = 12$

b. $2(a + 1) = 8 + a$

c. $13 - (5 + n) = 6$

20 Look back at the statements of the Commutative and Associative Properties of Addition on page 220.

a. There are corresponding properties of multiplication. Write statements for the corresponding properties.

b. Give examples showing how the Commutative and Associative Properties of Multiplication can be used in writing equivalent algebraic expressions.

21 The properties of numbers and operations discussed in this lesson can be applied to write equivalent expressions for any expression, not just linear expressions.

a. Consider the rule suggested for the income *I* from the Five Star bungee jump as a function of ticket price *p* from "Physics and Business at Five Star Amusement Park" in Unit 1.

$$I = p(50 - p)$$

Expand the expression $p(50 - p)$.

b. Consider the rule some students wrote for estimating the total population of Brazil *NEXT* year given the population *NOW*.

$$NEXT = 0.01 \cdot NOW + NOW - 0.009 \cdot NOW$$

Combine like terms to write a shorter expression on the right-hand side of the rule.

22 Use the distributive property to write the expression $(x + 2)(x + 3)$ in expanded form. Is this a linear expression? Explain how you know.

23 Write the following expressions in factored form.

a. $8x^2 + 12x$

b. $10x - 15x^2$

c. $3x^3 - 27x^2 + 18x$

24 You have learned how a CAS can be used to expand or factor expressions, test the equivalence of two expressions, and solve equations. How could you solve a system of linear equations using a CAS? Test your ideas using the system below from Lesson 2 (page 199). Compare the solution with the solution you previously found.

Surf City Business Center: $y_1 = 3.95 + 0.05x$

Byte to Eat Café: $y_2 = 2 + 0.10x$

Extensions

19   **a.** $x = 8$; $3(8 - 4) = 12$

     b. $a = 6$; $2(6 + 1) = 14$ and $8 + 6 = 14$

     c. $n = 2$; $13 - (5 + 2) = 6$

20   **a.** The Commutative Property of Multiplication: For any numbers a and b, $a \cdot b = b \cdot a$.

       The Associative Property of Multiplication: For any numbers a, b, and c, $a(bc) = (ab)c$.

     b. Students will have different examples. (Encourage them to have one example that combines the two properties, such as $x(3x) = (3x)x = 3(x^2)$.)

21   **a.** $p(50 - p) = 50p - p^2$

     b. $NEXT = 0.01(NOW) + NOW - 0.009(NOW)$
              $= 1.001NOW$

22 $(x + 2)(x + 3) = (x + 2)x + (x + 2)3$
                      $= x^2 + 2x + 3x + 6$
                      $= x^2 + 5x + 6$

This is not a linear expression because of the x^2 term. The expression cannot be simplified to the general linear form $a + bx$, and its graph is not a line.

23   **a.** $4x(2x + 3)$

     b. $5x(2 - 3x)$

     c. $3x(x^2 - 9x + 6)$

24

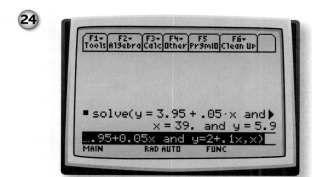

Review

25 Write equations for the lines satisfying these conditions.

   a. passing through the point (0, 4) and having slope 3

   b. passing through the points (10, 7) and (20, 12)

   c. passing through the points (−3, 5) and (1, −3)

26 Recall the Pythagorean Theorem which states that if a and b are the lengths of the legs of a right triangle and c is the length of the hypotenuse, then $a^2 + b^2 = c^2$. There are many right triangles for which the hypotenuse has length 5. For example, if $a = 1$ and $c = 5$ then $1^2 + b^2 = 5^2$, or $b^2 = 24$. So, b must be about 4.9 units long.

   a. Complete the table below by assigning different values to the leg length a and calculating the length b of the other leg.

a	1	2	3	4
b	4.9			
c	5	5	5	5

   b. Is the pattern of change in b as a increases a linear pattern? Explain.

27 Consider the two functions $y = 2 + 0.25x$ and $y = -8 + 1.5x$. Use tables or graphs to estimate solutions for these equations and inequalities.

   a. $2 + 0.25x = 0$ **b.** $2 + 0.25x = -8 + 1.5x$

   c. $-8 + 1.5x > 0$ **d.** $2 + 0.25x \leq -8 + 1.5x$

28 Consider the quadrilaterals shown below. Assume that segments that look parallel are parallel, and that segments or angles that look congruent are congruent.

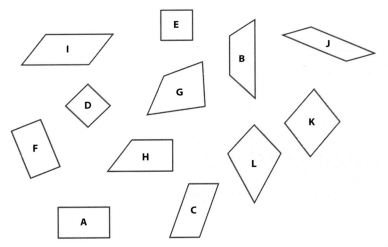

Review

25
 a. $y = 4 + 3x$

 b. $y = \frac{1}{2}x + 2$

 Students might notice that the second point is over 10 and up 5 to reason that the slope is 2. They also could reason that left 10 and down 5 gives the y-intercept $(0, 2)$.

 c. $y = -2x - 1$

 $\frac{\triangle y}{\triangle x} = \frac{8}{-4} = -2$. So the y-intercept can be found from $(1, -3)$ by adding 2 to the y-coordinate of -3.

26 a.

a	1	2	3	4
b	4.9	4.6	4	3
c	5	5	5	5

 b. The values of b do not change by a constant amount as a changes in a uniform way. Thus the pattern is not linear.

27 a. $x = -8$

 b. $x = 8$

 c. $x > 5\frac{1}{3}$

 d. $x \geq 8$

a. Identify all figures that are squares.

b. Identify all figures that are rectangles.

c. Identify all figures that are parallelograms.

d. Identify all figures that are trapezoids.

29 The histogram below displays the number of books read over the summer by all of the ninth grade students at Treadwell High School.

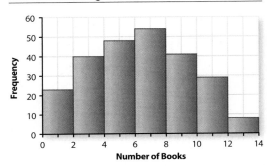

Summer Reading of Ninth Grade Students

a. Emily estimated that the median of these data is about 8 books. Do you think she is correct? Explain your reasoning.

b. Will estimated that the mean of these data is about 6 books and the standard deviation is about 4 books. Do his estimates seem reasonable? Explain your reasoning.

30 Using the diagram below, determine if each statement is true or false. In each case, explain your reasoning.

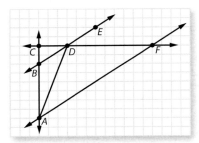

a. $\overleftrightarrow{AC} \perp \overleftrightarrow{DF}$

b. $m\angle FDA < m\angle CDA$

c. $\overleftrightarrow{BE} \parallel \overrightarrow{AF}$

d. $AD = DF$

28 **DEFINITION NOTE** Historically, some mathematics textbooks define a trapezoid as a quadrilateral with exactly one pair of parallel sides and some textbooks define a trapezoid as a quadrilateral with at least one pair of parallel sides. The "exactly one pair of parallel sides" definition means that parallelograms are not traezoids (exclusive definition). The "at least one pair of parallel sides definition" means that parallelograms are also trapezoids (inclusive definition). Students in your class may have been introduced to either or both of these definitions in elementary and middle school. Depending on that issue and your particular class, you may wish to address the issue of definitions in mathematics. (See the Course 3, Unit 1 *Teacher's Guide* for additional comments on the two alternative definitions of a trapezoid.)

  a. D and E are squares.

  b. A, D, E, and F are rectangles.

  c. A, C, D, E, F, I, J, and K are parallelograms.

  d. B and H are trapezoids. If one accepts the alternative definition (see Course 3, Unit 1, page 7) that a trapezoid is a quadrilateral with at least one pair of parallel sides, then the quadrilaterals listed in Part c are also trapezoids. G and L are the only figures that should not be listed.

29 **a.** The estimate of a median of 8 seems high since over half of the frequencies are below 8.

  b. These estimates are reasonable. The balance point of the histogram is near 6 books, and about 68% of the frequencies are between 2 and 10. Since this distribution is only somewhat approximately normal, it is difficult to accurately estimate the standard deviation.

30 **a.** True. Since $\overleftrightarrow{AC}$ is vertical and $\overleftrightarrow{DF}$ is horizontal, $\overleftrightarrow{AC} \perp \overleftrightarrow{DF}$.

  b. False. $\angle FDA$ is an obtuse angle and $\angle CDA$ is an acute angle. So m$\angle FDA$ > m$\angle CDA$.

  c. True. The slope of both lines is $\frac{2}{3}$.

  d. False. $DF = 9$ units. $AC = 8$ units. Using that value and the Pythagorean Theorem, $AD = \sqrt{3^2 + 8^2} \approx 8.5$.

Teaching Resources

Assessment Masters 192–197.

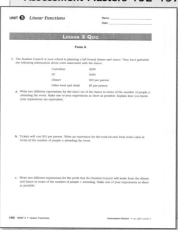

Looking Back

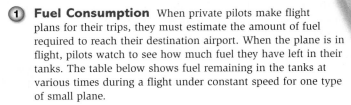

Through the lessons of this unit, you have seen that variables in many situations are related by linear functions. You have learned how to find rules that describe those functions. You also have learned how to use equations to answer questions about the variables and relations. This final lesson of the unit provides problems that will help you review, pull together, and apply your new knowledge.

1 **Fuel Consumption** When private pilots make flight plans for their trips, they must estimate the amount of fuel required to reach their destination airport. When the plane is in flight, pilots watch to see how much fuel they have left in their tanks. The table below shows fuel remaining in the tanks at various times during a flight under constant speed for one type of small plane.

Fuel Consumption

Time in Flight (in minutes)	40	60	80	100	120
Fuel Remaining (in gallons)	50	45	40	35	30

  a. Is fuel remaining a linear function of the time in flight? How do you know?

  b. Determine the rate of change in fuel remaining as time in flight increases. What units describe this rate of change?

  c. How much fuel was in the tanks at the start of the flight?

  d. Write a rule that shows how to calculate the amount of fuel remaining in the *NEXT* hour given the amount of fuel remaining in gallons *NOW*.

  e. Write a rule that shows how to calculate the amount of fuel remaining F after t minutes in flight.

  f. How much fuel remained in the tanks after 1.5 hours? After 3 hours?

  g. At one point in the flight, the pilot observes that 5 gallons of fuel remain in the tanks. How much flying time is left?

2 **Health and Nutrition** Even if we do not always eat what is best for us, most Americans can afford nutritious and varied diets. In many countries of the world, life is a constant struggle to find enough food. This struggle causes health problems such as reduced life expectancy and infant mortality.

This lesson includes explorations of linear functions, integrating the issues of the preceding lessons of the unit. Task 1 involves analyzing data about fuel consumption for one type of small aircraft; Task 2 involves analyzing data concerning calories and life expectancy; Task 3 involves analysis of a demand function; and Task 5 involves analysis of a school dance budget. Tasks 4, 6, and 7 involve symbolic work with linear functions, expressions, equations, and inequalities.

1   **a.** Yes. As the time in flight changes at a uniform rate, the fuel remaining also changes at a constant rate.

     b. The rate of change is -0.25 gallons per minute.

     c. The pattern would indicate that there were 60 gallons of fuel at the start of the flight.

     d. *NEXT = NOW* $-$ 0.25, starting at 60

     e. $F = 60 - 0.25t$

     f. 1.5 hours is 90 minutes, so there are 37.5 gallons remaining. After 3 hours, 15 gallons remain.

     g. 20 minutes

2   **INSTRUCTIONAL NOTE** This task asks students to explore data that suggest two fundamental and striking relations between nutrition and health. Before having students look at the data in the table, ask them to give their conjectures about factors that would cause different countries to have different life expectancies, infant mortality rates, or other general health indicators. You might ask them how much difference they think there might be between various familiar countries. Data in the table from a sample of countries suggest that there is a trend showing increase in life expectancy and decrease in infant mortality for increase in daily caloric intake. This is not a perfect relation because, for instance, Japanese people average only about 75% of the daily caloric intake of Americans, but have a similar life span. Furthermore, it is unreasonable to think that greatly increased caloric intake will produce increased life span or decreased infant mortality; eating too much is not good. Clearly there are other factors, like general public health conditions, that also affect life span and infant mortality rates.

a. The data in the table below show how average daily food supply (in calories) is related to life expectancy (in years) and infant mortality rates (in deaths per 1,000 births) in a sample of countries. Make scatterplots of the (*daily calories, life expectancy*) and (*daily calories, infant mortality*) data.

Health and Nutrition

Country	Daily Calories	Life Expectancy	Infant Mortality
Argentina	3,136	74	20
Bolivia	2,170	64	56
Dominican Republic	2,316	67	36
Haiti	1,855	53	61
Mexico	3,137	73	28
New Zealand	3,405	78	6
Paraguay	2,485	71	37
United States	3,642	78	7

Source: *The New York Times 2003 Almanac.* New York, NY: Penguin Company, 2002.

Study the patterns in the table and the scatterplots. Then answer these questions.

   i. What seems to be the general relation between daily calories and life expectancy in the sample countries?

   ii. What seems to be the general relation between daily calories and infant mortality in the sample countries?

   iii. What factors other than daily calorie supply might affect life expectancy and infant mortality?

b. Economists might use a linear model to predict the increase of life expectancy or decrease of infant mortality for various increases in food supply.

   i. Determine a linear regression model for calculating life expectancy from calories using the (*daily calories, life expectancy*) data pattern.

   ii. Determine a linear regression model for calculating infant mortality from calories using the (*daily calories, infant mortality*) data pattern.

   iii. What do the slopes of the graphs of your linear models say about the pattern relating life expectancy to daily calories in the sample countries? How about the relationship between infant mortality and daily calories?

c. Average daily calorie supply in Chile is 2,810. What life expectancy and infant mortality would you predict from the calorie data?

d. Brazil has a life expectancy of 68 years.

   i. For what daily calorie supply would you predict this life expectancy?

a.

(Calories, Life Expectancy)

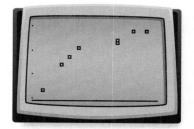 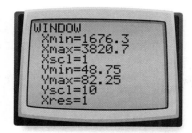

(*Calories, Infant Mortality*)

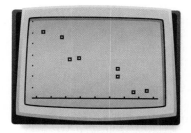 

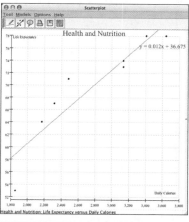

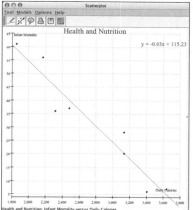

i. As average daily calories increase, the length of life also increases.

ii. As average daily calories increase, infant mortality rates decrease.

iii. Responses may vary. For example, life expectancy may be affected by exercise, smoking, stress, genetics, and access to and quality of health care. Infant mortality may be affected by the quality of prenatal care, the quality of medical care at birth, and the mother's health.

b. **i.** (*calories, life expectancy*): $y = 36.675 + 0.012x$

ii. (*calories, infant mortality*): $y = 115.230 - 0.030x$

iii. Slopes give rates at which life span increases and infant mortality rate decreases as daily caloric intake increases. For example,

- Each increase of 1 calorie leads to an increase of approximately 0.012 years in life span (100 calories gives approximately 1.2 years longer life).

- Each increase of 1 calorie leads to a decrease of approximately 0.030 in the infant mortality rate (100 calories decreases the infant mortality rate by about 3 deaths per 1,000 births).

c. Using the models from Part b, life span in Chile is predicted to be about 70 years, and infant mortality is predicted to be about 31 deaths per 1,000 births.

d. **i.** Using the model from Part b, a life expectancy of 68 years is predicted in Brazil for a calorie supply of 2,610 calories per day.

TECHNOLOGY NOTE These data are available to use with the custom tool "Modeling Line."

INSTRUCTIONAL NOTE
Make sure that students understand that infant mortality means the death rate for babies under 1 year of age.

A value of 20 means $\frac{20}{1,000}$, or 2% of the babies die before they reach the age of 1 year.

ii. The actual daily calorie supply for Brazil is 2,938 calories. What does the difference between the value suggested by the model and the actual value tell about the usefulness of the model you have found?

e. What life expectancy does your model predict for a daily calorie supply of 5,000? How close to that prediction would you expect the actual life expectancy to be in a country with a daily calorie supply of 5,000?

 Popcorn Sales Many people who go to movies like to have popcorn to munch on during the show. But movie theater popcorn is often expensive. The manager of a local theater wondered how much more she might sell if the price were lower. She also wondered whether such a reduced price would actually bring in more popcorn income.

One week she set the price for popcorn at $1.00 per cup and sold an average of 120 cups per night. The next week she set the price at $1.50 per cup and sold an average of 90 cups per night. She used that information to graph a linear model to predict number of cups sold at other possible prices.

a. Write a rule for the linear model. Explain what the slope and y-intercept of the model tell about the prospective number of popcorn cups sold at various prices.

b. Write and solve equations or inequalities to answer the following questions.

i. At what price does your model predict average daily sales of about 150 cups of popcorn?

ii. At what price does your model predict average daily sales of fewer than 60 cups of popcorn?

iii. How many cups of popcorn does your model predict will be sold per day at a price of $1.80 per cup?

c. Use the rule relating average daily number of cups sold to price to make a table relating price to income from popcorn sales. Explain what the pattern in the table tells about the relation between price and income.

Popcorn Sales

Graph titled "Popcorn Sales" with vertical axis "Average Number of Cups Sold" marked 0, 40, 80, 120, 160, 200 and horizontal axis "Popcorn Price (in dollars)" marked 0, 0.5, 1, 1.5, 2, 2.5. A decreasing line passes through points (1, 120) and (1.5, 90).

4 Solve the following equations and inequalities. Use each of the following methods of solving—table, graph, and algebraic reasoning— at least twice. Check your answers.

a. $9 + 6x = 24$ **b.** $286 = 7p + 69$

c. $6 - 4x \le 34$ **d.** $8 + 1.1x = -25$

e. $20 = 3 + 5(x - 1)$ **f.** $17y - 34 = 8y - 16$

g. $1.5x + 8 \le 3 + 2x$ **h.** $14 + 3k > 27 - 10k$

ii. The difference between an actual data value and a prediction from the model (in this case, about 330 calories) can be due to local factors that make those countries atypical, and the fact that the model is only an approximation to a rough trend, not an exact physical law. Differences remind us that models are only general summaries of patterns, and we must exercise judgment and caution in reasoning from them.

e. Using the model from Part b, a life span of approximately 96.7 years is predicted for a daily caloric intake of 5,000 calories. However, it seems quite likely that beyond some optimal point, increase of calorie intake will actually diminish life span. Again, this reminds us that often models cannot be extrapolated too far beyond the data available.

③
a. $y = 180 - 60x$, where x represents the popcorn price in dollars and y represents the number of cups sold. The y-intercept of $(0, 180)$ means that if the popcorn were free, 180 cups of popcorn would be given away. The slope of -60 indicates that for every dollar increase in the price of popcorn, the average number of cups sold in a night decreases by 60.

b. **i.** $150 = 180 - 60x$; $x = 0.5$; Daily sales of 150 cups of popcorn are predicted when the price of popcorn is set at $0.50 a cup.

ii. $180 - 60x < 60$; $x > 2$; If the price is greater than $2 per cup, fewer than 60 cups of popcorn are predicted to be sold each night.

iii. $y = 180 - 60(1.8)$; $y = 72$; If the price of popcorn is $1.80 per cup, then sales are predicted to be 72 cups per night.

c. In the table below, the price is given in column X, the number of cups of popcorn sold per night is listed in column Y_1, and the income $(X \cdot Y_1)$ is in column Y_2. The table shows that as price increases, the income starts to increase until it reaches a maximum of $135 when the price is $1.50, and then it starts to decrease.

④ Students should solve these equations and inequalities using a variety of methods and check their answers as indicated in the student text.

a. $x = 2.5$ **b.** $p = 31$

c. $x \geq -7$ **d.** $x = -30$

e. $x = \dfrac{22}{5} = 4.4$ **f.** $y = 2$

g. $x \geq 10$ **h.** $k > 1$

⑤ **Party Planning** The ninth grade class at Freedom High School traditionally has an end-of-year dance party. The class officers researched costs for the dance and came up with these items to consider.

Party Planning

Item	Cost
DJ for the dance	$350
Food	$3.75 per student
Drinks	$1.50 per student
Custodians, Security	$225

The question is whether the class treasury has enough money to pay for the dance or whether they will have to sell tickets.

a. Which of the following function rules correctly express dance cost C as a function of the number of students N who plan to come to the dance? Explain your reasoning.

$C = 350 + 3.75N + 1.50N + 225$
$C = 5.25N + 575$
$C = 575 + 5.25N$
$C = 580.25N$

b. Write and solve an equation or inequality to determine how many students could come to the dance without a ticket charge if the class treasury has $950.

c. Write and solve an equation or inequality to determine how many students could come to the dance with a ticket charge of only $2 if the class treasury has $950.

⑥ Using algebraic expressions to help make sense out of problem situations is an important part of mathematics. Writing expressions and function rules is often a first step. Being able to recognize and generate equivalent algebraic expressions is another important skill.

a. Write rules for the linear functions with graphs passing through the indicated points.

   i. $(0, -3)$ and $(4, 1)$

  ii. $(0, 3)$ and $(6, 0)$

 iii. $(2, -6)$ and $(8, 12)$

b. Write rules for the linear functions with graphs having the given slopes and passing through the given points.

   i. slope $= 3$; passes through $(4, 12)$

  ii. slope $= \frac{2}{3}$; passes through $(-6, -1)$

 iii. slope $= -4$; passes through $(17, 82)$

LESSON 4 • Looking Back **235**

5

a. Only the last rule is incorrect. The first rule shows each component of the cost. The second and third rules show the combined fixed costs plus the combined cost per student.

b. $5.25N + 575 = 950$; $N = 71.43$; up to 71 students could come to the dance without a ticket charge if the class treasury has $950.

c. $950 + 2N = 5.25N + 575$; $N = 115.38$; up to 115 students could come to the dance with a ticket charge of only $2 if the class treasury has $950.

6

a. **i.** $y = x - 3$

   ii. $y = 3 - 0.5x$

   iii. $y = 3x - 12$

b. **i.** $y = 3x$

   ii. $y = \frac{2}{3}x + 3$

   iii. $y = -4x + 150$

Unit 3

c. Compare the following pairs of linear expressions to see if they are equivalent. Explain your reasoning in each case.

    i. $4.2x + 6$ and $(1 - 0.7x)6$

    ii. $4C - 3(C + 2)$ and $-6 + C$

    iii. $0.3S - 0.4S + 2$ and $\dfrac{20 - S}{10}$

7 Solve the following system of equations using calculator- or computer-based methods and by algebraic reasoning.

$$\begin{cases} y = 35 + 0.2x \\ y = 85 + 0.7x \end{cases}$$

Summarize the Mathematics

Linear functions can be recognized in graphs, tables, and symbolic rules, or in verbal descriptions.

a Describe how you can tell whether two variables are related by a linear function by looking at:

    i. a scatterplot   **ii.** a table of values

    iii. the form of the function rule   **iv.** a description of the situation

Linear functions often describe relationships between an input variable x and an output variable y.

b Write a general rule for a linear function. What do the parts of the rule tell you about the function it represents?

c Explain how to find a value of y corresponding to a given value of x, using:

    i. a graph   **ii.** a table   **iii.** a symbolic rule

d Explain how to determine the rate of change in y as x increases, using:

    i. a graph   **ii.** a table   **iii.** a symbolic rule

e Explain how you can solve a linear equation or inequality using:

    i. a graph   **ii.** a table   **iii.** algebraic reasoning

f Explain how you can solve a system of linear equations using:

    i. a graph   **ii.** a table   **iii.** algebraic reasoning

Be prepared to share your descriptions and explanations with the whole class.

✓Check Your Understanding

Write, in outline form, a summary of the important mathematical concepts and methods developed in this unit. Organize your summary so that it can be used as a quick reference in future units and courses.

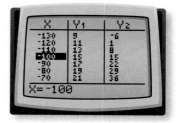

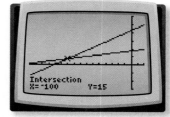

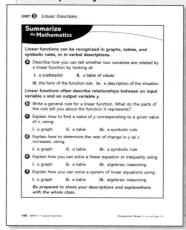

c. **i.** Not equivalent; $4.2(10) + 6 = 48$, and $(1 - 0.7(10))6 = -36$.

    ii. Equivalent. $4C - 3(C + 2) = 4C - 3C - 6 = -6 + C$

    iii. Equivalent. Both expressions can be rewritten as $2 - 0.1S$.

(7) The solution to the system is $x = -100$ and $y = 15$. Students should determine the solution algebraically and by either tables or graphs.

Summary

By asking for many student descriptions, students should begin to realize that you are not always seeking additional responses because the first response is incorrect or incomplete, but that there is often more than one correct description.

Summarize
the Mathematics

(a) **i.** In a scatterplot, look for data that show a linear pattern or seem to show a fairly consistent upward, downward, or horizontal trend.

    ii. In a table of values, a constant or nearly constant difference between y values as x values change uniformly.

    iii. In a function rule, after removing parentheses and combining like terms if necessary, look for a number multiplied by x and perhaps a number added or subtracted. The form would be $y = a + bx$, or $y = mx + b$.

    iv. Think about how the dependent variable changes as the independent variable changes and whether a constant rate of change makes sense in the situation.

(b) $y = a + bx$ or $y = mx + b$, where the constant term is the y-coordinate of the y-intercept, or the value of y when $x = 0$, and the coefficient of x is the rate of change in y as x increases. If the coefficient of x is positive, then y increases as x increases, and if the coefficient of x is negative, then y decreases as x increases.

(c) **i.** Using a graph, locate the given value of x on the x-axis, move up or down to the line, and read the corresponding y value. Or trace along the line to locate the given x value and identify the y value.

    ii. Using a table, find the given value of x and read the corresponding y value. Table extending or refining may be needed.

    iii. Using a rule, substitute the given value for x and solve for y.

(d) **i.** Using a graph, locate two points on the line with identifiable coordinates. Use these coordinates to find the ratio of the change in y values to the change in x values. (Divide the "rise" between any two points on the graph by the "run.")

    ii. Using a table, divide the change in y values between any two entries by the corresponding change in x values.

Teaching Resources

Transparency Master 198.

INSTRUCTIONAL NOTE
Encourage students to look at their notes in their Math Toolkits to help refresh their ideas about these questions if they need help.

iii. When the rule is written in the "$y = ...$" form, the coefficient of x gives the rate of change in y as x increases.

(e)

i. Using a graph, enter each side of the equation as a function. Find the value of the x-coordinate of the point of intersection. For inequality, the solution will be all x values either greater or less than the intersection point's x value.

ii. Using a table, enter each side of the equation as a function. Find the value of x for which the two y values are equal. An inequality solution will then be all values either greater or less than this x value, depending on which inequality is desired.

iii. Use undoing operations until the value of x is given, remembering to switch the direction of the inequality symbol when multiplying or dividing both sides of the inequality by a negative number.

(f)

i. Using a graph, trace to where the lines intersect and read the coordinates of the point of intersection.

ii. Using a table, find the x value for which the two y values are the same. Report the pair (x, y) as the solution.

iii. Set the two expressions for y equal to each other and solve for x by undoing operations. Then substitute the value for x into either "$y = ...$" rule to determine the value of y. Report the pair (x, y) as the solution.

Teaching Resources

Student Masters 199–201.

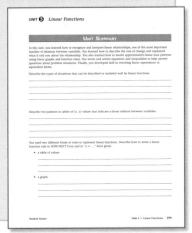

✓Check Your Understanding

Responses will vary. Above all, this should be something that is useful to the individual student. You may wish to have students use the Teaching Master, *Linear Functions* Unit Summary, to help them organize the information.

Practicing for Standardized Tests

Each Practicing for Standardized Tests master presents ten questions that draw on all content strands. The questions are presented in the form of test items similar to how they often appear in standardized tests such as state assessment tests, the Preliminary Scholastic Aptitude Test (PSAT), or the ACT PLAN. We suggest using these practice sets following the unit assessment so students can become familiar with the formats of standardized tests and develop effective test-taking strategies for performing well on such tests. Answers are provided below.

Teaching Resources

Student Masters 220–221.

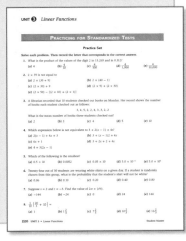

Answers to Practice Set 3

1. (e)   **2.** (c)   **3.** (b)   **4.** (e)   **5.** (d)

6. (c)   **7.** (b)   **8.** (b)   **9.** (b)   **10.** (b)

Assessment Masters 202–211.

UNIT **3** *Linear Functions*

Name _____

Date _____

UNIT TEST

Form A

1. Suppose Derek has not had the opportunity to take the mathematics class that you are taking. He is writing a report on the history of McDonald's restaurants. He learns that a regular McDonald's hamburger typically cost 19¢ in 1963 and 89¢ in 2003. He decides to use the line through these two data points to predict the price of a McDonald's hamburger in any year between 1963 and 2003.

   a. What would be Derek's prediction of the price in 1975? Explain how you got your answer.

   Prediction for 1975 _____

   Explanation:

   b. Use algebraic reasoning to write a rule relating price in cents of a McDonald's hamburger *p* to number of years since 1963 *n*.

   c. Write a rule relating *NOW* to *NEXT* that could be used to find the price of a McDonald's hamburger from one year to the next during this time period.

   d. Describe the rate of change in the price of a hamburger.

202   UNIT 3 • Linear Functions   Assessment Master

Assessment Masters 212–215.

UNIT **3** *Linear Functions*

TAKE-HOME ASSESSMENTS

1. Look in past newspapers or magazines at the library to find relationships that seem to be linear. Sports, business, and science are good topics. *USA Today* is a good source for graphs. Find at least two linear graphs or tables that give different information about a single topic. Write a brief report on how each linear graph or table is used to present information and to make predictions. If the graph or table was used incorrectly or could have been put to better use in the article you found, describe how it should have been used. Write a report about your findings, demonstrating your understanding of the important ideas of this unit.

2. Here is a mathematical puzzle that will surprise your friends. Have at least three people try it at once to get the full effect of the surprise. Have each person follow the steps below.

   Example

   (1) Write down any whole number between 50 and 99. Do not show it to anyone.   87

   (2) Add 74 to your number.   87 + 74 = 161

   (3) Strike off the hundreds digit and add it to the resulting two-digit number.   161 → 61   61 + 1 = 62

   (4) Subtract the result in step 3 from your original number.   87 − 62 = 25

   The result is always 25 no matter what number is picked originally. After trying a number of examples and having some friends do the same, explain why this trick works. (Hint: Represent the original number by a letter, say n. Perform each of the steps on n, writing the result of the step in terms of n.)

3. The table below provides the asking price in dollars and the square footage of 15 homes that were for sale in Rio Rancho, New Mexico, during the fall of 2005.

Asking Price (in $)	Square Footage		Asking Price (in $)	Square Footage
62,000	800		112,900	1,476
79,900	964		119,900	1,800
79,900	1,004		130,000	1,808
90,000	1,250		159,900	2,213
99,500	1,278		129,900	1,865
101,000	1,325		152,000	2,097
109,900	1,511		127,500	1,682
110,000	1,407			

212   UNIT 3 • Linear Functions   Assessment Master

Assessment Masters 216–219.

UNIT **3** *Linear Functions*

Name _____

Date _____

PROJECT

Exploring Relationships for Linearity

Purpose

Related pairs of variables are everywhere. Some have a linear, or approximately linear, relationship; others do not. Many such relationships were described in this unit and in the previous one. In this project, you will need to choose pairs of real-world variables, collect data, and describe the relationship between these variables.

Directions

1. You are to choose simple relationships between two variables that you and a partner can collect data on at home. For example, you might consider the following pairs.
   • number of pages in a book and thickness of the book in inches
   • number of words in a line in a magazine and length of the line in inches
   • width of a picture on the wall in your home and the height of the same picture
   • U.S. athletic shoe size and European shoe size for a pair of shoes
   • volume of water obtained from a running tap and the elapsed time since turning on the tap
   There are many other possibilities that you may find more interesting. Choose three pairs of variables.

2. For each pair of variables you choose, collect at least 10 pairs of data points. This means, for the examples above, you would need to examine 10 books, 10 magazines, 10 pictures, 10 shoe sizes, or collect water over a 10-second interval and make the appropriate measurements.

3. For each set of data, organize the data into a table and make a scatterplot. Using the scatterplot, describe the relationship between the variables. In particular, comment on whether a linear model would fit the trend in the data.

4. For each set of data, find the linear regression model for your data and draw it on your scatterplot. Explain the strengths and limitations of the linear regression model for your data.

5. Organize all of your data, plots, and explanations into a report according to the guidelines your teacher provides. Include a final section of your report in which you explain how to judge, before collecting data, whether a pair of variables has a linear relationship.

216   UNIT 3 • Linear Functions   Assessment Master

UNIT 4

VERTEX-EDGE GRAPHS

Many situations involve paths and networks, like bus routes and computer networks. *Vertex-edge graphs* can be used as mathematical models to help analyze such situations. A vertex-edge graph is a diagram consisting of points (vertices) and arcs or line segments (edges) connecting some of the points. Such graphs are part of geometry, as well as part of an important contemporary field called *discrete mathematics*.

In this unit, you will use vertex-edge graphs and Euler circuits to help find optimum paths, such as the best route to collect money from parking meters, deliver newspapers, or plow snow from city streets. You will also use vertex coloring of graphs to avoid conflict among objects, such as scheduling conflicts among meetings or broadcast interference among nearby radio stations.

You will develop the understanding and skill needed to solve problems about optimum paths and conflict through your work in two lessons.

Lessons

1 **Euler Circuits: Finding the Best Path**

Use Euler circuits and their properties to solve problems about optimum circuits.

2 **Vertex Coloring: Avoiding Conflict**

Use vertex coloring to solve problems related to avoiding conflict in a variety of settings.

VERTEX-EDGE GRAPHS

Unit Overview

There are four interwoven strands of mathematics in the Core-Plus Mathematics curriculum—algebra and functions, geometry and trigonometry, statistics and probability, and discrete mathematics. Although each unit makes connections among all four strands, most units have a primary emphasis on one of the strands. This unit begins the study of vertex-edge graphs, which is one important part of discrete mathematics. Other discrete math topics in Core-Plus Mathematics are counting, matrices, recursion, and the mathematics of voting and information processing. Core-Plus students will be well prepared to take a Discrete Mathematics course in college. Such a course is required for all computer science majors and many math majors. Also, some of these discrete mathematics topics are included in college business management courses.

Vertex-Edge Graphs Vertex-edge graphs are diagrams consisting of vertices and edges that can be used to model and solve problems related to paths, networks, and relationships among a finite number of objects. They are part of discrete mathematics, and also part of geometry since they are geometric diagrams with vertices and edges. In fact, they can be thought of as *discrete geometric models* in that they are discrete (consisting of vertices and edges), they are geometric diagrams, and they are powerful mathematical models used extensively in business and industry. In contrast to the importance of size and shape in most school geometry, size and shape are not essential features of vertex-edge graphs. All that really matters is how the vertices are connected to each other by the edges. The term "vertex-edge graph" is used to distinguish this type of graph from others, like function graphs or graphs used in data analysis. It is also common to simply use the term "graph." These materials use both terms as appropriate.

In the two main lessons of this unit, students use vertex-edge graphs to solve a variety of problems dealing with paths and relationships among objects. In addition, students explore and reason about properties and algorithms. Lesson 1 is about Euler circuits, which are circuits through a graph that use each edge of the graph exactly once. Students learn about vertex-coloring in Lesson 2, and how this idea can be used to solve problems related to avoiding conflicts. Other types of graph problems will be studied in later courses, including critical paths, minimum spanning trees, and the Traveling Salesperson Problem.

These graph problems are studied because they are accessible, fundamental, powerful, and commonly applied in the real world. Furthermore, an important outcome of this unit is the development of students' skills in mathematical modeling. Working with graph models provides students with explicit and invaluable experience in building and using mathematical models. In each lesson, students first build a graph model that represents a given situation;

then they use the model to find a mathematical solution; and finally, they interpret the solution in terms of the original situation. Being able to model and solve problems with vertex-edge graphs will provide students with additional and essential mathematical power.

Teachers report that this unit provides an opportunity to engage all students in investigating and learning mathematics, even if they have not been successful previously. This material often creates a level playing field for all students, and they typically find it enjoyable and refreshing.

NOTE NCTM's *Principles and Standards for School Mathematics* recommends that "discrete mathematics should be an integral part of the school mathematics curriculum, ..." (page 31).

Unit Objectives

- Understand and apply Euler paths and vertex coloring
- Use vertex-edge graphs to represent and solve problems related to paths, networks, and relationships among a finite number of objects
- Gain further experience in mathematical modeling by building and using vertex-edge graph models to solve problems in a variety of settings
- Develop skill in algorithmic problem solving: designing, using, and analyzing systematic procedures for solving problems
- Further develop skill in mathematical reasoning by exploring and reasoning about properties of vertex-edge graphs

CPMP-Tools

In this unit, many problems offer students an opportunity to create complex vertex-edge graphs, investigate characteristics of graphs, and apply algorithms. In some cases, you may wish to have students access *CPMP-Tools* from the Web while at home to do this work. Problems in which the vertex-edge graph software or custom tools can be used include

Lesson 1—pages 244, 248, 254, 258, 259
Lesson 2—pages 269, 278, 279, 282

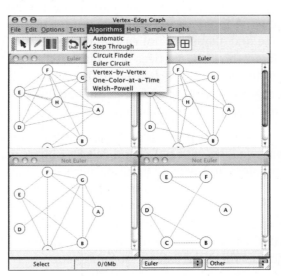

Suggestions to integrate this technology are included in the student text and teaching notes at point of use.

Discrete Mathematics in Course 1

Discrete mathematics in Course 1 is focused on vertex-edge graphs, specifically Euler paths and vertex coloring. All three themes of discrete mathematics are developed: discrete mathematical modeling, algorithmic problem solving, and optimization. An Euler path is a route through a graph that uses each edge of the graph exactly once. Euler paths can be used to model and solve problems such as finding the most efficient snow plowing route or newspaper delivery route through a neighborhood. Vertex-coloring problems are concerned with finding the fewest colors needed to color the vertices of a graph in such a way that adjacent vertices have different colors. Vertex coloring can be used to model and solve problems related to avoiding conflicts such as scheduling conflicts or radio station interference. Algorithms for finding Euler circuits and coloring vertices are investigated and analyzed. For more information on discrete mathematics, see *Implementing Core-Plus Mathematics*.

References

If you choose to use videos, referenced below, consider carefully the content of each video. It is important to keep the investigative nature of this unit intact. For example, some videos may present the main point of the investigation and so should be shown after, not before, the investigation. On the other hand, some parts of some videos may serve well as part of a lesson launch.

General (includes Euler paths and vertex coloring)

Consortium for Mathematics and its Applications (COMAP). *For All Practical Purposes*, 6th ed. New York: W. H. Freeman and Company, 2003.

COMAP. *For All Practical Purposes Video Series*. Washington, DC: Annenberg Media, 1988.

Cozzens, Margaret B. and Porter, Richard D. *Problem Solving Using Graphs*, HiMAP Module 6. Lexington, MA: COMAP, 1987.

Crisler, Nancy, Fisher, Patience, and Froelich, Gary. *Discrete Mathematics Through Applications*, 2nd ed. New York: W. H. Freeman and Company, 2000.

Dossey, John A., Otte, Albert D., Spence, Lawrence E., Vanden Eynden, Charles. *Discrete Mathematics* 4th ed. Boston, MA: Addison-Wesley, 2002.

Geometry: New Tools for New Technologies. VHS. Lexington, MA: COMAP, 1992.

Hart, Eric W., Kenney, Margaret J., DeBellis, Valerie A., Rosenstein, Joseph G. *Navigating Through Discrete Mathematics in Grades 6–12*. National Council of Teachers of Mathematics, 2007.

Hirsch, Christian R., Kenney, Margaret J. (eds.). *Discrete Mathematics Across the Curriculum*, K–12. Reston, VA: National Council of Teachers of Mathematics, 1991 NCTM Yearbook, 1991.

Ore, Oystein. *Graphs and Their Uses* (revised and updated by Robin Wilson). Washington, DC: Mathematical Association of America, New Mathematical Library 34, 1990.

ORSA promotional video. VHS. Operations Research Society of America, 1990.

Patterns: Networks, Paths, and Knots. VHS. Sunburst, 1993.

Tannenbaum, Peter. *Excursions in Modern Mathematics.* 5th ed. Upper Saddle River, NJ: Pearson Prentice Hall, 2004.

Wilson, Robin J. and Watkins, John J. *Graphs: An Introductory Approach.* New York: John Wiley and Sons, 1990.

Euler Paths

Ascher, Marcia. *Ethnomathematics: A Multicultural View of Mathematical Ideas.* Belmont, CA: Wadsworth, Inc., 1991.

Chavey, Darrah. *Drawing Pictures with One Line: Exploring Graph Theory.* HistoMAP Module 21. VHS. Lexington, MA: COMAP, 1992.

Geometry: New Tools for New Technologies. VHS. Lexington, MA: COMAP, 1992.

Math TV: Management Science, Program 104. VHS. Lexington, MA: COMAP, 1986.

Vertex Coloring

Barnette, David. *Map Coloring, Polyhedra, and the Four-Color Problem.* Dolciani Mathematical Expositions No. 8. Washington, DC: MAA, 1983.

Geometry: New Tools for New Technologies. VHS. Lexington, MA: COMAP, 1992.

Malkevitch, Joseph. *Applications of Vertex-Coloring Problems for Graphs.* UMAP Module 442. Lexington, MA: COMAP, 1981.

Lesson Objectives	On Your Own Assignments*	Suggested Pacing	Materials
Lesson 1 *Euler Circuits: Finding the Best Path* • Use vertex-edge graphs to model problems related to finding efficient routes—in this case, routes that use each edge exactly once • Use Euler circuits, circuits through a graph that use each edge exactly once, to help solve such problems • Learn and reason about properties of graphs and Euler circuits • Investigate algorithms for constructing Euler circuits • Use matrices to represent and analyze graphs	**After Investigation 1:** A1 or A2, C10, R15 or R16, Rv30–Rv33 **After Investigation 2:** A3 or A4, A5, A6 or A9, C11 or C12, choose two of R17–R19, E21, choice of E22–E25, Rv34, Rv35 **After Investigation 3:** A7, A8, C13 or C14, choose two of R18–R20, choice of E26–E29, Rv36–Rv38	5 days (including quizzing)	• *CPMP-Tools* vertex-edge graph software • Unit Resources
Lesson 2 *Vertex Coloring: Avoiding Conflict* • Use vertex-edge graphs to model problems related to avoiding conflict in a variety of settings • Color the vertices of a graph so that adjacent vertices have different colors • Investigate algorithms for vertex coloring • Use vertex coloring to solve a variety of problems, including assigning frequencies to radio stations, scheduling club meetings, and coloring the countries of a map	**After Investigation 1:** C5, C6 or C7, C8, E18, Rv19–Rv24 **After Investigation 2:** A1 or A2, A3 or A4, C9, R10, R11 or R12, E13 or E14, choice of E15–E17, Rv25, Rv26	4 days (including quizzing)	• *CPMP-Tools* vertex-edge graph software • *Optional:* Colored pencils • Unit Resources
Lesson 3 *Looking Back* • Review and synthesize the major objectives of the unit		2–3 days (including testing)	• Unit Resources

* When choice is indicated, it is important to leave the choice to the student.

Note: *It is best if Connections tasks are discussed as a whole class after they have been assigned as homework.*

Unit 4

Euler Circuits: Finding the Best Path

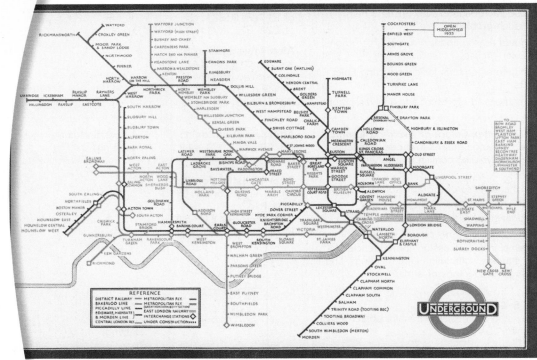

Source: London Transport Museum Guide

Often when solving problems using geometric figures or diagrams, you are concerned with their size, shape, or position. However, sometimes a geometric diagram is used to represent a situation in which size, shape, and position are not important. Instead, connections are what really matter. In this unit, you will study geometric diagrams made up of vertices and edges in which size and shape are not essential characteristics, but how the vertices are connected is very important.

A subway map is one common example of a geometric diagram with vertices and edges for which precise size and shape are not crucial. Perhaps the first such map was the 1933 London Underground map shown above.

Euler Circuits: Finding the Best Path

In this lesson, students first use vertex-edge graphs to model a variety of problems related to finding optimal routes. They then use Euler circuits—circuits through a graph that use each edge exactly once, to help solve the problems. They also learn and reason about properties of graphs and Euler circuits, and they investigate algorithms for constructing Euler circuits. Finally, they learn how to use matrices to represent and analyze graphs.

Lesson Objectives

- Use vertex-edge graphs to model problems related to finding efficient routes—in this case, routes that use each edge exactly once
- Use Euler circuits, circuits through a graph that use each edge exactly once, to help solve such problems
- Learn and reason about properties of graphs and Euler circuits
- Investigate algorithms for constructing Euler circuits
- Use matrices to represent and analyze graphs

Think About This Situation

Examine the Underground map and think about how a visitor to London might have used the map.

a What information is conveyed by the map? What information about the city is not conveyed by the map?

b Why are the size and shape of the map layout not essential?

c What are important features of subway maps like the one above?

d Describe other geometric diagrams with vertices and edges for which *connections* are important, but exact size and shape are not essential.

Geometric diagrams made up of vertices and edges, in which connections are important but exact size, shape, and position are not essential, are sometimes called *vertex-edge graphs*, or simply *graphs*. In this lesson, you will learn how to use vertex-edge graphs to find optimum routes.

Investigation 1 Planning Efficient Routes

You can save time, energy, and expense by studying a complex project before you begin your work. There may be many ways to carry out the project. However, one way may be judged to be the "best" or *optimum*, in some sense. As you work on this investigation, think about this question:

How can you create and use a mathematical model to find an optimum solution to problems such as the following locker-painting problem?

Locker Painting Suppose you are hired to paint all the lockers around eight classrooms on the first floor of a high school. The lockers are located along the walls of the halls as shown in the diagram to the right. Letters are placed at points where you would stop painting one row of lockers and start painting another. Five-gallon buckets of paint, a spray paint compressor, and other equipment are located in the first-floor equipment room *E*. You must move this bulky equipment with you as you paint the lockers. You also must return it to the equipment room when you are finished painting. (The lockers in the center hall must be painted one side at a time.)

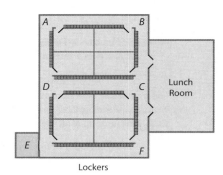

Lockers

Before addressing Part b of the Think About This Situation, you may wish to ask students to describe the positioning of the lines (vertical, horizontal, or multiples of 45°). A general description of the map from the Museum Guide is provided in Reflections Task 14. Students are asked to analyze it more carefully at that time.

Think About This Situation

a The map shows the general direction and order of stops, locations where two lines intersect, and the side of the river where stops are located. The distances between stops is not to scale, and it is likely that not all the curves in subway lines are displayed.

b Since people ride the subway underground, they do not need to know all the details of shape, size, and exact geographical location on the surface. The simplicity of the map more directly meets the need to know about connections and routes.

c Students may have experience using subway maps. The important features are showing relative position and connections.

d Students might describe diagrams such as electrical wiring diagrams, assembly diagrams for toys, flowcharts, family trees, organizational charts, makeup of chemical compounds, DNA chains.

Teaching Resources

Transparency Master 222.

UNIT ❹ *Vertex-Edge Graphs*

Think About This Situation

Examine the Underground map and think about how a visitor to London might have used the map.

ⓐ What information is conveyed by the map? What information about the city is not conveyed by the map?

ⓑ Why are the size and shape of the map layout not essential?

ⓒ What are important features of subway maps like the one above?

ⓓ Describe other geometric diagrams with vertices and edges for which connections are important, but exact size and shape are not essential.

222 UNIT 4 • *Vertex-Edge Graphs*   Transparency Master • *see with page 239*

Unit 4

Investigation 1 — Planning Efficient Routes

Vertex-edge graphs can be used to model and solve optimization problems. In this investigation, students explore one example related to finding an efficient route for painting school lockers. The objectives are for students to understand how to create a vertex-edge graph model and to formulate the conditions for this particular type of efficient route (which will be identified as an Euler circuit in the next investigation).

COLLABORATION SKILL
Include every group member in discussions.

1 Since you are being paid for the job, not by the hour, you would like to paint the lockers as quickly and efficiently as possible.

  a. Which row would you paint first? Is there more than one choice for the first row to paint?

  b. Which row would you paint last? Why?

2 Here are three plans that have been suggested for painting the lockers.

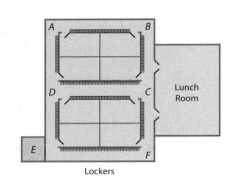

Lockers

Plan I: Paint from *E* to *F*, *F* to *C*, *C* to *D* (one side), *D* to *E*, *D* to *A*, *A* to *B*, *B* to *C*, *C* to *D* (the other side).

Plan II: Paint from *A* to *B*, *B* to *C*, *C* to *D* (one side), *D* to *A*, *D* to *C* (other side), *C* to *F*, *F* to *E*, *E* to *D*.

Plan III: Paint from *E* to *D*, *D* to *A*, *A* to *B*, *B* to *C*, *C* to *F*, *F* to *E*, *D* to *C* (one side), *C* to *D* (other side).

  a. Which, if any, of these plans do you think is optimum; that is, the "best" way to do the painting? If a plan is not optimum, explain why not.

  b. Without help from your classmates, prepare a plan you think is optimum for painting the lockers.

  c. Compare your plan with those of others.

   i. How are they alike? How are they different?

   ii. Agree on a list of criteria that can be used to decide whether a plan is optimum.

3 A **mathematical model** is a symbolic or pictorial representation including only the essential features of a problem situation. The floor-plan map of the first floor of the school shows the rows of lockers, classrooms, lunch room, equipment room, hallways, and outer walls. There are some features of this map that you do not need in order to solve the locker-painting problem.

  a. Which of the features of the map did you use as you tried to solve the locker-painting problem? Which features were not needed?

  b. Refer to the first-floor map of the school above. Think about a simplified diagram (a mathematical model) that includes only the essential features of the locker-painting problem. For example, the lettered points on the map are important because *E* is the beginning and ending point, and the other letters mark where one row of lockers ends and another begins. Complete a copy of the diagram below so that it is a mathematical model for the locker-painting problem.

A •   • B

D •   • C

E •   • F

1 **a.** Paint either row *ED* or *EF* first so you do not have to move the equipment past unpainted lockers.

b. End at *E* so the equipment can be left there. A key point is that the painting should begin and end at the corner closest to the equipment room. Beginning or ending anywhere else means the equipment must be moved past lockers that either need paint or are already painted.

2 **a.** **INSTRUCTIONAL NOTE** Accept any response for which the student exhibits good reasoning. None of the paths seem optimal because they pass lockers without painting them and do not end at the equipment room. Some students may respond with a route that they believe is better than any of the three given paths, in which case they already will have done Part b. Students may be wrestling with what "optimal" means. Let them; don't give them a definition yet. In this situation, optimal will mean a route in which the equipment is moved past as few lockers as possible while not painting. Creativity should be encouraged, but students eventually should arrive at the criteria in Part c.

Plans I and III seem the optimal choices of these three.
Possible explanations for why the given plans are not optimal:
  Plan I: In this plan, you pass the row of lockers between *D* and *E* after it is painted (i.e., *DE* is repeated) and you do not end at the equipment room.
  Plan II: In this plan, you go past two sets of lockers before beginning to paint. Also, you pass row *A* to *D* when it is already painted. Thus, *AD* and *DE* are repeated. And you do not end at the equipment room.
  Plan III: In this plan, you must go back to paint both sides of the center hall, and you end in the center hall. In this plan, *DE* is passed twice after it is painted to return to the equipment room.

b. Responses may vary. Some optimal orders:
E to *F*, *F* to *C*, *C* to *D* (one side), *D* to *A*, *A* to *B*, *B* to *C*, *C* to *D* (other side), *D* to *E*; *E* to *F*, *F* to *C*, *C* to *D*, *D* to *C*, *C* to *B*, *B* to *A*, *A* to *D*, *D* to *E*; *E* to *D*, *D* to *C*, *C* to *B*, *B* to *A*, *A* to *D*, *D* to *C*, *C* to *F*, *F* to *E*.

c. **i.** Plans should all start and end at the equipment room and not require moving equipment along a row of lockers while not painting them. Plans may be different in the order that they paint the lockers.

  ii. Students should identify these two key criteria.

   • Start and end at the equipment room.

   • Never move past a row you are not painting. This criterion might be more succinctly stated as, "don't repeat any rows" or "move past each row exactly once." (This last statement leads directly to Euler paths.)

3 **a.** In the locker-painting problems, features like the lunch room and the outer walls are irrelevant to the solution of the problem. The essential features are the various rows of lockers, since they are to be painted, and the points marked by the letters in the diagram where one row ends and one or more other rows begin.

b. Responses may vary. Most students will likely connect the points in the diagram in some meaningful way to represent the rows of lockers. Discussion may focus on what is essential and why it is essential.

A diagram consisting of a set of points along with segments or arcs joining some of the points is called a **vertex-edge graph**, or simply a **graph**. The points are called **vertices**, and each point is called a **vertex**. The segments or arcs joining the vertices are called **edges**. The word "graph" is used to mean different things at different times in mathematics. In this unit, the word "graph" typically refers to a diagram consisting of vertices and edges.

4 Now examine the vertex-edge graph models drawn by some other students.

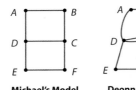

Michael's Model Deonna's Model Amy's Model

a. Does Michael's vertex-edge graph show all the essential features of the locker-painting problem? If so, explain. If not, describe what is needed.

b. Is Deonna's vertex-edge graph an appropriate model for the locker-painting problem? Why do you think Deonna joined vertices C and D with 2 edges?

c. Is Amy's graph an appropriate model for the locker-painting problem? Explain.

5 In Problem 2, you were asked to find an optimum plan for painting the first-floor lockers.

a. Use that plan to trace an optimum painting route on the vertex-edge graph you drew in Problem 3. If you cannot trace your optimum route on your graph, carefully check both your optimum plan and your graph.

b. Trace the same painting route on Deonna's graph. Does it matter if the vertices are connected by straight line segments or curved arcs? Does it matter how long the edges are?

6 Below is a vertex-edge graph that models a different arrangement of lockers.

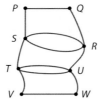

a. Draw a school floor-plan map that corresponds to this graph. Assume that the equipment room is at V.

b. Find, if possible, an optimum route for painting these lockers.

4 **a.** The diagram fails to show the fact that both sides of the hall joining C and D must be painted, so it does not show all essential features of the problem.

b. Yes, it is an appropriate model because it shows all the essential features of the problem. The segments and arcs represent rows of lockers. The vertices represent where the rows of lockers meet. Deonna used two edges between C and D because there are two rows of lockers which need to be painted, one row at a time. Notice that even though Deonna's drawing is "crooked," her model is still fine since exact size and shape are not essential features of this situation. This point is emphasized in Problem 5, Part b, below.

c. Amy's graph is also an accurate and appropriate model. An explanation follows but students may not catch all the subtleties at this point in their work. In Deonna's graph, the vertices are taken to be as given in the statement of the problem. That is, a vertex is a point "where you would stop painting one row of lockers and start painting another" or "where one row of lockers ends and another begins." In Amy's graph, she chose to ignore the corners at A, B, and F, which is fine since decisions about the painting route are not affected by those corners. For Amy, the vertices are defined as places where you need to make a decision about which row to paint next. Thus, the vertices are at the starting point (the equipment room, E) and at the two "hallway intersections," C and D. (If students are confused about why Amy's graph is an acceptable model, you might ask them to think about how the C-B-A-D section of lockers is really just one extended row of lockers since there are no branching points.)

5 **a.** Responses may vary. Students should find that their optimal plan works on their model. Be sure students do not include walking from one row of lockers in the middle hall to the other or going from the equipment room to the first row as separate edges.

b. The intent here is to emphasize that the lengths and shapes of the edges are irrelevant in the models. All that matters is that the definitions of the vertices and edges and how the vertices are connected to each other by the edges accurately represent the problem.

6 **a.** Responses may vary. See the examples below.

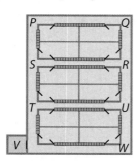 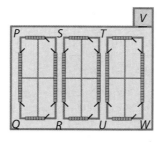

b. One possible optimal route is V-W-U-T-U-R-S-R-Q-P-S-T-V.

Unit 4

Summarize
the Mathematics

In this investigation, you explored how vertex-edge graphs can be used to model situations in which an efficient route is to be found.

a What is the difference between a floor-plan map of a school showing the lockers to be painted and a mathematical model of the locker-painting problem?

b A key step in modeling a problem situation with a graph is to decide what the vertices and edges will represent. Refer back to Problem 4. Both Deonna's and Amy's models are appropriate. What do the vertices and edges represent in each of these graphs in terms of the locker-painting problem?

c Can two vertex-edge graphs that have different shapes represent the same problem situation? Can two graphs that have different numbers of vertices and edges represent the same problem situation? Explain.

d In Problem 2, you wrote a list of criteria for an optimum locker-painting plan. Restate those criteria in terms of tracing around a vertex-edge graph that models the situation.

Be prepared to share your ideas with the entire class.

✔Check Your Understanding

Suppose the lockers and an equipment room on the west wing of a high school are located as shown below.

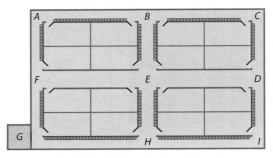

a. If you were to model the problem of painting these lockers with a vertex-edge graph, what would the vertices represent? The edges?

b. Draw a graph that models this problem.

c. Determine an optimum plan for painting the lockers. Check your plan against the criteria for tracing the edges and vertices of a graph that you prepared in Part d of the Summarize the Mathematics.

Summarize
the Mathematics

(a) The floor-plan map shows features, such as the lunch room, walls, and doors, that are irrelevant, that is, they are not needed to solve the problem at hand. A mathematical model shows only the essential features of the problem situation.

(b) In Deonna's model, the vertices are as given in the problem statement. That is, the vertices are the points where you would stop painting one row of lockers and start painting another row. The edges represent the rows of lockers. In Amy's model, the vertices represent the "hallway intersections" and the starting point (the equipment room). The edges represent the "extended" or single rows of lockers between those vertices. Both models accurately represent the problem situation. (This raises the interesting point that although this is a very concrete situation, nevertheless the definition of the vertices can be abstract and subtle. In particular, it is not correct to define the vertices as "corners of rows of lockers" and the edges as the rows of lockers between corners. This would lead to 8 vertices and would split the graph model into two disconnected pieces, which is not a representation that fits the problem situation.)

(c) It is important for students to understand that two graphs can have different shapes, sizes, and even different numbers of vertices and edges, and yet still accurately represent the same situation. For example, consider Deonna's and Amy's graphs for the locker-painting problem (and see Part b just above). Furthermore, two graphs are "the same" (i.e., isomorphic) if they have identical vertex-edge relationships, even if they look different in terms of shape or size. As an optional activity, you or your students could use software such as vertex-edge graph software in *CPMP-Tools* to help illustrate this point by drawing a graph and then dragging the vertices and deforming the edges.

(d) Students should state criteria that are equivalent to the following. You want to trace the graph so that (a) you start and stop at the same vertex, and (b) you trace each edge exactly once.

PROCESSING PROMPT
I made sure _____
(person)
was included in our
discussions by … .

✓Check Your Understanding

a. Responses may vary. One solution is to let the edges represent the rows of lockers. The vertices, corresponding to the points in the diagram of the lockers, represent points at which one row of lockers ends and another begins.

b. Responses may vary. Two possible graph models are shown at the right.

c. Plans may vary. *G* is the equipment room, so plans should begin and end at *G*. One possible plan is *G-H-I-D-C-B-E-H-E-B-A-F-G*.

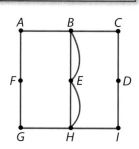

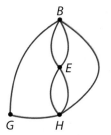

Euler Circuits: Finding the Best Path **T242**

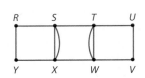

Investigation 2   Making the Circuit

Your criteria for the optimum sequence for painting the lockers in the previous investigation are the defining characteristics of an important property of a graph. An **Euler** (pronounced *oy' lur*) **circuit** is a route through a connected graph such that (1) each edge of the graph is traced exactly once, and (2) the route starts and ends at the same vertex.

You only consider Euler circuits in connected graphs. A **connected graph** is a graph that is all in one piece. That is, from each vertex there is at least one path to every other vertex. Given a connected graph, it often is helpful to know if it has an Euler circuit. (The name "Euler" is in recognition of the eighteenth-century Swiss mathematician Leonhard Euler. He was the first to study and write about these circuits.) As you work through this investigation, look for clues that help you answer these questions:

How can you tell if a graph has an Euler circuit?
If a graph has an Euler circuit, how can you systematically find it?

1 Graph models of the sidewalks in two sections of a town are shown below. Parking meters are placed along these sidewalks.

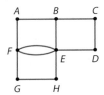
East Town Model

West Town Model

    a. Why would it be helpful for a parking-control officer to know if these graphs have Euler circuits?

    b. Does the graph that models the east section of town have an Euler circuit? Explain your reasoning.

    c. Does the graph that models the west section of town have an Euler circuit? Does it have more than one Euler circuit? Explain.

2 The three graphs at the top of the next page are similar to puzzles enjoyed by people all over the world. In each case, the challenge is to trace the figure. You must trace every edge exactly once without lifting your pencil and return to where you started. That is, the challenge is to trace an Euler circuit through the figure or graph. Place a sheet of paper over each graph and try to trace an Euler circuit. If the graph has an Euler circuit, write down the vertices in order as you trace the circuit. (Note that in the graph in Part c, only the points with letter labels are vertices. The other edge crossings are not vertices; you can think of them like overpasses in a road system.)

In this investigation, students learn that the solution to the locker-painting problem involves finding an Euler circuit, and so they investigate Euler circuits. They see that Euler circuits apply to other problem situations. Most of the investigation is devoted to finding conditions (a theorem) for when a graph has an Euler circuit, and investigating algorithms for constructing Euler circuits.

Students use reasoned trial and error to solve Problems 1 and 2. These problems set the stage for the current investigation and connect to the previous investigation. More systematic methods for finding circuits will be developed in later problems.

> **DIFFERENTIATION** It may be possible in some classes or with some students to teach this investigation in a very open-ended way, by simply presenting the two italicized focus questions and then turning students loose to find answers.

1. a. Parking-control officers would want to check each meter without walking a street twice. To minimize walking, they also might wish to begin and end at their parked cars.

   b. No, vertices B and E are problems. You can get into them, but not out again without retracing a path.

   c. Yes. Yes. Each edge can be traced exactly once starting and ending at the same vertex, for any vertex.

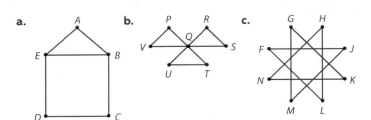

a.

b.

c.

③ By looking at the form of a function rule, you often can predict the shape of the graph of the function without plotting any points. Similarly, it would be helpful to be able to examine a vertex-edge graph and predict if it has an Euler circuit without trying to trace it.

a. Have each member of your group draw a graph with five or more edges that has an Euler circuit. On a separate sheet of paper, have each group member draw a connected graph with five or more edges that does *not* have an Euler circuit. Alternatively, use vertex-edge graph software to generate several graphs that have an Euler circuit and several graphs that do not.

b. Sort your group's graphs into two collections, those that have an Euler circuit and those that do not.

c. Examine the graphs in the two collections. Describe key ways in which graphs that have Euler circuits differ from those that do not.

d. Try to figure out a way to predict if a graph has an Euler circuit simply by examining its vertices.

   i. Test your method of prediction using the graphs in Problem 2.

   ii. If you have access to vertex-edge graph software, generate several additional general graphs to test your method.

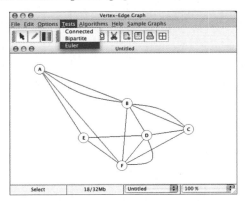

e. Make a conjecture about the properties of a graph that has an Euler circuit. Explain why you think your conjecture is true for *any* graph that has an Euler circuit. Compare and test your conjecture with other students' conjectures and graphs. Modify your conjecture and explanation as needed.

2 **a.** There is no Euler circuit.

b. There are Euler circuits from each vertex. The order of tracings may vary.

c. There are Euler circuits from each vertex. The order of tracings may vary.

3 **INSTRUCTIONAL NOTE** Make sure each student draws only one graph on each piece of paper. You might want to have some pieces of scrap paper available. It may be difficult for students to see that a graph has an Euler circuit if and only if there is an even number of edge-touchings at each vertex. Let them wrestle with it a bit before giving hints about looking at vertices and number of edge-touchings. Finding patterns is an important part of mathematics, and some students will get it!

a. See student-produced graphs.

b. Group work; no response is expected.

c. Students may focus on a variety of graph characteristics, like number of vertices and edges, shape of graph, types of subgraphs, etc. It may be that their particular collection of sample graphs will lead them to incorrect or insufficient conjectures, such as (1) graphs that look like polygons have Euler circuits (or they might say graphs that look like "cycles") or (2) graphs where each vertex has 2 or 4 edges touching it have Euler circuits.

d. If students did not focus on vertices in Part c, then they will here. (Ultimately, students need to look at number of edge-touchings at each vertex. Give them a chance to move in this direction before giving them too many hints.)

e. Conjecture: A connected graph has an Euler circuit when each vertex has an even number of edges touching it. Graphs with no Euler circuit have some vertices that have an odd number of edges touching them. (Note that if students generate graphs with loops, then a loop counts as 2 edge-touchings—see Problem 4 on page 245.) Rough Explanation: The key idea is that as you trace an Euler circuit you go in and out of vertices, and each in-out means two edge-touchings. Thus, a graph that has an Euler circuit will have an even number of edge-touchings at each vertex.

TECHNOLOGY NOTE You may wish to set up a computer and printer to allow students to create graphs using the "Euler and non-Euler Graphs" custom tool.

INSTRUCTIONAL NOTE You may want to be prepared to show counterexample graphs.

Unit 4

4 In your conjecture from Problem 3 Part e about which graphs have an Euler circuit, you probably counted the number of edges at each vertex of the graph. The number of edges touching a vertex is called the **degree of the vertex**. Restate your conjecture in terms of the degrees of the vertices. (If an edge loops back to the same vertex, that counts as two edge touchings. For an example see Extensions Task 29 on page 262.)

5 Once you can predict whether a graph has an Euler circuit, it is often still necessary to find the circuit. Consider the graphs below.

Graph I   **Graph II**

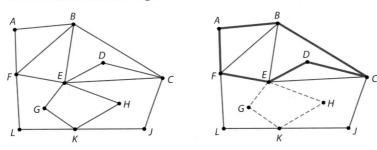

a. For each graph, predict whether it has an Euler circuit.

b. If the graph has an Euler circuit, find it.

c. Describe the method you used to find your Euler circuit. Describe other possible methods for finding Euler circuits.

6 One systematic method for finding an Euler circuit is to trace the circuit in stages. For example, suppose you and your classmates want to find an Euler circuit that begins and ends at *A* in the graph below. You can trace the circuit in several stages.

Stage I: Alicia began by drawing a circuit that begins and ends at *A*. The circuit she drew, shown in the diagram by the heavy edges, was *A-B-C-D-E-F-A*. But this does not trace all edges.

Stage II: George added another circuit shown by the dashed edges starting at *E*: *E-G-K-H-E*.

a. Alicia's and George's circuits can be combined to form a single circuit beginning and ending at *A*. List the order of vertices for that combined circuit.

4 Conjecture: A connected graph has an Euler circuit if and only if each vertex has even degree.

5 **a.** Using their work from Problems 3 and 4, students should predict if an Euler circuit exists. The goal here is to predict existence or nonexistence without actually trying to trace the circuit. Graph I has an Euler circuit, but Graph II does not.

b. There are many circuits that students can trace in Graph I.

c. Students should describe the methods or strategies they used to find an Euler circuit. This problem brings up an important distinction in mathematics: it's one thing to say something exists; it's quite another to find it.

6 **NOTE** This problem continues development of the skill of algorithmic problem solving. Here students will analyze a given algorithm, which is sometimes called Hierholzer's Algorithm or the Onionskin Algorithm.

a. One such circuit is *A-B-C-D-E-G-K-H-E-F-A*.

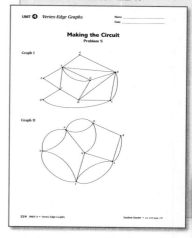
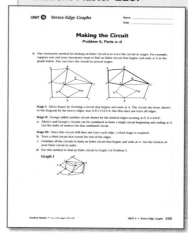

Stage III: Since this circuit still does not trace each edge, a third stage is required.

b. Trace a third circuit which covers the rest of the edges.

c. Combine all the circuits to form an Euler circuit that begins and ends at *A*. List the vertices of your Euler circuit in order.

d. Use this method to find an Euler circuit in Graph I of Problem 5.

7 Choose your preferred method for finding Euler circuits from Problems 5 and 6. Write specific step-by-step instructions that describe the method you chose. Your instructions should be written so that they apply to *any* graph, not just the one that you may be working on at the moment. Such a list of step-by-step instructions is called an **algorithm**.

Creating algorithms is an important aspect of mathematics. Algorithms are especially important when programming computers to solve problems. Two questions you should ask about any algorithm are *Does it always work?* and *Is it efficient?* You will consider these questions in more detail in the next lesson.

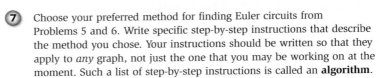

Summarize
the Mathematics

It is possible to examine a graph to decide if it has an Euler circuit. If it does, there are algorithms to find such a circuit.

a How can you tell if a graph like the one below has an Euler circuit without actually trying to trace the graph?

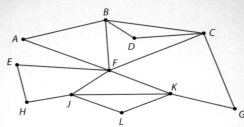

b Use your algorithm from Problem 7 to find an Euler circuit in the graph shown here.

Be prepared to explain your thinking and algorithm to the class.

b. One such circuit is *B-E-C-J-K-L-F-B*.

c. One possible circuit is *A-B-E-C-J-K-L-F-B-C-D-E-G-K-H-E-F-A*.

d. Students should apply this algorithm to other graphs.

(7) Students' instructions will vary. It is important for students to describe carefully their preferred method.

One description of the Onionskin Algorithm:

Step 1: Start at any vertex and begin tracing, going as long as you can without reusing edges. (Since all vertices are touched by an even number of edges, you can enter on one edge and leave on another. The starting vertex is the only vertex where you will need to stop.)

Step 2: When you get back to the starting vertex, check to see if you have an Euler circuit. If not, retrace your circuit, and when you reach a vertex *V* with an edge that you did not trace, trace it and continue drawing until you get back to *V* (which will happen for the same reason given in Step 1). Do not trace over edges you traced previously.

Step 3: Continue from *V* along your first path tracing. If you reach another vertex with an untraced edge, go back to Step 2.

Step 4: Continue this process of including more and more edges in your circuit until you eventually include them all, and you have an Euler circuit.

NOTE Although answering questions about whether or not algorithms always work and are efficient generally requires advanced mathematics beyond this course, students will informally investigate these questions in the next lesson and in the *Network Optimization* unit in Course 2. Note that the algorithm in Problem 6 above does, in fact, always work to find an Euler circuit when one exists.

Summary

During STM discussion, provide an opportunity for students to compare their algorithms in terms of similarities and differences.

Summarize
the Mathematics

(a) A connected graph has an Euler circuit if and only if each vertex has an even number of edge-touchings, that is, each vertex has even degree. (See notes on page T247.) Since the given graph has all even-degree vertices, it has an Euler circuit.

(b) Responses may vary. One possibility is *A-F-E-H-J-L-K-J-F-K-G-C-F-B-D-C-B-A*.

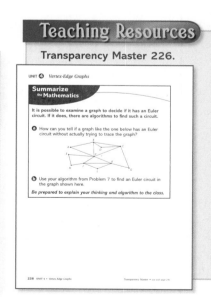
MATH TOOLKIT Sketch a connected graph with 8 vertices that has an Euler circuit. Explain how you know a circuit exists and how you can find an Euler circuit.

✓ Check Your Understanding

For each of the graphs below, decide if the graph has an Euler circuit. If there is an Euler circuit, use your algorithm to find it. If not, explain how you know that no Euler circuit exists.

a.
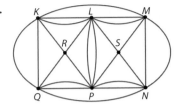

b.
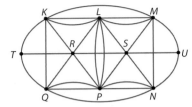

Investigation 3 — Graphs and Matrices

Information is often organized and displayed in tables. The use of tables to summarize information can be seen in almost every section of most newspapers. As you work on the problems in this investigation, look for answers to this question:

> *How can table-like arrays be used to represent vertex-edge graphs and help reason about information contained in the graphs?*

1. Examine this information on gold (1st place), silver (2nd place), and bronze (3rd place) medals awarded in the 2006 Winter Olympics.

Medal Count

Country	G	S	B	Total
Germany	11	12	6	29
United States	9	9	7	25
Austria	9	7	7	23
Russian Fed.	8	6	8	22
Canada	7	10	7	24
Sweden	7	2	5	14

Source: www.torino2006.org

a. What do each of the numbers in the row labeled Germany represent?

b. What is the meaning of the number in the fifth row and second column? (Don't count the row and column headings.) In the third row and third column?

c. Finland did not win any gold medals. However, the Finnish team did take home 6 silver medals and 3 bronze medals. How could you modify this chart to include this additional information?

EXTENSIONS AND SOME TECHNICAL DETAILS If a graph contains a loop (1 edge leading in and out of the same vertex), it counts as 2 edge-touchings. This allows for an even number of edge-touchings to be maintained when a loop is added to a graph that has an Euler circuit. See Extensions Tasks 28 and 29.

An *Euler path* is a route through a graph that uses each edge exactly once, and which may or may not start and end at the same vertex. Thus, an Euler circuit is a special case of an Euler path. A connected graph has an Euler path that is not a circuit if and only if there are exactly two odd-degree vertices in the graph (and these two vertices are the starting and ending vertices of the Euler path). Some students may notice this extension of what they have been doing in this lesson, but it is not required. For some exploration of Euler paths that are not circuits, see Applications Tasks 3, 5, and Connections Task 11.

 Check Your Understanding

a. This graph has an Euler circuit since all vertices have even degree. The specific circuit found will vary.

b. This graph has no Euler circuit, since 2 vertices, *T* and *U*, have odd degree.

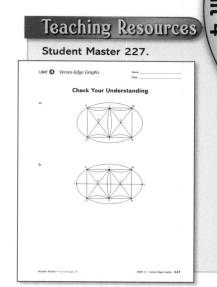

Investigation 3 · Graphs and Matrices

This investigation introduces matrices, mostly in the context of vertex-edge graphs. Students learn how to construct and interpret an adjacency matrix for a graph. They also learn about and use the row sum operation. They will learn much more about matrices and their uses in future units, particularly *Matrix Methods* and *Coordinate Methods* in Course 2.

1 **a.** The numbers of gold, silver, and bronze medals won by Germany in the 2006 Winter Olympics

b. Canada won 10 silver medals. Austria won 7 bronze medals.

c. Add a seventh row labeled "Finland" with these numbers: 0, 6, 3, and 9.

2 Rectangular arrays of numbers, like the one below, are sometimes called **matrices**. Matrices can be used to represent graphs. One way in which a graph can be represented by a **matrix** is shown by the partially completed matrix below.

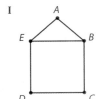

$$\begin{array}{c c} & \begin{array}{cccccc} A & B & C & D & E & F \end{array} \\ \begin{array}{c} A \\ B \\ C \\ D \\ E \\ F \end{array} & \left[\begin{array}{cccccc} 0 & 1 & 0 & 1 & 0 & 0 \\ - & - & - & - & - & - \\ - & - & - & - & - & - \\ 1 & 0 & 2 & 0 & 1 & 0 \\ - & - & - & - & - & - \\ - & - & - & - & - & - \end{array}\right] \end{array}$$

a. Study the first and fourth rows of the matrix. Explain what each entry means in terms of the graph.

b. Copy the matrix and then fill in the missing entries.

c. Vertices in a graph that are connected by an edge are said to be **adjacent vertices**. The matrix you constructed in Part b is called an **adjacency matrix** for the graph, since it contains information about vertices that are adjacent. Each entry in an adjacency matrix is the number of direct connections (edges) between the corresponding pair of vertices. Construct an adjacency matrix for each of the three graphs below.

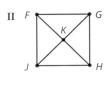

d. It is time-consuming to construct an adjacency matrix for a large graph. If you have access to vertex-edge graph software, construct an adjacency matrix for several graphs (without loops) that contain at least 6 vertices. Click on the entries of the matrix to see the corresponding edge(s) in the graph. Construct a circuit in the graph (not necessarily an Euler circuit) by clicking on entries in the adjacency matrix.

3 Now examine some common properties of the adjacency matrices you have constructed.

a. The **main diagonal** of a matrix like these consists of the entries in the diagonal running from the top-left corner of the matrix to the bottom-right corner. What do you notice about the main diagonal in these adjacency matrices? Explain this pattern. (The graphs you have worked with so far do not contain loops. To see how loops affect an adjacency matrix, see Extensions Task 28 on page 262.)

b. Describe and explain any symmetry you see in these adjacency matrices.

a. Each entry shows the number of single edges between the 2 vertices. For example, the "2" in the *D-C* cell means that there are 2 edges connecting *D* and *C*.

b.

$$\begin{array}{c c} & \begin{matrix} A & B & C & D & E & F \end{matrix} \\ \begin{matrix} A \\ B \\ C \\ D \\ E \\ F \end{matrix} & \begin{bmatrix} 0 & 1 & 0 & 1 & 0 & 0 \\ 1 & 0 & 1 & 0 & 0 & 0 \\ 0 & 1 & 0 & 2 & 0 & 1 \\ 1 & 0 & 2 & 0 & 1 & 0 \\ 0 & 0 & 0 & 1 & 0 & 1 \\ 0 & 0 & 1 & 0 & 1 & 0 \end{bmatrix} \end{array}$$

c.

I
$$\begin{array}{c c} & \begin{matrix} A & B & C & D & E \end{matrix} \\ \begin{matrix} A \\ B \\ C \\ D \\ E \end{matrix} & \begin{bmatrix} 0 & 1 & 0 & 0 & 1 \\ 1 & 0 & 1 & 0 & 1 \\ 0 & 1 & 0 & 1 & 0 \\ 0 & 0 & 1 & 0 & 1 \\ 1 & 1 & 0 & 1 & 0 \end{bmatrix} \end{array}$$

II
$$\begin{array}{c c} & \begin{matrix} F & G & H & J & K \end{matrix} \\ \begin{matrix} F \\ G \\ H \\ J \\ K \end{matrix} & \begin{bmatrix} 0 & 1 & 0 & 1 & 1 \\ 1 & 0 & 1 & 0 & 1 \\ 0 & 1 & 0 & 1 & 1 \\ 1 & 0 & 1 & 0 & 1 \\ 1 & 1 & 1 & 1 & 0 \end{bmatrix} \end{array}$$

III
$$\begin{array}{c c} & \begin{matrix} L & M & N \end{matrix} \\ \begin{matrix} L \\ M \\ N \end{matrix} & \begin{bmatrix} 0 & 1 & 1 \\ 1 & 0 & 2 \\ 1 & 2 & 0 \end{bmatrix} \end{array}$$

d. This part is optional. The *CPMP-Tools* vertex-edge graph software allows students to quickly construct adjacency matrices. It also highlights the connection between a graph and its adjacency matrix. (This task could be assigned as homework. Results could be printed for sharing the next day.)

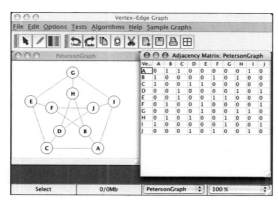

> **TECHNOLOGY NOTE**
> *CPMP-Tools*, vertex-edge graph software can be used to dynamically show the connection between edges in a graph and entries in its adjacency matrix.

  a. The main diagonal in each of the matrices consists of all zeros. This is because there are no loops in any of these graphs. See Extensions Task 27 to see how loops affect the adjacency matrix.

b. All of these matrices are symmetric about the main diagonal. This is because the edges connect two vertices, so that if vertex *X* is adjacent to vertex *Y*, then *Y* is also adjacent to *X*. (Note that this symmetry would not necessarily appear in the adjacency matrix for a *directed graph*, that is, a graph in which the edges are directed arrows. Directed graphs are not studied in this unit, except very briefly in Extensions Problem 26. Directed graphs will be studied in the Course 2 unit, *Network Optimization*.)

(4) The sums of the numbers in each row of a matrix are called the **row sums** of the matrix.

   a. Find the row sums of each of the adjacency matrices in Problem 2 Part c. What do these row sums represent in the graphs?

   b. Is it possible to tell by looking at the adjacency matrix for a graph whether the graph has an Euler circuit? Justify your response.

Summarize
the Mathematics

In this investigation, you learned how a matrix can be used to represent and help analyze a graph.

a An adjacency matrix corresponding to a graph that has 5 vertices, *A*, *B*, *C*, *D*, and *E*, listed in the matrix in that order, has a 2 in the third row, fifth column. What does the 2 represent? What does a 1 in the first row, second column mean?

b How do the row sums of adjacency matrices for graphs that do and do not have Euler circuits differ? Explain.

Be prepared to share your thinking with the entire class.

✔ Check Your Understanding

Examine the adjacency matrices below, and answer the following questions.

$$
\mathbf{I} \quad
\begin{array}{c c c c}
 & A & B & C \\
A & \begin{bmatrix} 0 \\ 2 \\ 0 \end{bmatrix} & \begin{matrix} 2 \\ 0 \\ 1 \end{matrix} & \begin{bmatrix} 0 \\ 1 \\ 0 \end{bmatrix}
\end{array}
$$

I   A   B   C

A $\begin{bmatrix} 0 & 2 & 0 \\ 2 & 0 & 1 \\ 0 & 1 & 0 \end{bmatrix}$

II   P   Q   R   S

$\begin{matrix} P \\ Q \\ R \\ S \end{matrix} \begin{bmatrix} 0 & 1 & 2 & 1 \\ 1 & 0 & 1 & 2 \\ 2 & 1 & 0 & 2 \\ 1 & 2 & 2 & 0 \end{bmatrix}$

   a. Does each of the graphs with an adjacency matrix given above have an Euler circuit? How can you tell without drawing the graphs?

   b. Draw and label a graph corresponding to each adjacency matrix. Find an Euler circuit if there is one.

4 a. i. 2, 3, 2, 2, 3   **ii.** 3, 3, 3, 3, 4   **iii.** 2, 3, 3

Each row sum is the degree of the vertex that corresponds to that row.

b. A connected graph has an Euler circuit if, and only if, all the row sums are even numbers. (This rule does not work when a graph has a loop, that is, an edge that joins a vertex to itself. Extensions Task 28 explores this situation in more detail.)

Summarize
the Mathematics

a Two in the third row, fifth column, means 2 edges join vertices *C* and *E*. One in the first row, second column, means 1 edge joins *A* and *B*.

b As long as the graph has no loops, the graph has an Euler circuit whenever all row sums are even.

Unit 4

POSSIBLE ERROR An entry in an adjacency matrix is the number of direct connections (edges) between the corresponding pair of vertices. It is not the number of edges in a path between 2 vertices. (Do not mention this issue unless students raise it.)

✔ Check Your Understanding

a. Neither graph has an Euler circuit, since some of the row sums are odd in each case.

b. Sample graphs are shown below. Neither has an Euler circuit.

I

II

On Your Own

Applications

1. Suppose the lockers on the second floor of a high school are located as shown at the right. Suppose the equipment room located at *G* is at the bottom of a stairway leading to the second floor. Find two optimum plans for painting the lockers that satisfy the optimum criteria you listed in Investigation 1, Problem 2 Part c (page 240).

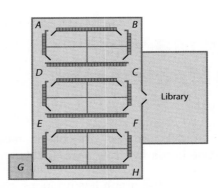

2. The Pregolya River runs through the Russian city of Kaliningrad. In the eighteenth century, the river was called the Pregel and the city was named Königsberg. Four parts of the city were connected by 7 bridges as illustrated here. Citizens often took walking tours of the city by crossing over the bridges. Some people wondered whether it was possible to tour the city by beginning at a point on land, walking across each bridge exactly once, and returning to the same point. This problem, called the *Königsberg bridges problem*, intrigued the mathematician Leonhard Euler, who lived at that time. The paper Euler wrote in 1736 containing the solution to this problem is widely considered to be the first paper on the theory of vertex-edge graphs. Ironically, Euler did not use an actual vertex-edge graph diagram as part of his solution, although his results clearly apply to such graphs. (Euler considered his work on this problem to be part of an area of mathematics informally discussed then as "the geometry of position," since it dealt with relative position, but not distance.)

   a. Draw a graph in which the vertices represent the 4 land areas (lettered in the figure) and the edges represent bridges.

   b. What is the solution to the Königsberg bridges problem? Explain your response.

   c. In the time since Euler solved the problem, two more bridges were built. One bridge was added at the left to connect areas labeled *L* and *P*. Another bridge was added to connect areas labeled *N* and *P*.

      i. Draw a graph that models this new situation of land areas and bridges.

      ii. Use your graph to determine if it is possible to take a tour of the city that crosses each of the 9 bridges exactly once and allows you to return to the point where you started.

On Your Own

Applications

1 Responses may vary. Some optimal plans follow:
G to H, H to F, F to E, E to F, F to C, C to D, D to C, C to B, B to A,
A to D, D to E, E to G;
G to E, E to D, D to C, C to D, D to A, A to B, B to C, C to F, F to E,
E to F, F to H, H to G;
G to E, E to F, F to E, E to D, D to A, A to B, B to C, C to D, D to C,
C to F, F to H, H to G.

TECHNOLOGY NOTE Since *CPMP-Tools* is available on the Web, some students may wish to use the vertex-edge graph software at home for some tasks such as On Your Own tasks 9, 16, and 21.

2 It's interesting that in Euler's 1736 paper he did not prove all of Euler's Theorem! He only proved half of the "if and only if" statement— if the vertex degrees are not all even, then there is no Euler circuit.

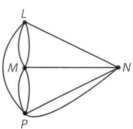

a. Graphs should have edges connecting vertices in the same relationship as in the graph at the right.

b. The walk is not possible since the graph does not have an Euler circuit. All vertices have odd degree.

c. **i.** See the graph at the right.

   ii. No, there is still not an Euler circuit. Vertices M and P have odd degree.

Euler Circuits: Finding the Best Path **T250**

3 The Bushoong are a subgroup of the Kuba chiefdom in the Democratic Republic of Congo (changed from Zaire in 1997). Bushoong children have a long tradition of playing games that involve tracing figures in the sand using a stick. The challenge is to trace each line once and only once without lifting the stick from the sand. Two such figures are given below. (Problem adapted from *Ethnomathematics: A Multicultural View of Mathematical Ideas*, Brooks/ Cole Publishing Company, 1991.)

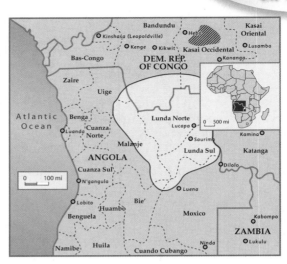

Figure I

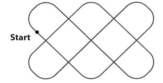

Start

Figure II

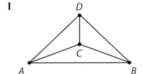

Start

Place a sheet of paper over the figures.

a. Trace each figure without lifting your pencil and without any retracing. Your tracing does not need to end at the same place it started.

b. Try tracing each figure using different "start" points. Summarize your findings.

4 Some popular puzzles involve trying to trace a figure starting and ending at the same vertex without lifting your pencil or tracing an edge more than once. That is, you try to find an Euler circuit.

a. Identify which of the following graphs do not have an Euler circuit. Explain why they do not.

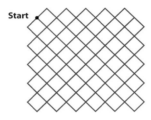

3 **a–b.** Figure I can be traced starting and returning to any point.
Figure II can be traced as required. You can start at the designated
vertex and end at the similarly configured vertex at the upper right
of the figure. You could also trace switching the "start" and "end"
points. (This type of tracing is called an *Euler path*, not a circuit.
See Applications Task 5 and Connections Task 11 for more about
Euler paths.)

4 **a.** Graphs I and II do not have Euler circuits since some of the vertices
have odd degree (in fact, all vertices have odd degree).

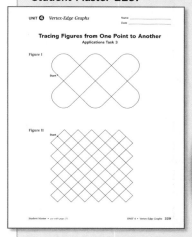
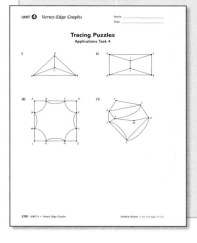
Unit 4

III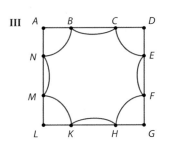

IV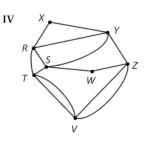

b. For each of the graphs that has an Euler circuit, use the algorithm you developed to find a circuit. Write down the sequence of vertices visited as you trace the circuit.

c. Draw two graphs that would be difficult or impossible to trace without lifting your pencil from the page or tracing an edge more than once—draw one so that it has an Euler circuit and the other so that it does not.

d. Use your graphs from Part c to amaze and teach someone outside of class, as follows. Challenge some people to trace your graphs, without lifting their pencil or tracing any edge more than once and starting and ending at the same point. Then ask them to challenge you in the same way with any graph they draw. See if you can amaze them with how quickly you can tell whether or not it is possible to trace the graph. Then teach them about Euler circuits so they will know the secret too.

5 Suppose the lockers on the second floor of the high school in the locker-painting problem on page 239 are located as shown here.

a. Draw a graph that represents this situation. Be sure to describe what the vertices and edges of your graph represent.

b. Is there a way to paint the lockers by starting and ending at the equipment room and never moving equipment down a hall without painting lockers on one side? Explain.

c. Is there a way to paint the lockers by starting at *D* and ending at *C* and never moving equipment down a hall without painting lockers on one side? Compare the degree of vertices *D* and *C* to the degrees of the other vertices. Make a conjecture about graphs in which there is a route through the graph that starts at one vertex, ends at another, and traverses each edge exactly once.

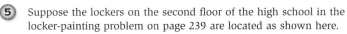

Second-Floor Lockers

6 A newspaper carrier wants to complete a delivery route without retracing steps. Some streets on the route have houses facing each other. Whenever there are houses on both sides of a street, papers are delivered to both sides by making all deliveries to one side and then along the other side.

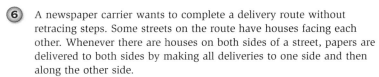

b. Graphs III and IV do have Euler circuits. A circuit for Graph III is
A-B-C-D-E-F-G-H-K-L-M-N-B-C-E-F-H-K-M-N-A. A circuit for Graph IV is
X-Y-Z-V-T-R-Y-S-W-Z-V-T-S-R-X.

c. Students should draw two graphs such that all the vertices have even
degree in one of the graphs but not in the other.

d. Student responses will vary. A point to notice here is that Euler circuits
only apply to connected graphs, and for very complicated graphs it
may be difficult to immediately see if they are connected. For example,
see Extensions Task 21.

a. The edges represent rows of lockers, *E* represents
the equipment room, and the other vertices represent
the end of one row of lockers and the beginning of
another. One possible graph is shown at the right.

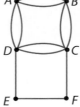

b. No, such a route is not possible, since not all vertices
have even degree.

c. Yes, it is possible to paint the lockers by starting at *D*
and ending at *C*. *D* and *C* have odd degree, while all
the other vertices have even degree. Conjecture: There is an Euler path
that is not a circuit if and only if all vertices have even degree except
for 2 odd-degree vertices, which will be the starting and ending
vertices of the Euler path. (See Connections Task 11 for more explicit
work with Euler paths.)

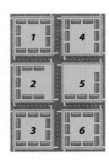

a. Suppose the paper carrier only delivers to the houses on blocks 1, 2, and 3. Construct a vertex-edge graph model for this situation. What do the edges and vertices represent? Find an optimum delivery route.

b. Suppose the paper carrier delivers to the houses on all 6 blocks. Construct a vertex-edge graph model for this situation. Find an optimum delivery route.

c. Now assume that *all* blocks have houses on all 4 sides and all streets continue in both directions.

   i. Add 3 more blocks that are adjacent to the given blocks on the street map. Find an optimum delivery route.

   ii. Can you find an Euler circuit no matter where the 3 new blocks are placed on the route? Explain your response.

   iii. Is it possible to place any number of new blocks on the route and still have an Euler circuit? Explain your reasoning.

7. The map below shows the trails in Tongas State Park. The labeled dots represent rest areas scattered throughout the park.

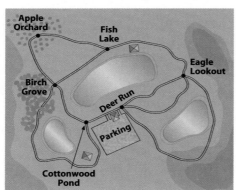

6 **a.** The vertices represent street corners; the edges represent rows of houses. Students may decide that there is no optimal delivery route. Two vertices have odd degree so there is not an Euler circuit. Thus, there is no "optimal" route if optimal is defined in terms of an Euler circuit.

(However, students may legitimately argue for the best possible route. For example, they may find an Euler path: *L-K-L-J-H-K-M-N-M-P-R-N*, but this is not a circuit. Here all the edges are used and none are repeated, but you don't start and end at the same vertex. Students also might argue for walking from *N* to *L* even though there are no houses there and thus no edge. See the graph at the right.)

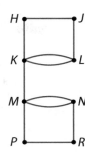

b. The vertices represent street corners; the edges represent rows of houses. All vertices are even. An optimal delivery route is *H-K-L-K-M-N-M-P-R-N-R-W-V-N-V-T-S-J-L-J-H*. See the graph at the right.

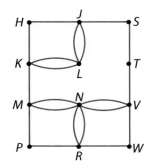

c. **i.** One possible optimal delivery route would be *H-J-S-T-V-W-V-T-S-X-Y-U-V-N-M-N-V-U-Z-W-R-N-L-J-L-N-R-P-M-K-L-T-Y-T-L-K-H*. See the graph at the right.

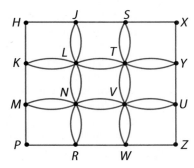

ii. Yes, no matter where the 3 blocks are placed, the vertices will have degrees of 2, 4, 6, or 8.

iii. Yes, there will be an Euler circuit because the vertices will have degrees of 2, 4, 6, or 8.

a. How would a graph model of this situation differ from the map? Is it necessary or useful to draw a graph model in this situation? Why or why not?

b. Construct an adjacency matrix related to the park map.

c. Is it possible to hike each of the trails in the park once and return to your car in the parking lot? Explain your answer by using the adjacency matrix from Part b and your knowledge of Euler circuits.

d. The Park Department has received money to build additional trails. Between which rest stops should they build a new trail (or trails) so that people can hike each trail once and return to their cars?

8 Certain towns in southern Alaska are on islands or isolated by mountain ranges. When traveling between these communities, you must take a boat or a plane. Listed below are the routes provided by a local airline.

Routes between:

Anchorage and Cordova
Anchorage and Juneau
Cordova and Yakutat
Juneau and Ketchikan
Juneau and Petersburg
Juneau and Sitka
Petersburg and Wrangell
Sitka and Ketchikan
Wrangell and Ketchikan
Yakutat and Juneau

a. Draw a vertex-edge graph that models this situation.

b. In what ways is your graph model like the map? In what ways is it different?

c. An airline inspector wants to evaluate the airline's operations by flying each route. It is sufficient to fly each route one-way. Can the inspector start in Juneau, fly all the routes exactly once, and end in Juneau?

d. How would an adjacency matrix for the graph show whether or not there is a route as described in Part c?

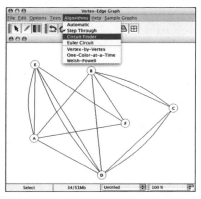

9 In Problem 6 of Investigation 2 (page 245), you learned about an algorithm for finding Euler circuits. Vertex-edge graph software can help you practice and understand this algorithm.

a. Generate an Euler graph from the Sample Graphs menu. (Create several Duplicate Graphs so they will be available to work with as needed.) Use different colors to identify partial circuits in the graph. Then choose black to select and color the edges of the final combined circuit.

b. Generate another Euler graph and use the Circuit Finder algorithm to find an Euler circuit. Use the algorithm in both Automatic and Step Through modes.

7 **a.** The park trails themselves could be a graph for the situation. Other graph models could be built to represent the park trails, but it is not necessary.

b. Using the first letter of each rest area name for the vertex name, we get the following matrix:

$$
\begin{array}{c c}
 & \begin{array}{cccccc} A & B & C & D & E & F \end{array} \\
\begin{array}{c} A \\ B \\ C \\ D \\ E \\ F \end{array} &
\left[\begin{array}{cccccc}
0 & 1 & 0 & 0 & 0 & 1 \\
1 & 0 & 2 & 0 & 0 & 1 \\
0 & 2 & 0 & 1 & 0 & 0 \\
0 & 0 & 1 & 0 & 3 & 0 \\
0 & 0 & 0 & 3 & 0 & 1 \\
1 & 1 & 0 & 0 & 1 & 0
\end{array}\right]
\end{array}
$$

c. No, when you sum the rows of the matrix, notice that both *C* and *F* are odd vertices. The park trails have an Euler path (see Applications Task 5) from *C* to *F*. However, no Euler circuit exists, so hikers cannot get back to the parking lot without repeating or omitting some trails.

d. Possible solutions:

- One trail could be added between Fish Lake and Cottonwood Pond. This might be the least expensive, unless it is too long and an additional rest stop is needed.

- Using existing rest stops, new paths could be added from Fish Lake to Birch Grove and then on to Cottonwood Pond.

- Using existing rest stops, new paths could be added from Fish Lake to Eagle Lookout to Deer Run to Cottonwood Pond.

8 **a.** Responses will vary by location of points and length of edges. If each edge represents a route between the cities (in either direction), one solution is shown. (Graphs that have edges that intersect are also acceptable.)

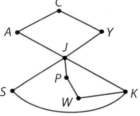

b. The graph is very different from the map. The only similarity is that the cities on the map are also on the graph. The graph does not show the geographical location of the cities, or even their relative position. The graph shows just the essential features of the problem, which in this case are the airline route connections.

c. No, *J* and *K* are odd vertices, so no Euler circuit is possible.

d. The row sums of the adjacency matrix for rows *J* and *K* would be odd.

9 **a–b.** Using the vertex-edge graph software in *CPMP-Tools* will help students better understand and apply the algorithm.

Connections

10 The following graphs separate the plane into several *regions*. The exterior of the graph is an infinite region. The interior regions are enclosed by the edges. For example, Graph I separates the plane into four regions (three are enclosed by the graph and the fourth is outside the graph).

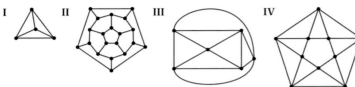

a. Complete a table like the one that follows using the graphs above. Be sure to count the exterior of the graph as one region.

Graph	Number of Vertices (V)	Number of Regions (R)	Number of Edges (E)
I			
II			
III			
IV			

b. Find a formula relating the numbers of vertices V, regions R, and edges E, by using addition or subtraction to combine V, R, and E.

c. Draw several more graphs, and count V, R, and E. Does your formula also work for these graphs?

d. Use your formula to predict how many regions would be formed by an appropriate graph with 5 vertices and 12 edges. Draw such a graph to verify your answer.

11 In this lesson, you discovered that some graphs do not have an Euler circuit.

a. If you are *not* required to start and end at the same vertex, do you think every graph has a path that traces every edge of the graph exactly once? Why or why not?

b. Place a sheet of paper over the graphs below. Try to copy the graphs by tracing each edge exactly once. You don't have to start and end at the same vertex.

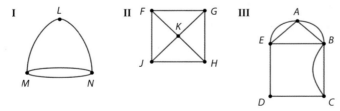

Connections

 10 **a.**

Graph	Number of Vertices (V)	Number of Regions (R)	Number of Edges (E)
I	4	4	6
II	20	12	30
III	6	8	12
IV	10	12	20

b. For example, $V + R = E + 2$ or $V + R - 2 = E$ or $V - E + R = 2$.

c. See the graphs below. The formula fails when (1) edges cross at points which are not vertices, in which case regions cannot be identified; or (2) the graph is not connected, in which case there are too few edges. For graphs where (1) and (2) do not occur, the formula $V + R = E + 2$ always holds.

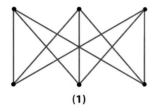

(1)

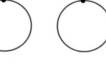

(2)

d. If the graph has no edge-crossings (except at vertices) and it is connected, then the formula $V + R = E + 2$ applies. In this case, we get $5 + R = 12 + 2$, so $R = 9$.

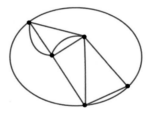

11 **a.** What is important for students to notice here is that some graphs in which not all the vertices are even can be traced, using each edge exactly once, starting and ending at different vertices. In this case, as students will see in the following parts of this problem, the starting and ending vertices have odd degree and all others have even degree. Students should also have noticed that some graphs cannot be so traced (those with more than two odd vertices).

b. Graphs I and III can be so traced.

c. For those graphs that can be traced in this manner, how do the starting and ending vertices differ from the other vertices?

d. An **Euler path** is a route through a connected graph that traces each edge of the graph exactly once. Thus an Euler circuit is a special type of Euler path, one in which the starting and ending vertices must be the same. State a rule for determining whether or not a graph has an Euler path in which the starting vertex is different from the ending vertex.

12 Tracing continuous figures is exhibited in cultures around the world. The Malekula live on an island in the South Pacific chain of some eighty islands that comprise the Republic of Vanuatu. As with the Bushoong in Africa (see Applications Task 3), the Malekula also have figures that represent objects or symbols of the culture. For example, Figure I below represents a yam. Figure II is called "the stone of Ambat." (Problem adapted from *Ethnomathematics: A Multicultural View of Mathematical Ideas*, Brooks/Cole Publishing Company, 1991.)

Figure I   **Figure II**

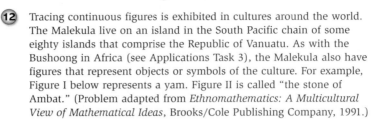

a. Can you trace each of these figures without lifting your pencil or tracing any edges more than once?

b. Describe any *symmetry* you see in each figure.

13 For vertex-edge graphs, the position of the vertices and the length and straightness of the edges are not critical. What is important is the way in which the edges connect the vertices. Consider the following matrix. Each entry shows the shortest distance, in miles, between two corresponding towns.

$$
\begin{array}{c c}
 & \begin{array}{ccc} W & R & T \end{array} \\
\begin{array}{c} \text{Woebegone (W)} \\ \text{Rivendell (R)} \\ \text{Troy (T)} \end{array} &
\left[\begin{array}{ccc}
- & 60 & 100 \\
60 & - & 80 \\
100 & 80 & -
\end{array} \right]
\end{array}
$$

a. Draw a vertex-edge graph that represents the information in the matrix.

c. For the graphs that can be traced in this manner, the starting and ending vertices have odd degree while all the other vertices have even degree.

d. A connected graph has an Euler path in which the starting vertex is different from the ending vertex if and only if the starting and ending vertices have odd degree and all the other vertices have even degree. (This theorem is also investigated in Applications Task 5, Part e.)

12 a. Both figures can be traced in many ways with an Euler circuit.

b. Figure I has reflection symmetries about vertical, horizontal, and diagonal lines. It also has 90°, 180°, and 270° rotational symmetries. Figure II has reflection symmetries about vertical and horizontal lines, and it has 180° rotational symmetry about a point in the center of the figure.

13 a. Accurate vertex-edge graphs will have 3 vertices with an edge between each pair of vertices. The edges could be curved or straight; the exact length of the edges and the exact location of the vertices does not matter. Students may also place the number representing each distance on the appropriate edge.

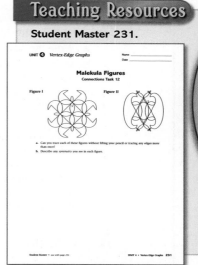

Teaching Resources

Student Master 231.

UNIT 4 *Vertex-Edge Graphs* Name ___ Date ___

Malekula Figures
Connections Task 12

Figure I   Figure II

a. Can you trace each of these figures without lifting your pencil or tracing any edges more than once?
b. Describe any symmetry you see in each figure.

Student Master • see unit page 256   UNIT 4 • Vertex-Edge Graphs **231**

Unit 4

b. Use a compass and ruler to draw a scale diagram showing the distances between the towns. Assume straight-line roads between the towns.

c. State a question involving these three towns that is best answered using the scale diagram.

d. State a question that could be answered using either the scale diagram or the graph.

14 The figure below is a *pentagon*. It has 5 vertices and 5 edges. Think about the figure as a vertex-edge graph.

a. Write the adjacency matrix for this graph.

b. Modify a copy of this graph by adding all the *diagonals*. (A diagonal is a line segment connecting 2 vertices that are not adjacent.) Write the adjacency matrix for this modified graph.

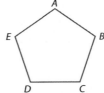

c. Write a description of the adjacency matrix for a graph in the shape of a *polygon* with n sides. (A polygon with n sides is similar to the pentagon shown here, but there are n vertices and n edges.) How would you modify the description of the adjacency matrix if the graph consisted of the polygon *and* its diagonals?

Reflections

15 Recall the original 1933 London Underground map on page 238. This is an example of a geometric diagram with vertices and edges for which precise size and shape is not crucial. The cartoon shown here accompanied the introduction of the map. The guide for the London Transport Museum describes the map as follows.

"Producing a map showing the different lines of the Underground system was particularly complicated. At first the Underground lines were shown geographically. A draughtsman, Harry Beck, devised his diagram in 1931. It uses only vertical, horizontal, or 45° diagonals and bears no relation to the real geography of London. At first the publicity department rejected it as too radical, finally publishing it in 1933 to instant enthusiasm from passengers. It was so simple and easy to use that the design is still used today and has been adapted by other cities around the world. It is a design classic." (London Transport Museum Guide)

a. Why do you think the publicity department thought the map was "too radical"?

b. Why do you think the map was received with "instant enthusiasm" by the passengers?

b. Scale drawings should be accurate. The scale drawing will almost certainly look different than the vertex-edge graph in Part a. Students will see that the vertex-edge graph can be drawn quickly, since it only shows connections, while the scale drawing takes time and must be drawn very carefully. By drawing these two diagrams students see in a very concrete way that vertex-edge graphs are quite different from geometric diagrams in which shape and size are essential.

c. Possible questions include the following: Which town is farthest away from Rivendell? If you travel from Woebegone through Rivendell to Troy, how many miles will you travel?

d. Possible questions include the following: Can you get from Rivendell to Troy? Can you get from every town to every other town?

(14) **a.**

$$\begin{array}{c} \\ A \\ B \\ C \\ D \\ E \end{array} \begin{array}{c} A\ \ B\ \ C\ \ D\ \ E \\ \begin{bmatrix} 0 & 1 & 0 & 0 & 1 \\ 1 & 0 & 1 & 0 & 0 \\ 0 & 1 & 0 & 1 & 0 \\ 0 & 0 & 1 & 0 & 1 \\ 1 & 0 & 0 & 1 & 0 \end{bmatrix} \end{array}$$

b.

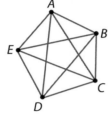

$$\begin{array}{c} \\ A \\ B \\ C \\ D \\ E \end{array} \begin{array}{c} A\ \ B\ \ C\ \ D\ \ E \\ \begin{bmatrix} 0 & 1 & 1 & 1 & 1 \\ 1 & 0 & 1 & 1 & 1 \\ 1 & 1 & 0 & 1 & 1 \\ 1 & 1 & 1 & 0 & 1 \\ 1 & 1 & 1 & 1 & 0 \end{bmatrix} \end{array}$$

c. The adjacency matrix for a regular polygon would have 2 ones in each row. The adjacency matrix for the modified regular polygon would have zeros on the main diagonal and ones elsewhere.

Reflections

(15) **a.** They probably thought it was too radical since it was so different from maps they were used to that showed distance and directly represented the geography of a region.

b. Passengers probably received it with "instant enthusiasm" because the map so simply and clearly shows how to navigate the subway system.

16 Two students have each drawn a graph that represents the combined routes of several school buses, as shown below. The vertices represent bus stops. Explain why the two graphs represent the same information. Label corresponding vertices with the same letter. If you have access to vertex-edge graph software, draw one of the graphs, then drag the vertices until it looks like the other graph.

17 Think of a problem different from those in this lesson that could be modeled with a vertex-edge graph and solved by using Euler circuits. Write a description of the problem and the solution.

18 Decide whether you agree with the following statement, and then write an argument to support your position: If a graph has an Euler circuit that begins and ends at a particular vertex, then it will have an Euler circuit that begins and ends at any vertex of the graph.

19 The algorithm for finding an Euler circuit in Problem 6 of Investigation 2 on page 245 is sometimes called the *onionskin algorithm*. Explain how this name describes what the algorithm does.

20 You might think that every matrix can be the adjacency matrix for some graph.

   a. Try to draw graphs that have the following adjacency matrices.

   i. $\begin{bmatrix} 0 & 3 \\ 3 & 0 \end{bmatrix}$
   ii. $\begin{bmatrix} 0 & 1 & 2 \\ 1 & 0 & 1 \\ 2 & 1 & 0 \end{bmatrix}$
   iii. $\begin{bmatrix} 0 & 2 & 1 \\ 2 & 0 & 2 \\ 1 & 1 & 0 \end{bmatrix}$

   b. Some matrices cannot be adjacency matrices for graphs. Write a description of the characteristics of a matrix that *could* be the adjacency matrix for a graph.

16 These two graphs represent the same information because there are the same numbers of vertices and edges, and the vertices are connected by the edges in the same way, as shown by the labeling below. (By using vertex-edge graph software, students can deform one graph so that it looks like the other.)

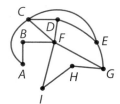 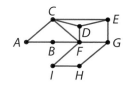

17 Problems will vary.

18 Students should agree with the statement because an Euler circuit is, in fact, a circuit. Thus, it has the property that you can start anywhere, go all the way around, and end where you started.

19 The name "onionskin algorithm" seems fitting since the algorithm works by peeling off partial circuits, like the skin of an onion.

20 a. See below for graphs that correspond to matrices in parts i and ii. The matrix in part iii cannot be the adjacency matrix of a graph. A "2" in the second row, third column, and a "1" in the third row, second column, both indicate the number of edges joining vertices B and C. These numbers must be equal in an adjacency matrix.

i.

ii.

b. The matrix must be symmetric across the diagonal from upper left to lower right. That is, it must have the same entry in the ith row, jth column, as in the jth row, ith column.

Unit 4

Extensions

21 Graphs have interesting properties that can be discovered by collecting data and looking for patterns.

I  II   III 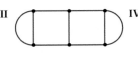 IV

a. Complete a table like the one that follows using the graphs above.

Graph	Sum of the Degrees of All Vertices	Number of Vertices of Odd Degree
I	30	
II		2
III		
IV		

b. Write down any patterns you see in the table.

c. See if the patterns continue when you collect more data. That is, draw a few more graphs, enter the information into the table, and check to see if the patterns you described in Part b are still valid. You might use vertex-edge graph software to help you generate graphs and information quickly.

d. Explain why the sum of the degrees of all the vertices in *any* graph is an even number.

e. Explain why *every* graph has an even number of vertices with odd degree.

22 Most of the graphs you have studied in this lesson have the key property of being *connected*. That is, they are all in one piece. Another way of thinking about connected graphs is that in a connected graph, there is a path from any vertex to any other vertex. Sometimes the way a graph is presented makes it difficult to tell whether or not it is connected.

a. Determine if the following graphs are connected.

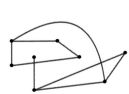 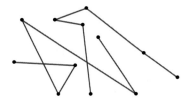

b. Describe a systematic method you could use to check to see if a given graph is connected.

Extensions

 21 **a.**

Graph	Sum of the Degrees of All Vertices	Number of Vertices of Odd Degree
I	30	0
II	18	2
III	18	6
IV	28	6

b. Possible patterns students may notice: The sum of the degrees and the number of odd vertices are both even numbers.

c. Students can use the vertex-edge graph software in *CPMP-Tools* to generate graphs, collect more data, and check their conjectures from Part b.

d. Every edge adds 2 to the sum of degrees. Thus, an easy way to obtain the sum of degrees is to count the edges and double that number. This will yield an even number.

e. For every graph, the sum of degrees is even (see Part d). The number of odd-degree vertices must be even; otherwise the sum of degrees would not be even. (Note that *odd + even = odd, odd + odd = even*, and *even + even = even*.)

 22 **a.** The first graph is connected; the second graph is not (it is in two pieces).

b. Responses may vary. Checking by "inspection" is not an adequate strategy, since for large or complicated graphs it is not practical. One definition of connectedness, given in the statement of the task, is that there is a path from every vertex to every other vertex. Thus, students may suggest that you could check this condition for every vertex. This is more systematic than "inspection," but issues of efficiency and exact procedures are problematic. A more systematic method is to choose one vertex, say *A*, show there is a path from *A* to every other vertex, and thus there is a path from everywhere to everywhere (through *A*), and therefore the graph is connected. To check whether or not every vertex can be reached from *A*, students might use a "breadth-first" algorithm. That is, start at *A* and follow each edge out of *A* to reach all the vertices adjacent to *A*, then, for each of those vertices, find all their adjacent vertices, and continue in this way until you do, or do not, reach all the vertices in the graph.

23 Decide whether each of the following statements is true (always true) or false (sometimes false). If a statement is true, explain as precisely as you can why it is true. If a statement is false, draw a *counterexample* that illustrates why it is false.

   a. Every vertex of a graph with an Euler circuit has degree greater than 1.

   b. If every vertex of a graph has the same degree, the graph has an Euler circuit.

24 In this lesson, you discovered and used an important result about Euler circuits. Now think more carefully about that result.

   a. Explain as precisely as you can why this statement is true.

   *If a graph has an Euler circuit, then
   all of its vertices have even degree.*

   b. Explain why or why not the following statement is true.

   *If all the vertices of a connected graph have
   even degree, then the graph has an Euler circuit.*

25 Dominoes are rectangular tiles used to play a game. Each tile is divided into 2 squares with a number of dots in each square, as in the figure below.

The standard set of dominoes has from 0 to 6 dots in each square. A deluxe set of dominoes has from 0 to 9 dots in each square. In each set, there is exactly one tile representing each possible number-pair combination. To play the game of dominoes, you take turns trying to place dominoes end-to-end by matching the number of dots. For example, for the three dominoes pictured below, the 3-5 domino can be placed next to the 1-3 domino, but the 0-2 domino cannot be placed next to either of the other dominoes.

Is it possible to form a ring of all the dominoes in a standard set placed end-to-end according to the rule above? How about for a deluxe set of dominoes? Explain your answers by reasoning about Euler circuits.

26 Euler circuits are also useful in manufacturing processes where a piece of metal is cut with a mechanical torch. To reduce the number of times the torch is turned on and off, it is desirable to make the cut continuous. For additional efficiency, the torch should not pass along an edge that has already been cut.

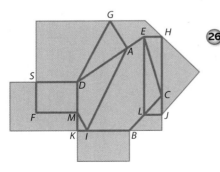

23 a. True. A graph with an Euler circuit must be connected and every vertex must be of even degree. Since the graph is connected, there can be no vertex of degree 0, otherwise that vertex would be disconnected from the rest of the graph. Thus, since all vertices have even degree, every vertex is of degree 2 or higher. So, every vertex has degree greater than 1.

b. False. An example is a graph where every vertex is of degree 3, like the one at the right.

 24 a. As you travel along this route, every time you come into a vertex, you also go out of it, until you have used every edge and you are back at the start. Each "going in" and "going out" adds 2 to the degree of the vertex. Thus, the degree of each vertex is a sum of 2s, and therefore the degree must be an even number.

b. Suppose each vertex of the connected graph has even degree. Choose any vertex for the start and begin traveling through the graph at random, never reusing an edge. Because the vertices all have even degree, every time you go into a vertex you can come out of it as well. By wandering through the graph in this way you will eventually end up back at the start. If this random route through the graph has used all the edges, then you have found an Euler circuit and you are done. If your route does not use all the edges, then choose a vertex on the route that has an unused edge coming out of it. Start at this vertex and travel again at random through the graph on unused edges and, again since all vertices have even degree, you will eventually end up back at your new starting vertex. Maybe now you have used all the edges in the graph. If so, just string the two circuits together to get an Euler circuit for the whole graph. If not, then repeat this procedure. By stringing together all the circuits you create in this way you will get an Euler circuit for the graph. This argument supports the statement that if all the vertices of a connected graph have even degree, then the graph has an Euler circuit.

> **NOTE** For a rigorous proof of the statement in Part b, see *Graphs, Models, and Finite Mathematics*, by Malkevitch, J. and Meyer, W. Prentice-Hall, 1974; or *Graphs: An Introductory Approach*, by Wilson, R. and Watkins, J., John Wiley and Sons, 1990.

 25 For a six-dot set, construct a vertex-edge graph by letting each number from 0 to 6 be a vertex, and drawing edges between pairs of vertices to correspond to the number pairs on the dominoes. For example, the 2-3 domino corresponds to an edge between the vertex representing 2 and the vertex representing 3. Since there is a domino for each number pair, there is an edge between each pair of vertices. In addition, there is a loop at each vertex corresponding to the "doubles" dominoes. Thus, the degree of each vertex is the sum of 6 (each vertex has an edge to the 6 other vertices) and 2 (there is a loop with 2 edge-touchings at each vertex). So, the degree of each vertex is $6 + 2 = 8$. Thus, every vertex has even degree, and therefore there is an Euler circuit through the graph. An Euler circuit corresponds to a ring of all the dominoes placed end-to-end according to the rule given in the statement of the task. Thus, such a ring is possible for a 6-dot standard set of dominoes.

Using similar reasoning, a 9-dot deluxe set corresponds to a graph in which each vertex has degree $9 + 2 = 11$. In this case, each vertex has odd degree so there is no Euler circuit and it is not possible to form a ring with all the dominoes.

The metal piece must be clamped in air so that the torch does not burn the surface of the workbench. This leads to another condition; namely, any piece that falls off should not require additional cutting. Otherwise, it would have to be picked up and reclamped, a time-consuming process. Find a way to make all the cuts indicated on the pictured piece of metal, so that you begin and end at point *S* and the above conditions are satisfied.

27. RNA (ribonucleic acid) is a messenger molecule associated with DNA (deoxyribonucleic acid). RNA molecules consist of a chain of bases. Each base is one of 4 chemicals: U (uracil), C (cytosine), A (adenine), and G (guanine). It is difficult to observe exactly what an entire RNA chain looks like, but it is sometimes possible to observe fragments of a chain by breaking up the chain with certain enzymes. Armed with knowledge about the fragments, you can sometimes determine the makeup of the entire chain. One type of enzyme that breaks up an RNA chain is a "G-enzyme." The G-enzyme will break an RNA chain after each G link. For example, consider the following chain.

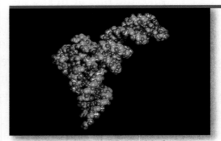

Computer-rendered molecular model of t-RNA

AUUGCGAUC

A G-enzyme will break up this chain into the following fragments.

AUUG   CG   AUC

Unfortunately, the fragments of a broken-up chain are usually mixed up and in the wrong order. In this task, you will figure out how to reconstruct the chain when given some mixed-up fragments.

a. Suppose a different RNA chain is broken by a G-enzyme into the following fragments (although not necessarily in this order).

AUG   AAC   CG   AG

Explain why the AAC fragment must be the end of the chain.

b. There is another enzyme, called a U-C enzyme, that breaks an RNA chain after each U or C link. For the unknown RNA chain in Part a, the U-C enzyme breaks the chain into the following fragments.

GC   GAAC   AGAU

As the final step in this chain-breaking process, the fragments are now further broken up using the other enzyme. That is, the fragments formed by the G-enzyme are now broken again, if possible, using the U-C enzyme, and vice versa. The resulting fragments from this process are shown in the table at the right. Each row of the table shows the break-up of each of the 7 fragments above. Complete the table by finding the rest of the final split fragments.

Original Fragment	Final Split Fragments
AUG	AU G
AAC	Not possible to split
CG	
AG	
GC	
GAAC	
AGAU	AG AU

26 The cuts indicated on the pictured piece of metal form a graph in which all vertices have even degree. Thus, an Euler circuit exists, and therefore the stated conditions of making the cut continuous and not passing along an edge that has already been cut can be met. However, not every Euler circuit will satisfy the additional condition that a piece that falls off should not require additional cutting. Referring to the diagram below, placing a clamp on piece 14 and then a cutting path that satisfies all of the conditions is *S, F, M, K, B, L, J, H, E, C, L, E, A, I, M, D, A, G, D, S, M, L, S.* The pieces fall off in the labeled order. (*Note:* Additional applications of this sort can be found in *Drawing Pictures with One Line* by Darrah Chavey, published by COMAP.)

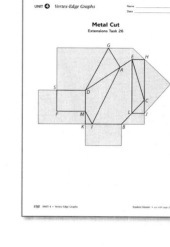

Teaching Resources

Student Master 232.

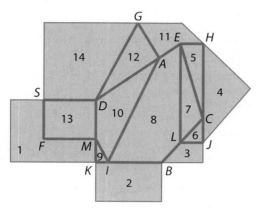

Unit 4

27 **a.** A G-enzyme breaks the chain after every G, so every segment must end in G, except for possibly the segment at the end of the chain. Thus, any segment, like AAC, that does not end with G must be the end of the chain.

b. See the completed table below.

Original Fragment	Final Split Fragments
AUG	AU G
AAC	Not possible to split
CG	C G
AG	Not possible to split
GC	G C
GAAC	G AAC
AGAU	AG AU

c. Mathematicians and biologists have discovered an amazing technique using Euler paths to reconstruct the unknown RNA chain. Carry out this technique, as follows:

Step 1: Draw vertices for each of the different final split fragments.

Step 2: Draw a **directed edge** (an arrow) from one vertex to another if the two split fragments are part of the same original fragment. The arrow should indicate how the two split fragments are recombined to get the original fragment.

Step 3: You now have a **directed graph**, that is, a graph where the edges have a direction. Find an Euler path through this graph (the start and end are not the same). Keep in mind that as you trace an Euler path, you must move in the direction shown by the directed edges.

Step 4: Put the fragments together as you traverse the Euler path. This will give you the original RNA chain.

28 A **loop** is an edge connecting a vertex to itself. When constructing an adjacency matrix for a graph with loops, a 1 is placed in the position in the matrix that corresponds with an edge joining a vertex to itself. An example of such a graph and its adjacency matrix is shown at the right.

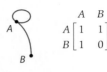

$$\begin{array}{c c} & \begin{array}{c c} A & B \end{array} \\ \begin{array}{c} A \\ B \end{array} & \left[\begin{array}{c c} 1 & 1 \\ 1 & 0 \end{array} \right] \end{array}$$

a. Recall that the degree of a vertex is the number of edges touching the vertex, except that a loop counts for 2 edge touchings. What is the degree of vertex *A*?

b. What is the row sum of the first row of the adjacency matrix above? In Investigation 3 of this lesson, you found a connection between row sums of an adjacency matrix and the degree of the corresponding vertex. Does this connection still hold for graphs with loops like the one above?

29 Some housing developments have houses built on a street that is a "cul-de-sac" so that traffic passing the houses is minimized.

a. Suppose a cul-de-sac is located at the end of the street between blocks 5 and 6 as shown here. Draw a vertex-edge graph that represents this housing development.

b. Find an optimum path for delivering papers to houses in this development.

c. See graph below. The Euler path is AG → AU → G → C → G → AAC, which produces the original chain: AGAUGCGAAC.

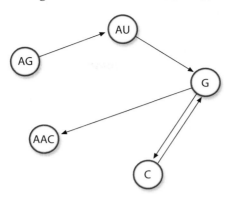

28 **a.** The degree of vertex *A* is 3.

b. The row sum of the first row is 2, but the degree of vertex *A* is 3. Therefore, the connection does not hold. (Note that it is unfortunate that this connection between adjacency matrix row sums and vertex degrees fails. We could fix it by making a new definition in the case of loops and say that we will put a 2 in the corresponding matrix entry. However, this new definition would then spoil another important property of adjacency matrices, whereby their powers tell us about paths of certain lengths in the corresponding graph. This is in fact a very useful property, and will be developed in the *Matrix Methods* unit in Course 2. Thus, mathematicians have chosen to keep the adjacency matrix definition for loops as stated in this problem.)

29 **a.** For example, see below.

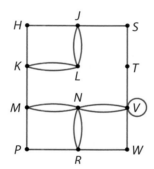

b. Many circuits exist. One possible circuit is *H-K-M-P-R-N-M-N-V-N-R-W-V-V-T-S-J-L-K-L-J-H*.

Unit 4

c. You know from this lesson that the degree of a vertex is the number of edges that touch it, except that loops count as two edge touchings. Find the degree of each vertex in your graph.

d. Repeat Parts a, b, and c with a second cul-de-sac constructed at the end of blocks 1 and 4.

e. How does adding a cul-de-sac affect the graph? How does adding a cul-de-sac affect the optimum path for delivering papers to houses in the development?

f. Does the condition about degrees of vertices for graphs with Euler circuits still hold for graphs with loops?

Review

30 Although distance and position are not crucial features of vertex-edge graphs, these features are important in many geometric settings. Consider points in the grid below.

a. What is the distance between points C and B? Between points C and A? Explain how to find those distances using the Pythagorean Theorem.

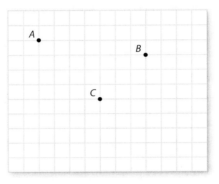

b. Starting at point C, move 3 units to the right and 4 units down. Mark the point at this location. How far is this point from point C?

c. Find a point that is exactly 10 units from point A, but is not directly above or below or directly to the right or left. What geometric shape is formed by all the points that are exactly 10 units from point A?

31 Place the following quantities in increasing order without using your calculator. Explain your method.

$$5\%, \frac{1}{10}, 0.5, \frac{1}{9}, \frac{4}{9}, 49\%$$

c. The degrees of the vertices are as follows:

H: 2	J: 4	S: 2
K: 4	L: 4	T: 2
M: 4	N: 6	V: 6
P: 2	R: 4	W: 2

d. The new cul-de-sac is a loop at *J* in the diagram above. The optimal path in Part b can be modified by traveling the loop when vertex *J* is first reached. The only change in the degrees is vertex *J* will have degree 6.

e. Adding a cul-de-sac just adds loops to the graph. The optimal route will include edges in the same order as before the loop was added to the graph. In addition, when arriving at a vertex that has an untraversed loop, traverse the loop and then continue on the previous optimal route.

f. Since a loop adds 2 to the degree of a vertex, it doesn't change the degree of a vertex from odd to even or vice versa. Thus, the condition for even vertices whenever a graph has an Euler circuit still holds for graphs with loops.

Review

30 **a.** The distance between *C* and *B* is $\sqrt{18}$ units. The distance between *C* and *A* is $\sqrt{32}$ units.

b. $\sqrt{9 + 16} = \sqrt{25} = 5$ units

c. For example, consider a point that is 8 units to the right of *A* and then 6 units down from there. The distance between this point and point *A* is 10 units. All points exactly 10 units from *A* form a circle centered at *A*.

 Just in Time

31 $5\%, \frac{1}{10}, \frac{1}{9}, \frac{4}{9}, 49\%, 0.5$

Student methods will vary.

32 Study the relations represented in the following tables. If a relation is linear, find the slope of the graph representing the relationship.

a.

x	4	6	8	10	12
y	1	0	−1	−2	−3

b.

x	0	1	3	8
y	2	4	6	8

c.

x	0	0.1	0.2	0.3
y	3	2.95	2.9	2.85

33 In a recent poll, 630 students were asked if they like Chinese food. The circle graph below shows the results of the poll. Determine as precisely as possible how many people gave each response.

34 Complete a table like the one below showing some possible lengths, widths, and perimeters for a rectangle with an area of 24 square units.

L	1	2	3	4	5	6	7	8	9	10	11	12	24
W	24	12											
P	50	28											

a. Describe the pattern of change in *W* as *L* changes.

b. Describe the pattern of change in *P* as *L* changes.

c. Find formulas to represent *W* as a function of *L*, and *P* as a function of *L*.

d. Are either of the patterns of change linear?

35 Solve each equation or inequality.

a. $5x - 6 = 20$

b. $4.85 = 1.25x + 6.1$

c. $80 - \frac{3}{4}x < 20$

d. $75 \le 15x + 100$

Just in Time

32 **a.** Linear; $-\frac{1}{2}$

     b. Not linear

     c. Linear; $-\frac{1}{2}$

INSTRUCTIONAL NOTE
Students will need a protractor to measure the angles.

33 Like: $\frac{160}{360} \cdot 630 = 280$ students

    Dislike: $\frac{120}{360} \cdot 630 = 210$ students

    No opinion: $\frac{80}{360} \cdot 630 = 140$ students

 Just in Time

34 **a.**

L	1	2	3	4	5	6	7	8	9	10	11	12	24
W	24	12	8	6	4.8	4	3.4	3	2.67	2.4	2.18	2	1
P	50	28	22	20	19.6	20	20.8	22	23.34	24.8	26.36	28	50

    a. As L increases, W decreases at a decreasing rate.

    b. As L increases, P decreases to a minimum of around 19.6 units and then increases again.

    c. $W = \frac{24}{L}$ and $P = 2L + 2W = 2L + 2 \cdot \frac{24}{L} = 2L + \frac{48}{L}$.

    d. No. The table shows a nonconstant rate of change for both W and P.

35 **a.** $x = 5.2$

    b. $x = -1$

    c. $x > 80$

    d. $x \geq -\frac{5}{3}$

Unit 4

36 Without using your calculator, match each equation with a possible graph of the equation.

a. $y = x - 5$

b. $y = -x + 5$

c. $y = x$

d. $y = -x - 5$

e. $y = x + 5$

f. $y = 5$

I

II

III
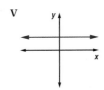

IV

V

VI

37 Determine if the expressions in each pair are equivalent.

a. 6.02×10^{21} and 602×10^{19}

b. 980×10^{10} and 9.8×10^{8}

c. 0.034×10^{12} and 340×10^{8}

38 Draw sketches of a cone and a cylinder.

36 a. IV

b. III

c. I

d. VI

e. II

f. V

 Just in Time

37 a. Equivalent

b. Not equivalent

c. Not equivalent

38

Cone   Cylinder

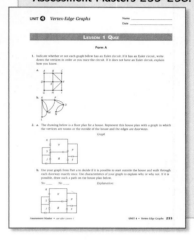
Unit 4

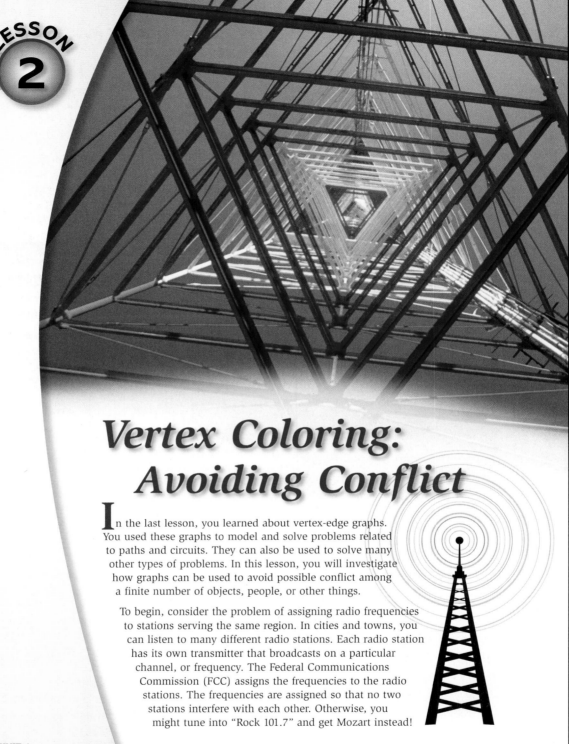

LESSON
2

Vertex Coloring: Avoiding Conflict

In the last lesson, you learned about vertex-edge graphs. You used these graphs to model and solve problems related to paths and circuits. They can also be used to solve many other types of problems. In this lesson, you will investigate how graphs can be used to avoid possible conflict among a finite number of objects, people, or other things.

To begin, consider the problem of assigning radio frequencies to stations serving the same region. In cities and towns, you can listen to many different radio stations. Each radio station has its own transmitter that broadcasts on a particular channel, or frequency. The Federal Communications Commission (FCC) assigns the frequencies to the radio stations. The frequencies are assigned so that no two stations interfere with each other. Otherwise, you might tune into "Rock 101.7" and get Mozart instead!

266 UNIT 4

Vertex Coloring: Avoiding Conflict

In this lesson, students learn how to use graphs to solve problems related to avoiding conflict among a finite number of objects. In particular, they learn some basic concepts and methods of vertex coloring. Vertex coloring is a powerful mathematical optimization technique. The optimization contexts explored in this lesson are interference of radio station broadcasts, scheduling conflicts, and map coloring.

See page T275B for a brief history of map coloring.

Lesson Objectives

- Use vertex-edge graphs to model problems related to avoiding conflict in a variety of settings
- Color the vertices of a graph so that adjacent vertices have different colors
- Investigate algorithms for vertex coloring
- Use vertex coloring to solve a variety of problems, including assigning frequencies to radio stations, scheduling club meetings, and coloring the countries of a map

Think About This Situation

Suppose 7 new radio stations have applied for permits to start broadcasting in the same region of the country. Some stations may interfere with each other, others may not.

a What are some factors that may determine whether or not stations interfere with each other?

b How does this situation involve "conflict"?

c How do you think the FCC should assign frequencies to the 7 stations?

d Why do you think the FCC might like to assign the fewest possible number of new frequencies for the 7 stations?

In this lesson, you will learn how to use vertex-edge graphs to solve problems about avoiding conflicts, such as assigning noninterfering radio frequencies, using a technique called *vertex coloring*.

Investigation 1   Building a Model

Suppose the 7 new radio stations that have applied for broadcast permits are located as shown on the grid below. A side of each small square on the grid represents 100 miles. The FCC wants to assign a frequency to each station so that no 2 stations interfere with each other. The FCC also wants to assign the fewest possible number of new frequencies. Suppose that because of geographic conditions and the strength of each station's transmitter, the FCC determines that stations within 500 miles of each other will not interfere with each other.

Your work on the problems of this investigation will help you answer the question:

How can vertex-edge graphs be used to assign frequencies to these 7 radio stations so that as few frequencies as possible are used and none of the stations interfere with each other?

1 For a small problem like this, you could solve it by trial and error. However, a more systematic method is needed for more complicated situations. Working on your own, begin modeling this problem with a graph. Remember, to model a problem with a graph, you must first decide what the vertices and edges represent.

a. What should the vertices represent?

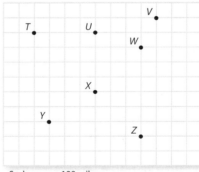

Scale: ⊢——⊣ = 100 miles

Think About This Situation

Teaching Resources

Transparency Master 239.

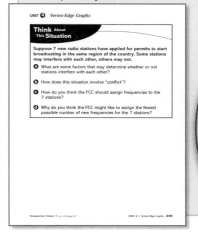

a Factors may include the power of the transmitters, the local geography, the regional atmospheric conditions, the distance between stations, and legal restrictions.

b There would be "conflict" in this situation if the radio broadcasts from the seven new stations interfered with each other, so that a listener trying to tune in would hear interfering broadcasts from more than one station.

c Strategies could be to assign a different frequency to each of the stations or assign the same frequency to all stations. In the former case, this would certainly avoid interference, but it may be that some of the stations could have the same frequency and yet still not interfere with each other because of, say, distance, geographical location, or transmission power. So, possibly fewer frequencies could be used. On the other hand, assigning them all the same frequency would probably cause some interference. Thus, some strategy that assigns more than one but less than seven frequencies may be preferable. (A specific method for doing this is needed, and will be learned in this lesson.)

d It might be the case that there are a limited number of frequencies available. So, assigning them in an optimal manner, using as few frequencies as possible, is desirable. (Note that this is another case of optimization. Many problems in discrete mathematics, and graph theory in particular, are optimization problems.)

In this investigation, students solve the radio-station problem by building and analyzing a vertex-edge graph model. In particular, they learn how to color the vertices of a graph to solve the problem.

Background information on conflict and compatibility as modeled by the graphs in Problem 3: The 500-miles-or-less and more-than-500-miles graphs represent two kinds of graph models. If edges correspond to 500 miles or less, then adjacent vertices are those in conflict (radio stations that will interfere with each other) and the graph model becomes a vertex-coloring model. In vertex-coloring problems, you try to optimally avoid conflict by minimizing the number of colors needed to color all the vertices. If edges correspond to more than 500 miles, then adjacent vertices are "compatible" (radio stations that can share the same frequency) and the graph model is a compatibility graph. In this case, the goal is to maximize compatibility in some sense by looking for the largest complete subgraphs. (A complete subgraph is a collection of vertices and edges in the graph such that all the vertices are connected to each other by the edges. For example, T, W, Y, and Z in Problem 3, Part b are vertices of a complete subgraph.) Both these models are valid and useful, and are initially explored in this investigation. However, since vertex coloring is more widely used, we will emphasize vertex coloring for most of this lesson.

COLLABORATION SKILL Taking time to ensure all group members understand

1   **a.** Most students will represent the radio stations with vertices.

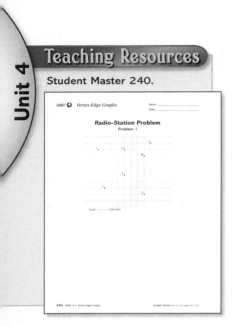

Teaching Resources

Student Master 240.

Think About This Situation, *page 267*

Teacher: Have you ever been on a long road trip, and the radio station that you were listening to starts turning into another station? *(Several students nod yes.)* Don't you hate it when you finally find a station that you like, and an hour or so later, you start hearing some other type of music or talking break through. Well you see, in each particular area (of each state, for instance), the radio frequencies are assigned so that no two radio stations interfere with each other if they are in the same area. So in our area the radio station LQZW has a frequency of 97.9 and the station MQA has the frequency 94.5 so that those two stations don't interfere with each other. *(Insert your own local stations.)* However, once you start heading out of our area toward Chicago, for instance, 97.9 becomes TSPN, and for a while TSPN and LQZW might even interfere with each other.

Suppose seven new radio stations have applied for permits to start broadcasting in the same region of the country. Some may interfere with each other, and others may not. What are some factors that might determine whether or not stations interfere with each other?

Student 1: They might have the same number, like 97.9.

Student 2: Yeah, but maybe they are far apart.

Teacher: Why would being far apart matter?

Student 2: Well, if they were really far apart and you were driving, then by the time one station completely faded away, the other one wouldn't be in range yet, so they would never interfere with each other.

Teacher: Okay, so having the same frequency (number) and distance apart are two factors that might determine whether or not radio stations interfere with each other. What are some other factors?

Student 3: Do you need to know how far the transmitter for the radio station can go? *(Other students agree.)*

Student 4: Hills or valleys might limit how far the radio station can transmit, so even if it's really strong it might not interfere with a station on the other side of a mountain.

Teacher: Okay. So signal strength and mountains are factors. Do you have any other important factors? *(No responses.)* Then, how does this situation involve "conflict"?

Student 5: There is a conflict when the stations are too close and they have the same channel.

Student 6: And no big hills in the way.

Teacher: What happens when all those factors are there?

Many students: They interfere.

Teacher: So, do we agree that radio stations are in conflict if their broadcasts interfere with each other?

Many students: Yes.

Student 7: They could just give each station a different frequency.

Teacher: That would work. Any other ideas? *(No response.)* What if they gave every station the same frequency? *(Many say there would be interference.)* Any ideas on how to assign less than 7 frequencies but more than 1?

Student 8: We could pick a radio station and give it a frequency. Then, we could give the radio stations right next to that one different frequencies. And then give the ones next to those stations different frequencies, and so on.

Student 9: But we might be able to use the first frequency again after you give different frequencies to the stations next to the original one you started with.

Teacher: Those are some good ideas. In mathematics and the real world, we often try to find efficient and systematic methods, and we'll learn about that in this lesson. Another important goal is to find the best solution. In this case, thinking about the best solution, why would the FCC want to assign the fewest number of frequencies?

Student 10: There's only so much room on the radio. So, you want to let in as many stations as you can.

Student 11: Yeah, but with satellite radio there's plenty of room for hundreds of stations and they don't fade out!

Teacher: That's a good point. Distance and mountains wouldn't be factors for interference, or conflict, in the case of satellite radio. In that case, there are other conflict issues like conflicting satellite orbits. But in this problem we're only dealing with ground-based radio stations. And we have a good start on this problem. In this lesson, you will figure out how to use some new mathematical methods and models to solve conflict problems like the radio station frequency problem we've been talking about.

b. How will you decide whether or not to connect 2 vertices with an edge? Complete this statement:

Two vertices are connected by an edge if … .

c. Now that you have specified the vertices and edges, draw a graph for this problem.

2 Compare your graph with those of your classmates.

a. Did everyone define the vertices and edges in the same way? Discuss any differences.

b. For a given situation, suppose two people define the vertices and edges in two different ways. Is it possible that both ways accurately represent the situation? Explain your reasoning.

c. For a given situation, suppose two people define the vertices and edges in the same way. Is it possible that their graphs have different shapes but both are correct? Explain your reasoning.

3 A common choice for the vertices is to let them represent the radio stations. Edges might be thought of in two ways, as described in Parts a and b below.

a. You might connect 2 vertices by an edge whenever the stations they represent are 500 miles or *less* apart. Did you represent the situation this way? If not, draw a graph where two vertices are connected by an edge whenever the stations they represent are 500 miles or *less* apart.

b. You might connect 2 vertices by an edge whenever the stations they represent are *more* than 500 miles apart. Did you represent the situation this way? If not, draw a graph where 2 vertices are connected by an edge whenever the stations they represent are *more* than 500 miles apart.

c. Compare the graphs from Parts a and b.

  i. Are both graphs accurate ways of representing the situation?

  ii. Which graph do you think will be more useful and easier to use as a mathematical model for this situation? Why?

4 For the rest of this investigation, use the graph where edges connect vertices that are 500 miles or less apart. Make sure you have a neat copy of this graph.

a. Are vertices (stations) *X* and *W* connected by an edge? Are they 500 miles or less apart? Will their broadcasts interfere with each other?

b. Are vertices (stations) *Y* and *Z* connected by an edge? Will their broadcasts interfere with each other?

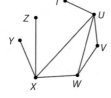

c. Compare your graph to the graph at the left.

  i. Explain why this graph also accurately represents the radio-station problem.

b. It is likely that different students will represent the edges in different ways. The most obvious alternatives are edges that represent pairs of vertices more than 500 miles apart or edges that represent pairs of vertices less than 500 miles apart. (Students are confronted with these two alternatives in Problem 3. For now, let them proceed with whatever representation they choose. Note that after Problem 3, only the 500-miles-or-less representation is explored, since this captures the notion of "conflict," but it is important in the beginning of the modeling process for them to wrestle with both alternatives.)

c. The graph will depend on the definition of vertices and edges. (A variety of definitions and graphs are possible and desirable at this point.)

2 **a.** Students should discuss and see that different alternatives are possible. They are prompted to consider certain alternatives below.

b. Yes, but the alternative definitions of vertices and edges must match the problem situation.

c. Yes, because the size and shape of a vertex-edge graph is not essential, only the vertices, edges, and how the vertices are connected by the edges are essential.

Unit 4

3 **a.** One possible graph when vertices are connected whenever stations are 500 miles or less apart is shown at the right.

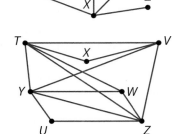

b. One possible graph when vertices are connected whenever stations are more than 500 miles apart is shown at the right.

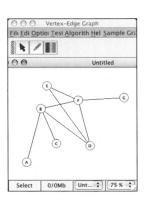

c. **i.** Both representations are accurate models of the problem.

ii. In this case, the 500-miles-or-less graph is much simpler and easier to analyze.

4 **a.** Yes. They are less than 500 miles apart. (None of the seven stations were exactly 500 miles apart.)

b. No. They are more than 500 miles apart.

c. **i.** Because the stations (vertices) that are less than 500 miles apart are connected by an edge. This graph may look different than the graph students drew in Problem 3, Part a.

KEY IDEA It is important for students to understand that there may be different ways of modeling a given situation, and that some models may be more appropriate than others.

TECHNOLOGY NOTE You may wish to have students create graphs using the vertex-edge graph software in *CPMP-Tools*. They can then dynamically drag the graphs to emphasize that size and shape can change while relationships between vertices and edges remain the same.

ii. Describe what it means for two graphs to be "the same" even if their appearances are different.

iii. If you have access to vertex-edge graph software, draw this graph and then drag its vertices so it looks like your graph in Problem 3, Part a.

5 Remember that the problem is to assign frequencies so that there will be no interference between radio stations. So far, your graph models this problem as follows. Vertices represent the radio stations. Two vertices are connected by an edge if the corresponding radio stations are within 500 miles of each other. Here's the last step in building the graph model—represent the frequencies as *colors*. So now, assigning frequencies to radio stations means to assign colors to the vertices.

Examine the statements in the following partially completed table. Translate each statement about stations and frequencies into a statement about vertices and colors. (The first one is already done for you.)

Statements about Stations and Frequencies	Statements about Vertices and Colors
Two stations have different frequencies.	Two vertices have different colors.
Find a way to assign frequencies so that stations within 500 miles of each other get different frequencies.	
Use the fewest number of frequencies.	

6 Now use as few colors as possible to **color the graph** for the radio-station problem. That is, assign a color to each vertex so that any 2 vertices that are connected by an edge have different colors. You can use colored pencils or just the names of some colors to do the coloring. Color or write a color code next to each vertex. Try to use the smallest number of colors possible.

7 Compare your coloring with another student's coloring.

a. Do both colorings satisfy the condition that vertices connected by an edge must have different colors?

b. Do both colorings use the same number of colors to color the vertices of the graph? Reach agreement about the minimum number of colors needed.

c. Explain, in writing, why the graph cannot be colored with fewer colors.

d. For 2 particular vertices, suppose one student colors both vertices red while another student colors 1 vertex red and the other blue. Is it possible that both colorings are acceptable? Explain your reasoning.

e. Describe the connection between graph coloring and assigning frequencies to radio stations.

ii. INSTRUCTIONAL NOTE In Problem 4, Part c, iii, students consider two graphs that look different, and not only do they both accurately represent the situation, but they are actually "the same." Two graphs are considered to be "the same" if they have the same numbers of vertices and edges and the vertices are connected by the edges in the same way. The technical term for two such graphs is that they are *isomorphic*. You don't need to stress this technical point with students, but students should understand that graphs can have different appearances and yet still have the same vertex-edge relationships.

Students have explored two related and important points about comparing two graph models: Two graphs can look different and yet both accurately represent the same situation. Or, two graphs can look different and yet be "the same." In Problem 3 students explored the former case when they examined two graph models and found that in each case the vertices, edges, and connections accurately represent the given situation, even though the graphs are very different.

⑤

Statements about stations and frequencies	Statements about vertices and colors
Two stations have different frequencies.	Two vertices have different colors.
Find a way to assign frequencies so that stations within 500 miles of each other get different frequencies.	Find a way to assign colors to the vertices so that vertices connected by an edge have different colors.
Use the fewest number of frequencies.	Use the fewest number of colors.

⑥ One possible coloring is shown at the right. (Students may not have the fewest number of colors here, but by the time Problem 7 is finished, students should reach agreement that 3 is the minimum number of colors.)

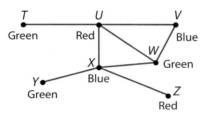

⑦ **a.** Adjacent vertices should have different colors.

b. Different groups may have used different numbers of colors. They should resolve their differences here and in Part c.

c. Students might point out that there are 3 vertices in the graph that are all adjacent to each other, and such a configuration requires 3 colors. So, the graph cannot be colored with fewer than 3 colors.

d. Yes. For example, *Y* and *Z* could be the same color or different colors as long as they do not match *X*.

e. The colors represent the different radio frequencies, so coloring the vertices is like assigning frequencies to the radio stations.

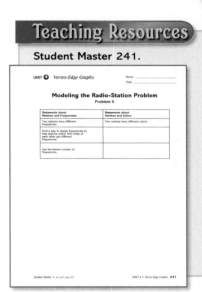

Summarize
the Mathematics

Some problems can be solved by coloring the vertices of an appropriate graph.

a What do the vertices, edges, and colors represent in the graph that you used to solve the radio-station problem?

b How did "coloring a graph" help solve the radio-station problem?

c In what ways can two graphs differ and yet still both accurately represent a situation?

Be prepared to share your ideas with the class.

✔ Check Your Understanding

Consider the graph at the right.

a. On a copy of the graph, color the vertices using as few colors as possible.

b. If possible, find a second coloring of the graph in which some of the vertices colored the same in Part a are no longer colored the same. Again use as few colors as possible.

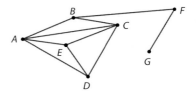

Investigation 2 · Scheduling, Mapmaking, and Algorithms

Now that you know how to color a graph, you can use graph coloring to solve many other types of problems. As you work on the problems in this investigation, look for answers to this question:

> *What are the basic steps of modeling and solving conflict problems using vertex-edge graphs?*

Scheduling Meetings There are 6 clubs at King High School that want to meet once a week for one hour, right after school lets out. The problem is that several students belong to more than one of the clubs, so not all the clubs can meet on the same day. Also, the school wants to schedule as few days per week for after-school club meetings as possible. Below is the list of the clubs and the club members who also belong to more than one club.

Summarize
the Mathematics

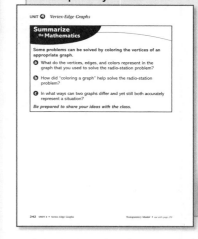

(a) Vertices represent stations; 2 vertices are connected by an edge if the 2 stations are 500 miles or less apart; and colors represent frequencies.

(b) Coloring the graph puts a color on each vertex (a frequency for each station) in such a way that 2 adjacent vertices (nearby stations) get different colors (different frequencies). Thus, there is no conflict. The stations do not interfere with each other.

(c) Two graphs may both accurately represent the situation and yet look different because of the placement of vertices, the length or shape of edges, or the colors of the vertices. Another way for two different-looking graphs to both accurately represent the situation is if the edges in one graph represent conflict (500 miles or less apart) while the edges in the other graph represent compatibility (more than 500 miles apart).

KEY IDEA Two graphs can differ and yet both be appropriate models and, in fact, they may even be "the same" (isomorphic) in that they have the same vertex-edge relationship.

PROCESSING PROMPT We made sure all members understood that two different-looking graphs can represent the same situation by ... .

✓ Check Your Understanding

a. The fewest number of colors is 4. One possible coloring: *A* and *F* are red; *C* and *G* are green; *B* and *E* are blue; and *D* is yellow
(Note that *ACED* forms a graph on 4 vertices in which all the vertices are adjacent to each other, so at least 4 colors are needed.)

b. Another possible coloring: *A* and *G* are red; *C* and *F* are green; *B* and *E* are blue; and *D* is yellow

Investigation 2 — Scheduling, Mapmaking, and Algorithms

In this investigation, students use vertex coloring to solve a variety of problems. They learn that vertex coloring can be a useful problem-solving technique for situations involving conflict among a finite number of objects. They also explore algorithms for vertex coloring.

In Problem 1, a key decision is what the vertices and edges should represent. In Part a, vertices might be chosen to be clubs or students. Then edges could be chosen based on conflict or compatibility. Thus, work in Part a can be very diverse. However, most students will probably decide to connect two vertices with an edge if the clubs they represent share a member and thus *cannot* meet on the same day. Some students might connect two vertices when the clubs *can* meet on the same day. This situation is analogous to the radio-station problem

Clubs and Members

Club	Students Belonging to More Than One Club
Varsity Club	Christina, Shanda, Carlos
Math Club	Christina, Carlos, Wendy
French Club	Shanda
Drama Club	Carlos, Vikas, Wendy
Computer Club	Vikas, Shanda
Art Club	Shanda

1. Consider the club-scheduling problem as a graph-coloring problem.

   a. Your goal is to assign a meeting day (Monday–Friday) to each club in such a way that no 2 clubs that share a member meet on the same day. Also, you want to use as few days as possible. Working on your own, decide what you think the vertices, edges, and colors should represent.

   b. Compare your representations with others. Decide as a group which representations are best. Complete these three statements.

   The vertices represent … .

   Two vertices are connected by an edge if … .

   The colors represent … .

   c. Draw a graph that models the problem.

   d. Color the club-scheduling graph using as few colors as possible.

2. Use your graph coloring in Problem 1 to answer these questions.

   a. Is it possible for every club to meet once per week?

   b. What is the fewest number of days needed to schedule all the club meetings?

   c. On what day should each club meeting be scheduled?

   d. Explain how your coloring of the graph helps you answer each of the questions above.

Coloring Maps Another class of problems for which graph coloring is useful involves coloring maps. You may have noticed in your geography or social-studies course that maps are always colored so that neighboring countries do not have the same color. This is done so that the countries are easily distinguished and don't blend into each other. In the following problems, you will explore the number of different colors necessary to color *any* map in such a way that no 2 countries that share a border have the same color. This is a problem that mathematicians worked on for many years, resulting in a lot of new and useful mathematics. For this problem, *countries* are assumed to be regions that are contiguous (not broken up into separate parts), and *border* means a common boundary of some length (touching at points doesn't matter).

LESSON 2 • Vertex Coloring: Avoiding Conflict **271**

where students could focus on stations that *cannot* have the same frequency (500 miles or less apart) or *can* have the same frequency (more than 500 miles apart). In the radio-station problem, the conflict graph was simpler. It is interesting that in this club-scheduling problem the "compatibility" (nonconflict) graph is simpler.

DIFFERENTIATION As an extension for some students, you could have them solve the problem with the compatibility graph. (For example, they could find complete subgraphs within the compatibility graph.) However, vertex coloring with a conflict graph is a more common and useful technique, so emphasize that.

1 **a.** Individual students should make their own assignments for vertices, edges, and colors. Work here could be very diverse. However, the statement of the problem, with emphasis on clubs, assigning days to clubs, and clubs that share a member, will probably lead most students to let clubs be the vertices. Then an edge can represent when 2 clubs share a member, and colors can be the days for the clubs to meet. In any case, after a brief time encourage students to move on to Part b, where they will reach agreement about how to represent this problem situation.

INSTRUCTIONAL NOTE Students may approach Problem 1 in diverse ways, which is fine. However, by Part b be sure they are focused on the vertex coloring conflict approach.

b. The vertices represent <u>the different clubs</u>.
Two vertices are connected by an edge if <u>the clubs they represent share a member</u>.
The colors represent <u>the days of the week</u>.

INSTRUCTIONAL NOTE If students respond to the edge placement sentence by saying, "there is a conflict," acknowledge that as a good general answer and then press for an answer specific to this context.

c. One possible model:
VC = Varsity Club
MC = Math Club
FC = French Club
DC = Drama Club
CC = Computer Club
AC = Art Club
(Some of the names are added to edges for reference and to highlight the conflicts.)

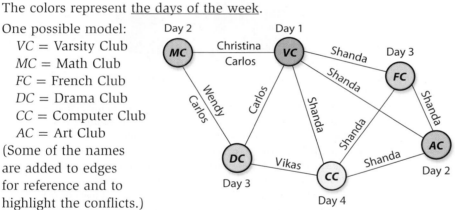

d. The fewest number of colors is 4. See graph above. (Note that VC-FC-AC-CC forms a graph on 4 vertices in which all the vertices are adjacent to each other, so at least 4 colors are needed, and the coloring above does it with 4.)

2 **a.** Yes

b. 4 days

c. One possible schedule, corresponding to the coloring above:
Varsity Club meets on Monday, Art and Math Clubs meet on Tuesday, Drama and French Clubs meet on Wednesday, and Computer Club meets on Thursday.

d. Since the graph needed 4 colors, the clubs can all meet within 4 days (once each week). The graph model does not help you decide which exact days to meet, only which clubs cannot meet the same day.

Unit 4

3 Shown here is an uncolored map of a portion of southern Africa.

  a. Using a copy of this map, color the map so that no 2 countries that share a border have the same color. (For this problem, you may assume that Botswana and Zambia intersect only at a point, though in fact they share a border about 10 miles long.)

  b. How many colors did you use? Try to color the map with fewer colors.

  c. Compare your map coloring with that of other classmates.

   i. Are the colorings different?

   ii. Are the colorings legitimate; that is, do neighboring countries have different colors? If a coloring is not legitimate, fix it.

  d. What is the fewest number of colors needed to color this map?

4 In Problem 3, you found the fewest number of colors needed to color the Africa map. Now think about the fewest number of colors needed to color *any* map.

  a. Do you think you can color *any* map with at most 5 different colors? Can the map of Africa be colored with 5 colors?

  b. The map below has been colored with 5 colors. Is it possible to color the map with fewer than 5 colors? If so, make a copy of the map and color it with as few colors as possible.

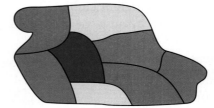

  c. What do you think is the *fewest* number of colors needed to color *any* map? Make a conjecture.

   i. Compare your conjecture to the conjectures of your classmates. Briefly discuss any differences. Revise your conjecture if you think you should. Test your conjecture as follows, in part ii.

   ii. Over the next few days, test your conjecture on other maps outside of class. Revise your conjecture as necessary. Compare and discuss again with your classmates and teacher.

Maps can be colored by working directly with the maps, as you have been doing. But it is also possible to turn a map-coloring problem into a graph-coloring problem. This can be helpful since it allows you to use all the properties and techniques for graphs to help you understand and solve map-coloring problems.

3 **a.** One possible coloring is shown below.

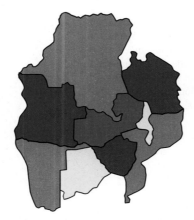

b. Responses may vary. The minimum needed is four colors. (Students may not at this time be sure that 4 is the minimum number of colors needed. They will examine a vertex-edge graph that represents this map in Problem 6 on page 273. By analyzing that graph, you can be sure that 4 is the minimum number of colors.)

c. **i.** Within the class, there should be different colorings.

  ii. Students should fix their coloring if necessary.

d. 4 colors—see Part b.

4 **a.** Students will probably not be sure whether or not every map can be colored with 5 colors, but they should realize that the map of southern Africa can be colored with 5, since they colored it with 4 colors in Problem 3. It's always easier to color with more colors; the challenge is to color with fewer.

b. Yes, it is possible to color the map with three colors as shown.

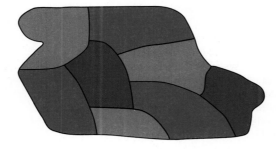

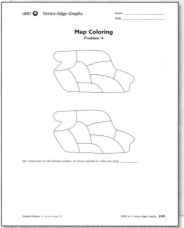
c. Students will now have seen two maps that can be colored with 5 colors, the Africa map and the generic map in Part b, but both can be colored with fewer colors as well. For now, they should guess the fewest number of colors needed for any map and test and revise their guess over the next few days.

INSTRUCTIONAL NOTE This is the famous Four-Color Theorem. Students should be encouraged to make conjectures and try them on some maps and compare with classmates. Let them play with this for at least a day or two before giving the answer, or maybe let some students give a report. When the answer is given, be sure to emphasize how recent and famous the result is and how long mathematicians worked on the problem. This is an example of "cutting edge" mathematics that is accessible to students. A brief history of map coloring is provided on page T275B.

⑤ To find a graph that models a map-coloring problem, first think about what you did with the radio-station and club-scheduling problems. In both of those problems, the edges were used to indicate some kind of *conflict* between the vertices. The vertices in conflict were connected by an edge and colored different colors. A crucial step in building a graph-coloring model is to decide what the conflict is. Once you know the conflict, you can figure out what the vertices, edges, and colors should represent.

a. What was the conflict in the club-scheduling problem? What was the conflict in the radio-station problem?

b. Make and complete a table like the one below.

Modeling Conflicts

Problem	Conflict if:	Vertices	Connect with an Edge if:	Colors
Radio-station problem	*2 radio stations are 500 miles or less apart*	*radio stations*		*frequencies*
Club-scheduling problem	*two clubs* _____			
Map-coloring problem	*two countries* _____			

⑥ Consider the map of a portion of southern Africa in Problem 3.

a. Use the information in the table above to create a vertex-edge graph that represents the map.

b. Color the vertices of the graph. Remember that coloring always means that vertices connected by an edge must have different colors. Also, as usual, use as few colors as possible.

c. Compare your coloring with those of other classmates.

  i. Are all the colorings legitimate?

  ii. Reach agreement on the fewest number of colors needed to color the graph.

  iii. Is the minimum number of colors for this *graph*-coloring problem the same as the minimum number of colors for the *map*-coloring problem in Part d of Problem 3? Explain.

Algorithms You have now used vertex coloring to solve several problems. In each problem, you used some method to color the vertices of a graph using as few colors as possible. Recall that a systematic step-by-step method is called an *algorithm*. Finding good graph-coloring algorithms is an active area of mathematical research with many applications. It has proven quite difficult to find an algorithm that colors the vertices of any graph using as few colors as possible. You often can figure out how to do this for a given small graph, as you have done in this lesson. However, no one knows an efficient algorithm that will color *any* graph with the *fewest* number of colors! This is a famous unsolved problem in mathematics. Think about methods you have used to color a graph.

LESSON 2 • Vertex Coloring: Avoiding Conflict   **273**

5 **a.** Some students were members of more than one club. Frequencies would interfere with each other if the stations were too close.

b. **Modeling Conflicts**

Problem	Conflict if:	Vertices	Connect with an Edge if:	Colors
Radio-station problem	*two radio stations are within 500 miles of each other*	*radio stations*	*stations are 500 miles apart or less*	*frequencies*
Club-scheduling problem	*two clubs share members*	*clubs*	*clubs share a member*	*days of the week*
Map-coloring problem	*two countries share a border*	*countries*	*countries have a common border*	*colors on the map*

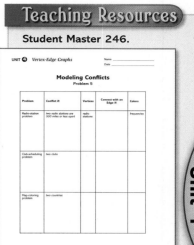
6 **a.** The vertices represent countries and the edges represent shared borders.

b. Two countries must be colored with different colors if they share a border, so 2 vertices connected by an edge must have different colors. See the possible coloring below.

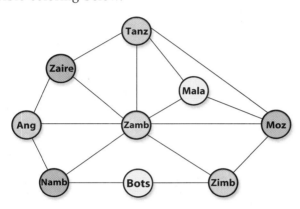

c. **i.** Students should verify, in any legitimate coloring, that adjacent vertices must have different colors.

ii. The fewest number of colors needed to color the graph is 4. We can prove that 4 is the fewest number because (a) we've colored the graph above using 4 colors; and (b) it must take at least 4 colors since there are 4 vertices in the graph that are all adjacent to each other: Tanz-Mala-Moz-Zamb.

iii. Yes, the minimum in both cases is 4 colors. The graph is just a model of the map on page 272 (which is just a model of the southern portion of Africa).

7 Describe some strategies or algorithms you have used to color the vertices of a graph using the fewest number of colors. Compare and discuss algorithms with your classmates.

8 One commonly used algorithm is sometimes called the **Welsh-Powell algorithm**. Here's how it works:

Step 1: Begin by making a list of all the vertices starting with the ones of highest degree and ending with those of lowest degree.

Step 2: Color the first uncolored vertex on your list with an unused color.

Step 3: Go down the list coloring as many uncolored vertices with the current color as you can, following the rule that vertices connected by an edge must be different colors.

Step 4: If all the vertices are now colored, you're done. If not, go back to Step 2.

a. Follow the Welsh-Powell algorithm, step by step, to color the two graphs below.

 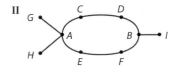

b. Does the Welsh-Powell algorithm always yield a coloring that uses the fewest number of colors possible? Explain your reasoning.

c. Use the Welsh-Powell algorithm to color each graph below and compare your coloring with your previous results.

   i. radio-station graph (Investigation 1, Problem 6)

   ii. club-scheduling graph (Investigation 2, Problem 1, Parts c and d)

7 Student strategies may include coloring the vertices with highest degree first, coloring from the outside in or from the inside out (thinking of the shape of the graph), coloring as many vertices as possible with one color, or coloring one vertex and then simply continue vertex by vertex. Note that the last two strategies are discussed in more detail as the One-Color-at-a-Time and Vertex-by-Vertex algorithms in Extensions Problem 15.

8 **a.** Here are the steps for coloring Graph I.

Step 1: List the vertices according to degree: *D, A, B, E, C, F.*

Step 2: *D* is at the top of the list. Color *D* red.

Step 3: Going down the list, we find that no other vertex can be colored red.

Step 4: Choose a new color, green, for the highest uncolored vertex, *A.*

Step 5: Going down the list, we color *C* and *F* green.

Step 6: Choose a new color, blue, for the highest uncolored vertex, *B.*

Step 7: Going down the list, color *E* blue.

For II, we must put *A* followed by *B* at the head of the list of vertices because they have the highest degrees. The Welsh-Powell algorithm will give *A* and *B* the same color. Then *C, E, G, H,* and *I* will have the second color, and *D* and *F* will have the third.

b. No. In Graph I in Part a, it does produce a minimal coloring, which can be explained by the fact that 3 colors are used and there is a "triangle" in the graph so no fewer than 3 colors can be used. However, for Graph II the Welsh-Powell algorithm uses 3 colors, but actually you can color this graph with 2 colors: give *A, D, F,* and *I* color 1, and give *C, E, G, H,* and *B* color 2.

c. For these situations, the Welsh-Powell algorithm gives the same result as the technique used by students in the investigation.

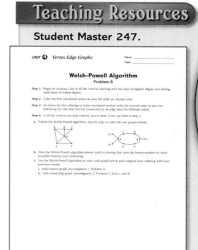

Teaching Resources

Student Master 247.

KEY IDEAS Graph II was chosen to highlight the fact that the Welsh-Powell algorithm does not always give the fewest number of colors, although adjacent vertices will get different colors.

i. Radio-Station Graph: Create a list of vertices with lower degrees later, for example, *U, X, W, V, Z, T, Y.* Then the Welsh-Powell algorithm yields the following result: on the first pass through the list, color *U, Y,* and *Z* red; on the second pass, color *X, V,* and *T* green; and on the third pass, color *W* blue.

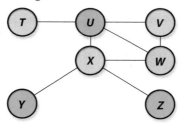

ii. Club-Scheduling Graph: Using the list *VC, CC, FC, AC, DC,* and *MC,* we find that *VC* is colored red in the first pass, *CC* and *MC* are colored green in the second, *FC* and *DC* are colored blue in the third, and *AC* is colored yellow in the fourth.

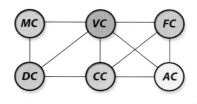

Unit 4

Summarize
the Mathematics

In this lesson, you used graphs to avoid conflict in three seemingly different problems.

a Explain how each of the three main problems you solved in this lesson—assigning radio frequencies, club scheduling, and map coloring—involved "conflict among a finite number of objects."

b Describe the basic steps of modeling and solving a conflict problem with a graph.

c The **chromatic number** of a graph is the fewest number of colors needed to color all its vertices so that 2 vertices connected by an edge have different colors. What is the chromatic number of the graphs for each of the three problems in this lesson (radio stations, club meetings, and map coloring)? How is this number related to the solution for each problem?

Be prepared to share your responses with the entire class.

✓Check Your Understanding

Hospitals must have comprehensive and up-to-date evacuation plans in case of an emergency. A combination of buses and ambulances can be used to evacuate most patients. Of particular concern are patients under quarantine in the contagious disease wards. These patients cannot ride in buses with nonquarantine patients. However, some quarantine patients can be transported together. The records of who can be bused together and who cannot are updated daily.

Suppose that on a given day there are 6 patients in the contagious disease wards. The patients are identified by letters. Here is the list of who cannot ride with whom:

A cannot ride with *B*, *C*, or *D*.   *D* cannot ride with *A* or *C*.
B cannot ride with *A*, *C*, or *E*.   *E* cannot ride with *F* or *B*.
C cannot ride with *A*, *B*, or *D*.   *F* cannot ride with *E*.

The problem is to determine how many vehicles are needed to evacuate these 6 patients. Use graph coloring to solve this problem. Describe the conflict, and state what the vertices, edges, and colors represent.

LESSON 2 • Vertex Coloring: Avoiding Conflict **275**

Summarize
the Mathematics

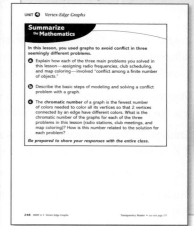

a For the problem of assigning radio frequencies, "conflict among a finite number of objects" is interference among 7 radio stations; for the club-scheduling problem, "conflict among a finite number of objects" is scheduling conflict among 6 clubs; for the map-coloring problem, "conflict among a finite number of objects" is shared borders among a finite number of countries.

b First identify the conflict. This will help you decide how to define the vertices and edges, since the vertices are the objects that are potentially in conflict and the edges show which objects are actually in conflict. Sketch a graph that models the situation based on your definitions of vertices and edges. Then color the vertices such that adjacent vertices have different colors. This results in avoiding conflicts. Use the fewest number of colors for an optimal solution that avoids conflict.

c The chromatic numbers of the graphs for the radio stations, club meetings, and map coloring are 3, 4, and 4, respectively. These numbers give the minimum number of frequencies, meeting days, and country colors, respectively.

MATH TOOLKIT Describe the basic steps of modeling and solving a conflict problem with a graph.

✓ Check Your Understanding

The conflict in this situation involves patients who cannot ride with each other due to contagious disease. Let vertices represent the patients—*A, B, C, D, E, F*. Two vertices will be connected by an edge if the 2 patients cannot ride in the same ambulance. The colors represent ambulances transporting patients. Three ambulances are needed. For example, patients *A* and *E* can ride in one, *B* and *D* in another, and *C* and *F* in the third. Patient *F* also can ride with *B* and *D* instead.

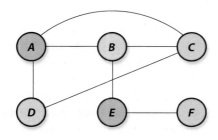

Promoting Mathematical Discourse

Summarize the Mathematics, *page 275*

Teacher: In this lesson, we used graphs to avoid conflict in three different problems. How did each of those situations involve "conflict among a finite number of objects"?

Student 1: In the first problem about radio stations, the conflict was the stations' broadcasts interfering with each other.

Student 2: Yeah, the radio stations would interfere with each other if they were too close. That was the conflict.

Teacher: Did we have a finite number of objects?

Student 3: Yes, we had 7 radio stations. Those were the objects that our vertices represented.

Student 4: Then we did the problem about the clubs. Let's see *(looking back at her notes)*, were the objects the people or the clubs?

Student 5: What did our vertices represent?

Student 4: The clubs. Okay, so the objects were the 6 clubs.

Student 6: The conflict was 2 clubs with at least one member in both. This was because members need to go to all the meetings.

Teacher: Has Student 6 made a clear statement of the conflict that you can agree with? *(Students agree.)* Okay. Then what was the third problem situation?

Student 7: The third problem was about the map of Africa. The objects were a finite number of countries. And the conflict was when 2 countries were bordering each other because then they couldn't be the same color.

Teacher: Do you all agree? *(Students agree.)* Next, we are going to make a list on the board of the basic steps of modeling and solving a conflict problem with a graph. Who would like to give us the first step and write it up on the board?

Student 8: Do we first have to determine what the objects are?

Student 9: Yeah, I think so, because those are the vertices and you have to draw the vertices first.

Student 10: But sometimes there is more than just one kind of object in the problem. I think you have to figure out what the conflict is first. So, then you know that the objects are the things that are in conflict with each other.

Student 8: I agree. So, step one should be to determine what the conflict is.

Teacher: Go ahead, Student 8, start it off *(on the board)*.

Student 11: Step 2 is to identify the objects and make those your vertices. *(Writes Step 2 on the board.)*

Student 12: Step 3 is to make a graph. You need to draw and label the vertices and draw the edges between the objects that are in conflict. *(Student 12 writes Step 3 on the board.)*

Student 13: Wait a minute! When I think about the conflict in the problem, I'm really thinking about both what the vertices and edges mean at the same time. It is really one step. Remember when we did the table about Modeling Conflicts? We said, "Two radio stations are 500 miles or less apart." Do you see what I mean?

Student 10: Yeah, I guess that is right. You kind of think "conflict" between "objects" together. Let's just make that one step.

Teacher: *(To class)* Well, what do you think? Shall we rewrite our first step? *(Class agrees.)*

Student 1: Okay, how about this? Step 1: Determine what the conflict is between.

Teacher: Any edits to this suggestion? *(No edits are offered.)* Well, is our previous Step 3 workable as our new Step 2? *(Students agree.)*

Student 2: Next, we have to color the vertices so that vertices that are connected by an edge have different colors. Should I make that Step 3? *(Students agree and he writes it on the board.)*

Student 3: Don't forget we want to use the least number of colors. *(Student 13 adds this on the board.)*

Student 4: I guess the last thing is to use the colors to avoid your conflict. Like in the radio-station problem, all the stations that were yellow could be the same frequency, and so on. The colors kind of form the different groups of things. *(Student 15 writes "Use colors to avoid the conflicts in the particular problem.")*

Teacher: Are we satisfied with our modeling method? *(Students nod.)* If you think that summarizing these steps in the modeling and solving of conflict would be helpful for you, then you should enter this in your toolkit. The last question deals with something called the **chromatic number**. The chromatic number of a graph is just the fewest number of colors needed to color all its vertices so that 2 vertices connected by an edge have different colors. So, what was the chromatic number of each of the graphs for these three problems that we have been discussing?

Student 5: For the radio-station problem, we used 3 colors.

Student 6: Yep, and for the problem about the school clubs we used 4 right? *(Students agree.)*

Student 7: And we used 4 colors for the map of Africa.

Teacher: Good, now keep those steps in mind as you work on these different problem situations that involve graph coloring. *(Teacher then gives the homework assignment.)*

Brief History of Map-Coloring Problem

The problem is to find the smallest number of colors necessary to color the countries (or states or regions) of any map so that each two countries with a common border have different colors. Note that we only allow "countries" that are all contiguous. So, for example, Michigan would not count as a single "country" because the state of Michigan is comprised of two land masses that are separated by water. Different maps require more or less colors than other maps, but the problem is to find the smallest number of colors that will color any map.

It all began in October 1852. While coloring regions on a map of England, Francis Guthrie discovered that he could color all the counties of England with just four colors. Through his brother, Guthrie asked Augustus De Morgan, a mathematician at University College, London, if four colors would suffice for all possible maps. De Morgan thought it obvious but could not prove it, and neither could anyone else for more than 100 years.

De Morgan communicated the problem to his colleague Sir William Rowan Hamilton, who was not particularly impressed with it. However, the problem became famous when, on June 13, 1878, at a meeting of the London Mathematical Society, Arthur Cayley asked if anyone could solve it. No one could. And from that moment on it was known as the Four-Color Problem, and it became one of the most famous unsolved problems in all of mathematics.

In 1879, Alfred Kempe, a London barrister, announced what he thought was a proof of the Four-Color Problem. The proof was accepted for eleven years, until P. J. Heawood found an error in it in 1890. Heawood couldn't fix the proof, but he did prove that any map could be colored with five colors. No one could prove whether or not four colors were enough until 1976, when Kenneth Appel and Wolfgang Haken from the University of Illinois finally settled the matter. Using over 1,000 hours of computer time, and a proof running several hundred pages, with some 10,000 diagrams, Appel and Haken finally proved that four colors will suffice to color any map.

Work on this proof by many mathematicians over the course of more than a century stimulated much of what is called combinatorial mathematics. The applications of the mathematics generated by this simple yet difficult problem now go far beyond the realm of map coloring.

On Your Own

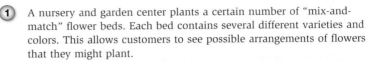

Applications

1. A nursery and garden center plants a certain number of "mix-and-match" flower beds. Each bed contains several different varieties and colors. This allows customers to see possible arrangements of flowers that they might plant.

   However, the beds are planted so that no bed contains two colors of the same variety. For example, no bed contains both red roses and coral roses. Also, no bed contains two varieties of the same color. For example, no bed contains both yellow tulips and yellow marigolds. This is done so that the customer can distinguish among and appreciate the different colors and varieties. A list of the varieties and colors that will be planted follows.

Flower Beds

Varieties	Colors
Roses	Red, Coral, White
Tulips	Yellow, Purple, Red
Marigolds	Yellow, Orange

The nursery wants to plant as few mix-and-match beds as possible. In this task, you will determine the minimum number of mix-and-match flower beds.

a. The varieties and colors listed above yield 8 different types of flowers, such as red roses, red tulips, and yellow tulips. List all the other types of flowers that are possible.

b. It is the types of flowers from Part a that will be planted in the mix-and-match beds. The problem is to figure out the minimum number of beds needed to plant these types of flowers so that no bed contains flowers that are the same variety or the same color. First, you need to build a graph-coloring model.

   i. What should the vertices represent?

   ii. What should the edges represent? Why?

   iii. What should the colors of the graph represent?

c. Draw the graph model and color it with as few colors as possible.

Applications

1 **a.** The types (including the three listed in the text) are red roses (rR), coral roses (cR), white roses (wR), yellow tulips (yT), purple tulips (pT), red tulips (rT), yellow marigolds (yM), and orange marigolds (oM).

   b. i. Vertices should represent the 8 types of flowers (color/variety).

   ii. The edges should represent when flower types are of the same variety or color so that the edges represent conflicting flower types.

   iii. The colors of the graph should represent the flower beds needed.

   c. Here is one of many arrangements.

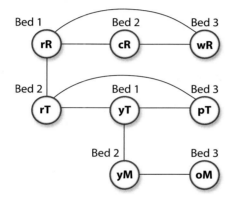

d. What is the minimum number of mix-and-match beds needed?

e. Use your graph coloring to recommend to the nursery which types of flowers should go in each of the mix-and-match beds.

f. When using a graph-coloring model, you connect vertices by an edge whenever there is some kind of conflict between the vertices. What was the conflict in this task?

2 A local zoo wants to take visitors on animal-feeding tours. They propose the following tours.

Tour 1 Visit lions, elephants, buffaloes

Tour 2 Visit monkeys, hippos, deer

Tour 3 Visit elephants, zebras, giraffes

Tour 4 Visit hippos, reptiles, bears

Tour 5 Visit kangaroos, monkeys, seals

The animals are fed only once a day. Also, there is only room for 1 tour group at a time at any 1 site. What is the fewest number of days needed to schedule all 5 tours? Explain your answer in terms of graph coloring.

3 You often can color small maps directly from the map, without translating to a graph model. However, using a graph model is essential when the maps are more complicated. The map of South America shown here can be colored either directly or by using a graph-coloring model.

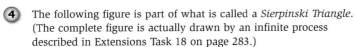

a. Color a copy of the map of South America directly. Use as few colors as possible and make sure that no two bordering countries have the same color.

b. Represent the map as a graph. Then color the vertices of the graph with as few colors as possible.

c. Did you use the same number of colors in Parts a and b?

4 The following figure is part of what is called a *Sierpinski Triangle*. (The complete figure is actually drawn by an infinite process described in Extensions Task 18 on page 283.)

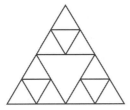

LESSON 2 • Vertex Coloring: Avoiding Conflict **277**

d. 3 beds

e. One solution is to put red roses and yellow tulips in Bed 1; coral roses, red tulips, and yellow marigolds in Bed 2; and white roses, purple tulips, and orange marigolds in Bed 3. Other solutions are possible (for example, orange marigolds could be in Bed 1).

f. The conflict was having the same color or the same variety in a single bed.

2 Let the vertices represent the different tours and connect 2 vertices if the 2 tours visit a common animal. This graph can be colored with only 2 colors; hence these tours can be scheduled in 2 days with no conflicts. One possible schedule is given here.

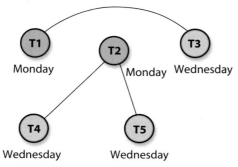

3 **a.** Four colors are needed to color this map. One coloring is below.

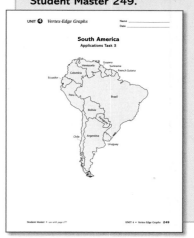

b.

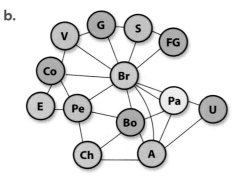

c. Yes, 4 colors.

a. Think of this figure as a map in which each triangle *not* containing another triangle is a country. Make and color a copy of the map with as few colors as possible.

b. Construct a graph that represents this map. Color the vertices of the graph with as few colors as possible. Compare the number of colors used with that in Part a.

c. Think of this figure as a map as Sierpinski did: the triangles with points upwards are countries, and the triangles with points downwards are bodies of water, "Sierpinski oceans," that separate the countries. Using this interpretation of countries, color a copy of the map with as few colors as possible. (Leave the Sierpinski oceans uncolored.)

d. Construct a graph for this second map. Color this graph with as few colors as possible. Did you use the same number of colors as in Part c?

Connections

5 Shown here is a student's proposal for a graph that models the radio-station problem from page 267.

a. Is this a legitimate model for the radio-station problem? Explain your reasoning.

b. In this graph model, some edges intersect at places that are not vertices. Can the graph be redrawn without edge-crossings? If so, do so.

c. Graphs that *can* be drawn in the plane with edges intersecting only at the vertices are called **planar graphs**. Which of the graphs below are planar graphs? (Use available software to demonstrate).

I   II   III

6 This task explores some properties of *complete graphs*. A **complete graph** is a graph that has exactly one edge between every pair of vertices. Complete graphs with 3 and 5 vertices are shown below.

a. Draw a complete graph with 4 vertices. Draw a complete graph with 6 vertices.

4 **a.** Only 2 colors are needed to color this map, shown below.

b. Looking at the figure without actually removing the middle third triangle (hence, not a true Sierpinski Triangle), we have the "maps" and graphs shown below. We assume that sharing a point or corner of the triangle does not mean sharing a boundary, which is the usual interpretation.

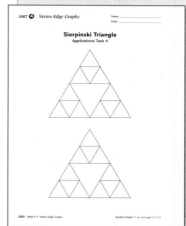

4a.

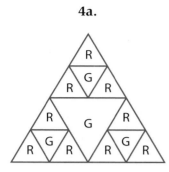

4b.

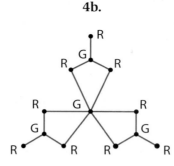

c. Assume that touching at a point does not constitute sharing a boundary. Every middle triangle is removed so these removed triangles do not represent a country and are not colored. The result should be that this figure needs only one color despite how complicated the figure looks in detail.

d. As in Part c, only 1 color is needed. There are no edges representing conflict (i.e., touching borders).

4c.

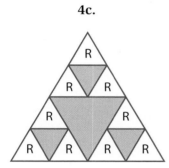

4d.

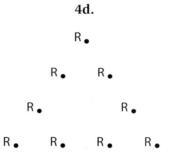

Connections

5 **a.** Yes, because the relationships between vertices and edges are the same as in their previous model. Alternatively, students may say that the radio stations 500 miles or less apart are connected by edges.

b. Yes. One possible redrawing is shown at the right.

c. Graphs I and II are planar. (Graph I can be redrawn so no edges intersect.)

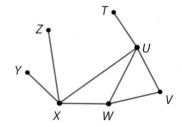

6 **a.**

Four Vertices

Six Vertices

TECHNOLOGY NOTE
CPMP-Tools vertex-edge graph software can be used in Tasks 5–8 to help investigate planar, complete, and cycle graphs.

b. Make a table that shows the number of edges for complete graphs with 3, 4, 5, and 6 vertices.

c. Look for a pattern in your table. How many edges does a complete graph with 7 vertices have? A complete graph with n vertices?

7 Refer to the definition of a complete graph given in Connections Task 6.

a. What is the minimum number of colors needed to color the vertices of a complete graph with 3 vertices? A complete graph with 4 vertices? A complete graph with 5 vertices?

b. Make a table showing the number of vertices and the corresponding minimum number of colors needed to color a complete graph with that many vertices. Enter your answers from Part a into the table. Find two more entries for the table.

c. Describe any patterns you see in the table.

d. What is the minimum number of colors needed to color a complete graph with 100 vertices? With n vertices?

8 A **cycle graph** is a graph consisting of a single *cycle* (a route that uses each edge and vertex exactly once and ends where it started).

a. Color the vertices of each of the cycle graphs below using as few colors as possible.

b. Make a conjecture about the minimum number of colors needed to color cycle graphs. Write an argument supporting your conjecture. Test your conjecture by drawing and coloring some large cycle graphs using vertex-edge graph software if available.

9 Besides coloring graphs, it is also possible to color other geometric figures. The three-dimensional figures below are three of the five *regular polyhedra*. You will learn more about regular polyhedra in Unit 6 *Patterns in Shape*. For now, you just need to visualize these three objects.

Tetrahedron   **Hexahedron**   **Octahedron**

Complete Parts a, b, and c for each of the above polyhedra. Record your answers for each of these coloring schemes in a table like the one on the next page.

LESSON 2 • Vertex Coloring: Avoiding Conflict **279**

b.

Number of Vertices	Number of Edges
3	3
4	6
5	10
6	15

c. Add the number of vertices in a given row to the number of edges in the same row to get the number of edges in the next row. So, to get the number of edges for a complete graph with 7 vertices (E_7), add $6 + E_6$ to get $6 + 15$ or 21 edges. Thus, the number of edges in a complete graph with n vertices is $(n - 1) + E_{n-1}$. (This is also $\frac{n^2 - n}{2}$ edges.)

7 **a.** Students will likely sketch complete graphs and color the vertices.

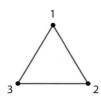 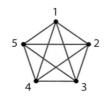

b.

Number of Vertices	Minimum Number of Colors
3	3
4	4
5	5
6	6
7	7

c. The number of vertices equals the minimum number of colors needed to color the vertices of a complete graph.

d. 100 colors; n colors

8 **a.**

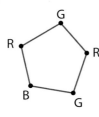 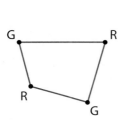 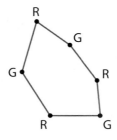 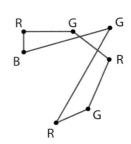

    3 colors   **2 colors**   **2 colors**   **3 colors**

b. Cycle graphs with an even number of vertices need 2 colors; those with an odd number of vertices need 3 colors.

> **TECHNOLOGY NOTE**
> The vertex-edge graph software in *CPMP-Tools* can be used to create cycle graphs and to color the graphs.

Unit 4

Coloring Polyhedra

Regular Polyhedron	Minimum Number of Colors		
	for Vertices	for Edges	for Faces
Tetrahedron			
Hexahedron			
Octahedron			

a. Color the vertices. Use the minimum number of colors. (Vertices connected by an edge must have different colors.)

b. Color the edges. Use the minimum number of colors. (Edges that share a vertex must have different colors.)

c. Color the faces. Use the minimum number of colors. (Faces that are adjacent must have different colors.)

Reflections

10 Throughout this course, and this unit in particular, you have been doing *mathematical modeling*. Below is a diagram that summarizes the process of mathematical modeling.

Process of Mathematical Modeling

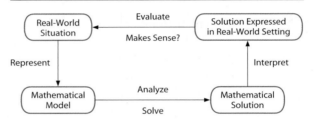

Choose one example of mathematical modeling from this lesson. Use the example to illustrate each part of the diagram.

11 Think of a problem situation different from any in this lesson that could be solved by vertex coloring. Describe the problem and the solution.

12 In this lesson, as well as in previous units, you have engaged in important kinds of mathematical thinking. From time to time, it is helpful to step back and reflect on the kinds of thinking that are broadly useful in doing mathematics. Look back over Lessons 1 and 2 and consider some of the mathematical thinking you have done. Describe an example where you did each of the following.

a. Search for and describe patterns

b. Formulate or find a mathematical model

c. Make and check conjectures

d. Describe and use algorithms

e. Use different representations of the same idea

9 **a–c.** **Coloring Polyhedra**

Regular Polyhedron	Minimum Number of Colors		
	for Vertices	for Edges	for Faces
Tetrahedron	4	3	4
Hexahedron	2	3	3
Octahedron	3	4	2

Teaching Resources

Student Master 251.

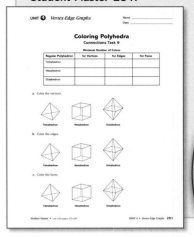

Reflections

10 A sample response based on the radio-station problem follows.

Real-World Situation—Assign frequencies to 7 radio stations so that there will be no interference between stations and the fewest possible number of new frequencies are used.

Represent this real-world situation with a graph model.

Mathematical Model—Build a vertex-edge graph to model this situation, where the vertices represent radio stations, the edges correspond to 2 radio stations that need different frequencies to avoid interference, and the colors represent frequencies. Thus, the real-world problem now becomes a graph-coloring problem.

Solve the mathematical problem, in this case by coloring the vertices of the graph with the fewest possible number of colors, by using some systematic procedure (algorithm).

Mathematical Solution—A coloring of the graph so that 2 vertices connected by an edge have different colors and the fewest possible number of different colors are used. In this example, 3 colors are needed.

Interpret the solution in terms of the real-world situation.

Solution Expressed in Real-World Setting—The fewest number of frequencies needed is the same as the fewest number of colors needed. Thus in this example, 3 frequencies are needed for the 7 radio stations. Further, the vertex coloring will tell you which frequencies to assign which stations.

Does this solution make sense? For example, if we had come up with 10 frequencies needed, we would know that something went wrong since there are only 7 radio stations.

Evaluate the solution. For example, what coloring algorithm was used? Could it be used to color other graphs? How do we know that 3 is the fewest number of colors needed?

11 There are many possibilities. For example, students could look at business or industry where certain items must be kept separate.

12 Some examples of these types of mathematical thinking are given.

   a. *search for and describe patterns*: relating vertices, regions, and edges of graphs; relating the number of edges and vertices for complete graphs

   b. *formulate or find a mathematical model*: locker painting models and other Applications tasks from Lesson 1, adjacency matrices, radio-station and club-scheduling conflict models; and maps as graphs

> **NOTE** The remaining answers to Problem 12 can be found on page T281.

Extensions

13. Search the Internet or a library for information on mathematicians who have worked on map coloring. Write a one-page report on one mathematician's contribution to the field.

14. In the nineteenth century, mathematicians made a conjecture about the minimum number of colors needed to color any map so that regions with a common boundary have different colors. This conjecture became one of the most famous unsolved problems in mathematics—until 1976 when the problem was solved. Based on your work in this lesson, how many colors do you think are needed to color *any* map? Only consider maps where the regions are connected. So, for example, do not consider a map that has a country that is split into two parts separated by another country.

    a. Try to draw a map that requires 3 colors and cannot be colored with fewer colors.

    b. Try to draw a map that requires 4 colors and cannot be colored with fewer colors.

    c. Try to draw a map that requires 5 colors and cannot be colored with fewer colors.

    d. How many colors do you think are necessary to color any map? After you have worked on this problem for a while, search the Internet or a library for recent information on graph theory and map coloring. Find the answer and compare it to your answer. Write a brief report on your findings.

15. In Problem 7 on page 274, you described algorithms that you used to color a graph. You may have described one of the following two algorithms (adapted from the description in *Discrete Algorithmic Mathematics, 3rd Edition*, A K Peters, Ltd, 2004, page 294).

Ken Appel and colleague Wolfgang Haken of the University of Illinois used 1,200 hours of computer time to help solve the map-coloring problem.

Vertex-by-Vertex Algorithm

Step 1: Arbitrarily number all the vertices of the graph: Vertex 1, Vertex 2, Vertex 3, and so on. Also, number the colors: Color 1, Color 2, and so on.

Step 2: Color the first vertex on your list with the first color.

Step 3: Color the next vertex on your list with the lowest-numbered color not already used for an adjacent vertex.

Step 4: Continue vertex-by-vertex until all vertices are colored.

One-Color-at-a-Time Algorithm

Step 1: Arbitrarily number all the vertices of the graph: Vertex 1, Vertex 2, Vertex 3, and so on.

Step 2: Color the lowest-numbered vertex with an unused color.

Step 3: Go down the list of vertices coloring as many uncolored vertices with the current color as you can, following the rule that adjacent vertices must be different colors.

Step 4: If all the vertices are now colored, you're done. If not, go back to Step 2.

LESSON 2 • Vertex Coloring: Avoiding Conflict   **281**

c. *make and check conjectures*: for Euler circuits, for graph-coloring algorithms; for the minimum number of colors needed to color graphs; and possibly conjectures related to the One-Color-at-a-Time and Welsh-Powell algorithms

d. *describe and use algorithms*: methods for finding Euler circuits, applying the Welsh-Powell algorithm, and possibly the algorithm in Extensions Task 26 (pages 260–261)

e. *use different representations of the same idea*: problem situation in words and a vertex-edge representation, graphs and matrices for connections between vertices, a matrix and a scale drawing for distance (pages 256–257), different vertex-edge graphs for same context such as 500 miles or less apart and more than 500 miles apart

Extensions

13 Here you might start with some histories of mathematics. Three very good sources are: Boyer, Carl. *A History of Mathematics*, Second Edition. New York, NY: John Wiley and Sons, 1991., Kline, Morris. *Mathematical Thought from Ancient to Modern Times.* New York, NY: Oxford University Press, 1990., and Holt, Howard Eves. *An Introduction to the History of Mathematics,* Fourth Edition. New York, NY: Holt, Rinehart, and Winston, 1976. Mathematicians who have contributed to map coloring include Francis Guthrie, Augustus De Morgan, Sir William Rowan Hamilton, A. F. Mobins, Arthur Cayley, A. B. Kempe, P. J. Heawood, P. G. Tait, Kenneth Appel, and Wolfgang Haken. Students also could interview a mathematician at a local college, university, or company who is interested in graph coloring or who specializes in discrete or applied mathematics.

14 **a.** One possibility is shown.

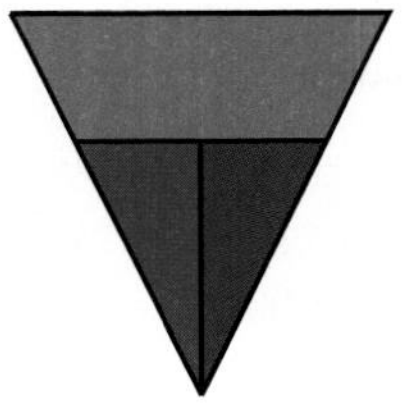

b. One possibility is shown.

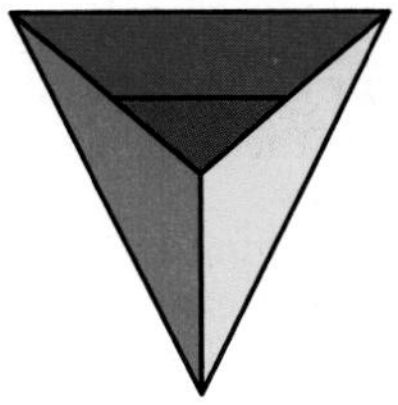

c. A famous theorem proved in 1976 shows that every map can be colored with at most 4 colors (see page T275B for a historical discussion of this theorem). Thus, students will not be able to draw a map that requires 5 colors and cannot be colored with fewer colors. The map at the right is an example of the complicated types of maps that students have tried.

d. Two good resources:

Barnette, David. *Map Coloring, Polyhedra, and the Four-Color Problem*. Washington, DC: Dolciani Mathematical Expositions No. 8, *Mathematical Association of America*, 1983.

Wilson, Robin J. and Watkins, John J. *Graphs: An Introductory Approach*. New York, NY: John Wiley and Sons, 1990.

a. Color the graph below (from Problem 8 on page 274) using each of the two algorithms above. For this problem, number the vertices in the same way for each algorithm.

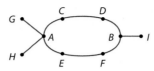

b. Compare the colorings from Part a.

　i. Make a conjecture about the colorings produced by these two algorithms for any graph.

　ii. Use vertex-edge graph software to test your conjecture with other graphs. For example, load some of the specific graph examples from the Sample Graphs menu. Then color using both algorithms, as found in the Algorithms menu. Each time you apply one of these algorithms, the software creates a random numbering of the vertices of the graph. What happens when the two algorithms are used with the same numbering of the vertices?

　iii. Explain why you think your conjecture is true.

c. Compare the One-Color-at-a-Time algorithm to the Welsh-Powell algorithm in Problem 8 on page 274. Describe similarities and differences.

d. Use vertex-edge graph software to help you further investigate the three algorithms you have considered in this task: the Vertex-by-Vertex algorithm, the One-Color-at-a-Time algorithm, and the Welsh-Powell algorithm. Explore the following questions. Write a brief report summarizing your findings. Include examples, counterexamples, and explanations as needed.

　i. What happens when you change the order in which you list the vertices? Do some types of orderings seem to generally be better than others?

　ii. Does one algorithm always yield a coloring with fewer colors than the others?

　iii. Will any of the algorithms always produce the chromatic number when applied to any graph?

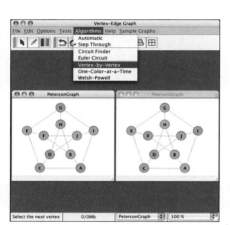

16 In this lesson, coloring a graph has always meant coloring the *vertices* of the graph. It also can be useful to think about **coloring the edges** of a graph. For example, suppose there are 6 teams in a basketball tournament and each team plays every other team exactly once. Games involving different pairs of teams can be played during the same round, that is, at the same time. The problem is to figure out the fewest number of rounds that must be played. One way to solve this problem is to represent it as a graph and then color the *edges*.

a. Represent the teams as vertices. Connect 2 vertices with an edge if the 2 teams will play each other in the tournament. Draw the graph model.

15 **a.** For both of these algorithms the coloring can change depending on how the vertices are ordered (see Step 1). In this problem students are asked to use the same ordering for each algorithm implementation. Using the Vertex-by-Vertex algorithm with vertices ordered alphabetically (for example), you get the following coloring: *A* and *B* are color 1; *C, E, G, H,* and *I* are color 2; *D* and *F* are color 3. Using the One-Color-at-a-Time algorithm with the vertices ordered in the same alphabetical order, you get: *A* and *B* are color 1; *C, E, G, H,* and *I* are color 2; *D* and *F* are color 3. (Just for comparison, note that using the One-Color-at-a-Time algorithm with reverse alphabetical order you get: *I, H, G, F, D* are color 1; *E, C, B* are color 2; *A* is color 3.)

TECHNOLOGY NOTE
CPMP-Tools, Vertex-edge graph software can be used with this task.

b. **i.** Based on the one example in Part a, students may conjecture that these two algorithms produce the same coloring when the vertices are ordered in the same way.

ii. Trying several more graphs, possibly using *CPMP-Tools,* Vertex-edge graph software to quickly generate and check, should support this conjecture.

iii. Students might explain why they think this conjecture is true as follows. For the One-Color-at-a-Time algorithm you start with color 1 and go down the list of ordered vertices coloring as many as possible with color 1. When you reach a vertex that you can't color with color 1, call it vertex *X*, you leave it blank and go on to the next vertex, and then vertex *X* will become the first one to be colored with color 2 next time through. In contrast, when using the Vertex-by-Vertex algorithm vertex *X*, which was skipped in the first pass above and later colored with color 2, is not skipped and is assigned color 2 right away. In either case, all the vertices ordered before vertex *X* get color 1 and vertex *X* gets color 2. Reasoning in this way, students may explain their conjecture.

c. The Welsh-Powell algorithm and the One-Color-at-a-Time algorithm are identical if the vertex ordering chosen for the One-Color-at-a-Time algorithm is from highest degree to lowest degree.

d. **i.** Generally, ordering from highest degree to lowest degree is better, but not always for all graphs.

ii. One algorithm is not always better than another for every graph.

iii. None of the algorithms produces the chromatic number when applied to any graph with a given ordering of vertices.

16 **a–b.**

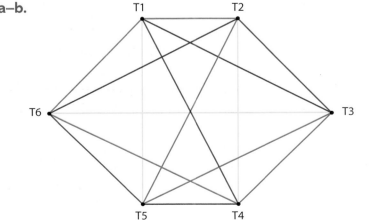

INSTRUCTIONAL NOTE Be sure that students realize that this and Extensions Task 17 are the only tasks that involve edge coloring. The rest of the lesson is concerned with conflict and vertex coloring.

Unit 4

b. Color the edges of the graph so *edges that share a vertex have different colors.* Use as few colors as possible.

c. Think about what the colors mean in terms of the tournament and the number of rounds that must be played. Use the edge coloring to answer these questions.

  i. What is the fewest number of rounds needed for the tournament?

  ii. Which teams play in which rounds?

d. Describe another problem situation that could be solved by edge coloring.

17 Here is an interesting game involving a type of edge coloring that you can play with a friend.

  • Place 6 points on a sheet of paper to mark the vertices of a *regular hexagon,* as shown here.

  • Each player selects a color different from the other.

  • Take turns connecting 2 vertices with an edge. Each player should use his or her color when adding an edge.

  • The first player who is forced to form a triangle of his or her own color loses. (Only triangles with vertices among the 6 starting vertices count.)

a. Play this game several times and then answer the questions below.

  i. Is there always a winner?

  ii. Which player has the better chance of winning? Explain.

b. Use the results of Part a to help you solve the following problem.

  Of any 6 students who are in a room, must there be at least 3 mutual acquaintances or at least 3 mutual strangers?

18 The Sierpinski Triangle is a very interesting geometric figure. If you try to draw it, you will never finish. That's because it is defined by an infinitely repetitive set of instructions. Here are the instructions.

Step 1: Draw an equilateral triangle.

Step 2: Find the midpoint of each side.

Step 3: Connect the midpoints. This will subdivide the triangle into 4 smaller triangles.

Step 4: Remove the center triangle. (Don't actually cut it out, just think about it as being removed. If you wish, you can shade it with a pencil to remind yourself it has been "removed.") Now there are 3 smaller triangles left.

Step 5: Repeat Steps 2–4 with each of the remaining triangles. Continue this process with successively smaller triangles. The first two passes through the instructions are illustrated at the top of the next page.

Sierpinski Triangle quilt made by Diana Venters.

LESSON 2 • Vertex Coloring: Avoiding Conflict **283**

c. **i.** The fewest number of rounds is 5.

ii. One possible schedule is shown here.

Round 1 Red	Round 2 Blue	Round 3 Pink	Round 4 Green	Round 5 Yellow
T1 vs. T2	T1 vs. T3	T1 vs. T6	T1 vs. T4	T1 vs. T5
T3 vs. T5	T2 vs. T6	T2 vs. T5	T2 vs. T3	T2 vs. T4
T4 vs. T6	T5 vs. T4	T3 vs. T4	T5 vs. T6	T3 vs. T6

d. There are other problems which involve timetables; for example, teacher schedules.

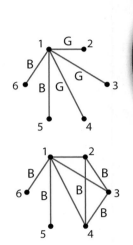

17 **a.** **i.** Yes, by the time all 15 possible edges are drawn, a triangle of 1 color will be formed. To explain why there is always a winner, consider the following argument:

> For every vertex, there are 5 edges containing that vertex. At least 3 of these edges will be the same color, say green. Label the other 2 edges blue. If vertices 2, 3, and 4 are joined, in any order by a green edge, then a green triangle is formed. So, join them as blue edges. But then we have a blue triangle. So, either way a triangle of 1 color is formed.

ii. The second player has the better chance. If the second player chooses carefully and does not form a triangle, the first player will be forced to form a triangle by the last (15th) play.

b. Yes, if one edge color represents acquaintances and the other edge color represents strangers, then at least one set of 3 mutual acquaintances or strangers will occur corresponding to one triangle of the same color formed. (Note that the problem relates to Ramsey Numbers, R(m, n). R(m, n) is the minimum number of people in a room that will guarantee that there are either **m** mutual aquaintances or **n** mutual strangers in the room. This problem, with a bit of additional work, shows that R(3, 3) = 6. You can learn more about Ramsey Numbers, which are a current area of mathematical research, at http://mathworld.wolfram.com/RamseyNumber.html.)

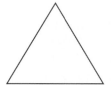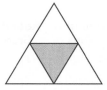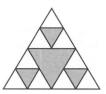

If you continue this process, you never get finished with these instructions because there always will be smaller and smaller triangles to subdivide.

a. On an enlarged copy of the third stage, draw the next stage of the process.

b. Stretch your imagination and think of the Sierpinski Triangle as a map, where the countries are the triangles that don't get removed. What is the minimum number of colors needed to color the map?

Review

19 Each table below represents a linear relation. Complete the table and find the equation of the line.

a.

x	0	1	2	3	4	5	6
y	0			7			

b.

x	0	1	2	3	4	5	6
y	4			7			

c.

x	0	1	2	3	4	5	6
y				7			7

d.

x	0	1	2	3	4	5	6
y				7		3	

20 Try to answer these questions without the use of a calculator. Think about how your answer for one part can help you determine an answer for another part.

a. What percent is 80 of 800?　　**b.** What percent is 8 of 800?

c. What percent is 0.8 of 800?　　**d.** What percent is 4 of 800?

e. What percent is 1 of 800?　　　**f.** What percent is 0.5 of 800?

21 Solve $3(x - 1) = 7x + 5$ by any method. Explain your method.

22 Donna wants to buy a painting that regularly sells for a price of $55 but is on sale for 20% off. If the sales tax is 7%, how much money will Donna need in order to buy the painting?

18 **a.** **Third Stage** **Next Stage**

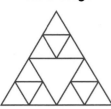 

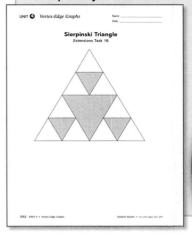
b. Since the infinite process never creates a common edge, the Sierpinski Triangle can be colored with one color. (Also see Applications Task 4 on page 278.)

Review

19 **a.**

x	0	1	2	3	4	5	6
y	0	$\frac{7}{3}$	$\frac{14}{3}$	7	$\frac{28}{3}$	$\frac{35}{3}$	14

$y = \frac{7}{3}x$

Students might use $(0, 0)$ and $(3, 7)$ to establish that the slope is $\frac{7}{3}$ and that the equation is $y = \frac{7}{3}x$. Then they can use the equation to fill out the table. Or they might reason proportionally that to make the 3 "steps" from $y = 0$ to $y = 7$, each step must be $\frac{7}{3}$.

b.

x	0	1	2	3	4	5	6
y	4	5	6	7	8	9	10

$y = 1x + 4$

Rate of change (slope) = 1, y-intercept = 4.

c.

x	0	1	2	3	4	5	6
y	7	7	7	7	7	7	7

$y = 7$

Rate of change is 0.

d.

x	0	1	2	3	4	5	6
y	13	11	9	7	5	3	1

$y = -2x + 13$

Rate of change is -2, y-intercept is 13.

20 **a.** $\frac{80}{800} = \frac{1}{10} = 10\%$

b. Students might reason that $\frac{8}{800} = \frac{1}{100} = 1\%$, or they might reason from the previous result.

c. 0.8 is a tenth of 8, so this answer is a tenth of the previous result. 0.1%.

d. Half of the result in Part b. $\frac{1}{2}$ of 1% is 0.5%.

e. $\frac{1}{8}$ of the result in Part b. $\frac{1}{8}$ of 1% is 0.125%.

f. Half of the result in Part e. $\frac{1}{2}$ of 0.125 is 0.0625%.

21 Students might use tables or graphs or a symbolic method to solve this equation. The solution is $x = -2$.

22 $47.08

> **INSTRUCTIONAL NOTE**
> This task helps students practice the use of percents and mental arithmetic. You may wish to have students share their approaches to finding $\frac{1}{8}$ of 1%. Some students may take $\frac{1}{2}$ of $\frac{1}{2}$ of $\frac{1}{2}$ of 1%.

23 Sketch a graph of each equation.

a. $y = 3x + 4$

b. $y = -\frac{2}{3}x + 6$

c. $y = -2 + \frac{1}{4}x$

d. $y = 3$

24 Without using a calculator, find the value of each expression.

a. $-5^2 + 10$

b. $3^3 - 2^3$

c. $(-2)^2 - 4(-5)$

d. $6(4)^3$

e. $8(0.5)^2$

f. $\frac{3(2^3)}{6}$

25 Calculate the area of each shape.

a. a right triangle that has a base of 7 inches and a height of 4 inches

b. a parallelogram with length 8 cm and height 5 cm

c. a square with perimeter 64 feet

26 Assume that the polygons in each pair shown below are similar with corresponding sides and angles as suggested by the diagrams. Find the unknown side lengths and angle measurements x, y, z, p, w, and t.

a.

b.

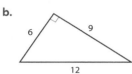

c.

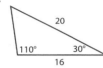

23 **a.**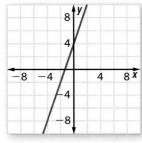

b.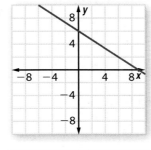

c.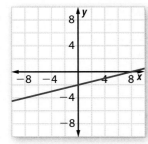

d.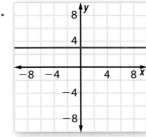

24 **a.** -15 **b.** 19

c. 24 **d.** 384

e. 2 **f.** 4

25 **a.** Area of triangle $= 0.5(7)(4) = 14$ square in.

b. Area $= (8)(5) = 40$ square cm

c. Area $= \left(\dfrac{64}{4}\right)^2 = 256$ square ft

 Just in Time

26 **a.** $\dfrac{6}{10} = \dfrac{4}{x}$, $x = 6.\overline{6}$

b. $y = 90°$

$\dfrac{z}{15} = \dfrac{9}{12}$, $z = 11.25$

c. $p = 30°$

$w = 110°$

$t = 10$

Teaching Resources

Assessment Masters 253–258.

Looking Back

I n this unit, you have studied a type of geometric diagram consisting of vertices and edges called a *graph*, or sometimes *vertex-edge graph*. The essential characteristic of these graphs is the relationship among the vertices, as defined by how the edges connect the vertices. These vertex-edge graphs can be used as models to help understand and solve many interesting types of problems.

You have used Euler circuits and vertex coloring to find optimum circuits and to manage conflicts in a variety of settings. The tasks in this final lesson will help you review and organize your thinking about the use of vertex-edge graphs as mathematical models.

1. One city's Department of Sanitation organizes garbage collection by setting up precise garbage truck routes. Each route takes one day. Some sites that need garbage collection more often are on more than one route. However, if a site is on more than one route, the routes should not visit that site on the same day. Here is a list of routes and the sites on each route that are also on other routes.

   Route 1: Site A, Site C

   Route 2: Site D, Site A, Site F

   Route 3: Site C, Site D, Site G

   Route 4: Site G

   Route 5: Site B, Site F

   Route 6: Site D

   Route 7: Site C, Site F, Site B

   a. Can all 7 routes be scheduled in one week (Monday–Friday)? What is the fewest number of days needed to schedule all 7 routes?

   b. Set up a schedule for the garbage truck routes, showing which routes run on which day of the week.

In this lesson, students will have the opportunity to select the type of graph model that is best suited to each of the three tasks, and then use the model to solve the problem. Also, the general process of mathematical modeling is explicitly described and reviewed.

1   **a.** Since only 4 colors are needed to color this graph, the routes can be scheduled in one week. The fewest number of days needed to schedule all 7 routes is 4.
Vertices represent routes.
Edges represent routes with common sites.
Goal: Minimize the number of vertex colors or the number of days needed for all routes.
(The edges labeled with "F" are an example showing that site F is common to routes 2, 5, and 7.)

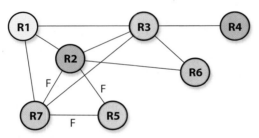

b. One schedule might be as below (since only 4 days are needed to cover all sites, there are many other possibilities). Students should be able to state and understand reasoning such as the following: Vertices 2 and 4 have the same color, which means they are not connected by an edge. This is because routes 2 and 4 do not conflict, that is, they do not share a site. Because of this, they can be scheduled on the same day, for example, on Monday.

Mon (Red)	Tues (Blue)	Wed (Green)	Thurs (Yellow)	Fri
Route 2 Route 4	Route 6 Route 7	Route 3 Route 5	Route 1	Take the day off or use for other arrangements

2 The security guard for an office building must check the building several times throughout the night. The diagrams below are the floor plans for office complexes on two floors of the building. An outer corridor surrounds each office complex. In order to check the electronic security system completely, the guard must pass through each door at least once.

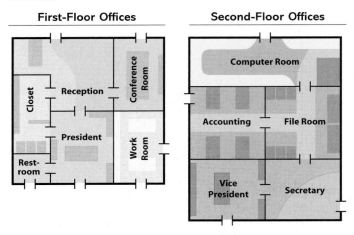

First-Floor Offices

Second-Floor Offices

a. For each office complex, can the guard walk through each door exactly once, starting and ending in the outer corridor? If so, show the route the guard could take. If not, explain why not.

b. If it is not possible to walk through each door exactly once starting and ending in the outer corridor, what is the fewest number of doors that need to be passed through more than once? Show a route the guard should take. Indicate the doors that are passed through more than once.

c. Construct an adjacency matrix for the graph modeling the first-floor offices problem. Explain how to use the matrix to solve the problem.

3 Traffic lights are essential for controlling the flow of traffic on city streets, but nobody wants to wait at a light any longer than necessary. Consider the intersection diagrammed below. The arrows show the streams of traffic. There is a set of traffic lights in the center of the intersection.

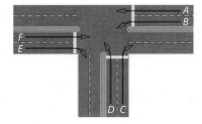

a. The guard can walk through each door exactly once, starting and ending in the outer corridor, for the first-floor office complex, but not for the second floor. This can be modeled as an Euler path problem, where the vertices are the rooms and two vertices are connected with an edge if there is a door between the rooms. In graph terms, the problem is asking for an Euler circuit.

The first-floor graph has all even vertices, thus an Euler circuit exists. Here's one: Corridor—President—Restroom—Corridor—Reception—Closet—President—Reception—Conference Room—Corridor—Work Room—Corridor.

The second-floor graph does not have all even vertices, so there is not an Euler circuit.

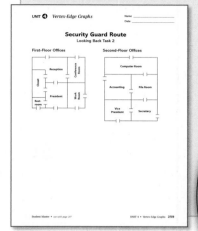
First-Floor Office Complex

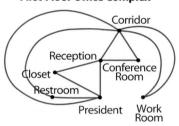

Second-Floor Office Complex

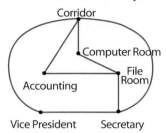

b. It is not possible to walk through each door exactly once, starting and ending in the corridor, for the second-floor office complex. This is because "File Room" and "Secretary" are vertices of odd degree. One solution is to make all vertices even by adding in imaginary edges corresponding to repeated edges. These added edges represent doors that are passed through more than once. Putting in one imaginary edge between "File Room" and "Secretary" will make all vertices even. Thus, only one door—the door between the file room and the secretary's office—needs to be passed through more than once.

Here is one route that the guard could take: Corridor—Vice President—Secretary—File Room—Accounting—Corridor— Computer Room—File Room—Secretary—Corridor.

c.

	C	CR	COR	P	R	RR	W
C	0	0	0	1	1	0	0
CR	0	0	1	0	1	0	0
COR	0	1	0	1	1	1	2
P	1	0	1	0	1	1	0
R	1	1	1	1	0	0	0
RR	0	0	1	1	0	0	0
W	0	0	2	0	0	0	0

The row sums are all even, so there is an Euler circuit, so the guard can take the desired route.

a. Can traffic streams *B* and *D* have a green light at the same time? How about *B* and *C*? List all the traffic streams that conflict with *B*.

b. Streams of traffic that have a green light at the same time are said to be on the same green-light cycle. What is the fewest number of green-light cycles necessary to safely accommodate all 6 streams of traffic?

c. For each of the green-light cycles you found in Part b, list the streams of traffic that can be on that cycle.

Summarize
the Mathematics

In this unit, you have used vertex-edge graphs as mathematical models to help solve a variety of problems.

a When constructing a mathematical model, you look for and mathematically represent the essential features of a problem situation. For each of the three tasks in this lesson, describe the essential features of the problem situation and how they are represented in the graph model you used. Be sure to describe what the vertices, edges, and colors (if needed) represent in each case.

b Key mathematical topics in this unit are Euler circuits and vertex coloring.

  i. What is an Euler circuit?

  ii. How can you tell if a graph has an Euler circuit?

  iii. Describe the types of problems that can be solved with Euler circuits.

  iv. Describe what it means to "color the vertices of a graph."

  v. Describe the types of problems that can be solved by vertex coloring.

Be prepared to share your descriptions and reasoning with the class.

✔ Check Your Understanding

Write, in outline form, a summary of the important mathematical concepts and methods developed in this unit. Organize your summary so that it can be used as a quick reference in future units and courses.

3   **a.** *B* and *D* cannot have a green light at the same time since those streams of traffic cross each other.

   B and *C* do not interfere with each other, so they can go on the same green-light cycle.

   The traffic streams that conflict with *B* are *D*, *E*, and *F*.

b. The fewest number of green-light cycles is 3. This can be modeled as a graph-coloring problem where the vertices are the streams of traffic, 2 vertices are connected by an edge if the streams of traffic conflict with each other, and colors correspond to different green-light cycles. The fewest number of colors needed to color all the vertices is 3.

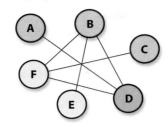

c. There are many different acceptable answers, depending on how the coloring is done and how the question is interpreted. Based on the above coloring, the most "routine" answer would probably be that *A*, *B*, and *C* are on one green-light cycle; *F* and *E* are on the second cycle; and *D* is on the third cycle.

   However, in this task it is possible for a stream of traffic to go on more than one green-light cycle, and in fact it is desirable to have as many streams going on each green light as possible. So, other acceptable answers could have several compatible streams going on each green light. *A-B-C*, *A-E-F*, *A-C-E*, and *C-D-E* are sets of compatible streams. Thus, an example of another acceptable answer is *A*, *B*, and *C* go on the first green light; *A*, *E*, and *F* on the second green light; and *C*, *D*, and *E* on the third green light. There are other combinations that work as well.

   Finding the compatible streams of traffic is another way to think about this problem. There are several ways to find the compatible streams—you can see them by examining all the different vertex colorings; or by directly examining the conflict graph from the perspective of compatibility (vertices that are not joined by an edge) rather than conflict (vertices that are joined by an edge); or by building a different graph model where you connect vertices by an edge if the streams of traffic are compatible (such a graph is called a compatibility graph and is another useful graph model).

ELL TIPS After all students have completed the lesson, it's time to evaluate what worked and what didn't work. Examine how students performed and determine if the methods you employed were successful. A professional log is helpful in tracking methods and can be used for future reference. Indicate what worked well in aiding ELL students and in which situation. This approach can help fine-tune your methods as you begin to see patterns emerge. Rely on your past evaluations to help you prepare for your next lesson or unit of study.

INSTRUCTIONAL NOTE
Note also there may be some difference of opinion about whether *E* conflicts with *B*. Traffic experts (e.g., police) would consider *B* and *E* in conflict. The same comment also applies to *C* and *F*.

INSTRUCTIONAL NOTE It is best not to use traffic-light colors to color the graph, as this can lead to confusion.

Unit 4

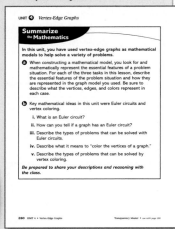

Unit 4

Summarize the Mathematics

a Many possible student responses are summarized in this chart.

Problem	Graph Model	Vertices	Edges	Colors	Why Chosen
Garbage Collector	vertex coloring	routes	two routes, common site	days	to avoid conflicts between routes
Office Complex	Euler paths or circuits	rooms	doors		to determine an optimal route
Traffic Lights	vertex coloring	stream of traffic	conflicting traffic	green-light cycles	to minimize green-light cycles

b

i. An Euler circuit for a vertex-edge graph is a path that uses each edge of the graph exactly once and begins and ends at the same vertex.

ii. A graph will have an Euler circuit iff each vertex has an even number of edge-touchings, that is, even degree. So, you must be able to check each of the finite number of vertices to find out whether they all have even degree. When the graph is represented with an adjacency matrix, the row sums can be checked to see whether or not they are even.

iii. Problems that involve covering or tracing a route and returning to the place of origin may be solved with Euler circuits. (Students should give examples from this unit as well as those that they might have learned about from other sources.)

iv. To "color the vertices of a graph" means to assign colors to all the vertices such that adjacent vertices (i.e., vertices that are connected by an edge) have different colors. The edges represent the conflict between the objects. By coloring adjacent vertices differently, you are indicating that those objects need a different treatment, such as different frequencies, different days of the week, or different cages.

v. Problems that have objects that cannot be treated the same because of some "conflict" may be solved with vertex coloring.

✔ Check Your Understanding

You may wish to have students use the Teaching Master, *Vertex-Edge Graphs Unit Summary*, to help them organize the information. Above all, this should be something that is useful to the individual student.

Practicing for Standardized Tests

Each Practicing for Standardized Tests master presents 10 questions that draw on all content strands. The questions are presented in the form of test items similar to how they often appear in standardized tests such as state assessment tests, the Preliminary Scholastic Aptitude Test (PSAT), or the ACT PLAN. We suggest using these practice sets following the unit assessment so students can become familiar with the formats of standardized tests and develop effective test-taking strategies for performing well on such tests. Answers are provided below.

Answers to Practice Set 4

1. (b)	**2.** (c)	**3.** (d)	**4.** (a)	**5.** (e)
6. (c)	**7.** (e)	**8.** (c)	**9.** (e)	**10.** (e)

Midterm Assessments

A bank of assessment tasks from which to construct a midterm exam that fits your particular class needs and emphases is provided in the Unit 4 Resource Masters and the TeacherWorks CD. In addition to problems similar in form to those on quizzes and tests, these assessment banks include several multiple-choice tasks for each unit.

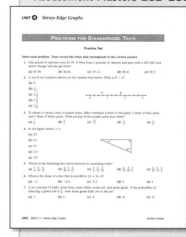

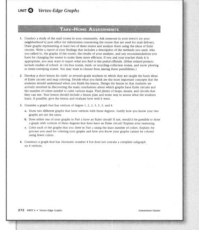

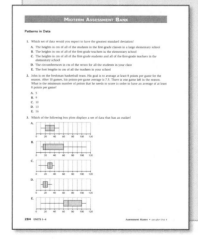

Glossary/Glosario

Math nline A mathematics multilingual glossary is available at www.math.glencoe.com/multilingual_glossary. The Glossary includes the following languages:

Arabic	English	Korean	Tagalog
Bengali	Hatian Creole	Russian	Urdu
Cantonese	Hmong	Spanish	Vietnamese

English	**Español**

A

Acute triangle (p. 68) A triangle with three *acute angles* (angles whose measures are less than 90°).

Triángulo acutángulo (pág. 68) Triángulo con tres *ángulos agudos* (ángulos cuyas medidas son menos de 90°).

Adjacency matrix (p. 248) A matrix representation of a vertex-edge graph in which each entry of the matrix is the number of edges between the corresponding pair of vertices.

Matriz de adyacencia (pág. 248) Representación matricial de un grafo en que cada entrada de la matriz es el número de aristas entre pares correspondientes de vértices.

Adjacent vertices (p. 248) Two vertices are adjacent if there is an edge between them.

Vértices adyacentes (pág. 248) Dos vértices son adyacentes si hay una arista entre ellos.

Algorithm (p. 246) A list of step-by-step instructions or a systematic step-by-step procedure.

Algoritmo (pág. 246) Lista de instrucciones detalladas o procedimiento detallado.

Altitude In a triangle, the perpendicular segment from a side to the opposite vertex (p. 389). In a parallelogram, a perpendicular segment from the line containing the base to the opposite side (p. 389). In a prism, a segment that is perpendicular to the planes of both bases (p. 428). In a pyramid, the perpendicular segment from the plane of the base to the apex (p. 428). In a cone, the perpendicular segment from the plane of the base to the vertex. In a cylinder, a perpendicular from the plane of one base to the plane of the other base.

Altura En un triángulo, el segmento perpendicular de un lado al vértice opuesto (pág. 389). En un paralelogramo, un segmento perpendicular de la recta que contiene la base al lado opuesto (pág. 389). En un prisma, segmento perpendicular a ambas bases (pág. 428). En una pirámide, el segmento perpendicular del plano de la base al vértice (pág. 428). En un cono, el segmento perpendicular del plano de la base al vértice. En un cilindro, la perpendicular del plano de una de las bases al plano de la otra.

Apex *see* **pyramid**

Vértice *véase* **pirámide**

Approximately normal distribution (mound-shaped) (p. 77) A data or probability distribution that has one peak and tapers off on both sides. Normal distributions are **symmetric**—the two halves look like mirror images of each other.

Distribución aproximadamente normal (campaniforme) (pág. 77) Datos o distribución probabilística que tiene un pico y que disminuye en ambos lados. Las distribuciones normales son **simétricas**: las dos mitades son imágenes especulares mutuas.

B

Back-to-back stemplot (p. 98) A stemplot used to compare two sets of data. The center column contains the stem of the data, while the right leaf contains one data set and the left leaf the other.

Esquema de tallos consecutivo (pág. 98) Un esquema de tallos que se usa para comparar dos conjuntos de datos. La columna central lleva los tallos de los datos, la hoja derecha lleva uno de los conjuntos de datos y la izquierda el otro.

Base *see* **exponential expression, parallelogram, prism, pyramid,** and **triangle**

Base *véase* **expresión exponencial, paralelogramo, prisma, pirámide** y **triángulo**

Base angles of a triangle (p. 372) Angles opposite the congruent sides of an isosceles triangle. These angles are congruent.

Ángulos basales de un triángulo (pág. 372) Ángulos opuestos a los lados congruentes de un triángulo isósceles. Dichos ángulos son congruentes.

Glossary/Glosario

English

Bimodal distribution (p. 96) A distribution with two well-defined peaks.

Bisector of an angle (p. 385) A ray that begins at the vertex of an angle and divides the angle into two angles of equal measure.

Box plot (box-and-whiskers plot) (p. 109) A statistical graphic in which only the minimum, lower quartile, median, upper quartile, maximum, and outliers are displayed.

ⓒ

Categorical data (p. 94) Data that fall into categories such as male/female or freshman/sophomore/junior/senior.

Central angle of a regular polygon (p. 401) An angle whose vertex is at the center of the polygon and whose sides (rays) extend through the endpoints of a side of the polygon.

Chromatic number (p. 275) The smallest number of colors needed to color all the vertices of a graph. (*see* **color a graph**)

Coefficient (p. 157) A number in front of a variable. For example, in the expression $x^2 - 10x + 25$, the coefficient of x^2 is 1 and the coefficient of x is -10.

Color a graph (p. 269) Assign a color to each vertex of a graph so that adjacent vertices have different colors. This may also be referred to as *graph coloring* or *vertex coloring*.

Coloring the edges (p. 282) Assign a color to each edge of a graph so that edges that share a vertex have different colors.

Computer Algebra System (CAS) (p. 54) Software that directs a calculator or computer to perform numeric, graphic, and symbolic mathematical operations required in arithmetic, algebra, calculus, and beyond.

Cone (p. 430) A figure formed by a circular region (the *base*), a point (the *vertex*) not in the plane of the base, and all of the segments joining the vertex to the base.

Español

Distribución bimodal (pág. 96) Distribución con dos picos bien definidos.

Bisectriz de un ángulo (pág. 385) Rayo que parte del vértice de un ángulo y que lo divide en dos ángulos congruentes.

Diagrama de caja (diagrama de caja y patillas) (pág. 109) Gráfica estadística en que sólo se muestran el mínimo, el cuartil inferior, la mediana, el cuartil superior, el máximo y los valores atípicos.

Datos categóricos (pág. 94) Datos que caen en categorías como masculino/femenino o primer año/segundo año/tercer año/cuarto año.

Ángulo central de un polígono regular (pág. 401) Ángulo cuyo vértice está en el centro del polígono y cuyos lados (rayos) se extienden por los extremos de un lado del polígono.

Número cromático (pág. 275) Mínimo de colores que se requieren para pintar todos los vértices de un grafo. (*véase* **coloración de un grafo**)

Coeficiente (pág. 157) Número delante de una variable. Por ejemplo, en la expresión $x^2 - 10x + 25$, el coeficiente de x^2 es 1 y el de x es -10.

Colorear un grafo (pág. 269) Asignación de un color a cada vértice de un grafo de modo que vértices adyacentes tengan colores distintos. Esto se llama también *coloración de un grafo* o *coloración de vértices*.

Coloración de aristas (pág. 282) Asignación de un color a cada arista de un grafo de modo que las aristas con vértices comunes tengan colores distintos.

Sistema algebraico computacional (SAC) (pág. 54) Programas que hacen que una computadora ejecute operaciones matemáticas numéricas, gráficas o simbólicas que se requieren en aritmética, álgebra, cálculo y otros.

Cono (pág. 430) Figura formada por una región circular (*la base*), un punto (*el vértice*) fuera del plano de la base y todos los segmentos que unen el vértice a la base.

Glossary/Glosario

English	Español

Congruent figures (p. 370) Figures that have the same shape and size, regardless of position or orientation.

Figuras congruentes (pág. 370) Figuras de la misma forma y tamaño, sea cual sea su posición u orientación.

Connected graph (p. 243) A graph that is all in one piece. That is, from each vertex there is at least one path to every other vertex.

Grafo conexo (pág. 243) Un grafo que es de una sola pieza, o sea, de cada vértice hay por lo menos un camino a cada uno de los otros vértices.

Consecutive angles (p. 387) In a polygon, two angles whose vertices are adjacent.

Ángulos consecutivos (pág. 387) En un polígono, dos ángulos cuyos vértices son adyacentes.

Constant term (p. 157) The term in an algebraic expression in which a variable does not appear. For example, in the expression $x^2 - 10x + 25$, the 25 is the constant term.

Término constante (pág. 157) Término de una expresión algebraica sin variables. Por ejemplo, en la expresión $x^2 - 10x + 25$, 25 es un término constante.

Counterexample (p. 451) A statement or diagram that shows that a given statement is not always true.

Contraejemplo (pág. 451) Enunciado o diagrama que prueba que un enunciado dado no es verdadero.

Converse (p. 380) A statement formed by interchanging the "if"-clause and the "then"-clause of a given "if-then" statement.

Recíproco (pág. 380) Enunciado que resulta al intercambiar las cláusulas "si" y "entonces" de un enunciado "si-entonces."

Convex polygon (p. 404) A polygon in which no segment connecting any two vertices of the polygon contains points in the exterior of the polygon. Otherwise the polygon is called *nonconvex*.

Polígono convexo (pág. 404) Polígono en que no hay segmento que una dos de sus vértices y que contenga puntos fuera del mismo. De lo contrario, el polígono se llama *no convexo*.

Convex polyhedron (p. 426) A polyhedron in which no segment connecting any two vertices of the polyhedron contains points in the exterior of the polyhedron. Otherwise the polyhedron is called *nonconvex*.

Poliedro convexo (pág. 426) Poliedro en que no hay segmento que una dos de sus vértices y que contenga puntos fuera del mismo. De lo contrario, el poliedro se llama *no convexo*.

Cube (regular hexahedron) (p. 427) A regular polyhedron with six congruent, square faces.

Cubo (hexaedro regular) (pág. 427) Poliedro regular con seis caras cuadradas congruentes.

Cycle graph (p. 279) A vertex-edge graph consisting of a single cycle—a route that uses each edge and vertex exactly once and ends where it started.

Grafo cíclico (pág. 279) Grafo que consta de un solo ciclo: un camino que pasa por cada arista y cada vértice solo una vez y que termina donde empezó.

Cylinder (p. 430) A figure formed by two congruent circular regions (the *bases*) contained in parallel planes along with all segments having an endpoint on each base and parallel to the line joining the centers of the bases.

Cilindro (pág. 430) Figura formada por dos regiones circulares congruentes (las *bases*) contenidas en planos paralelos, junto con todos los segmentos que tienen un extremo en cada base y que son paralelos a la recta que une los centros de las bases.

· · · · · · · · · · · · · · · · · (D) · · · · · · · · · · · · · · · · ·

Dart (p. 422) A nonconvex quadrilateral with two distinct pairs of consecutive sides the same length.

Dardo (pág. 422) Cuadrilátero no convexo con dos pares de lados consecutivos que tienen la misma longitud.

Data distribution (pp. 75–82) The collection of data values, typically summarized in a table or plotted so that the number or proportion of times that each value occurs can be observed.

Distribución de datos (págs. 75–82) Conjunto de datos típicamente tabulados o graficados de modo que pueda observarse el número o proporción de veces que ocurre cada valor.

Glossary/Glosario

English	**Español**

Data transformation (p. 124) A change in each value in a set of data such as adding the same constant to each value, taking the square root of each value, or dividing each value by the same constant; often used to change units of measure.

Transformación de datos (pág. 124) Cambio de cada valor en un conjunto de datos, como la adición de la misma constante a cada valor, la extracción de la raíz cuadrada de cada valor o la división de cada valor entre la misma constante; se usan a menudo para convertir unidades de medida.

Degree of a vertex (p. 245) The number of edges touching a vertex. If an edge loops back to the same vertex, that counts as two edge-touchings.

Grado de un vértice (pág. 245) Número de aristas que concurren en un vértice. Los lazos se cuentan dos veces.

Dependent variable (p. 6) A dependent variable is one whose value changes in response to change in one or more related independent variables.

Variable dependiente (pág. 6) Variable cuyos valores cambian en respuesta a cambios en una o más variables independientes relacionadas.

Deviation from the mean (p. 118) The difference between a data value and the mean of its distribution.

Desviación de la media (pág. 118) Diferencia entre un dato y la media de su distribución.

Directed edge (p. 262) An edge in a vertex-edge graph with a direction indicated.

Arista dirigida (pág. 262) Arista de un grafo en que se indica la dirección de la misma.

Directed graph (digraph) (p. 262) A vertex-edge graph in which all the edges are directed.

Grafo dirigido (digrafo) (pág. 262) Grafo en que todas las aristas poseen dirección.

Dot plot (number line plot) (p. 76) A statistical graphic where dots that represent data values are plotted above a number line.

Esquema de puntos (esquema lineal numérico) (pág. 76) Gráfica estadística en que puntos que corresponden a los datos se grafican encima de una recta numérica.

Doubling time (p. 314) For a quantity growing exponentially, the time it takes for the quantity to double.

Tiempo de duplicación (pág. 314) Tiempo que tarda en duplicarse una cantidad que crece exponencialmente.

Dual of a tessellation (p. 418) A tessellation obtained by connecting the centers of regular polygons that share a common edge in a given tessellation of regular polygons.

Dual de un teselado (pág. 418) En un teselado dado de polígonos regulares, teselado que se obtiene al unir los centros de los polígonos regulares que tienen una arista común.

· ·

Edge (of a vertex-edge graph) (p. 241) Segment or arc joining two vertices in a vertex-edge graph.

Arista (de un grafo) (pág. 241) Segmento o arco que une dos vértices de un grafo.

Equally-likely outcomes (p. 534) Outcomes that all have the same probability of occurring.

Resultados equiprobables (pág. 534) Resultados que tienen la misma probabilidad de ocurrir.

Equation A statement using symbols indicating that two expressions are equivalent.

Ecuación Enunciado que usa símbolos y que indica que dos expresiones son iguales.

Equilateral polygon (p. 419) A polygon in which all sides have equal length.

Polígono equilátero (pág. 419) Polígono cuyos lados tienen todos la misma longitud.

Equivalent expressions (p. 215) Expressions that produce equal output values from all possible equal input values.

Expresiones equivalentes (pág. 215) Expresiones que producen los mismos valores de salida para todos los valores de entrada posibles iguales.

Glossary/Glosario

English	Español

Euler circuit (p. 243) A route through a connected graph such that (1) each edge is used exactly once, and (2) the route starts and ends at the same vertex.

Circuito de Euler (pág. 243) Camino en un grafo conexo de modo que (1) cada arista se recorre sólo una vez y (2) el camino empieza y termina en el mismo vértice.

Euler path (p. 256) A route through a connected graph that traces each edge of the graph exactly once.

Camino de Euler (pág. 256) Camino en un grafo conexo que traza cada arista sólo una vez.

Expanding (p. 221) Rewriting an algebraic expression with parentheses as an equivalent expression that does not contain parentheses.

Desarrollo (pág. 221) Volver a escribir una expresión algebraica con paréntesis como una expresión equivalente sin paréntesis.

Exponent (power) *see* **exponential expression**

Exponente (potencia) *véase* **expresión exponencial**

Exponential decay (p. 323) Process in which change of the dependent variable can be modeled by an exponential function with rule in the form $y = a(b^x)$ where $a > 0$ and $0 < b < 1$.

Desintegración exponencial (pág. 323) Proceso en que el cambio de la variable dependiente viene dado por una función exponencial de la forma $y = a(b^x)$, con $a > 0$ y $0 < b < 1$.

Exponential expression (p. 304) An algebraic expression in the form b^n, where b and n are real numbers or variables. The number b is called the *base* of the exponential expression, and n is called the **exponent** or the **power**.

Expresión exponencial (pág. 304) Expresión algebraica de la forma b^n, con b y n números reales o variables. El número b es la base de la expresión exponencial y n es su **exponente** o **potencia**.

Exponential function (pp. 296, 328) A function of the form $y = a(b^x)$ where $a \neq 0$ and $0 < b < 1$ or $b > 1$.

Función exponencial (págs. 296, 328) Función de la forma $y = a(b^x)$, con $a \neq 0$ y $0 < b < 1$ ó $b > 1$.

Exponential growth (p. 291) Process in which change of the dependent variable can be modeled by an exponential function with rule in the form $y = a(b^x)$ where $a > 0$ and $b > 1$.

Crecimiento exponencial (pág. 291) Proceso en que el cambio de la variable dependiente viene dado por una función exponencial de la forma $y = a(b^x)$, con $a > 0$ y $b > 1$.

Expression A symbolic representation of a calculation procedure.

Expresión Representación simbólica de un procedimiento de cálculo.

Exterior angle of a convex polygon (p. 405) An angle formed at a vertex of the polygon by one side and the extension of the adjacent side.

Ángulo exterior de un polígono convexo (pág. 405) Ángulo formado en un vértice del polígono por un lado y la extensión del lado adyacente.

· · · · · · · · · · · · · · · · · · (F) · · · · · · · · · · · · · · · · · ·

Factoring (p. 221) Rewriting an algebraic expression in an equivalent form as a product of several expressions.

Factorización (pág. 221) Replanteamiento de una expresión algebraica en una equivalente que sea un producto de varias expresiones.

Fibonacci sequence (p. 35) The sequence of numbers 1, 1, 2, 3, 5, 8, 13, 21, 34, ...

Sucesión de Fibonacci (pág. 35) La sucesión de números 1, 1, 2, 3, 5, 8, 13, 21, 34, ...

Five-number summary (p. 108) The minimum, lower quartile (Q_1), median (Q_2), upper quartile (Q_3), and maximum of a data set.

Resumen de cinco números (pág. 108) El mínimo, el cuartil inferior (Q_1), la mediana (Q_2), el cuartil superior (Q_3) y el máximo de un conjunto de datos.

Glossary/Glosario

English	Español
Frequency table (p. 87) A summary table for numerical data, where typically the column on the left gives the different data values and the column on the right gives the number of times each value occurs.	**Tabla de frecuencias** (pág. 87) Una tabla sumarial de datos numéricos, donde la columna de la izquierda lleva típicamente los diversos valores de los datos y la columna de la derecha lleva el número de veces que aparece cada valor.
Function (in one variable) (p. 69) A relationship between two variables in which each value of the independent variable corresponds to exactly one value of the dependent variable.	**Función (de una variable)** (pág. 69) Relación entre dos variables en que a cada valor de la variable independiente corresponde un solo valor de la variable dependiente.
Function graph The set of points (x, y) on a coordinate grid whose coordinates are related by a function.	**Gráfica de una función** El conjunto de puntos (x, y) en un cuadriculado cuyas coordenadas están relacionadas por una función.

(G)

Graph *see* **vertex-edge graph, function graph**	**Gráfica** *véase* **grafo, gráfica de función**
Graph coloring *see* **color a graph**	**Coloración de un grafo** *véase* **colorear un grafo**

(H)

Half-life (p. 327) For a quantity decaying exponentially, the amount of time it takes for the quantity to diminish by half.	**Media vida** (pág. 327) Tiempo que tarda en reducirse a la mitad una cantidad que decrece exponencialmente.
Height of a figure (p. 389) The length of the figure's altitude. (*see* **altitude**)	**Altura de una figura** (pág. 389) Longitud de la altura de una figura. (*véase* **altura**)
Histogram (p. 78) A statistical graphic for numerical data, where the height of a bar shows the *frequency* or count of the values that lie within the interval covered by the bar.	**Histograma** (pág. 78) Gráfica estadística para datos numéricos en que la altura de una barra muestra la *frecuencia* o cuenta de los valores que yacen en el intervalo cubierto por la barra.

(I)

Independent variable (p. 6) Variables whose values are free to be changed in ways that are restricted by the context of the problem or by mathematical restrictions on allowed values. These variables influence the values of other variables called *dependent variables*.	**Variable independiente** (pág. 6) Variable cuyos valores cambian libremente según las restricciones de un problema o por restricciones matemáticas sobre los valores permisibles. Estas variables influyen en los valores de otras variables, las llamadas *variables dependientes*.
Interquartile range (IQR) (p. 108) A measure of spread; the distance between the first and third quartiles.	**Rango intercuartílico (RI)** (pág. 108) Medida de dispersión; distancia entre los cuartiles primero y tercero.
Isosceles triangle (p. 68) A triangle with at least two sides of equal length. The noncongruent side, if any, is called the *base*, and the angles that lie opposite the congruent sides are called the *base angles*.	**Triángulo isósceles** (pág. 68) Triángulo con por lo menos dos lados congruentes. El lado no congruente, si es que existe, se llama *base* y los ángulos opuestos a los lados congruentes se llaman *ángulos basales*.

Glossary/Glosario

English	**Español**

(K)

Kite (p. 366) A convex quadrilateral with two distinct pairs of consecutive sides the same length.

Deltoide (pág. 366) Cuadrilátero convexo con dos pares distintos de lados consecutivos de la misma longitud.

(L)

Lateral face *see* **prism, pyramid**

Cara lateral *véase* **prisma, pirámide**

Linear equation (p. 189) An equation in which expressions on both sides of the equal sign are either numbers or linear expressions.

Ecuación lineal (pág. 189) Ecuación en que las expresiones en ambos lados del signo de igualdad son números o expresiones lineales.

Linear expression (p. 216) An expression that defines a linear function.

Expresión lineal (pág. 216) Expresión que define una función lineal.

Linear function (p. 150) A function of the form $y = a + bx$ where a and b are real numbers.

Función lineal (pág. 150) Función de la forma $y = a + bx$, donde a y b números reales.

Linear inequality (p. 189) An inequality in which expressions on both sides of the inequality sign are either numbers or linear expressions.

Desigualdad lineal (pág. 189) Desigualdad en que las expresiones en ambos lados del signo de desigualdad son o números o expresiones lineales.

Linear regression (p. 166) A systematic method of finding linear mathematical models for patterns in (x, y) data sets.

Regresión lineal (pág. 166) Método sistemático para hallar modelos matemáticos lineales de patrones en conjuntos de datos de la forma (x, y).

Loop (p. 262) An edge in a graph connecting a vertex to itself.

Lazo (pág. 262) Arista de un grafo que une un vértice a sí mismo.

(M)

Main diagonal of a matrix (p. 248) The entries in a square matrix running from the top-left corner of the matrix to the bottom-right corner.

Diagonal principal de una matriz (pág. 248) Las entradas de una matriz que van de la esquina superior izquierda de la matriz a la esquina inferior derecha.

Mathematical model (pp. 162; 240) A symbolic or pictorial representation including only the essential features of a problem situation.

Modelo matemático (págs. 162; 240) Representación simbólica o pictórica de un problema que sólo incluye sus características esenciales.

Matrix (plural: matrices) (p. 248) A rectangular array of numbers.

Matriz (plural: Matrices) (pág. 248) Arreglo rectangular de números.

Mean (arithmetic average) (p. 84) The sum of the values in a data set divided by how many values there are; the balance point of the distribution.

Media (promedio aritmético) (pág. 84) Suma de los valores de un conjunto de datos dividida entre el número de valores; punto de equilibrio de la distribución.

Mean absolute deviation (MAD) (p. 140) A measure of variability in a data set found by computing the mean of the absolute values of the deviations from the mean of the distribution.

Desviación absoluta media (DAM) (pág. 140) Medida de variabilidad de un conjunto de datos que se halla calculando la media de los valores absolutos de las desviaciones de la media de la distribución.

Glossary/Glosario

English	**Español**

Measure of center (p. 83) Numerical summary of the center of a distribution, such as the mean or median.

Measure of position (p. 104) A number that tells the position of a data value in its distribution, such as a percentile or a deviation from the mean.

Measure of spread (measure of variability) Numerical summary of the variability of the values in a distribution, such as the range, interquartile range, or standard deviation.

Median (second quartile, Q₂) (p. 84) The value in the middle of an ordered list of data; the 50th percentile. If there are an even number of values, the mean of the two values in the middle.

Median of a triangle (p. 95) The line segment joining a vertex to the midpoint of the opposite side.

Mode (p. 94) The most frequent value in a set of numerical data; the category with the highest frequency in a set of categorical data is called the modal category.

Mutually-exclusive events (disjoint) (p. 539) Events that cannot occur on the same outcome of a probability experiment.

Medida central (pág. 83) Resumen numérico del centro de una distribución, como la media o la mediana.

Medida de posición (pág. 104) Número que indica la posición de un dato en su distribución, como el percentil o la desviación de la media.

Medida de dispersión (medida de variabilidad) Resumen numérico de la variabilidad de los valores de una distribución, como el rango, el rango intercuartílico o la desviación estándar.

Mediana (segundo cuartil, Q₂) (pág. 84) Valor central de una lista ordenada de datos; percentil quincuagésimo. Si hay un número par de valores, la mediana es la media de los dos valores centrales.

Mediana de un triángulo (pág. 95) Segmento de recta que une un vértice al punto medio del lado opuesto.

Moda (pág. 94) Valor más frecuente de un conjunto de datos numéricos; en un conjunto de datos categóricos, la categoría de mayor frecuencia, la llamada categoría modal.

Eventos mutuamente excluyentes (disjuntos) (pág. 539) Eventos que no pueden ocurrir en el mismo resultado de un experimento probabilístico.

— **N** —

Net (p. 426) A two-dimensional pattern consisting of polygons that can be folded along edges to form a polyhedron.

Nonconvex *see* **convex**

Nonperiodic tessellation *see* **periodic tessellation**

Normal distribution *see* **approximately normal**

NOW-NEXT rule (p. 29) An equation that shows how to calculate the value of the next term in a sequence from the value of the current term.

Red (pág. 426) Patrón bidimensional que consta de polígonos que forman un poliedro al plegarse a lo largo de sus aristas.

No convexo *véase* **convexo**

Teselado aperiódico *véase* **teselado periódico**

Distribución normal *véase* **aproximadamente normal**

Regla de recurrencia (pág. 29) Ecuación que muestra cómo hallar el valor del término siguiente a partir del valor del término actual.

— **O** —

Oblique drawing (p. 433) A way to depict three-dimensional objects that maintains parallelism of lines.

Proyección oblicua (pág. 433) Forma de presentar sólidos, que mantiene el paralelismo de rectas.

Glossary/Glosario

English	Español

Oblique prism (p. 428) A prism in which some lateral faces are parallelograms that are not rectangles.

Obtuse triangle (p. 68) A triangle with an *obtuse angle* (an angle with measure greater than 90°).

Opposite angles (p. 375) In a triangle △*ABC*, ∠*A* is opposite $\overline{BC}$, ∠*B* is opposite $\overline{AC}$, and ∠*C* is opposite $\overline{AB}$. In a quadrilateral *ABCD* ∠*A* is opposite ∠*C* and ∠*B* is opposite ∠*D*.

Orthographic drawing (p. 432) A way to depict three-dimensional objects by sketching several two-dimensional face-views such as a top view, a front view, and a right-side view.

Outlier (p. 77) A data value that lies far away from the bulk of the other values; for single-variable data, an unusually large or an unusually small value.

- (P) -

P(A and B) (p. 540) The probability that *A* and *B* both happen on the same outcome.

P(A or B) (p. 540) The probability that *A* or *B* occurs.

Parabola (p. 470) The shape of the graph of a quadratic function.

Parallel lines (p. 177) Lines that are coplanar and do not intersect.

Parallel planes Planes that do not intersect.

Parallelogram (pp. 365, 389) A quadrilateral with opposite sides of equal length. Any side may be designated the *base*, and an *altitude* to that base is a perpendicular segment from the line containing the base to the opposite side.

Percentile (p. 104) A way of describing the position of a value in a distribution. The 60th percentile, for example, is the value that separates the smallest 60% of the data values from the largest 40%.

Periodic tessellation (p. 421) A tessellation that fits exactly on itself when translated in different directions. Such a tessellation has translation symmetry. A tessellation that does not have any translation symmetry is called *nonperiodic*.

Prisma oblicuo (pág. 428) Prisma en que algunas caras laterales son paralelogramos que no son rectángulos.

Triángulo obtusángulo (pág. 68) Triángulo con un ángulo obtuso (uno que mide más de 90°).

Ángulos opuestos (pág. 375) En un triángulo △*ABC*, ∠*A* se opone a $\overline{BC}$, ∠*B* se opone a $\overline{AC}$, y ∠*C* se opone a $\overline{AB}$. En un cuadrilátero *ABCD* ∠*A* se opone a ∠*C* y ∠*B* se opone a ∠*D*.

Proyección ortogonal (pág. 432) Forma de presentar sólidos mediante el bosquejo de varias vistas fisonómicas bidimensionales, como las vistas superior, frontal o derecha.

Valor atípico (pág. 77) Dato que está muy alejado del grueso de los otros valores; para datos de una variable, un valor inusualmente grande o inusualmente pequeño.

P(A y B) (pág. 540) Probabilidad que *A* y *B* ocurran ambos en el mismo resultado.

P(A o B) (pág. 540) Probabilidad de que ocurra *A* o *B*.

Parábola (pág. 470) La forma de la gráfica de una función cuadrática.

Rectas paralelas (pág. 177) Rectas coplanarias que no se intersecan.

Planos paralelos Planos que no se intersecan.

Paralelogramo (págs. 365, 389) Cuadrilátero de lados opuestos de la misma longitud. Cualquier lado es la *base* y la *altura* correspondiente es el segmento perpendicular trazado de la recta que contiene la base al lado opuesto.

Percentil (pág. 104) Forma de describir la posición de un valor en una distribución. El percentil sexagésimo, por ejemplo, es el valor que separa el 60% inferior de los datos del 40% superior de los mismos.

Teselado periódico (pág. 421) Teselado que encaja perfectamente en sí mismo cuando se traslada en diversas direcciones. Tal teselado posee simetría de traslación. Un teselado que carece de tal simetría se llama *aperiódico*.

Glossary/Glosario

English

Permutation (p. 581) A rearrangement of a finite set of objects.

Perpendicular bisector of a segment (p. 374) A line that is perpendicular to a segment and contains its midpoint.

Perpendicular lines (p. 396) Lines that intersect to form a right angle (an angle with measure of 90°).

Planar graph (p. 278) A vertex-edge graph that can be drawn in the plane so that edges intersect only at the vertices.

Polygon (p. 398) A closed figure in a plane, formed by connecting line segments (sides) endpoint-to-endpoint (vertices) with each segment meeting exactly two other segments. Polygons with four, five, six, seven, and eights sides are called quadrilaterals, pentagons, hexagons, septagons, and octagons respectively. An *n*-gon is a polygon with *n* sides.

Polyhedron (*plural:* polyhedra) (p. 426) A three-dimensional counterpart of a polygon, made up of a set of polygons that encloses a single region of space. Exactly two polygons (faces) meet at each edge and three or more edges meet at each vertex.

Prism (p. 428) A polyhedron with two congruent polygonal faces, called *bases*, contained in parallel planes, and joined by parallelogram faces called *lateral faces*.

Probability distribution (p. 534) A description of all possible numerical outcomes of a random situation, along with the probability that each occurs; may be in table, formula, or graphical form.

Pyramid (p. 428) A polyhedron in which all but one of the faces must be triangular and share a common vertex. The triangular faces are called *lateral faces*, and the *apex* is the vertex that is common to the lateral faces. The *base* is the face that does not contain the apex.

Quadratic equation (p. 511) An equation in which expressions on both sides of the equal sign are either numbers, linear expressions, or quadratic expressions and at least one of those expressions is quadratic.

Español

Permutación (pág. 581) Una reordenación de un conjunto finito de objetos.

Mediatriz de un segmento (pág. 374) Recta perpendicular a un segmento y que contiene por su punto medio.

Rectas perpendiculares (pág. 396) Rectas que se intersecan en ángulo recto (uno que mide 90°).

Grafo planar (pág. 278) Grafo que puede trazarse en el plano de modo que sus aristas se intersequen sólo en los vértices.

Polígono (pág. 398) Figura cerrada planar, que consta de segmentos de recta (los lados), unidos extremo a extremo (los vértices) y cada segmento sólo interseca a otros dos segmentos. Los polígonos de cuatro, cinco, seis, siete y ocho lados se llaman cuadriláteros, pentágonos, hexágonos, heptágonos y octágonos, respectivamente. Un *en*ágono es un polígono de *n* lados.

Poliedro (pág. 426) Homólogo tridimensional de un polígono, compuesto por un conjunto de polígonos que encierran una sola región del espacio. Sólo se intersecan dos polígonos (caras) en cada arista y tres o más aristas concurren en cada vértice.

Prisma (pág. 428) Poliedro con dos polígonos congruentes y paralelos (las bases), unidas por paralelogramos (las caras laterales).

Distribución probabilística (pág. 534) Descripción de todos los resultados numéricos posibles de una situación aleatoria, junto con la probabilidad de cada uno; puede darse en una tabla, fórmula o gráfica.

Pirámide (pág. 428) Poliedro en que todas las caras, salvo una, son triangulares y tienen un vértice común. Las caras triangulares se llaman *caras laterales* y el *vértice* es común a todas ellas. La *base* es la cara que no contiene el vértice.

Ecuación cuadrática (pág. 511) Ecuación con por lo menos una expresión cuadrática y en la cual las expresiones en ambos lados del signo de igualdad son números, expresiones lineales o expresiones cuadráticas.

Glossary/Glosario

Quadratic expression (p. 494) An expression that defines a quadratic function.

Quadratic function (p. 470) A function of the form $y = ax^2 + bx + c$ where a, b, and c are real numbers and $a \neq 0$.

Quartile, lower (first quartile, Q_1) (p. 108) The value that divides the ordered list of data into the smallest one-fourth and the largest three-fourths; the median of the smaller half of the values; the 25th percentile.

Quartile, upper (third quartile, Q_3) (p. 108) The value that divides the ordered list of data into the smallest three-fourths and the largest one-fourth; the median of the larger half of the values; the 75th percentile.

(R)

Random digit (p. 558) A digit selected from 0, 1, 2, 3, 4, 5, 6, 7, 8, 9 in a way that makes each of the digits equally likely to be chosen (has probability $\frac{1}{10}$); successive random digits should be independent, which means that if you know what random digits have already been selected, each digit from 0 through 9 still has probability $\frac{1}{10}$ of being the next digit.

Range (p. 77) A measure of spread; the difference between the largest value and the smallest value in a data set.

Rate of change (p. 155) The ratio of change in value of a dependent variable to change in value of a corresponding independent variable.

Rectangle A parallelogram with one right angle.

Rectangular distribution (uniform) (p. 96) A distribution where all values in intervals of equal length are equally likely to occur.

Reflection symmetry (p. 401) In two dimensions, a figure has reflection symmetry if there is a line (called the *line of symmetry*) that divides the figure into mirror-image halves. Also called *mirror symmetry*. In three dimensions, a figure has reflection symmetry if there is a plane (called the *symmetry plane*) that divides the figure into mirror-image halves. Also called *plane symmetry*.

Expresión cuadrática (pág. 494) Expresión que define una función cuadrática.

Función cuadrática (pág. 470) Función de la forma $y = ax^2 + bx + c$, donde a, b, c son números reales y $a \neq 0$.

Cuartil inferior (primer cuartil, Q_1) (pág. 108) Valor que divide una lista ordenada de datos en el cuarto inferior y los tres cuartos superiores; mediana de la mitad inferior de los valores; percentil vigésimo quinto.

Cuartil superior (tercer cuartil, Q_3) (pág. 108) Valor que divide una lista ordenada de datos en los tres cuartos inferiores y el cuarto superior; mediana de la mitad superior de los valores; percentil septuagésimo quinto.

Dígito aleatorio (pág. 558) Dígito escogido de 0, 1, 2, 3, 4, 5, 6, 7, 8, 9, de modo que cada uno tenga la misma probabilidad de elegirse que cualquier otro (tiene probabilidad $\frac{1}{10}$); los dígitos aleatorios consecutivos deben ser independientes, o sea, si conoces los dígitos aleatorios ya escogidos, cada dígito de 0 a 9 aún tiene $\frac{1}{10}$ de probabilidad de escogerse como el dígito siguiente.

Rango (pág. 77) Medida de dispersión; diferencia entre los valores máximo y mínimo de un conjunto de datos.

Tasa de cambio (pág. 155) La razón de cambio en valor de una variable dependiente al cambio en valor de la variable independiente correspondiente.

Rectángule Un paralelogramo con un ángulo recto.

Distribución rectangular (uniforme) (pág. 96) Distribución en que todos los valores en intervalos de la misma longitud son equiprobables.

Simetría de reflexión (pág. 401) En dos dimensiones, una figura posee simetría de reflexión si hay una recta (el *eje de simetría*) que la divide en mitades especulares. También llamada *simetría especular*. En tres dimensiones, una figura posee simetría de reflexión si hay un plano (el *plano de simetría*) que la divide en mitades especulares. También llamada *simetría con respecto a un plano*.

Glossary/Glosario

English	**Español**

Regular dodecahedron (p. 441) A regular polyhedron with twelve congruent, regular pentagonal faces.

Regular hexahedron *see* **cube**

Regular icosahedron (p. 441) A regular polyhedron with twenty congruent, equilateral triangular faces.

Regular octahedron (p. 441) A regular polyhedron with eight congruent, equilateral triangular faces.

Regular polygon (p. 400) A polygon in which all sides are congruent and all angles are congruent.

Regular polyhedron (platonic solid) (p. 439) A polyhedron in which all faces are congruent, regular polygons, and the arrangement of faces and edges is the same at each vertex.

Regular tessellation (p. 409) A tessellation that consists of repeated copies of a single regular polygon.

Regular tetrahedron (equilateral triangular pyramid) (p. 441) A regular polyhedron with four congruent, equilateral triangular faces.

Relative frequency histogram (p. 79) A histogram that shows the proportion or percentage that fall into the interval covered by each bar, rather than the frequency or count.

Relative frequency table (p. 100) A summary table for numerical data, where typically the column on the left gives the different data values and the column on the right gives the proportion (*relative frequency*) of measurements that have that value.

Resistant to outliers (less sensitive to outliers) (p. 86) Condition where a summary statistic does not change much when an outlier is removed from a set of data.

Rhombus (p. 366) A quadrilateral with all four sides of equal length.

Right triangle (p. 45) A triangle with a *right angle* (an angle with measure of 90°). The side opposite the right angle is the *hypotenuse*. The other two sides are the *legs*.

Dodecaedro regular (pág. 441) Poliedro regular con doce caras pentagonales regulares congruentes.

Hexaedro regular *véase* **cubo**

Icosaedro regular (pág. 441) Poliedro regular con veinte caras triangulares equiláteras congruentes.

Octaedro regular (pág. 441) Poliedro regular con ocho caras triangulares equiláteras congruentes.

Polígono regular (pág. 400) Polígono cuyos lados son todos congruentes y cuyos ángulos son todos congruentes.

Poliedro regular (sólido platónico) (pág. 439) Poliedro cuyas caras son todas polígonos regulares congruentes y la disposición de caras y aristas en cada vértice es la misma.

Teselado regular (pág. 409) Teselado que consta de copias de un solo polígono regular.

Tetraedro regular (pirámide triangular equilátera) (pág. 441) Poliedro regular con cuatro caras triangulares equiláteras congruentes.

Histograma de frecuencias relativas (pág. 79) Histograma que muestra la proporción o porcentaje que cae en el intervalo cubierto por cada barra, en vez de la frecuencia o cuenta.

Tabla de frecuencias relativas (pág. 100) Tabla sumarial de datos numéricos, donde la columna de la izquierda lleva típicamente los diversos valores de los datos y la columna de la derecha lleva la proporción (*frecuencia relativa*) de las medidas que tienen dicho valor.

Resistencia a los valores atípicos (menos susceptible a los valores atípicos) (pág. 86) Condición en que una estadística sumarial no cambia mucho cuando se elimina un valor atípico de un conjunto de datos.

Rombo (pág. 366) Cuadrilátero con cuatro lados que son de longitudes iguales.

Triángulo rectángulo (pág. 45) Triángulo con un *ángulo recto* (ángulo que mide 90°). El lado opuesto al ángulo recto se llama *hipotenusa* y los otros dos lados son los *catetos*.

Glossary/Glosario

English	Español

Rigid shapes (p. 366) Shapes that cannot flex when pressure is applied.

Formas rígidas (pág. 366) Formas que no se pueden doblar al aplicárseles presión.

Rotational symmetry (p. 401) In two dimensions, a figure has rotational symmetry if there is a point (called the *center of rotation*) about which the figure can be turned less than 360° in such a way that the rotated figure appears in exactly the same position as the original figure. In three dimensions, a figure has rotational symmetry if there is a line (called the *axis of symmetry*) about which the figure can be turned less than 360° in such a way that the rotated figure appears in exactly the same position as the original figure.

Simetría de rotación (pág. 401) En dos dimensiones, una figura posee simetría de rotación si hay un punto (el *centro de la rotación*) alrededor del cual la figura puede girar en menos de 360° de modo que la figura girada aparece en la misma posición que la figura original. En tres dimensiones, una figura posee simetría de rotación si hay una recta (el *eje de simetría*) alrededor de la cual la figura puede girar en menos de 360° de modo que la figura girada aparece en la misma posición que la figura original.

Row sum of a matrix (p. 249) The sum of the numbers in a row of a matrix.

Suma de fila de una matriz (pág. 249) Suma de las entradas de la fila de una matriz.

Run (trial) (p. 553) One repetition of a simulation.

Prueba (pág. 553) Una repetición de un simulacro.

Sample space (p. 534) The set of all possible outcomes of a chance situation.

Espacio muestral (pág. 534) Conjunto de todos los resultados posibles de una situación probabilística.

Scalene triangle (p. 68) A triangle with no two sides of equal length.

Triángulo escaleno (pág. 68) Triángulo sin ningún par de lados de la misma longitud.

Scatterplot (p. 5) A plot on a coordinate grid of the points whose (*x*, *y*) coordinates correspond to related data values of two variables.

Gráfica de dispersión (pág. 5) Gráfica en un cuadriculado de los puntos (*x*, *y*) cuyas coordenadas corresponden a datos relacionados de dos variables.

Schlegel diagram (p. 449) A vertex-edge graph resulting from "compressing" a three-dimensional object down into two dimensions.

Diagrama de Schlegel (pág. 449) Grafo que resulta de "comprimir" a dos dimensiones un objeto tridimensional.

Semiregular polyhedron (p. 442) A polyhedron whose faces are congruent copies of two or more different regular polygons and whose faces and edges have the same arrangement at each vertex.

Poliedro semirregular (pág. 442) Poliedro cuyas caras son copias congruentes de dos o más polígonos regulares distintos y cuyas caras y aristas poseen la misma disposición en cada vértice.

Semiregular tessellation (p. 410) A tessellation of two or more regular polygons that has the same arrangement of polygons at each vertex.

Teselado semirregular (pág. 410) Teselado de dos o más polígonos regulares que posee la misma disposición de polígonos en cada vértice.

Sensitive to outliers (p. 86) Condition where a summary statistic changes quite a bit when an outlier is removed from a set of data.

Susceptible a los valores atípicos (pág. 86) Condición en que una estadística sumarial cambia bastante cuando se elimina un valor atípico de un conjunto de datos.

Simulation (p. 553) Creating a mathematical model that copies (simulates) a real-life situation's essential characteristics.

Simulacro (pág. 553) Modelo matemático que copia (simula) las características esenciales de una situación concreta.

Glossary/Glosario

English	**Español**

Single-variable data (p. 75) Data where a single measurement or count is taken on each object of study, such as height of each person or age of each person.

Datos de una sola variable (pág. 75) Datos en que se ejecuta una sola medida o cuenta en cada objeto de estudio, como la estatura o la edad de una persona.

Skewed distribution (p. 77) A distribution that has a *tail* stretched either towards the larger values (*skewed right*) or towards the smaller values (*skewed left*).

Distribución asimétrica (pág. 77) Distribución que posee una *cola* extendida ya sea hacia los valores más grandes (*asimétrica derecha*) o hacia los valores más pequeños (*asimétrica izquierda*).

Slope-intercept form (p. 160) A linear function with rule in the form $y = mx + b$ is said to be written in slope-intercept form because the value of m indicates the slope of the graph and the value of b indicates the y-intercept of the graph.

Forma pendiente-intersección (pág. 160) Una función lineal de la forma $y = mx + b$ se dice que está escrita en la forma pendiente-intersección porque m es la pendiente de la gráfica y b es la intersección y de la misma.

Slope of a line (p. 155) Ratio of change in y-coordinates to change in x-coordinates between any two points on the line; $\frac{\text{change in } y}{\text{change in } x}$ or $\frac{\Delta y}{\Delta x}$; indicates the direction and steepness of a line.

Pendiente de una recta (pág. 155) Razón del cambio en las coordenadas y al cambio en las coordenadas x entre dos puntos de una recta; $\frac{\text{cambio en } y}{\text{cambio en } x}$ o $\frac{\Delta y}{\Delta x}$; indica la dirección e inclinación de la recta.

Solve (an equation, inequality, or system of equations) (p. 189) To find values of the variable(s) that make the statement(s) true.

Solución (de una ecuación, desigualdad o sistema de ecuaciones) (pág. 189) Calcular valores de la variable o variables que las satisfagan.

Speed (p. 11) When a person or object moves a distance d in a time t, the quotient $\frac{d}{t}$ gives the average speed of the motion. The units of speed are given as "distance per unit of time."

Rapidez (pág. 11) Cuando una persona o un cuerpo se desplaza una distancia d en un tiempo t, el cociente $\frac{d}{t}$ da la rapidez media del movimiento. Las unidades de rapidez son "distancia por unidad de tiempo."

Spreadsheet (p. 32) A spreadsheet is a two-dimensional grid of cells in which numerical data or words can be stored. Numerical values in the cells of a spreadsheet can be related by formulas, so that the entry in one cell can be calculated from values in other cells.

Hojas de cálculos (pág. 32) Cuadriculado bidimensional de celdas en que pueden almacenarse datos numéricos o palabras. Los valores numéricos en una hoja de cálculos pueden estar relacionados por fórmulas, de modo que la entrada en una celda puede calcularse de los valores en otras celdas.

Square A rhombus with one right angle.

Cuadrado Un rombo con un ángulo recto.

Square root (p. 335) If r is a number for which $r^2 = n$, then r is called a square root of n. Every positive number n has two square roots, denoted with the radical forms $\sqrt{n}$ and $-\sqrt{n}$.

Raíz cuadrada (pág. 335) Si r es un número que cumple $r^2 = n$, r se llama una raíz cuadrada de n. Todo número positivo r posee dos raíces cuadradas, designadas por los radicales $\sqrt{n}$ y $-\sqrt{n}$.

Standard deviation (s) (p. 116) A useful measure of spread; based on the sum of the squared deviations from the mean; in a normal distribution about 68% of the values lie no more than one standard deviation from the mean.

Desviación estándar (pág. 116) Medida útil de dispersión; se basa en la suma de las desviaciones al cuadrado de la media; en una distribución normal, cerca del 68% de los valores yacen a no más de una desviación estándar de la media.

Glossary/Glosario

English	Español

Stemplot (stem-and-leaf plot) (p. 97) A statistical display using certain digits (such as the tens place) as the "stem" and the remaining digit or digits (such as the ones place) as "leaves."

Summary statistic (p. 77) A numerical summary of the values in a distribution. For example, the mean, median, or range.

Symmetry plane (mirror plane) *see* **reflection symmetry**

System of equations (p. 199) Two or more equations. The *solution of a system* is the set of solutions that satisfy each equation in the system.

Diagrama de tallos (diagrama de tallo y hojas) (pág. 97) Presentación estadística en que se usan ciertos dígitos (las decenas, por ejemplo) como los "tallos" y el dígito o dígitos restantes (las unidades, por ejemplo) como "las hojas."

Estadística sumarial (pág. 77) Resumen numérico de los valores de una distribución. Por ejemplo, la media, la mediana o el rango.

Plano de simetría (plano especular) *véase* **simetría de reflexión**

Sistema de ecuaciones (pág. 199) Dos o más ecuaciones. La *solución de un sistema* es el conjunto de soluciones que satisfacen cada ecuación del sistema.

(T)

Tessellation (tiling) (p. 408) Repeated copies of one or more shapes so as to completely cover a planar region without overlaps or gaps.

Translation symmetry (p. 408) A pattern has translation symmetry if it coincides with itself under some translation (slide).

Triangle (p. 389) A polygon with three sides. A *base* of a triangle is the side of the triangle that is perpendicular to an altitude.

Triangulate (p. 366) To divide a polygon into a set of nonoverlapping triangles where the vertices of the triangles are the vertices of the polygon.

Teselado (embaldosado) (pág. 408) Copias repetidas de una o más formas que cubren una región plana completamente sin traslapos o espacios.

Simetría de traslación (pág. 408) Un patrón posee simetría de traslación si coincide consigo mismo bajo alguna traslación (deslizamiento).

Triángulo (pág. 389) Polígono con tres lados. Una *base* de un triángulo es un lado del mismo el cual es perpendicular a una altura.

Triangulación (pág. 366) División de un polígono en un conjunto de triángulos que no se traslapan y en que los vértices de los triángulos son los del polígono.

(V)

Variability (p. 103) The spread in the values in a distribution. (*see* **measure of spread**)

Variable A quantity that changes. Variables are commonly represented by letters like x, y, z, s, or t. (*see* **dependent variable** and **independent variable**)

Vertex (*plural:* vertices) (p. 241) A point where edges of a vertex-edge graph meet. Also, a point where two sides of a polygon meet.

Vertex angle defect (p. 437) In a convex polyhedron, the vertex angle defect is the positive difference between the sum of the measures of the *face angles* (the angle formed by two edges of a polyhedral angle) at that vertex and 360°.

Variabilidad (pág. 103) Dispersión de los valores de una distribución. (*véase* **medida de dispersión**)

Variable Cantidad que cambia. Se representan en general por letras como x, y, z, s o t. (*véanse* **variable dependiente** y **variable independiente**)

Vértice (pág. 241) Punto al que concurren aristas de un grafo. También, punto al que concurren dos lados de un polígono.

Defecto del ángulo de un vértice (pág. 437) En un polígono convexo, la diferencia positiva entre la suma de las medidas de los *ángulos de cara* (el ángulo formado por dos aristas de un ángulo poliedro) en ese vértice y 360°.

Glossary/Glosario

English	**Español**

Vertex coloring *see* **color a graph**

Vertex-edge graph (graph) (p. 241) A diagram consisting of a set of points (called *vertices*) along with segments or arcs (called *edges*) joining some of the points.

Vertical angles (p. 376) Two angles whose sides form two pairs of opposite rays.

Venn diagram (p. 540) A diagram involving circles that depicts collections of objects and the relationships between them.

Coloración de vértices *véase* **colorear un grafo**

Grafo (pág. 241) Diagrama que consta de un conjunto de puntos (los vértices) junto con segmentos o arcos (las aristas) que unen algunos de los puntos.

Ángulos opuestos por el vértice (pág. 376) Dos ángulos cuyos lados forman dos pares de rayos opuestos.

Diagrama de Venn (pág. 540) Diagrama que consta de círculos que exhiben colecciones de objetos y las relaciones entre ellos.

· **W** ·

With replacement (p. 562) Selecting a sample from a set so that each selection is replaced before selecting the next; thus, each member of the set can be selected more than once.

Without replacement (p. 562) Selecting a sample from a set so that each selection is not replaced before selecting the next; each member of the set cannot be selected more than once.

Con devolución (pág. 562) Selección de una muestra de un conjunto de modo que cada selección se devuelve antes de elegir la siguiente; así, cada miembro del conjunto puede escogerse más de una vez.

Sin devolución (pág. 562) Selección de una muestra de un conjunto de modo que cada selección no se devuelve antes de elegir la siguiente; así, cada miembro del conjunto no puede escogerse más de una vez.

· **X** ·

x-intercept of a graph (p. 477) The point(s) where the graph intersects the x-axis.

Intersección x de una gráfica (pág. 477) El punto o los puntos en que una gráfica interseca el eje x.

· **Y** ·

y-intercept of a graph (p. 155) The point(s) where the graph intersects the y-axis.

Intersección y de una gráfica (pág. 155) El punto o los puntos en que una gráfica interseca el eje y.

Index of Topics and Resources

Index of Topics and Resources *(continued)*

Index of Topics and Resources (continued)

Index of Topics and Resources (continued)

Index of Topics and Resources (continued)

Index of Contexts

Index of Contexts (continued)

Index of Contexts (continued)

Index of Contexts (continued)